NOBEL PRIZE LIBRARY

———

GIDE

GJELLERUP

HEYSE

Nobel Prize Library

PUBLISHED UNDER THE SPONSORSHIP OF THE
NOBEL FOUNDATION & THE SWEDISH ACADEMY

André Gide

Karl Gjellerup

Paul Heyse

ALEXIS GREGORY, *New York*, AND
CRM PUBLISHING, *Del Mar, California*

CONTENTS

André Gide

1947

"For his comprehensive and artistically significant writings, in which human problems and conditions have been presented with a fearless love of truth and keen psychological insight"

Illustrated by MICHEL RODDE

PRESENTATION ADDRESS

By *ANDERS ÖSTERLING*

PERMANENT SECRETARY
OF THE SWEDISH ACADEMY

———

On THE FIRST PAGE of the remarkable journal kept by André Gide for half a century, the author, then twenty years old, finds himself on the sixth floor of a building in the Latin Quarter, looking for a meeting place for "The Symbolists," the group of youths to which he belonged. From the window he looked at the Seine and Notre Dame during the sunset of an autumn day and felt like the hero of a Balzac novel, a Rastignac ready to conquer the city lying at his feet: "And now, we two!" However, Gide's ambition was to find long and twisting paths ahead; nor was it to be contented with easy victories.

The seventy-eight-year-old writer who this day is being honored with the award of the Nobel Prize has always been a controversial figure. From the beginning of his career he put himself in the first rank of the sowers of spiritual anxiety, but this does not keep him today from being counted almost everywhere among the first literary names of France, or from enjoying an influence that has persisted unabatedly through several generations. His first works appeared in the 1890s; his last one dates from the spring of 1947. A very important period in the spiritual history of Europe is outlined in his work, constituting a kind of dramatic foundation to his long life.

One may ask why the importance of this work has only so recently been appreciated at its true value: the reason is that André Gide belongs unquestionably to that class of writers whose real evaluation requires a long perspective and a space adequate for the three stages of the dialectic process. More than any of his contemporaries, Gide has been a man of contrasts, a veritable Proteus of perpetually changing attitudes, working tirelessly at opposite poles in order to strike flashing sparks. This is why his work gives the appearance of an uninterrupted dialogue in which faith constantly struggles against doubt, asceticism against the love of life, discipline against the need for freedom. Even his external life has been mobile and changing, and his famous voyages to the Congo in 1927 and to Soviet Russia in 1935—to cite only those—are proof enough that he did not want to be ranked among the peaceful stay-at-homes of literature.

Gide comes from a Protestant family whose social position permitted him to follow his vocation freely and to devote greater attention than most others can afford to the cultivation of his personality and to his inner development. He described this family milieu in his famous autobiography whose title *Si le grain ne meurt (If It Die* . . . , 1924) is taken from St. John's words about the grain of wheat that must die before its fruition. Although he has strongly reacted against his Puritan education, he has nonetheless all his life dwelled on the fundamental problems of morality and religion, and at times he has defined with rare purity the message of Christian love, particularly in his short novel, *La Porte étroite (Strait Is the Gate,* 1909), which deserves to be compared with the tragedies of Racine.

On the other hand, one finds in André Gide still stronger manifestations of that famous "immoralism"—a conception which his adversaries have often misinterpreted. In reality it designates the free act, the "gratuitous" act, the liberation from all repressions of conscience, something analagous to what the American recluse Thoreau expressed, "The worst thing is being the slave dealer of one's soul." One should always keep in mind that Gide found some difficulty in presenting as virtue that which is composed of the absence of generally recognized virtues. *Les Nourritures terrestres (Fruits of the Earth,* 1897) was a youthful attempt from which he later turned away, and the diverse delights he enthusiastically sings of evoke for us those beautiful fruits of southern lands which do not bear keeping. The exhortation which he addresses to his disciple and reader, "And now, throw away my book. Leave me!," has been followed first of all by himself in his later works.

But what leaves the strongest impression, in *Nourritures* as elsewhere, is the intense poetry of separation, of return, captured by him in so masterly a fashion in the flute song of his prose. One rediscovers it often; for example, in this brief journal entry, written later, near a mosque at Brusa on one May morning: "Ah! begin anew and on again afresh! Feel with rapture this exquisite tenderness of the cells in which emotion filters like milk. . . . Bush of the dense gardens, rose of purity, indolent rose in the shade of plane trees, can it be that thou hast not known my youth? Before? Is it a memory I dwell in? Is it indeed I who am seated in this little corner of the mosque, I who breathe and I who love thee? or do I only dream of loving thee? . . . If I were indeed real, would this swallow have stolen so close to me?"

Behind the strange and incessant shift in perspective that Gide's work offers to us, in the novels as well as in the essays, in the travel diaries, or in the analyses of contemporary events, we always find the same supple intelligence, the same incorruptible psychology, expressed in a language which, by that most sober means, attains a wholly classic limpidity and the most delicate variety. Without going into the details of the work, let us mention in this connection the celebrated *Les Faux Monnayeurs* (*The Counterfeiters,* 1926), with its bold and penetrating analysis of a group of young French people. Through the novelty of its technique, this novel has inspired a whole new orientation in the contemporary art of the narrative. Next to it, put the volume of memoirs already mentioned, in which the author intended to recount his life truthfully without adding anything that could be to his advantage or hiding what would be unpleasant. Rousseau had the same intention, with this difference, that Rousseau exhibits his faults in the conviction that all men being as evil as he, none will dare to judge or condemn him.

Gide, however, quite simply refuses to admit to his fellows the right to pass any judgment on him; he calls on a higher tribunal, a vaster perspective, in which he will present himself before the sovereign eye of God. The significance of these memoirs thus is indicated in the mysterious Biblical quotation of the "grain of wheat" which here represents the personality: as long as the latter is sentient, deliberate, and egocentric, it dwells alone and without germinating power; it is only at the price of its death and its transmutation that it will acquire life and be able to bear fruit. "I do not think," Gide writes, "that there is a way of looking at the moral and religious question or of acting in the face of it that I have not known and made my own at some moment in my life. In truth, I have wished to reconcile them all, the most diverse points of view, by excluding nothing and by being ready to entrust to Christ the solution of the contest between Dionysus and Apollo."

Such a statement throws light on the intellectual versatility for which Gide is often blamed and misunderstood, but which has never led him to betray himself. His philosophy has a tendency toward regeneration at any price and does not fail to evoke the miraculous phoenix which out of its nest of flames hurls itself to a new flight.

In circumstances like those of today, in which, filled with admiring gratitude, we linger before the rich motifs and the essential themes of this work, it is natural that we pass over the critical reservations which the author himself seems to enjoy provoking. For even in his ripe age, Gide has never argued in favor of a full and complete acceptance of his experiences and his conclusions. What he wishes above all is to stir up and present the problems. Even in the future, his influence will doubtless be noted less in a total acceptance than in a lively controversy about his work. And in this lies the foundation of his true greatness.

The work of André Gide contains pages which provoke with almost confessional audacity. He wishes to combat the Pharisees, but it is difficult, in the struggle, to avoid shocking certain rather delicate norms of human character. One must always remember that this manner of acting is a form of the impassioned love of truth which, since Montaigne and Rousseau, has been an axiom of French literature. Through all the phases of his evolution, Gide has appeared as a true defender of literary integrity, founded on the personality's right and duty to present all its problems resolutely and honestly. From this point of view, his long and varied activity, stimulated in so many ways, unquestionably represents an idealistic value.

Since Mr. André Gide, who has declared with great gratitude his acceptance of the distinction offered him, has unfortunately been prevented from coming here by reasons of health, his Prize will now be handed to His Excellency the French Ambassador.

ACCEPTANCE SPEECH

By ANDRÉ GIDE

IT WOULD NO DOUBT be of little purpose to dwell on my regrets at not being able to be present on this solemn occasion or to have my own voice bear witness to my gratitude, compelled as I am to forgo a trip that promised to be both pleasant and instructive.

I have, as you know, always declined honors, at least those which as a Frenchman I could expect from France. I confess, gentlemen, that it is with a sense of giddiness that I suddenly receive from you the highest honor to which a writer can aspire. For many years I thought that I was crying in the wilderness, later that I was speaking only to a very small number, but you have proved to me today that I was right to believe in the virtue of the small number and that sooner or later it would prevail.

It seems to me, gentlemen, that your votes were cast not so much for my work as for the independent spirit that animates it, that spirit which in our time faces attacks from all possible quarters. That you have recognized it in me, that you have felt the need to approve and support it, fills me with confidence and an intimate satisfaction. I cannot help thinking, however, that only recently another man in France represented this spirit even better than I do. I am thinking of Paul Valéry, for whom my admiration has steadily grown during a friendship of half a century and whose death alone prevents you from electing him in my place. I have often said with what friendly deference I have constantly and without weakness bowed to his genius, before which I have always felt "human, only too human." May his memory be present at this ceremony, which in my eyes takes on all the more brilliance as the darkness deepens. You invite the free spirit to triumph and through this signal award, given without regard for frontiers or the momentary dissensions of factions, you offer to this spirit the unexpected chance of extraordinary radiance.

STRAIT IS THE GATE

By ANDRÉ GIDE

Translated by Dorothy Bussy

1.

Some people might have made a book out of it; but the story I am going to tell is one that it took all my strength to live and over which I spent all my virtue. So I shall set down my recollections quite simply, and if in places they are ragged I shall have recourse to no invention and neither patch nor connect them; any effort I might make to dress them up would take away from the last pleasure I hope to get in telling them.

I lost my father before I was twelve years old. As there was nothing to keep my mother at Le Havre, where my father had had a practice as a doctor, she decided to go to Paris, where she thought I should be better able to finish my education. She took a small apartment near the Luxembourg and Miss Ashburton came to live with us. Miss Flora Ashburton, who had no relations of her own, had begun by being my mother's governess; she afterwards became her companion and later on her friend. I spent my childhood in the society of these two women, whom I remember as equally gentle and equally sad and always dressed in mourning. One day—it was a good long time, I think, after my father's death—my mother changed the black ribbon in her morning cap for a mauve one.

"Oh, mamma!" I cried. "That color doesn't suit you at all." The next morning the black ribbon was back again.

My health was delicate. My mother and Miss Ashburton had only one thought—to keep me from ailing. If I have not become an idler as a result of their solicitude, it must really be that my love of work is ingrained. At the very beginning of the fine weather they both used to persuade themselves that it was time for me to leave town, that I was growing pale. About the middle of June we would start for Fongueusemare in the neighborhood of Le Havre, where we used to spend the summer every year at my Uncle Bucolin's.

Standing in a garden that is neither very large nor very fine, and which has nothing special to distinguish it from a number of other Normandy gardens, the Bucolins' house, a white two-storied building, resembles a great many country houses of the century before last. A score of large windows look east onto the front of the garden; as many more onto the back; there are none at the sides. The windows have small panes; some of them, which have been recently replaced, seem too light in color among the old ones, which look green and dull beside them. Certain others have flaws in the glass which our parents used to call "bubbles";

a tree seen through them becomes distorted; when the postman passes, he suddenly develops a hump.

The garden is rectangular and is enclosed by a wall. The part that lies in front of the house consists of a fairly large, shady lawn with a gravel path all round it. On this side the wall is lower and allows a view of the farmyard and buildings that lie round the garden. The farm is bordered according to the custom of the country, by an avenue of beeches.

Behind the house on the west side the garden spreads more spaciously. A walk gay with flowers runs along the south espalier wall and is protected from the sea winds by a thick screen of Portugal laurel and a few trees. Another walk running along the north wall disappears under a mass of branches. My cousins used to call it the "dark walk" and would not venture along it after twilight. These two paths lead to the kitchen-garden, which continues the flower-garden on a lower level, and which you reach by a small flight of steps. Then, at the bottom of the kitchen-garden, a little gate with a secret fastening leads, on the other side of the wall, to a coppice in which the beech avenue terminates right and left. As one stands on the doorstep of the west front, one can look over the top of this clump of trees to the plateau beyond, with its admirable clothing of crops. On the horizon, at no great distance, can be seen the church of a little village and, when the air is still, the smoke rising from half-a-dozen houses.

Every fine summer evening after dinner we used to go down to the "lower garden." We went out by the little secret gate and walked as far as a bench in the avenue from which there was a view over the country; there, near the thatched roof of a deserted marl-pit, my uncle, my mother, and Miss Ashburton would sit down, before us the little valley filled with mist; and over the distant woods we

watched the sky turn golden. Afterwards we would linger for a while at the lower end of the garden, where it had already grown dark. When we came in we found my aunt in the drawing-room. She hardly ever went out with us. For us children the evening ended then; but very often we were still reading in our rooms when we heard our elders go up to bed.

Almost every hour of the day which we did not spend in the garden we spent in the "schoolroom," my uncle's study, in which some school desks had been placed for us. My cousin Robert and I worked side by side—behind us were Juliette and Alissa. Alissa was two years older than I, Juliette one year younger; Robert was the youngest of us four.

I am not writing here an account of my early recollections, but only of those which refer to my story. It really begins, I may say, in the year of my father's death. Perhaps my sensibility—over-stimulated as it had been by our bereavement and if not by my own grief at any rate by the sight of my mother's—predisposed me at this time to new emotions. I had matured precociously, so that when we went back to Fongueusemare that year, Juliette and Robert seemed to me all the younger by comparison. But when I saw Alissa, I understood on a sudden that we two had ceased to be children.

Yes, it was certainly the year of my father's death; my recollection is confirmed by a conversation that, I remember, took place between my mother and Miss Ashburton immediately after our arrival. I had come unexpectedly into the room where my mother and her friend were talking together; the subject of their talk was my aunt. My mother was indignant that she had not gone into mourning or had gone out again so soon. (To tell the truth it was as impossible for me to imagine Aunt Bucolin dressed in black as my mother in colors.) The day of our arrival, Lucile Bucolin, as far as I can remember, was wearing a muslin gown. Miss Ashburton, conciliatory as ever, was trying to calm my mother.

"After all," she argued timidly, "white is mourning too."

"And do you call that red shawl she has round her shoulders mourning too? Flora, I am ashamed of you," my mother cried.

It was only during the holidays that I saw my aunt, and no doubt the warm summer weather was the reason of her wearing the transparent, low-necked bodices in which I always remember her; but still more than the brilliant color of the scarves that she used to throw over her bare shoulders, it was my aunt's low necks that shocked my mother.

Lucile Bucolin was very beautiful. I still have by me a little portrait of her in which I can see her as she then was, looking so young that she might have been taken for the elder sister of her daughters, sitting sideways in an attitude habitual to her, her head leaning on her left hand, her little finger curved rather affectedly toward her lip. A large-meshed net confines the masses of her curly hair, which fall half-uncoiled upon her neck. In the opening of her bodice a locket of Italian mosaic hangs from a loosely tied black velvet neck ribbon. Her black velvet sash, with its wide floating bow, her broad-brimmed soft straw hat, which is dangling from the back of her chair—everything adds to the childishness of her appearance. Her right hand hangs by her side, holding a shut book.

Lucile Bucolin came from a West Indian family; she had either never known her parents or had lost them very early. My mother told me later that when she was left an orphan, or, possibly even deserted, she was taken in by Pasteur Vautier and his wife, who at that time had no children of their own. They left Martinique soon after, taking her with them to Le Havre, where the Bucolins were set-

tled. The Vautiers and the Bucolins used to see a good deal of each other. My uncle was at that time employed in a bank abroad, and it was only three years later, when he came home to stay with his people, that he saw little Lucile. He fell in love with her and at once asked her to marry him, to the great grief of his parents and of my mother. Lucile was then sixteen years old. In the meantime Madame Vautier had had two children; she was beginning to be anxious as to the influence their adopted sister—whose character was developing more and more oddly every month—might have over them; the household, moreover, was in straitened circumstances. My mother told me all this in order to explain why the Vautiers accepted her brother's proposal so gladly. What I suppose for my own part is, that Miss Lucile was becoming terribly embarrassing. I am well enough acquainted with Le Havre society to imagine the kind of reception that a girl of such fascinations would meet with. Pasteur Vautier, whom I knew later on, was a gentle creature, at once circumspect and ingenuous, incapable of coping with intrigue and quite defenseless against evil —the worthy man must have been at the end of his tether. I can say nothing of Madame Vautier; she died in giving birth to a fourth child about my own age who afterwards became my friend.

Lucile Bucolin took very little share in our life; she did not come downstairs from her room till after the midday meal was over, and then immediately stretched herself on the sofa or in a hammock and remained there till evening, when she would rise, no less languid than before. She used sometimes to raise a handkerchief to her forehead as if wiping away some imaginary moisture, though her skin was a perfection of smooth purity; this handkerchief of hers filled me with wonder because of its fineness and its scent, which seemed more like the perfume of a fruit than of a flower; sometimes she would draw from her waist a minute mirror with a sliding silver lid, which hung with various other objects from her watch-chain; she would look at herself, wet her finger at her lips, and then moisten the corner of her eyes. She used often to hold a book, but it was almost always shut; a tortoiseshell bookmarker was stuck between its pages. If you came near her she did not turn from the contemplation of her dreams to look at you. Often from her careless or tired hand, from the back of the sofa, or from a fold of her dress, her handkerchief would drop to the ground, or her book, or a flower, it might be, or the bookmarker. One day when I picked up her book—this is a childish memory I am telling you—I blushed to see that it was a book of poetry.

In the evening after dinner, Lucile Bucolin did not join our family party at the table, but sat down at the piano, where she took a kind of placid pleasure in playing one or other of Chopin's slow mazurkas; sometimes she would break off in the middle of a bar and pause, suspended motionless on a chord.

I used to experience a peculiar discomfort when I was with my aunt; it was a feeling of uneasiness, of disturbance, mingled with a kind of admiration and a kind of terror. Perhaps some obscure instinct set me against her; and then I felt that she despised Flora Ashburton and my mother, that Miss Ashburton was afraid of her, and that my mother disliked her.

Lucile Bucolin, I wish I no longer bore you malice; I wish I could forget for a moment how much harm you did . . . at any rate, I will try to speak of you without anger.

* * *

One day of that summer—or perhaps of the following, for as the place where the scene was laid never changed, my memories sometimes overlap and become confused—one day I went into the drawing-room to fetch a book; she was there. I was on the point of going away again when she called me back—she, who as a rule never seemed to see me.

"Why do you run away so fast, Jerome? Are you afraid of me?"

With a beating heart I drew near, forced myself to smile, put out my hand. She took my hand with one of hers and with the other stroked my cheek.

"How badly your mother dresses you, you poor little thing!" she said.

At that time I used to wear a sort of sailor suit with a large collar, which my aunt began pulling about.

"Sailor collars are worn much more open," said she, undoing a button of my shirt. "There, see if that doesn't look better!" and taking out her little mirror, she drew my face down to hers, passed her bare arm around my neck, put her hand into my shirt, asked me laughingly if I was ticklish—went on—farther. . . . I started so violently that my shirt tore across, and with a flaming face I fled, as she called after me: "Oh! the little stupid!"

I rushed away to the other end of the kitchen-garden, and there I dipped my handkerchief into a little tank, put it to my forehead—washed, scrubbed—my cheeks, my neck, every part of me the woman had touched.

On certain days Lucile Bucolin had her "attacks." They would come on suddenly and turn the whole house upside down. Miss Ashburton made haste to get the children out of the way and to distract their attention; but it was impossible to stifle or to prevent their hearing the dreadful screams that came from the bedroom or the drawing-room. My uncle lost his head; we heard him rushing along the passages, fetching towels and eau de Cologne and ether; in the evening at table, where my aunt was not yet able to appear, he looked anxious and aged.

When the attack was more or less over, Lucile Bucolin used to send for her children—that is, for Robert and Juliette— never for Alissa. On those melancholy days Alissa would shut herself up in her room, where her father sometimes joined her, for he used often to talk to Alissa.

My aunt's attacks made a great impression upon the servants. One evening when the attack had been particularly acute and I was being kept in my mother's room, where what was going on in the drawing-room was less noticeable, we heard the cook running along the passages calling out: "Sir, sir, come quick! My poor lady is dying."

My uncle had gone up to Alissa's room; my mother went out to meet him on his way down. A quarter of an hour later I heard them talking below the windows of the room where I had remained, and my mother's voice reached me. "Do you know what I think, my dear? The whole thing is play-acting." And she repeated the word several times over, emphasizing every syllable, "play-act-ing."

This was toward the end of the holidays and two years after our bereavement. I was not to see my aunt again very often. The unhappy event that shattered our family life was preceded by a little incident that occurred a short time before the final catastrophe and turned the uncertain and complex feeling I had previously experienced for Lucile Bucolin into pure hatred. But before relating this I must first speak of my cousin.

That Alissa Bucolin was pretty, I was incapable yet of perceiving; I was drawn and held to her by a charm other than mere beauty. No doubt she was very like her mother; but the expression of her eyes was so different that it was not till later that I became aware of this likeness. I cannot describe faces; the features and even the color of the eyes escape me; I can only recall the expression of her smile—a smile that was already almost sad—and the line of her eyebrows, which were so extraordinarily far from her eyes, raised above them in great circles. I have never seen any like them anywhere . . . stay, though! there is a Florentine statuette of the time of Dante; and I like to fancy that Beatrice as a child had eyebrows wide-arched like hers. They gave her look, her whole being, an expression of enquiry at once anxious and confident—yes, of passionate enquiry. She was all question and expectation. You will hear how this questioning took possession of me, became my life.

And yet Juliette might have been considered more beautiful; the brilliance of joy and health was upon her; but beside her sister's grace this beauty of hers seemed something external, something which lay open to the whole world at the first glance. As for Robert, there was nothing particular to distinguish him. He was merely a boy of about my own age; I used to play with him and Juliette; with Alissa I used to talk. She mixed very little in our games; as far back as I can remember, I see her serious, gently smiling, reflective. What did we talk about? What can two children talk about? I will try to tell you in a moment, but let me first finish what I have to say about my aunt, so as to have done with her.

Two years after my father's death, my mother and I spent the Easter holidays at Le Havre. We did not stay with the Bucolins, who had comparatively little room in their town house, but with an elder sister of my mother's, whose house was larger. Aunt Plantier, whom I rarely had the opportunity of seeing, had long since been left a widow; I hardly knew her children, who were much older than I was and very unlike me.

The Plantiers' house was not actually in the town, but halfway up the small hill called the "Côte" which overlooks it. The Bucolins lived in the business quarter; a steep shortcut led in a few minutes from one house to the other. I used to run up and down it several times a day.

On that particular day I had had lunch at my uncle's. After the meal was over, he went out, and I accompanied him as far as his office and then returned home to the Plantiers' to fetch my mother. There I heard that she had gone out with my aunt and would not be back till dinnertime. I immediately went down again to the town, where I was very rarely free to go by myself, and found my way to the port, which was dreary that day with a sea-fog; I loitered on the quays for an hour or so, and then suddenly I was seized with the desire to go back and take Alissa by surprise, though indeed I had only just left her. I ran back through the town and rang at the Bucolins' door. I was just darting upstairs when the maid who had let me in stopped me. "Don't go up, Master Jerome. Don't go up! Mistress is having an attack."

But I brushed past her. It was not my aunt I had come to see. . . . Alissa's room was on the third floor. On the first there were the drawing-room and the dining-room; on the second, my aunt's room, from which voices were coming. The door past which I had to go was open, and a flood of light came from the room and fell on the landing; afraid of being seen, I hesitated a moment and drew back into the dark. This is what I beheld to my unspeakable amazement: my aunt was lying on a sofa in the middle of the room; the curtains were drawn, and it was illuminated by the cheerful light of two candelabras full of candles; Robert and Juliette were at her feet, and behind her was a strange young man in a lieutenant's uniform. The presence of the two children seems to me today monstrous; at that time in my innocence I thought it reassuring rather than otherwise. They were laughing and looking at the stranger, who was saying in a piping voice: "Bucolin! Bucolin! . . . If I had a pet lamb I should certainly call it Bucolin."

My aunt herself burst out laughing. I saw her hold out a cigarette for the young man to light, smoke a few whiffs of it, and then let it fall to the floor. He rushed forward to pick it up, made as if he had caught his feet in a scarf, tripped, and fell on his knees before my aunt. Thanks to this ridiculous performance, I was able to slip by without being noticed.

I found myself outside Alissa's door. For a moment I waited. Bursts of laughter and voices came up from the floor below; perhaps they drowned the sound of my knock, for I heard no answer. I pushed the door, and it opened silently. The room was so dark that I did not at once distinguish Alissa; she was on her knees by the bedside; through the window behind her came the last glimmer of expiring daylight. She turned as I came near, but without getting up, and murmured: "Oh, Jerome, why have you come back?"

I bent down to kiss her; her face was bathed in tears. . . .

My whole life was decided by that moment; even to this day I cannot recall it without a pang of anguish. Doubtless I understood very imperfectly the cause of Alissa's wretchedness, but I felt intensely that it was far too strong for her little quivering soul, for her fragile body, shaken with sobs.

I remained standing beside her, while she remained on her knees. I could express nothing of the unfamiliar transport of my breast, but I pressed her head against my heart and pressed my lips to her forehead while my whole soul came flooding through them. Drunk with love, with pity, with an indistinguishable mixture of enthusiasm, self-sacrifice, and virtue, I appealed to God with all my strength—I offered myself up to Him, unable to conceive that existence could have any other object than to shelter this child from fear, from evil, from life. I knelt down at last, my whole being full of prayer. I gathered her to me; vaguely I heard her say: "Jerome! They didn't see you, did they? Oh! go away quickly. They mustn't see you." Then, lower still: "Jerome, don't tell anyone. Poor papa doesn't know about it. . . ."

I told my mother nothing therefore; but the interminable whisperings that went on between her and Aunt Plantier, the mysterious, preoccupied, distressed looks of the two women, the "Run along, my dear!" with which they would get rid of me whenever I came within earshot of their confabulations, all went to show that they were not wholly unsuspicious of the Bucolin family secret.

We had no sooner returned to Paris than a telegram recalled my mother to Le Havre. My aunt had run away.

"With anyone?" I asked Miss Ashburton, with whom my mother had left me.

"My dear, you must ask your mother. I can't tell you anything," said our dear old friend, whom this event had filled with consternation.

Two days later she and I set out to rejoin my mother. It was a Saturday. I should see my cousins the next day at church and that was the one idea that filled my mind; for in my childish thoughts I attached great importance to this sanctification of our meeting. After all, I cared very little for my aunt and made it a point of honor not to question my mother.

There were not many people that morning in the little chapel. Pasteur Vautier, no doubt intentionally, had chosen as his text Christ's words: *"Strive to enter in at the strait gate."*

Alissa was sitting a few seats in front of me. I saw her face in profile; I gazed at her so intently and with such self-oblivion that it seemed as though it was through her that I heard the words I listened to with such passionate eagerness. My uncle was sitting beside my mother, crying.

The pastor first read the whole text: *"Enter ye in at the strait gate: for wide is the gate and broad is the way that leadeth to destruction, and many there be which go in thereat. Because strait is the gate, and narrow is the way, which leadeth unto life, and few there be that find it."*

Then, under the different headings of his subject he spoke first of the broad way. . . . With a mind rapt and as in a dream, I saw my aunt's room; I saw her lying on the sofa, laughing; I saw the brilliant officer, laughing too . . . and the very idea of laughter and of joy became an offense and an outrage, became, as it were, the hateful exaggeration of sin!

"And many there be which go in thereat," went on the pastor. Then he painted, and I saw, a gaily dressed, laughing multitude advancing in joyous troops, whom I felt I could not and would not join because every step I took with them would lead me farther and farther from Alissa. Then the pastor took up again the first words of his text, and I saw that strait gate through which we must strive to enter. I fancied it, in the dream into which I was plunged, as a sort of press into which I passed with effort and with an extremity of pain, but which had in it as well a foretaste of heavenly felicity. And again this gate became the door of Alissa's room; in order to enter in at it, I squeezed myself—I emptied myself of all that I contained of selfishness. . . . *"Because strait is the gate which leadeth unto*

life," went on Pasteur Vautier; and beyond all maceration, beyond all sorrow, I imagined—I had the presentiment of another joy, pure, seraphic, mystic, for which my soul was already athirst. I imagined this joy like the song of a violin, at once strident and tender, like the pointed fierceness of a flame in which Alissa's heart and mine were consumed. We advanced together, clothed in those white robes of which the Apocalypse speaks, holding each other by the hand, looking forward to the same goal. . . . What if these childish dreams should call up a smile? I repeat them as they came, without alteration. Their apparent confusion lies only in the use of words and imperfect images to convey a feeling that was perfectly definite.

"And few there be that find it," ended the pastor. He explained how to find the strait gate. . . . *"Few there be"*—I would be one of those. . . .

At the end of the sermon I had reached such a pitch of moral tension that, without attempting to see my cousin, as soon as the service was over, I fled—out of pride, already desiring to put my resolutions (for I had made resolutions) to the test, and thinking that I should so best deserve her.

2.

This austere teaching found my soul ready prepared and naturally predisposed to duty. My father's and mother's example, added to the puritanical discipline to which they had submitted the earliest impulses of my heart, inclined me still more toward what I used to hear called "virtue." Self-control was as natural to me as self-indulgence to others, and this severity to which I was subjected, far from being irksome to me, was soothing. It was not so much happiness that I

sought in the future as the infinite effort to attain it, and in my mind I already confounded happiness with virtue. No doubt, like all boys of fourteen, I was still unformed and pliable, but my love for Alissa soon urged me farther and more deliberately along the road on which I had started. A sudden inward illumination made me acquainted with myself. I saw myself as a brooding, half-fledged, wistful creature, somewhat careless of others, somewhat unenterprising, and with no ambitions save for such victories as are to be gained over self. I was fond of my books and cared only for the games that need reflection or effort. I did not much frequent the society of my schoolfellows and when I did take part in their amusements, it was only out of affection or good nature. I made friends, however, with Abel Vautier, who, the following year, joined me in Paris and was in my class at school. He was an agreeable, indolent boy for whom I had more liking than esteem, but at any rate he was someone with whom I could talk about Fongueusemare and Le Havre, toward which my thoughts were continually flying.

As for my cousin Robert Bucolin, who had been sent to the same school, he was two classes below us, and I saw him only on Sundays. If he had not been the brother of my cousins, whom, however, he was very unlike, I should have taken no pleasure in his society.

I was at that time entirely engrossed by my love, and it was in its light alone that these two friendships had any importance for me. Alissa was the pearl of great price of which the Gospel spoke, and I was like him who went and sold all that he had to buy it. Child as I still was, am I wrong in talking of love, and in giving this name to the feeling I had for my cousin? Nothing that I experienced later seems to me worthier of that name—and moreover, when I became old enough to suffer from the more definite qualms of the flesh, my feeling did not greatly change in character; I never sought more directly to possess her whom, as a child, I had sought only to deserve. Work, efforts, pious acts, I offered them all up, mystically, to Alissa, and, indeed, invented a refinement of virtue by which I often left her in ignorance of what I had done only for her sake. In this way I became intoxicated, as it were, with the fumes of modesty, and accustomed myself, alas! regardless of my own comfort, to feel no satisfaction in anything that did not cost me an effort.

Was I alone in feeling the spur of emulation? I do not think that Alissa was touched by it, or that she did anything for my sake or for me, though all my efforts were only for her. Everything in her unaffected and artless soul was of the most natural beauty. Her virtue seemed like relaxation, so much there was in it of ease and grace. The gravity of her look was made charming by her childlike smile; I recall that gently and tenderly enquiring look as she raised her eyes, and can understand how my uncle, in his distress, sought support and counsel and comfort from his elder daughter. In the summer that followed I often saw him talking to her. His grief had greatly aged him; he spoke little at meals or sometimes displayed a kind of forced gaiety more painful than his silence. He remained smoking in his study until the hour of the evening when Alissa would go to fetch him. He had to be persuaded to go out; she led him off to the garden like a child. Together they would go down the flower-walk toward the place where we had put out a few chairs at the head of the steps leading down to the kitchen-garden.

One evening, I was lingering out of doors reading, and as I lay on the grass in the shade of one of the big copper beeches, separated from the flower-walk only by the laurel hedge, which prevented me from being seen but not from hearing, Alissa's and my uncle's voices reached me. They had no doubt been talking of Robert; then I heard my name uttered by Alissa, and I was just beginning to make out their words, when my uncle exclaimed: "He! Oh, he will always be fond of work."

An involuntary listener, at first I had the impulse to go away or at any rate to make some movement to show them that I was there; but what was I to do? Cough? Call out "I am here; I can hear you"? It was much more awkwardness and shyness than curiosity to hear more which kept me quiet. And besides, they were only passing by, and I heard what they said only very indistinctly. But they came on slowly. Alissa, no doubt, as was her habit, with a light basket on her arm, was cutting off the heads of faded flowers and picking up from under the espaliers the unripe fruit that the frequent sea-mists used so often to bring down. I heard her clear voice: "Papa, was Uncle Palissier a remarkable man?"

My uncle's voice was low and indistinct; I could not make out his answer.

Alissa insisted: "Very remarkable, do you think?"

Again an inaudible answer and again Alissa's voice: "Jerome is clever, isn't he?"

How could I help straining to hear? But no! I could make out nothing.

She went on: "Do you think he will become a remarkable man?"

Here my uncle raised his voice: "First, my dear, I should like to understand what you mean by 'remarkable.' One can be very remarkable without its showing—at any rate in the eyes of men—very remarkable in the eyes of God."

"Yes, that is what I mean," Alissa said.

"And then, one can't tell yet. He's too young. Yes, certainly, he's very promising, but that's not enough for success."

"What more must there be?"

"Oh, my child! I can hardly tell. There must be confidence, support, love—"

"What do you mean by support?" interrupted Alissa.

"The affection and esteem that have been lacking to me," answered my uncle, sadly; and then their voices finally died away.

When I said my prayers that evening, I felt remorse for my unintentional eavesdropping and resolved to confess it to my cousin. Perhaps this time there *was* a mixture of curiosity in my resolution.

At my first words the next day, she said: "But, Jerome, it's very wrong to listen like that. You ought to have told us you were there or else to have gone away."

"Really, I didn't listen—I just overheard you without meaning to. And you were only passing by."

"We were walking slowly."

"Yes, but I hardly heard anything. I stopped hearing almost at once. What did uncle answer when you asked him what was necessary for success?"

"Jerome," she said, laughing, "you heard perfectly well. You are just making me repeat it for your amusement."

"I really heard only the beginning—when he spoke of confidence and love."

"He said, afterwards, that a great many other things were necessary."

"And you, what did you answer?"

She suddenly became very serious. "When he spoke of support in life, I answered that you had your mother."

"Oh, Alissa, you know I shan't always have her—And then, it's not the same thing—"

She bent her head: "That's what he said too."

I took her hand, trembling. "Whatever I hope to become later is for you."

"But, Jerome, I may leave you too."

My soul went into my words: *"I shall never leave you."*

She raised her shoulders slightly:

"Aren't you strong enough to walk alone? We must each of us find God by ourselves."

"But you must show me the way."

"Why do you want any other guide but Christ? Do you think we are ever nearer to each other than when each of us forgets the other as we pray to God?"

"Yes," I interrupted, "that He may unite us. That is what I ask Him morning and evening."

"Don't you understand what communion in God means?"

"With my whole heart I understand. It means being rapturously united in the worship of the same thing. I think it is just because I want to be united to you that I worship what I know you worship too."

"Then your worship is not pure."

"Don't ask too much of me. I shouldn't care for Heaven if you were not there too."

She put her finger on her lips and answered with some solemnity: *"Seek ye first the kingdom of God and His righteousness."*

As I put down our words, I feel that they will seem very unchildlike to those who do not realize the deliberate seriousness with which some children talk to each other. What am I to do? Try to excuse them? No! no more than I will color them to make them look more natural.

We had procured the Gospels in the Vulgate and knew long passages of them by heart. Alissa had learned Latin with me under the plea of helping her brother, but really, I think, in order to follow me in my reading. And indeed I could hardly bring myself to take pleasure in any study in which I knew she would not keep me company. If this was sometimes a hindrance to me, it was not, as might be supposed, because it hampered the growth of my mind; on the contrary, it was she who seemed to be everywhere and easily ahead of me. But the course my mind pursued was always shaped with reference to her, and what preoccupied us at that time, what we called "thought," was often merely the pretext for some more subtle communion, merely the disguise of feeling, merely the covering of love.

My mother may at first, perhaps, have been anxious about a feeling whose depth she had not as yet gauged. But now that she felt her strength ebbing, she loved to gather us together in the same maternal embrace. The heart disease from which she had long been suffering began to be more and more troublesome. In the course of a particularly severe attack she sent for me: "My poor boy," she said, "I'm getting very old. Some day I shall leave you suddenly."

She stopped; her breathing was very difficult. Then I broke out, irresistibly, with what is seemed to me she was expecting me to say: "Mamma . . . you know I want to marry Alissa."

And my sentence was no doubt the continuation of her secret thoughts, for she went on at once: "Yes, that is what I want to speak to you about, my Jerome."

"Mamma," said I, sobbing, "you do think she loves me, don't you?"

"Yes, my child." And several times she repeated tenderly: "Yes, my child." She spoke with difficulty. She added: "You must leave it to the Lord." Then as I was stooping over her, she put her hand on my head and said: "May God keep you, my children! May God keep you both!" Then she fell into a doze from which I did not try to rouse her.

This conversation was never resumed. The next morning my mother felt better. I went back to school and silence closed again over this semiconfidence. In any case, what more could I have learned? That Alissa loved me I could not for a moment doubt. And even if I could, doubt would forever have vanished from my heart at the time of the melancholy event that occurred soon after.

My mother passed away very quietly one evening when Miss Ashburton and I were with her. The final attack that carried her off had not at first seemed worse than the preceding ones; it was only toward the end that it became alarming, and we had no time to send for any of our relations. It was with our old friend that I watched the first night beside my dear mother's body. I loved my mother deeply, and wondered that in spite of my tears I should feel so little sadness. If I wept, it was out of pity for Miss Ashburton, whose friend—so many years younger than herself—had thus been taken by God before her. But the secret thought that this bereavement would hasten an understanding with my cousin greatly predominated over my grief.

My uncle arrived the next morning. He handed me a letter from his daughter, who did not come till the day after with Aunt Plantier.

". . . Jerome, my friend, my brother" (she wrote), ". . . how grieved I am not to have been able to speak those few words to her before her death which would have given her that great happiness she desired. May she forgive me now! And may God alone guide us both henceforward! Good-bye, my poor friend.

"I am, more tenderly than ever,
        "YOUR ALISSA."

What could be the meaning of this letter? What were those words that she was grieved not to have uttered—what could they be but those with which she would have plighted our future? I was still so young, however, that I dared not ask her for her hand at once. And besides, what need had I of her promise? Were we not already as good as engaged? Our love was no secret from our relations; my uncle was no more opposed to it than my mother had been; on the contrary, he treated me already as a son.

I spent the Easter holidays, which began a few days later, at Le Havre, sleeping at Aunt Plantier's and taking nearly all my meals at Uncle Bucolin's. My aunt Félicie Plantier was the best of women, but neither my cousins nor I were on very intimate terms with her. She was in a continual state of breathless bustle; her gestures were ungentle and her voice was unmusical; she harried us with caresses and at odd moments of the day, when the need for effusion seized her, would suddenly overwhelm us with the floods of her affection. Uncle Bucolin was very fond of her, but merely from the tone of his voice when he spoke to her, it was easy to understand how greatly he had preferred my mother.

"My poor boy," she began one evening, "I don't know what you are meaning to do this summer, but I will wait to hear your plans before settling my own; if I can be useful to you—"

"I have not thought much about it yet," I answered. "Perhaps I shall travel."

She went on: "You know that both here and at Fongueusemare you will always be welcome. You will be doing your uncle and Juliette a pleasure by going to them. . . ."

"Alissa, you mean."

"Of course. I beg your pardon. . . . Would you believe it? I thought it was Juliette you were in love with! Until a month ago—when your uncle told me— you know I'm very fond of you all, but I don't know you very well; I've seen so little of you. . . . And then I'm not very observant; I have no time to mind other people's business. I always saw you playing with Juliette—I thought to myself, she's so pretty, so gay—"

"Yes, I like playing with her still, but it's Alissa I love."

"All right, all right! It's your affair. As for me, I hardly know her at all, so to speak. She talks less than her sister. I suppose as you've chosen her, you must have good reasons for it."

"But, Aunt, I didn't choose to love her, and I've never thought what reasons I had for—"

"Don't be cross, Jerome. I didn't mean anything. Now, you've made me forget what I wanted to say. Oh, yes! I suppose, of course, it'll all end with your marrying; but it wouldn't be quite proper for you to become engaged just yet because of your mourning—and then you're still very young. I thought, now that your mother isn't there, your staying at Fongueusemare mightn't be considered quite the thing."

"But, Aunt, that's just why I spoke of traveling."

"Oh, well, my dear, I thought that my presence there might make things easier and I've arranged to keep part of the summer free."

"If I asked Miss Ashburton, she would certainly come with pleasure."

"Yes, I know she's coming already. But that's not enough! I will come too. Oh! I don't pretend I shall take your poor mother's place," she added, suddenly bursting into sobs, "but I can look after the housekeeping—and—well—you and your uncle and Alissa needn't feel uncomfortable."

Aunt Félicie was mistaken as to the efficacy of her presence. To tell the truth, we were only uncomfortable because of her. In accord with her announcement, she settled herself at Fongueusemare at the beginning of July, and Miss Ashburton and I joined her there soon after.

Under the pretense of helping Alissa to look after it, she filled the house, which had always been so peaceful, with a continual hubbub. The zeal with which she set about being agreeable to us and "making things easier," as she called it, was so overdone that Alissa and I were nearly always constrained and practically speechless when she was near. She must have thought us very cold. . . . And even if we had not been silent, would she have been able to understand the nature of our love? Juliette's character, on the other hand, fitted in well enough with this exuberance; and perhaps my affection for my aunt was tinged with a certain resentment at seeing her show such a marked preference for the younger of her nieces.

One morning after the arrival of the post, she sent for me: "My poor Jerome," she said, "I'm absolutely heart-broken; my daughter is ill and wants me; I shall be obliged to leave you. . . ."

Puffed up with idle scruples, I went to find my uncle, not knowing whether I should dare to stay on at Fongueusemare after my aunt's departure.

But at my first words: "What," he cried, "will my poor sister think of next to complicate what is so very natural? Why should you leave us, Jerome? Aren't you already almost my child?"

My aunt had stayed barely a fortnight at Fongueusemare. As soon as she was gone, the house was able to sink back again into peace. There dwelt in it once more a serenity that was very like happiness. My mourning had not cast a shadow on our love, but had made it weightier. And in the monotonous course of the life that then began, each slightest stirring of our hearts was audible as if in some place of high resonance.

Some days after my aunt's departure I remember we were discussing her one evening at table: "What a commotion!" said we. "Is it possible that the stir of life should leave her soul so little respite? Fair image of love, what becomes of your reflection here?" . . . For we remembered Goethe's saying about Madame von Stein: "It would be beautiful to see

the world reflected in that soul." And we then and there established a kind of hierarchy, putting the contemplative faculties in the highest place.

My uncle, who up to then had been silent, reproved us, smiling sadly: "My children," said he, "God will recognize His image even though broken. Let us beware of judging men from a single moment of their lives. Everything you dislike in my poor sister is the result of circumstances with which I am too well acquainted to be able to criticize her as severely as you do. There is not a single pleasing quality of youth which may not deteriorate in old age. What you call 'commotion' in Félicie, was at first nothing but charming high spirits, spontaneity, impulsiveness, and grace. We were not very different, I assure you, from what you are today. I was rather like you, Jerome—more so, perhaps, than I imagine. Félicie greatly resembled Juliette as she now is—yes, even physically—and I catch a likeness to her by starts," he added, turning to his daughter, "in certain sounds of your voice; she had your smile—and that trick, which she soon lost, of sitting sometimes, like you, without doing anything, her elbows in front of her and her forehead pressed against the locked fingers of her hands."

Miss Ashburton turned toward me and said almost in a whisper: "It is your mother that Alissa is like."

The summer that year was splendid. The whole world seemed steeped in azure. Our fervor triumphed over evil—over death; the shades gave way before us. Every morning I was awakened by my joy; I rose at dawn and sprang to meet the coming day. . . . When I dream of that time, it comes back to me all fresh with dew. Juliette, an earlier riser than her sister, whose habit it was to sit up very late at night, used to come out into the garden with me. She was the messenger between her sister and me; I talked to her interminably of our love, and she never seemed tired of listening. I told her what I dared not tell Alissa, with whom excess of love made me constrained and shy. Alissa seemed to lend herself to this child's play and to be delighted that I should talk so happily to her sister, ignoring or feigning to ignore, that in reality we talked only of her.

Oh, lovely shifts of love, of love's very excess, by what hidden ways you led us, from laughter to tears, from the most artless joy to the exactions of virtue!

The summer sped by, so pure, so smooth, that of its swift-slipping days scarce anything remains in my memory. Its only events were talks and readings.

"I have had a melancholy dream," Alissa said to me on one of the last mornings of the holidays. "I was alive and you were dead. No, I didn't see you die. It was merely—that you were dead. It was horrible; it was so impossible, that I managed to get it granted for you to be simply absent. We were parted and I felt that there was a way of getting to you; I tried to find out how, and I made such an effort to succeed that it woke me up. This morning I think I was under the impression of my dream; it seemed as if it was still going on. I felt as if I were still parted from you—going to be parted from you for a long, long time—" and she added very low: "all my life—and that all our lives we should have to make a great effort. . . ."

"Why?"

"Each of us a great effort to come together again."

I did not take these words seriously, or perhaps I was afraid to take them seriously. With a beating heart, and in a sudden fit of courage, I said to her, as though protesting: "Well, as for me, this morning I dreamed that I was going to marry you—so surely, that nothing, nothing would be able to part us, except death."

"Do you think that death is able to part?" asked she.

"I mean—"

"I think that death, on the contrary, is able to bring together—yes, bring together what has been parted in life."

The whole of this conversation sank into us so deeply that I can still hear the very intonation of the words we used. And yet I did not realize all their gravity until later.

The summer sped by. Already nearly all the fields lay bare, with their wider spaces more emptied of hope. The evening before—no, two evenings before my departure, I went out with Juliette and we wandered down to the shrubbery at the end of the lower garden.

"What were you repeating yesterday to Alissa?" she asked.

"When do you mean?"

"When you stayed behind us on the quarry bench."

"Oh! Some verses of Baudelaire's, I think."

"What were they? Won't you say them to me?"

" 'Bientôt nous plongerons dans les froides ténèbres,' " I began rather ungraciously.

But no sooner had I started than she interrupted me and took up the lines in a changed and trembling voice: " 'Adieu! vive clarté de nos étés trop courts!' "

"What! you know them?" I cried, extremely astonished. "I thought you didn't care for poetry. . . ."

"Why? Because you never quote me any?" she said, laughing, though in rather a forced way. "Sometimes you seem to think I'm perfectly idiotic."

"It's quite possible to be very intelligent and not care for poetry. I've never heard you repeat any or ask me to quote you any."

"Because that's Alissa's business." She

was silent for a few minutes and then asked abruptly: "You're going away the day after tomorrow?"

"Yes, I must."

"What are you going to do this winter?"

"It's my first year at the École Normale."

"When do you think of marrying Alissa?"

"Not before I've done my military service. And indeed, not before I have a better idea of what I mean to do afterwards."

"Don't you know yet?"

"I don't want to know yet. Too many things appeal to me. I want to put off for as long as I can having to choose and settle down to only one thing."

"Is it reluctance to settle down that makes you put off getting engaged too?"

I shrugged my shoulders without answering.

She insisted: "Then, what are you waiting for? Why don't you get engaged at once?"

"Why should we get engaged? Isn't it enough to know that we do and shall belong to each other, without proclaiming it to the world? Since I choose to devote my whole life to her, do you think it would be nobler to bind my love by promises? Not I! Vows seem to me to be an insult to love. I should only want to be engaged if I distrusted her."

"It isn't Alissa that I distrust—"

We were walking slowly. We had reached that part of the garden where, in former days, I had unintentionally overheard the conversation between Alissa and her father. It suddenly occurred to me that perhaps Alissa, whom I had seen go out into the garden, was sitting at the head of the steps, and that she would be able to overhear us in the same manner; the possibility of making her listen to words that I dared not say to her openly, tempted me; I was amused by the artifice

and raising my voice: "Oh!" I exclaimed with the somewhat stilted vehemence of youth, and too much engrossed by my own words to hear in Juliette's all that she had left unsaid: "Oh, if only we could lean over the soul we love and see as in a mirror, the image we cast there!—read in another as in ourselves, better than in ourselves! What tranquillity there would be in our tenderness—what purity in our love!"

I had the conceit to take Juliette's emotion for an effect of my very indifferent flight of eloquence. She suddenly hid her face on my shoulder: "Jerome! Jerome! I wish I could be sure you would make her happy! If she were to suffer through you as well, I think I should detest you!"

"Why, Juliette," I cried, embracing her and raising her head, "I should detest myself. If you only knew! Why, it's only so that I may begin life better with her that I don't want to settle on my career yet! Why, it is upon her that I hang my whole future. Why, I want none of the things that I might be without her—"

"And what does she say when you speak to her so?"

"I never speak to her so! Never; and that's another reason why we're not engaged yet; there is never any question of marriage between us, nor of what we shall do hereafter. Oh, Juliette! life with her seems to me so lovely that I dare not —do you understand—I dare not speak to her about it."

"You want happiness to come upon her as a surprise."

"No! that's not it. But I'm frightened— of frightening her. Do you see? I'm afraid that the immense happiness that I foresee may frighten her. One day I asked her whether she wanted to travel. She said that she wanted nothing, that it was enough for her to know that foreign countries existed, and that they were beautiful, and that other people were able to go to them—"

"And you, Jerome, do you want to travel?"

"Yes, everywhere! All life seems to me like a long journey—with her, through books and people and countries. Have you ever thought of the meaning of the words 'weighing anchor'?"

"Yes, I often think of them," she murmured.

But barely listening to her, and letting her words drop to earth like poor, hurt birds, I went on: "To start one night; to wake up in the dazzling brilliancy of morning; to feel oneself together and alone on the uncertain waves—"

"To arrive in a port, which one has seen on the map as a child; where everything is strange—I imagine you on the gangway, leaving the boat with Alissa leaning on your arm."

"We should hurry off to the post," I added, laughing, "to get the letter which Juliette would have written to us—"

"From Fongueusemare, where she would have stayed behind, and which you would remember as—oh, so tiny, and so sad, and so far away—"

Were those her words exactly? I cannot be sure for, I repeat, I was so full of my love that, beside it, I was scarcely aware of any expression but its own.

We were drawing near the steps and were just going to turn back when Alissa suddenly appeared from out of the shade. She was so pale that Juliette uttered an exclamation.

"Yes, I don't feel very well," Alissa stammered hastily. "The air is rather chilly. I think I had better go in." And leaving us there and then, she went hurriedly back toward the house.

"She overheard what we were saying," Juliette cried as soon as she was a little way off.

"But we didn't say anything that could have vexed her. On the contrary—"

"Oh! Let me alone," she said, and darted off in pursuit of her sister.

That night I could not sleep. Alissa had come down to dinner, but had retired immediately afterwards, complaining of a headache. What had she heard of our conversation? I anxiously went over in my mind everything we had said. Then I thought that perhaps I had been wrong to walk so close to Juliette and to let my arm slip around her; but it was the habit of childhood, and many a time Alissa had seen us walking so. Ah! blind wretch that I was, groping after my own errors, not to have thought for a moment that Juliette's words, to which I had paid so little attention, and which I remembered so ill, might perhaps have been better understood by Alissa. No matter! Led astray by my anxiety, terrified at the idea that Alissa might distrust me, and imagining no other peril, I resolved, in spite of what I had said to Juliette, and perhaps influenced by what she had said to me—I resolved to overcome my scruples and apprehensions and to betroth myself the following day.

It was the eve of my departure. Her sadness, I thought, might be ascribed to that. She seemed to avoid me. The day passed without my being able to see her alone. The fear of being obliged to leave before speaking to her sent me to her room a little before dinner. She was putting on a coral necklace, and, her arms raised to fasten it, was bending forward with her back turned to the door, looking at herself over her shoulder in a mirror between two lighted candles. It was in the mirror that she first caught sight of me, and she continued to look at me in it for some moments without turning round.

"Why," she said, "wasn't the door shut?"

"I knocked, but you didn't answer. Alissa, you know I'm going tomorrow?"

She answered nothing, but laid down

the necklace, which she could not succeed in fastening. The word "engagement" seemed to me too bare, too brutal; I used I know not what periphrasis in its stead. As soon as Alissa understood what I meant, I thought I saw her sway and lean against the mantelpiece for support —but I myself was trembling so much that in my fearfulness I avoided looking at her.

I was near her, and, without raising my eyes, I took her hand; she did not free herself, but bending down her face a little and raising my hand a little, she put her lips on it and murmured, as she half leant against me: "No, Jerome, no. Don't, please, let us be engaged."

My heart was beating so fast, that I think she felt it, and she repeated, more tenderly: "No, not yet—"

And as I asked her: "Why?"

"It's I that ought to ask you why," she said. "Why change?"

I did not dare speak to her of yesterday's conversation, but no doubt she felt that I was thinking of it, and as if in answer to my thought, said, as she looked at me earnestly: "You are wrong, dear. I do not need so much happiness. Are we not happy enough as we are?" She tried in vain to smile.

"No, since I have to leave you."

"Listen, Jerome, I can't speak to you this evening—don't let's spoil our last minutes. No, no, I'm as fond of you as ever; don't be afraid. I'll write to you; I'll explain. I promise I'll write to you—tomorrow—as soon as you have gone. Leave me now! See, here I am crying. You must go."

She pushed me away, tore me gently from her—and that was our good-bye; for that evening I was not able to speak to her again, and the next morning, when it was time for me to leave, she shut herself up in her room. I saw her at her window waving good-bye to me as she watched my carriage drive off.

3.

I had hardly seen Abel Vautier that year; he had enlisted without waiting to be called up, while I, in the meantime, had been reading for my degree. I was two years younger than Abel, and had put off my military service until after leaving the École Normale, where we were both to go for our first term that year.

We met again with pleasure. After leaving the army, he had spent more than a month traveling. I was afraid of finding him changed; but he had merely acquired more confidence without losing any of his charm. We spent the afternoon before the opening day of the term in the Luxembourg Gardens; unable to restrain myself from confiding in him, I spoke to him at length about my love for Alissa, which, for that matter, he knew of already. During the last year he had acquired some experience of women, and, in consequence, put on rather a conceited and patronizing manner, which, however, did not offend me. He laughed at me for not having finally managed to clinch the matter, as he expressed it, giving forth as an axiom that a woman should never be given time to go back on herself. I let him talk, but thought to myself that his excellent arguments were not applicable either to her or to me, and simply showed that he did not understand us.

The day after our arrival, I received the following letter:

"My dear Jerome,

"I have been thinking a great deal about your suggestion. [My suggestion! What a way of speaking of our engagement!] I am afraid I am too old for you. Perhaps you don't think so now, because you have had no opportunity yet of seeing anything of other women. But I keep thinking of what I should suffer later on if, after I had given myself to you, I were to find out that you were no longer able to care for me. You will be very indignant, no doubt, as you read this; I think I hear you protesting; it's not that I doubt your love—I simply ask you to wait a little longer until you are rather better acquainted with life.

"Please understand that I am speaking only of you—as for myself, I feel sure that I shall never cease to love you.

"ALISSA."

Cease to love each other! Could there be any question of such a thing? I was more astonished than grieved, but so greatly disturbed, that I hurried off to show the letter to Abel.

"Well, what do you mean to do?" he asked after he had read the letter, shaking his head and screwing up his lips as he did so. I made a despairing gesture. "At any rate, I hope you aren't going to answer her! If you begin arguing with a woman you're lost. Listen to me: if we were to sleep at Le Havre on Saturday night, we might spend Sunday morning at Fongueusemare, and be back here in time for the lecture on Monday morning. I haven't seen your people since my military service. That's excuse enough, and a very creditable one. If Alissa sees that it's only an excuse, so much the better. I'll look after Juliette while you talk to her sister. Try not to play the fool. To tell you the truth, there's something I can't understand in your tale; you can't have told me everything. Never mind! I'll soon get to the bottom of it. Mind you don't let them know we're coming; you must take your cousin by surprise and not give her time to arm herself."

My heart was beating fast as I pushed open the garden gate. Juliette came running to meet us at once. Alissa, who was busy in the linen room, made no haste to come down. We were talking to my uncle and Miss Ashburton when at last she entered the drawing-room. If our sudden arrival had upset her, at any rate she managed to show no signs of it. I thought of what Abel had said, and that it was precisely with the intention of arming herself against me that she had been so long in making her appearance. Juliette's extreme animation made her reserve seem colder still. I felt that she disapproved of my return; at any rate she tried to show disapprobation in her manner, and I dared not imagine that behind this disapprobation there might be hidden another and a livelier feeling. Seated at some distance from us, in a corner near the window, she seemed absorbed in a piece of embroidery, the stitches of which she was counting below her breath. Abel talked—fortunately! for, as for me, I felt incapable of saying a word, and if it had not been for the tales he told of his year's service and his travels, this meeting would have had a dismal beginning. My uncle himself seemed unusually thoughtful.

Immediately after lunch, Juliette took me aside and drew me into the garden: "What do you think?" she said, when we were alone, "I've had an offer of marriage! Aunt Félicie wrote to papa yesterday to tell him she had had a proposal for me from a Nîmes vine-grower, a person who is very satisfactory in every way, she says; he met me at some parties last spring and fell in love with me."

"And did this individual make any impression on you?" I questioned, with an instinctive feeling of hostility toward the suitor.

"Yes, I think I remember him. A kind of cheery Don Quixote—not cultivated—very ugly—very vulgar—rather ridiculous. Aunt Félicie couldn't keep her countenance before him."

"Has he any—chance?" I asked, mockingly.

"Oh, Jerome! How can you? A man

who's in business! . . . If you'd seen him you wouldn't ask."

"And has my uncle answered?"

"He answered what I did—that I was too young to marry. Unfortunately," she added, laughing, "Aunt foresaw that objection; in a postscript she says that Monsieur Édouard Teissières—that's his name—is willing to wait, that he has simply declared himself so soon in order to be put 'on the ranks.' It's absurd, but what am I to do? All the same, I can't tell him he's too ugly."

"No, but you can say that you don't want to marry a vine-grower."

She shrugged her shoulders. "That's a kind of reason Aunt's mind is incapable of taking in. But let's talk of something else. Has Alissa written to you?"

She spoke with extreme volubility and seemed in great agitation. I handed her Alissa's letter, which she read, blushing deeply. I seemed to discern a note of anger in her voice as she asked me: "Then what are you going to do?"

"I don't know," I answered. "Now that I am here, I feel that it would have been easier to write, and I blame myself for coming. Can you understand what she means?"

"I understand that she wants to leave you free."

"Free! What do I care for freedom? And can you understand why she writes to me so?"

She answered "No!" so shortly that, without at all divining the truth, I at least felt persuaded from that moment that Juliette probably knew something about it. Then, abruptly turning back as we came to a bend in the path: "Let me be now," she said. "You haven't come here to talk to me. We have been together a great deal too long."

She fled off to the house, and a moment later I heard her at the piano.

When I went back to the drawing-room, she was talking to Abel, who had joined her there; she went on playing as she talked, though carelessly, and as if vaguely improvising. I left them. I went into the garden and wandered about some time, looking for Alissa.

She was at the bottom of the orchard, picking the first chrysanthemums at the foot of a low wall. The smell of the flowers mingled with that of the dead leaves in the beech copse, and the air was saturated with autumn. The sun did no more now than just warm the espaliers, but the sky was orientally pure. Her face was framed, hidden nearly, in the depths of a big Dutch peasant's cap that Abel had brought back from his travels, and which she had at once put on. She did not turn as I drew near, but I saw, by the slight tremor that she could not repress, that she had recognized my step; and I began at once to fortify myself against her reproaches and the severity that I felt her look was going to impose upon me. But when, as I came closer and, as if afraid, began to slacken my pace, she, though still she did not turn, but kept her head lowered as a sulky child might do, stretched out to me from behind her back her hand full of flowers, and seemed to beckon me on. And as, on the contrary, at sight of this gesture I came to a stand-still in a spirit of playfulness, she turned around at last and took a few steps toward me, raising her face; and I saw that it was full of smiles. The brightness of her look made everything seem on a sudden simple and easy again, so that without an effort and with an unaltered voice, I began: "It was your letter that brought me back."

"I thought so," she said, and then, softening the sharpness of her rebuke by the inflection of her voice: "and that is what vexed me. Why didn't you like what I said? It was very simple, though." (And indeed, sadness and difficulty seemed now nothing but imagination, seemed now to exist only in my mind.) "We were happy so; I told you we were; why be astonished at my refusing when you ask me to change?"

And indeed I felt happy with her, so perfectly happy that the one desire of my mind was that it should differ in nothing from hers, and already I wished for nothing beyond her smile and to walk with her thus hand in hand along a sun-warmed, flower-bordered path.

"If you prefer it," I said gravely, renouncing at one stroke every other hope and giving myself up to the perfect happiness of the present, ". . . if you prefer it, we will not be engaged. When I got your letter, I did in fact realize that I was happy and that my happiness was going to cease. Oh! give me back the happiness that I had; I can't do without it. I love you well enough to wait for you all my life, but that you should cease to love me or that you should doubt my love, that thought, Alissa, is unbearable to me."

"Alas! Jerome, I cannot doubt it."

And her voice, as she said this, was at once calm and sad; but the smile that illuminated her remained so serenely beautiful that I was ashamed of my fears and protestations; it seemed to me then that from them alone came that touch of sadness which I felt lurking in her voice. Without any transition, I began speaking of my plans and of the new life from which I was expecting to derive so much benefit. The École Normale was not at that time what it has since become; its somewhat rigorous discipline, irksome only to young men of an indolent or refractory disposition, was helpful to those whose minds were bent on study. I was glad that this almost monastic way of life should preserve me from the world, which at best attracted me but little; the knowledge that Alissa feared it for me would have been enough to make it appear hateful. Miss Ashburton had kept the apartment she had shared with my mother in Paris. As Abel and I knew hardly anyone in Paris, we should spend some hours of every Sunday with her; every Sunday I should write to Alissa and keep her informed of every detail of my life.

We were now sitting on the edge of an open garden frame through which sprawled huge stalks of cucumber plants, the last fruits of which had been gathered. Alissa listened to me, questioned me. I had never felt her tenderness more solicitous, her affection more pressing. Fear, care, the slightest stir of emotion even, evaporated in her smile, melted away in this delightful intimacy like mist in the perfect blueness of the sky.

Then, when Juliette and Abel came out to join us, we spent the rest of the day on a bench in the beech copse, reading aloud Swinburne's *Triumph of Time,* each of us taking a verse by turns. Evening drew in.

When the time came for us to be going, Alissa kissed me good-bye and then half playfully, but still with that elder-sister air, which was perhaps called for by my thoughtlessness, and which she was fond of assuming, said: "Come—promise me you won't be so romantic for the future."

"Well, are you engaged?" Abel asked as soon as we were again alone together.

"My dear fellow, there's no question of that now," I answered, adding at once in a tone that cut short any further questioning: "And a very good thing too. I have never been happier in my life than I am tonight."

"Nor I either!" he cried; then, abruptly flinging his arms round me: "I've got something wonderful to tell you, something extraordinary! Jerome, I'm madly in love with Juliette! I suspected as much as long ago as last year; but I've seen life since then, and I didn't want to tell you anything about it until I'd met your cousins again. Now it's all up with me! It's for life. *'J'aime, que dis-je aimer—j'idolâtre Juliette!'* I've thought for a long time past that I had a kind of brother-in-law's affection for you."

Then, laughing and joking, he embraced me again and again, flinging himself about like a child on the cushions of the railway carriage that was taking us to Paris. I was absolutely astounded by his announcement, and the slight strain of literary affectation which I felt in it jarred on me not a little. But how was it possible to hold out against such vehemence and such rapture?

"Well, what? Have you proposed to her?" I managed to ask between two bursts of excitement.

"No, no, certainly not!" he cried; "I don't want to skip the most charming part of the story. *'Le meilleur moment des amours n'est pas quand on dit: je t'aime. . . .'* Come now, you aren't going to reproach me with that, are you? You —such a past master of slowness yourself!"

"Well, at any rate," I said, slightly irritated, "do you think that she . . . ?"

"Didn't you notice her embarrassment when she saw me again? And the whole time of our visit, her agitation, and her blushes, and her volubility? No, you noticed nothing, of course! Because you're completely taken up with Alissa. And how she questioned me! How she drank in my words! Her intelligence has developed tremendously since last year. I don't know where you got it that she doesn't like reading; you always imagine that Alissa's the only person who can do anything! My dear boy, it's astonishing what she knows. Can you guess what we were amusing ourselves by doing before dinner? Repeating one of Dante's *Canzoni*! We each of us said a line, and when I went wrong she corrected me. You know, the one that begins: *'Amor che nella mente mi ragiona.'* You didn't tell me that she had learnt Italian."

"I didn't know it myself," I said, rather astonished.

"What? When we began the *Canzone*, she told me it was you who had shown it to her."

"She must have heard me read it to her sister one day when she was sitting with us doing her needlework, as she often does; but I'm blessed if she ever let on that she understood."

"Really! You and Alissa are amazing with your egoism. You are so much absorbed in your own love, that you can't spare a glance for the admirable flowering of an intelligence and a soul like hers! I don't want to flatter myself, but all the same it was high time that I appeared on the scene. No, no! I'm not angry with you, as you see," he said, embracing me again. "Only promise me—not a word of any of this to Alissa. I want to conduct my affairs by myself. Juliette is caught, that's certain, and fast enough for me to venture to leave her till next holidays. I think I shan't even write to her between this and then. But we will spend the Christmas vacations at Le Havre, and then—"

"And then?"

"Well, Alissa will suddenly learn of our engagement. I mean to push it through smartly. And do you know what will happen? Why! I shall get you Alissa's consent by force of our example. You can't pull it off for yourself, but we shall persuade her that we can't get married before you. . . ."

So he went on, drowning me in an inexhaustible flow of words which did not stop even on the train's arrival in Paris, even on our getting back to Normale, for though we walked all the way from the station to the school, he insisted, in spite of the lateness of the hour, on accompanying me to my room, where we went on talking till morning.

Abel's enthusiasm made short work of the present and the future. He already saw and described our double wedding; imagined and painted everybody's surprise and joy; became enamored of the beauty of our story, of our friendship, of the part he was to play in my love affair. Far from being proof against so flattering a warmth, I felt myself pervaded by it, and gently succumbed to the allurement of his fanciful suggestions. Thanks to our love, courage and ambition swelled in us; we were hardly to have left the École Normale when our double marriage (the ceremony to be performed by Pasteur Vautier) would take place and we should all four start on our wedding journey; then we were each to embark on some monumental work with our wives as collaborators. Abel, for whom the schoolmaster's profession had no attractions, and who thought he was born to be a writer, would rapidly earn the fortune of which he stood in need, by a few successful plays. As for me, more attracted by learning itself than by the thought of any gain that might accrue from it, my plan was to devote myself to the study of religious philosophy, of which I purposed writing the history—but what avails it now to recall so many hopes?

The next day we plunged into our work.

4.

The time till the Christmas holidays was so short that my faith, quickened as it had been by my last conversation with Alissa, never for a moment wavered. As I had resolved, I wrote to her at length every Sunday. During the rest of the week I kept apart from my fellow-students and frequented hardly anyone but Abel; I lived with the thought of Alissa, and covered my favorite books with notes meant for her eye, subordinating the interest I sought in them myself to the interest they might have for her. Her letters caused me some uneasiness; and though she answered mine rather regularly, her keenness to keep up with me seemed, I thought, to come more from anxiety to encourage my work than from her own spontaneous inclination; and it even seemed to me that while, on my part, reflections, discussions, criticisms were only means toward expressing my thoughts, she, on the contrary, took advantage of all these things to conceal hers. Sometimes I wondered whether she was not actually taking pleasure in this as in a kind of game. No matter! I was firmly resolved to complain of nothing, and I let no trace of anxiety appear in my letters.

Toward the end of December, then, Abel and I left for Le Havre.

I was to stay with Aunt Plantier. She was not in when I arrived, but I had hardly had time to settle in my room when a servant came to tell me that she was waiting for me in the drawing-room.

She had no sooner finished enquiring after my health, my surroundings, my studies, than, without more ado, she gave way to her affectionate curiosity: "You haven't told me yet, my dear, whether you were pleased with your stay at Fongueusemare? Were you able to advance matters at all?"

I had to put up with my aunt's good-natured tactlessness, however painful it might be to hear her speak so summarily of feelings for which the purest and gentlest words would still have seemed too brutal; yet her tone was so simple and so cordial that it would have been senseless to take offense. Nevertheless, I could not help objecting a little. "Didn't you say last spring that you thought an engagement would be premature?"

"Yes, I know; one always says that to begin with," she started off again, seizing one of my hands, which she pressed with emotion between both of hers. "Besides, on account of your studies and your military service, you won't be able to marry for several years, I know. Moreover, personally I don't approve of long engagements. They're trying for young girls, though sometimes it's very touching to see . . . for that matter it's not necessary to make the engagement public . . . only then one can give people to understand—oh! very discreetly—that there's no further need to be on the look-out; and besides, it authorizes your correspondence, your intimacy; and, moreover, if anyone else came forward—and it might very well happen," she insinuated with a knowing smile, "one is able just to hint that . . . no, it's not worth while. You know there's been an offer for Juliette! She has attracted a great deal of attention this winter. She's still rather young, which is what she answered; but the young man suggested waiting; he's not exactly a young man, either . . . in short, he's a very good match, a very reliable person. Well! you'll see him tomorrow; he's going to be at my Christmas Tree. You'll tell me what you think of him."

"I'm afraid, Aunt Félicie, that it's labor lost on his part, and that Juliette has someone else in her mind," I said, making a great effort not to mention Abel at once.

"Hum?" said Aunt Félicie, enquiringly, and putting her head on one side with an incredulous look. "You surprise me! Why should she not have told me anything about it?"

I bit my lips to prevent myself from saying anything more.

"Oh, well! we shall soon see. Juliette hasn't been very well lately," she went on. ". . . but we aren't speaking of her for the moment. Ah! Alissa is very charming too. Come now, did you or did you not make your declaration?"

Although rebelling with my whole heart against the word "declaration,"

which seemed to me so inappropriate and crude, I was incapable of replying by a falsehood to this direct question; I answered, "Yes," in some confusion, and felt my face flame as I did so.

"And what did she say?"

I bent my head; I should have liked not to answer. In still greater confusion and as though in spite of myself, I said, "She refused to be engaged."

"Well! the child was quite right," said my aunt. "You have plenty of time before you, Heaven knows. . . ."

"Oh! Aunt! that's enough now," I said, trying in vain to stop her.

"Besides, I'm not surprised; I always thought your cousin more sensible than you. . . ."

I do not know what came over me at this point; my nerves were no doubt exasperated by this cross-examination, for it seemed to me that on a sudden my heart burst; like a child, I buried my face in my kind aunt's lap and cried out, sobbing: "No, Aunt, no! You don't understand. She didn't ask me to wait—"

"What! Did she refuse you?" she asked in a tone of the kindest commiseration, raising my head with her hand.

"No—no—not exactly." I shook my head sadly.

"Are you afraid she doesn't love you any longer?"

"Oh, no! I'm not afraid of that."

"My poor boy, if you want me to understand, you must explain a little more clearly."

I was ashamed and vexed to have given way to my emotion; my aunt was doubtless incapable of understanding the reasons for my uncertainty; but if some special motive lay behind Alissa's refusal, Aunt Félicie, by questioning her gently, might perhaps help me to discover it. She soon reached the same conclusion for herself.

"Listen," she went on. "Alissa is coming tomorrow morning to help me decorate the Christmas tree; I shall soon see what is at the bottom of it all; I will let you know at lunchtime, and I'm sure you'll see there's nothing to be alarmed about."

* * *

I went to dine at the Bucolins'. Juliette, who had, it is true, been unwell for the preceding few days, seemed to me changed; her eyes had a *farouche,* an almost hard, expression, which made her more different than ever from her sister. I was not able to speak to either of them alone that evening; neither did I wish to, and as my uncle seemed tired I left soon after dinner.

At the Christmas Tree Aunt Plantier gave every year, there was always a large gathering of children, relations, and friends. It was set up in an inner hall that contained the staircase and out of which opened the entrance hall, the drawing-room, and the glass doors of a kind of winter-garden, where a buffet had been spread. The decoration of the tree was not finished, and on the morning of the party, which was the day after my arrival, Alissa, as my aunt had told me she would, came round rather early to help her hang the branches of the tree with ornaments, lights, fruits, sweets, and toys. I should have enjoyed very much sharing this task with her myself, but I had to let Aunt Félicie speak to her. I went out, therefore, without seeing her, and spent the whole morning trying to while away the anxious hours.

I first went to the Bucolins', as I wanted to see Juliette. But I heard that Abel had been before me, and as I was afraid of interrupting a crucial conversation, I left at once; then I wandered about the quays and streets till lunchtime.

"Great silly!" cried my aunt, when I saw her. "It's really inexcusable to make yourself so unhappy for nothing! There's not a single word of sense in anything you said to me yesterday. Oh! I didn't beat about the bush. I sent Miss Ashburton away, as she was tiring herself out helping us, and as soon as I was alone with Alissa I asked her straight out why she hadn't accepted you last summer. Do you suppose she minded? She wasn't embarrassed for a single moment and answered quite calmly that she didn't want to marry before her sister. If you had asked her frankly, she would have said the same thing to you; a fine thing to make such a fuss about, isn't it? You see, my dear, there's nothing like frankness. Poor Alissa! She spoke to me about her father, too, whom she can't leave. Oh! we had a long talk. Dear child. She's very sensible; she told me she wasn't perfectly sure yet that she was the right person for you; that she was afraid she was too old, and thought that somebody of Juliette's age. . . ."

My aunt went on, but I no longer listened; there was only one thing that mattered—Alissa refused to marry before her sister. But was not Abel there? After all, in his egregious conceit he was right; he was going to pull off, as he said, both our marriages at one blow.

I hid from my aunt, as best I could, the agitation into which this revelation, simple as it was, had plunged me, and showed her nothing but a delight, which she thought very natural, and with which she was all the more gratified as it seemed that it was through her that I had obtained it; but directly after luncheon I left her with some excuse or other, and hurried off to find Abel.

"Ah! what did I tell you?" said he, embracing me, as soon as I had confided my good news to him. "My dear fellow, I can tell you already that the conversation I had with Juliette this morning almost settled it, though we talked of hardly anything but you. But she seemed tired—nervous—I was afraid of agitating her by going too far, of over-exciting her if I stayed too long. But after what you tell me, I hesitate no longer! I snatch up my hat, dear boy, my stick, and I'm off. Come with me as far as the Bucolins' to hang on to my coat-tails for fear I shall fly away on the road; I feel lighter than Euphorion! When Juliette knows that it's only because of her that her sister has refused you—when I make my offer on the spot— Ah! my boy, I can see my father this evening beside the Christmas tree, praising the Lord and weeping with joy, as he extends his hands over the two couples kneeling at his feet; Miss Ashburton will flutter off in a sigh; Aunt Plantier will dissolve into her bodice, and the fiery tree will sing the glory of God and clap its hands like the mountains in the Scriptures."

It was toward evening that the Christmas tree was to be lighted, and that the party of children, relations, and friends was to assemble. Not knowing what to do with myself, sick with anxiety and impatience, after I had left Abel I started on a long walk over the cliffs so as to get over the time of waiting as best I could—lost my way, and altogether managed so cleverly, that when I got back to Aunt Plantier's the party was already in full swing.

As soon as I got into the hall, I caught sight of Alissa; she seemed to be waiting for me, and came toward me at once. She was wearing around her neck, in the opening of her bodice, a little, old, amethyst cross I had given her in memory of my mother, but which I had never seen her wear before. Her features were drawn, and the look of suffering on her face smote my heart.

"Why are you so late?" she asked rapidly and breathlessly. "I wanted to speak to you."

"I lost my way on the cliffs. . . . But you're ill. . . . Oh, Alissa! what is the matter?"

She stood before me a moment, as though struck dumb, her lips trembling.

So sickening a dread took hold of me that I dared not question her. She put her hand on my neck, as though to pull my face toward her; I saw that she wanted to speak, but at that moment some guests came in; disheartened, she let her hand drop. . . .

"It is too late," she murmured. Then, seeing my eyes fill with tears, she added in reply to my enquiring look—as though such a derisory explanation could suffice to tranquillize me!—"No . . . don't be alarmed: I've only a headache, the children make such a noise . . . I had to take refuge here . . . it's time to go back to them now."

She left me abruptly. Some people coming in separated me from her. I thought that I should be able to rejoin her in the drawing-room. I caught sight of her at the other end of the room, surrounded by a troop of children whose games she was organizing; between her and me there were a number of people whom I knew, and whom I should not have been able to venture past without running the risk of being stopped. I felt incapable of civilities, of conversations; perhaps if I edged along the wall . . . I tried.

Just as I was going to pass in front of the large glass doors that led into the garden, I felt my arm seized. Juliette was there, half hidden in the embrasure, behind the folds of the curtain.

"Let's go into the conservatory," she said, hastily. "I want to speak to you. Go on by yourself; I'll meet you there directly." Then, half opening the door for a moment, she slipped into the garden.

What had happened? I wished that I could see Abel. What had he said? What had he done? Returning to the hall, I made my way to the conservatory, where Juliette was waiting for me.

Her face was flaming; her frowning brows gave her look an expression of hardness and pain; her eyes shone as if she was feverish; even her voice was harsh and tense. A sort of fury inspired her; notwithstanding my anxiety I was astonished—embarrassed almost—by her beauty. We were alone.

"Has Alissa spoken to you?" she asked at once.

"Barely two words; I came in very late."

"You know she wants me to marry before she does?"

"Yes."

She looked at me fixedly. . . . "And do you know whom she wants me to marry?"

I did not answer.

"You!" she went on with a cry.

"Why! it's madness!"

"Yes! isn't it?" There was both despair and triumph in her voice. She straightened herself, or rather flung herself backwards. "Now I know what there remains for me to do," she added indistinctly as she opened the door of the garden, which she slammed violently behind her.

My brain and heart were in a whirl. I felt the blood throbbing in my temples. One sole idea survived in the confusion of my spirits—to find Abel; he, perhaps, would be able to explain the singular behavior of the two sisters. But I dared not go back to the drawing-room, where I thought everyone would see my agitation. I went out. The icy air of the garden calmed me; I stayed in it some time. Evening was falling, and the sea-mist hid the town; there were no leaves on the trees; earth and sky seemed one immense desolation. The sound of voices singing rose upon the air; no doubt it was the choir of children gathered round the Christmas tree. I went in by the entrance hall. The doors of the drawing-room and inner hall were open; in the drawing-room, which was now deserted, I caught sight of my aunt where she was sitting, partly concealed by the piano, talking to Juliette. In the inner hall the guests were thronging round the lighted tree. The children had finished their hymn; there was a silence, and Pasteur Vautier, standing up in front of the tree, began a sort of sermon. He never missed an opportunity of what he called "sowing the good seed." I felt the lights and heat uncomfortably oppressive, and was going out. Abel was standing beside the door; he had, no doubt, been there for some time. He was looking at me in a hostile manner, and when our eyes met he shrugged his shoulders. I went toward him.

"Fool!" he said in a whisper; and then, abruptly, "Oh, let's go out; I'm fed up with preaching." And as soon as we were outside, "You fool!" he said again, as I looked at him anxiously without speaking. "Why, it's you she loves, you fool! Couldn't you have told me?"

I was aghast. I tried not to understand.

"No, of course not! You couldn't even see it for yourself!" He had seized me by the arm and was shaking me furiously. His voice between his clenched teeth hissed and trembled.

"Abel, I implore you," I said after a moment's silence, and in a voice that trembled too, while he strode along at random, dragging me with him. "Instead of being so angry, try to tell me what has happened. I know nothing."

He stopped suddenly and scrutinized my face by the dim light of a streetlamp; then, drawing me quickly to him, he put his head upon my shoulder and murmured with a sob: "Forgive me! I'm an idiot too, and I didn't understand any better than you, my poor brother!" His tears seemed to calm him a little; he raised his head, started walking again, and went on: "What happened? What's the use of going over it again? I had talked to Juliette in the morning, as I told you. She was extraordinarily beautiful and animated; I thought it was because of me, but it was simply because we were talking of you."

"Didn't you realize it at the time?"

"No, not exactly; but now the smallest detail becomes clear."

"Are you sure you are not making a mistake?"

"A mistake! My dear fellow, you must be blind not to see that she's in love with you."

"Then Alissa. . . ."

"Then Alissa is sacrificing herself. She had found out her sister's secret and wanted to give you up to her. Really, old boy, it's not very difficult to understand! I wanted to speak to Juliette again; at my first words or, rather, as soon as she began to understand me, she got up from the sofa where she was sitting and repeated several times over, 'I was sure of it,' in the tone of voice of a person who was anything but sure."

"Oh! don't joke about it."

"Why not? I consider it a highly comic affair. She rushed into her sister's room; I overheard their voices raised excitedly in a way that alarmed me. I hoped to see Juliette again, but after a moment it was Alissa who came out. She had her hat on, seemed embarrassed at seeing me, said 'How do you do?' to me quickly as she went out—and that's all."

"Didn't you see Juliette again?"

Abel hesitated for a little. "Yes. After Alissa had gone, I pushed open the door of the room. Juliette was there motionless, standing in front of the chimney-piece, her elbows on the marble, her chin in her hands; she was staring at herself in the glass. When she heard me she didn't turn around, but stamped her foot, crying, 'Oh, leave me alone!' so harshly that I went away again without asking for more. That's all."

"And now?"

"Oh! talking to you has done me good. . . . And now? Well! You had better try to cure Juliette of her love; for, either I don't know Alissa, or else she won't have you before you do."

We walked on for some time silently. "Let's go back," he said at last. "The guests must have gone by now. I'm afraid my father will be waiting for me."

We went in. The drawing-room was, in fact, empty; and in the hall around the tree, whose branches had been stripped and whose lights had nearly all been extinguished, there remained only my aunt and two of her children, Uncle Bucolin, Miss Ashburton, the pastor, my cousins, and a rather ridiculous-looking individual whom I had noticed talking for a long time to my aunt, but whom I only at that moment recognized as the suitor Juliette had spoken to me about. Taller, stronger, more highly colored than any of us, almost bald, of a different class, a different world, a different race, he seemed to realize that he was a stranger among us; he wore an immense moustache and a grizzled imperial, which he was nervously twisting and tugging.

The entrance hall, the doors of which had been left open, was not lighted; we had come in noiselessly, and no one noticed our presence. A frightful foreboding shot through me.

"Stop!" Abel said, seizing me by the arm.

Then we saw the stranger draw near Juliette, and take the hand that she abandoned to him without resistance, without giving him a glance. Night shut down upon my heart.

"Oh, Abel! What is happening?" I whispered as if I did not understand yet, or hoped I did not understand aright.

"By Jove! the young one is going one better," he said in a hissing voice. "She doesn't want to be outdone by her sister. The angels are applauding in Heaven, and no mistake!"

My uncle went up to embrace Juliette, whom Miss Ashburton and my aunt were pressing around. Pasteur Vautier drew near. I took a step forward.

Alissa caught sight of me, ran up to me in a quiver of emotion. "Oh, Jerome! It mustn't be. She doesn't love him! Why, she told me so only this very morning! Try to prevent it, Jerome! Oh! what will become of her?"

She hung upon my shoulder with desperate entreaty. I would have given my life to lessen her anguish.

Suddenly there came a cry from near the tree, a confused stir. We rushed up. Juliette had fallen unconscious into my aunt's arms. They were all crowding around, hanging over her, so that I could hardly see her; her face, which had turned frightfully pale, looked as though it was being dragged backwards by the weight of her loosened hair. It seemed, from the convulsive movements of her body, that this was no ordinary faint.

"No, no!" my aunt said aloud, in order to reassure Uncle Bucolin, who was getting agitated, and whom Pasteur Vautier was already consoling with his forefinger pointed Heavenwards. "No, it's nothing. The effect of emotion. Just a nervous attack. Monsieur Teissières, please help me, you're so strong. We will carry her up to my room, on to my bed, on to my bed." Then she stooped toward the elder of her sons and whispered something in his ear; I saw him go off at once, no doubt to fetch a doctor.

My aunt and the stranger were supporting Juliette's shoulders as she lay, half reclining, in their arms. Alissa raised her sister's feet and embraced them tenderly. Abel held up her head, which would have fallen backwards, and I saw him bend down and cover her floating hair with kisses as he gathered it together.

Outside the door of the room I stopped. Juliette was laid on the bed; Alissa said a few words to M. Teissières and to Abel which I could not hear; she accompanied them to the door and begged us to leave her sister to rest; she

wished to remain alone with her, with no one else but Aunt Plantier. Abel caught hold of my arm and dragged me out of doors into the night, and there we walked on and on for a long time without purpose, without courage, without reflection.

5.

I seemed to have no reason for living other than my love, and to that I clung, expecting nothing, and with my mind made up to expect nothing but what should come to me from Alissa.

The next morning, as I was getting ready to go to see her, my aunt handed me the following letter, which she had just received:—

". . . Juliette's extreme restlessness did not yield to the doctor's prescriptions till toward morning. I beg Jerome not to come to see us for some days. Juliette might recognize his footstep or his voice, and she is in need of the greatest quiet.

"I am afraid Juliette's condition will keep me here. If I do not manage to see Jerome before he leaves, please tell him, dear Aunt, that I will write to him. . . ."

The Bucolins' door was shut only against me. My aunt or anyone else who chose was free to knock at it; and, indeed, my aunt was going there that very morning. I might make a noise! What a feeble excuse! No matter. "Very well," said I, "I won't go."

It cost me a great deal not to see Alissa again at once, and yet I was afraid of seeing her; I was afraid she might hold me responsible for her sister's condition, and it was easier to bear not seeing her again than to see her vexed.

At any rate, I determined I would see Abel. At his door, the maid gave me a note:—

"I am leaving you this time so that you mayn't be anxious. The idea of staying at Le Havre, so near Juliette, was intolerable. I embarked for Southampton last night, almost directly after I left you. I shall spend the rest of the holidays with S—— in London. We shall meet again at the School."

All human help failed me at one and the same time. I did not prolong a stay that could only prove painful to me, and went back to Paris before the beginning of the term. It was to God that I turned my looks, to Him "from Whom cometh down all true consolation and every good gift." It was to Him that I offered my trouble. I thought that Alissa, too, was taking refuge in Him, and the thought that she was praying encouraged and exalted my prayers.

There went by a long period of meditation and study, with no events other than Alissa's letters to me and mine to her. I have kept all her letters; by their help I can, from this time onwards, check my recollections when they become confused.

I had news of Le Havre from my aunt, and at first only from her; I learned through her what anxiety Juliette's unhappy condition had caused for the first few days. Twelve days after I had left, I at last received this letter from Alissa:—

"Forgive me, my dear Jerome, for not having written to you sooner. Our poor Juliette's state has allowed me very little time. Since you went away, I have hardly left her. I begged Aunt to give you news of us, and I suppose she has done so. So you know that Juliette has been better for the last three days. I already thank God, but I dare not feel happy yet."

Robert also, of whom I have so far told you very little, was able to give me news of his sisters when he returned to Paris a few days after me. For their sake, I spent more time with him than my disposition naturally would have inclined me to; whenever the School of Agriculture, where he was studying, left him free, I took him in charge and was at great pains to amuse him.

It was through him that I learned—what I had not dared ask either Alissa or my aunt—that Édouard Teissières had come to enquire for Juliette very assiduously, but that when Robert had left Le Havre she had not yet seen him. I learned also that Juliette had kept up an obstinate silence toward her sister which nothing had been able to break down.

Then I learned from my aunt a little later that Juliette insisted on her engagement being made public in spite of what I instinctively felt was Alissa's hope that it would be broken off at once. Advice, injunctions, entreaties, spent themselves in vain against this determination of Juliette's, which seemed fixed like a bar across her brow and a bandage over her eyes—which seemed to immure her in silence.

Time passed. I received from Alissa—to whom, indeed, I knew not what to write—nothing but the most elusive notes. The thick fogs of winter wrapped me round; my study lamp and all the fervor of my love and faith served but ill, alas! to keep the darkness and the cold from my heart.

Time passed. Then, one morning of sudden spring, came a letter from Alissa to my aunt, who was absent from Le Havre, a letter which my aunt sent on to me and from which I copy out the part that throws light on my story.

"Admire my docility. As you advised, I have seen M. Teissières and talked to him at length. I confess that his behavior has been perfect, and I have almost, I admit, come to the point of believing that the marriage may not turn out so badly as I feared at first. Certainly Juliette does not love him; but he seems to me every week to be less unworthy of her love. He speaks of the situation with great clear-sightedness and makes no mistake as to my sister's character; but he has great faith in the efficacy of his own love, and flatters himself that there is nothing his constancy will not be able to overcome. That is to say, he is very much in love.

"Yes! I am extremely touched to see Jerome take so much trouble over my brother. I imagine that he does so only out of a sense of duty, for Robert's character is very different from his—perhaps, too, in order to please me—but doubtless he has already come to understand that the more arduous the duty one assumes, the more it educates and uplifts the soul. You will think these very lofty reflections, but do not laugh at your foolish niece too much for it is these thoughts which give me support and which help me to try to look upon Juliette's marriage as a good thing.

"Dear Aunt, your affectionate solicitude is very precious to me. But do not think I am unhappy; I might almost say that the contrary is the case, for the trial through which Juliette has just gone has had its effect on me too. Those words of Scripture which I used to repeat without very well understanding them have suddenly become clear to me: 'Cursed be the man that trusteth in man.' Long before coming across them in my Bible, I had read them on a little Christmas card which Jerome sent me when he was not quite twelve years old and I was just four-teen. Beside the bunch of flowers which was painted on it, and which we then thought lovely, there were these lines, from a paraphrase of Corneille's:—

'Quel charme vainqueur du monde
Vers Dieu m'élève aujourd'hui?
Malheureux l'homme qui fonde
Sur les hommes son appui.'

"I confess I infinitely prefer the simple text out of Jeremiah. No doubt, Jerome chose the card at the time without paying much attention to the lines. But if I am to judge from his letters, his frame of mind at present is not unlike mine, and every day I thank God that He should have brought us both nearer to Him with one and the same stroke.

"I have not forgotten our conversation, and I am not writing to him so much as I used to do, so as not to disturb him in his work. You will no doubt think that I make up for it by talking about him all the more; lest I should go on too long, I will end my letter at once. Don't scold me too much this time."

What reflections this letter aroused in me! I cursed my aunt's meddling interference (what was the conversation to which Alissa alluded, and which was the cause of her silence?) and the clumsy good nature that made her send the letter on to me. It was already hard enough for me to bear Alissa's silence, and oh! would it not have been better a thousand times to have left me in ignorance that she was writing to another person what she no longer cared to say to me? Everything in the letter irritated me: to hear her speak to my aunt so easily of our little private affairs, as well as the naturalness of her tone, her composure, her seriousness, her pleasantry.

"No, no, my dear fellow! Nothing in the letter irritates you, except the fact that it isn't addressed to you," said Abel, who was my daily companion; for Abel was the only person to whom I could speak, and in my loneliness, I was constantly drawn to him afresh by weakness, by a wistful longing for sympathy, by diffidence, and, when I was at fault, by my belief in his advice, in spite of the difference of our natures—or rather, because of it.

"Let us study this paper," said he,

spreading the letter out on his writing-table.

Three nights had already passed over my vexation; for four days I had managed to keep it to myself! I led up almost naturally to a point when Abel said to me: "We'll consign the Juliette-Teissières affair to the fire of love—eh? We know what that flame is worth. Upon my word, Teissières seems just the kind of moth to singe his wings in it."

"That will do!" I said, for his banter was very distasteful to me. "Let's go on to the rest."

"The rest?" he said. "The rest is all for you. You haven't much to complain of. Not a line, not a word, that isn't filled with the thought of you. You may say the whole letter is addressed to you: when Aunt Félicie sent it on to you, she merely sent it to its rightful owner; Alissa writes to the good lady as a makeshift, in default of you. What can Corneille's lines (which, by the way, are by Racine) matter to your aunt? I tell you, it's to you she is talking; she's saying it all to you. You're nothing but a simpleton if a fortnight hence your cousin isn't writing to you just as lengthily, as easily, as agreeably. . . ."

"She doesn't seem to be taking the right road!"

"It only depends upon you for her to take it! Do you want my advice? Don't say a word for ever so long of love or marriage; don't you see that since her sister's misfortune, it's *that* she's set against? Harp on the fraternal string and talk to her untiringly of Robert—since you have the patience to look after the young ass. Just go on amusing her intelligence; all the rest will follow. Ah! if it were only I who had to write to her! You aren't worthy to love her."

Nevertheless, I followed Abel's advice; and, indeed, Alissa's letters soon began to get more animated; but I could not hope for any real joy on her part or that she would let herself go without reserve until Juliette's situation, if not her happiness, was assured.

The news Alissa gave me of her sister improved, however. Her marriage was to take place in July; Alissa wrote to me that she supposed that at this date Abel and I would be engaged in our studies. I understood that she judged it better for us not to appear at the ceremony, so we alleged some examination or other, and contented ourselves with sending our good wishes.

About a fortnight after the marriage this is what Alissa wrote to me:—

"My Dear Jerome,

"Imagine my astonishment yesterday when, on opening at random the charming Racine you gave me, I found the four lines that are on your little old Christmas card that I have kept in my Bible for the last ten years.

> 'Quel charme vainqueur du monde
> Vers Dieu m'élève aujourd'hui?
> Malheureux l'homme qui fonde
> Sur les hommes son appui!'

"I had thought they came from a paraphrase of Corneille's, and I admit I didn't think much of them. But as I went on reading the fourth *Cantique Spirituel*, I came across some verses which are so beautiful that I cannot resist copying them. No doubt you know them already, if I am to judge from the indiscreet initials which you have put in the margin of the book. [It is true that I had taken the habit of sprinkling my books and Alissa's with the first letter of her name, opposite all the passages I liked and wanted her to know.] Never mind! I write them out for my own pleasure. I was a little vexed at first to see that you had pointed out what I thought was a discovery of my own, but this naughty feeling soon gave way to my pleasure in thinking that you like them as much as I do. As I copy, I feel as if I were reading them over with you.

'De la sagesse immortelle
La voix tonne et nous instruit.
"Enfants des hommes," dit-elle,
"De vos soins quel est le fruit?
Par quelle erreur, âmes vaines,
Du plus pur sang de vos veines
Achetez-vous si souvent,
Non un pain qui vous repaisse,
Mais une ombre qui vous laisse
Plus affamés que devant? . . .

.   .   .

' "Le pain que je vous propose
Sert aux anges d'aliment:
Dieu lui-même le compose
De la fleur de son froment,
C'est ce pain si délectable
Que ne sert point à sa table
Le monde que vous suivez.
Je l'offre à qui veut me suivre.
Approchez. Voulez-vous vivre?
Prenez, mangez et vivez."

.   .   .

'L'âme heureusement captive
Sous ton joug trouve la paix,
Et s'abreuve d'une eau vive
Que ne s'épuise jamais.
Chacun peut boire en cette onde:
Elle invite tout le monde;
Mais nous courons follement
Chercher des sources bourbeuses
Ou des citernes trompeuses
D'où l'eau fuit à tout moment.'

"How beautiful! Jerome, how beautiful! Do you really think it as beautiful as I do? A little note in my edition says that Mme de Maintenon, when she heard Mlle d'Aumale sing this hymn, seemed struck with admiration, 'dropped a few tears,' and made her repeat a part of the piece. I know it by heart now, and never weary of saying it to myself. My only regret is that I haven't heard you read it.

"The news from our travelers continues to be very good. You know already how much Juliette enjoyed Bayonne and Biarritz in spite of the fearful heat. Since then they have visited Fontarabie, stayed at Burgos, and crossed the Pyrenees twice. Now she writes me an enthusiastic letter from Montserrat. They think of spending ten days longer at Barcelona before they return to Nîmes, where Édouard wants to be back before September so as to be able to look after the vintage.

"Father and I have been settled at Fongueusemare for a week now, and we expect Miss Ashburton and Robert in four days' time. You know the poor boy has failed in his examination; not that it was difficult, but the examiner asked him such peculiar questions that it confused him; I cannot believe, after what you told me about his keenness for work, that he hadn't prepared properly, but this examiner, it appears, takes a pleasure in putting people out.

"As for your successes, my dear, I can hardly say that I congratulate you. I have so much confidence in you, Jerome! Whenever I think of you, my heart fills with hope. Will you be able to begin the work you speak about at once?

"Nothing is changed here in the garden; but the house seems very empty! You will have understood—won't you?— why I asked you not to come this year. I feel it is better so; I tell myself so every day, for it is hard to stay so long without seeing you. Sometimes I look for you involuntarily; I stop in the middle of what I am reading, I turn my head quickly . . . it seems as though you were there!

"I continue my letter. It is night; everybody is asleep; I am sitting up late writing to you, before the open window. The garden is full of scents; the air is warm. Do you remember when we were children, whenever we saw or heard anything very beautiful, we used to say to ourselves, 'Thanks, Lord, for having created it.' Tonight I said to myself with my whole soul, 'Thanks, Lord, for having made the night so beautiful!' And suddenly I wanted you there—I felt you there, close to me—with such violence that perhaps you felt it.

"Yes, you were right in your letter when you said, 'In generous hearts admiration is lost in gratitude.' How many other things I should like to write to you. I think of the radiant land Juliette speaks of. I think of other lands, vaster, more radiant still, more desert-like. A *strange* conviction dwells in me that one day—but I cannot tell how—you and I shall see together some great mysterious land —but ah! I cannot tell which . . ."

No doubt you can easily imagine with what transports of joy I read this letter, with what sobs of love! Other letters followed. Alissa, it is true, thanked me for not coming to Fongueusemare; it is true she begged me not to try to see her again that year, but she regretted my absence, she wanted me; from page to page there sounded the same appeal. Where did I find strength to resist it? In Abel's advice, no doubt, and in the fear of suddenly ruining my joy, and in an instinctive stiffening of my will against the inclinations of my heart.

From the letters that followed I copy all that bears upon my tale:—

"Dear Jerome,

"My heart melts with joy as I read you. I was just going to answer your letter from Orvieto, when the one from Perugia and the one from Assisi arrived together. My mind has turned traveler; it is only my body that makes believe to stay behind here; in truth I am with you on the white roads of Umbria. I set out with you in the morning and watch the dawn with a fresh-created eye. . . . Did you really call me on the terrace of Cortona? I heard you. We were terribly thirsty on the hills above Assisi, but how good I thought the Franciscan's glass of water! Oh, my friend! It is through you that I look at all things. How much I like what you write about St. Francis! Yes, what we should seek for is indeed—is it not?— an exaltation and not an emancipation of the mind. The latter goes only with an abominable pride. Our ambition should lie not in revolt but in service.

"The news from Nîmes is so good that it seems to me I have God's permission to give way to joy. The only shadow this summer is my poor father's condition. In spite of all my care he still stays sad, or rather relapses into sadness the moment I leave him to himself, and it becomes less and less easy to get him out of it. All the joys of nature that are about us speak a language that has become foreign to him; he no longer even makes any effort to understand it. Miss Ashburton is well. I read your letters aloud to them both; each one gives us enough to talk about for three days, and then comes a fresh one.

"Robert left us the day before yesterday. He is going to spend the rest of his holidays with his friend R——, whose father is at the head of a model farm. Certainly the life we lead here is not very amusing for him. I could only encourage him in his idea when he spoke of leaving.

". . . I have so much to say to you. I thirst for a talk, such an endless talk! Sometimes I can find no words, no distinct ideas—this evening I am writing as in a dream—and all I realize is an almost oppressive sense of infinite riches to bestow and to receive.

"How did we manage to be silent during so many long months? No doubt we were hibernating. Oh! may that frightful winter of our silence be forever past! Now that I have found you again, life, thought, our souls—everything seems beautiful, adorable, inexhaustibly fertile."

12th September.

"I have got your letter from Pisa. The weather is splendid here, too. Never before have I thought Normandy so beautiful. The day before yesterday I took an enormously long walk, going across country at random. When I came in, I was not so much tired as excited, almost intoxicated with sun and joy. How beautiful the haystacks were in the burning sun! There was no need for me to imagine myself in Italy to think everything I saw wonderful.

"Yes, dear friend, it is as you say, an exhortation to joy which I hear and understand in Nature's 'mingled hymn.' I hear it in every bird's song; I breathe it in the scent of every flower, and I have reached the point of conceiving adoration as the only form of prayer, repeating over and over again with St. Francis: 'My God! My God! *e non altro*'—and nothing else—my heart filled with *inexpressible* love.

"Don't be afraid, though, of my becoming an ignoramus. I have been reading a great deal lately; with the help of a few rainy days I have, as it were, folded my adoration up into my books. Finished Malebranche and began at once Leibnitz's *Letters to Clarke*. Then, as a rest, read Shelley's *Cenci*—without pleasure; read *The Sensitive Plant* too. I shall make you very indignant, but I would give nearly all of Shelley and all of Byron for Keats's four odes, which we read together last summer; just as I would give all Hugo for a few of Baudelaire's sonnets. The words 'great poet' have no meaning —what is important is to be a *pure* poet. Oh, my brother! thank you for having taught me to understand and love these things.

"No, don't cut short your journey for the sake of a few days' meeting. Seriously, it is better that we should not see each other again just yet. Believe me, I could not think of you more if you were with me. I should be sorry to give you pain, but I have come to the point of no longer wanting your presence—now. Shall I confess? If I knew you were coming this evening I should fly away.

"Oh! don't ask me to explain this feeling, please. I only know that I think of you unceasingly (which ought to be enough for *your* happiness) and that I am happy so."

A short time after this last letter, and immediately after my return from Italy, I was called up for my military service and sent to Nancy. I did not know a living soul there, but I was glad to be alone, for it was thus more clearly apparent to my lover's pride and to Alissa herself that her letters were my only refuge, and that the thought of her was, as Ronsard would have said, "my only entelechy."

To tell the truth I bore very cheerily the pretty severe discipline to which we were subjected. I stiffened myself to endurance, and in my letters to Alissa complained only of absence. We even found in this long separation a trial worthy of our valor. *"You who never complain,"* wrote Alissa; *"you whom I cannot imagine faltering."* What would I not have endured to prove the truth of her words?

Almost a year had gone by since our last meeting. She seemed not to consider this, but to count her time of waiting only from now onwards. I reproached her with it.

"Was I not with you in Italy? [She replied.] Ungrateful! I never left you for a single day. You must understand that now, for a time, I can't follow you any longer, and it is that, only that, which I call separation. I try hard, it is true, to imagine you as a soldier. I can't succeed. At best I see you in the evening in your little room in the rue Gambetta, writing or reading—but no, not even that! In reality it is only at Fongueusemare or Le Havre that I can see you, a year from now.

"A year! I don't count the days that have already gone by; my hope fastens its gaze on that point in the future, which is slowly, slowly drawing nearer. Do you remember the low wall that shelters the chrysanthemums at the end of the garden, and how sometimes we used to venture along the top of it? Juliette and you walked on it as boldly as though you were Mussulmans going straight to Paradise; as for me, I was seized with giddiness after the first step or two, and you used to call to me from below: 'Don't look at your feet! Eyes front! Don't stop! Look at the goal!' And then, at last—and it was more of a help than your words—you would climb on to the wall at the other end and wait for me. Then I no longer trembled; I no longer felt giddy; I no longer saw anything but you; I ran until I reached your open arms.

"Without faith in you, Jerome, what would become of me? I have need to feel you strong; need to lean on you. Don't weaken."

Out of a sort of spirit of defiance, which made us deliberately prolong our time of waiting—out of fear, too, of an unsatisfactory meeting—we agreed that I should spend my few days' leave at Christmas with Miss Ashburton, in Paris.

I have already told you that I do not give all her letters. Here is one I received about the middle of February:—

"Great excitement the day before yesterday in passing along the rue de Paris to see Abel's book, very ostentatiously displayed in M——'s shop window. You had indeed announced its appearance, but I could not believe in its *reality*. I wasn't able to resist going in; but the title seemed to me so ridiculous that I hesitated to name it to the shopman; I was, in fact, on the point of going out again with any other book, no matter what. Fortunately a little pile of *Wantonness* was set out for customers near the counter, and I took a copy and put down my money, without having had to speak.

"I am grateful to Abel for not having sent me his book! I have not been able to look through it without shame; shame

not so much because of the book itself—in which, after all, I see more folly than indecency—but shame to think that Abel, Abel Vautier, your friend, should have written it. I searched in vain, from page to page, for the 'great talent' that the *Temps* reviewer has discovered in it. In our little society of Le Havre, where Abel is often mentioned, people say that the book is very successful. I hear his incurable futility of mind called 'lightness' and 'grace'; of course, I keep prudently silent, and have told no one but you that I have read it. Poor Pasteur Vautier, who at first looked deeply grieved—and very rightly —is now beginning to wonder whether, instead, he hasn't cause to feel proud; and all his acquaintance are doing their best to persuade him so. Yesterday, at Aunt Plantier's, when Mme V—— said to him abruptly: 'You must be very happy, Pasteur, over your son's wonderful success!' he answered, rather abashed: 'Oh! I haven't got as far as that yet!' 'But you will! But you will!' Aunt said, innocently no doubt, but in such an encouraging voice that everyone began to laugh, even he.

"What will it be when *The New Abelard* is brought out? I hear it is going to be acted at some theatre or other on the *boulevards,* and that the papers are beginning to talk of it already! Poor Abel! Is that really the success he wants? Will he be satisfied with that?

"Yesterday in the *Interior Consolation* I read these words: 'All human glory, indeed all temporal honor, all worldly grandeur, compared with Thy eternal glory, is vanity and foolishness.' And I thought: 'Oh, God! I thank Thee that Thou hast chosen Jerome for Thy eternal glory, compared with which the other is vanity and foolishness.' "

The weeks and months went by in monotonous occupations; but as there was nothing on which I could fasten my thoughts but memories or hopes, I hardly noticed how slow the time was, how long the hours.

My uncle and Alissa were to go in June to the neighborhood of Nîmes on a visit to Juliette, who was expecting her baby about that time. Less favorable news of her health made them hasten their departure.

"Your last letter, addressed to Le Havre, [wrote Alissa] arrived after we had left. I cannot explain by what accident it reached me here only a week later. During all that week I went about with a soul that was only half a soul, a shivering, pitiful, beggarly soul. Oh, my brother! I am only truly myself—more than myself—when I am with you.

"Juliette is better again. We are daily expecting her confinement, without undue anxiety. She knows that I am writing to you this morning. The day after our arrival at Aigues-Vives, she said to me: 'And Jerome? What has become of him? Does he write to you still?' And as I couldn't but tell her the truth: 'When you write to him,' she said, 'tell him that . . .' she hesitated a moment, and then, smiling very sweetly, went on: 'that I am cured.' I was rather afraid that in her letters, which are always so gay, she might be acting a part and taking herself in by it. The things she makes her happiness out of nowadays are so different from the things she had dreamed of, the things on which it seemed her happiness ought to have depended! . . . Ah! this which we call *happiness,* how intimate a part of the soul it is, and of what little importance are the outside elements that seem to go to its making! I spare you all the reflections I make during my walks along the *garigue,* when what astonishes me most is that I don't feel happier; Juliette's happiness ought to fill me with joy . . . why does my heart give way to an incomprehensible melancholy against

which I am unable to fight? The very beauty of the country, which I feel, which at any rate I recognize, adds still further to this inexplicable sadness. When you wrote to me from Italy, I was able to see everything through you; now I feel as if I were depriving you of whatever I look at without you. And then at Fongueusemare or at Le Havre I had made for myself a kind of rough-weather virtue for use on rainy days; here, this virtue seems out of place, and I feel uneasily that there is no occasion for it. The laughter of the people and the country jars upon me; perhaps what I call being sad is simply not being so noisy as they. No doubt there was some pride in my joy formerly, for at present, in the midst of this alien gaiety, what I feel is not unlike humiliation.

"I have scarcely been able to pray since I have been here: I have the childish feeling that God is no longer in the same place. Good-bye; I must stop now. I am ashamed of this blasphemy, and of my weakness, and of my sadness, and of confessing them, and of writing you all this which I should tear up tomorrow if it were not posted tonight. . . ."

The next letter spoke only of the birth of her niece, whose godmother she was to be, of Juliette's joy and of my uncle's. Of her own feelings there was no further question.

Then there were letters dated from Fongueusemare again, where Juliette went to stay with her in July.

"Édouard and Juliette left us this morning. It is my little niece whom I regret most; when I see her again in six months' time I shall no longer recognize every one of her movements; she had scarcely one that I hadn't seen her invent. Growth is always so mysterious and surprising; it is through failure of attention that we are not oftener astonished at it. How many hours I have spent bending over the little cradle where so many hopes lie centered. By what selfishness, by what conceit, by what lack of desire for improvement is it that development ceases so soon, and that every creature becomes definitive when still so far from God? Oh! if we could, if we would but approach nearer to Him . . . think, what emulation!

"Juliette seems very happy. I was grieved at first to find that she had given up her piano and her reading; but Édouard Teissières doesn't like music and hasn't much taste for books; no doubt Juliette is acting wisely in not seeking her pleasure where he cannot follow her. On the other hand, she takes an interest in her husband's occupations and he tells her all about his business. It has developed greatly this year; it pleases him to say that it is because of his marriage, which has brought him an important *clientèle* at Le Havre. Robert accompanied him the last time he went on a business journey. Édouard is very kind to him, declares he understands his character, and doesn't despair of seeing him take seriously to this kind of work.

"Father is much better; the sight of his daughter's happiness has made him young again; he is interesting himself again in the farm and the garden, and has just asked me to go on with our reading aloud, which we had begun with Miss Ashburton and which was interrupted by the Teissières' visit. I am reading them Baron Hübner's travels, and enjoy them very much myself. I shall have more time now for my own reading too; but I want some advice from you; this morning I took up several books, one after the other, without feeling a taste for any of them!"

Alissa's letters thenceforward became more troubled, more pressing.

"The fear of troubling you prevents me from telling you how much I want you. [She wrote toward the end of the summer.] Every day that has to be got through before I see you again weighs on me, oppresses me. Another two months! It seems longer than all the rest of the time that has already gone by without you! Everything I take up to while away the hours, seems nothing but an absurd stopgap, and I cannot set myself to anything. My books are without virtue and without charm; my walks have no attraction; Nature has lost her glamour; the garden is emptied of color, of scent. I envy you your fatigue-parties and your compulsory drills, which are constantly dragging you out of yourself, tiring you, hurrying along your days, and, at night, flinging you, wearied out, to your sleep. The stirring description you gave me of the maneuvers haunts me. For the last few nights I have been sleeping badly, and several times I have been awakened with a start by the bugles sounding reveillé . . . I actually heard them. I can so well imagine the intoxication of which you speak, the morning rapture, the lightheadedness almost. . . . How beautiful the plateau of Malzéville must have been in the icy radiance of dawn!

"I have not been quite so well lately; oh! nothing serious. I think I am just looking forward a little too much to your coming."

And six weeks later:

"This is my last letter, my friend. However uncertain the date of your return may be, it cannot be delayed much longer. I shall not be able to write to you any more. I should have preferred our meeting to have been at Fongueusemare, but the weather has broken; it is very cold, and Father talks of nothing but going back to town. Now that Juliette and Robert are no longer with us, we could easily take you in, but it is better that you should go to Aunt Félicie's, who will be glad, too, to have you.

"As the day of our meeting comes near, I look forward to it with growing anxiety, almost with apprehension. I seem now to dread your coming, which I so longed for; I try not to think of it; I imagine your ring at the bell, your step on the stairs, and my heart stops beating or hurts me. . . . And whatever you do, don't expect me to be able to speak to you. I feel my past comes to an end here; I see nothing beyond; my life stops. . . ."

Four days later, however—a week, that is, before I was liberated from my military service—I received one more letter, a very short one:

"My friend, I entirely approve of your not wanting to prolong beyond measure your stay at Le Havre and the time of our first meeting. What should we have to say to each other that we have not already written? So if the business connected with your examination calls you to Paris as early as the 28th, don't hesitate, don't even regret that you are not able to give us more than two days. Shall we not have all our lives?"

6.

It was at Aunt Plantier's that our first meeting took place. I suddenly felt that my military service had made me heavy and clumsy. . . . Later on I thought she must have found me altered. But why should this first deceptive impression have had any importance for us two? As for me, I was so much afraid of not recognizing the Alissa I knew that at first I hardly dared look at her. No! what was really embarrassing was the absurd position of being engaged, which they all forced upon us, and everybody's anxiety

to leave us alone and hurry away when we were there!

"Oh, Aunt! you are not the least in the way; we have nothing private to say to each other," Alissa cried at last, impatient at the tactless manner in which the excellent woman tried to efface herself.

"Yes, yes! my dears. I quite understand. When young people haven't seen each other for a long time, they always have lots of little things to tell each other."

"Please, Aunt! You really will annoy us if you go away!" and this was said in a tone that was almost angry, and in which I hardly recognized Alissa's voice.

"Aunt! I assure you that if you go away, we shan't utter a single other word!" I added, laughing, but myself filled with a certain apprehension at the idea of our being left alone. And then, with sham cheerfulness, we all three set to work to make conversation, trying to hide our embarrassment beneath the forced liveliness of our commonplace talk. We were to meet again the next day, as my uncle had invited me to lunch, so that we parted that evening without regret, glad to put an end to this absurd scene.

I arrived long before luncheon-time, but found Alissa talking to a girl friend whom she had not the strength of mind to send away, and who was not discreet enough to go. When at last she left us, I pretended to be surprised that Alissa had not kept her to lunch. We were both of us in a state of nervous tension and tired by a sleepless night. My uncle appeared. Alissa felt that I thought him aged. He had grown rather deaf, and heard my voice with difficulty; the necessity I was under of shouting so as to make myself understood made my talk dull and stupid.

After lunch Aunt Plantier, as had been arranged, came to take us out in her carriage; she drove us to Orcher with the idea of letting Alissa and me do the pleasantest part of the return journey on foot.

The weather was hot for the time of year. The part of the hill up which we had to walk was exposed to the sun and unattractive; the leafless trees gave us no shelter. In our anxiety to rejoin the carriage in which our aunt was to wait for us, we hastened our pace uncomfortably. My head was aching so badly that I could not extract a single idea from it; to keep myself in countenance, or because I thought that the gesture might serve instead of words, I had taken Alissa's hand, which she let me keep. Our emotion, the rapidity of our walk, and the awkwardness of our silence sent the blood to our faces; I felt my temples throbbing; Alissa's color was unpleasantly heightened; and soon the discomfort of feeling the contact of our damp hands made us unclasp them and let them drop sadly to our sides.

We had made too much haste; we arrived at the crossroads long before the carriage, which had taken another road and driven very slowly, because of my aunt's desire to leave us plenty of time for talking. We sat down on the bank at the side of the road; a cold wind, which suddenly got up, chilled us to the bone, for we were bathed in perspiration; then we walked on to meet the carriage. But the worst was again the pressing solicitude of our poor aunt, who was convinced that we had had a long and satisfactory talk and was longing to question us about our engagement. Alissa, unable to bear it, and with her eyes full of tears, alleged a violent headache, and we drove home in silence.

The next day I woke up with aching limbs and a bad chill, so unwell that I put off going to the Bucolins' till afternoon. By ill luck, Alissa was not alone. Madeleine Plantier, one of Aunt Félicie's granddaughters, was there. I knew that Alissa liked talking to her. She was stay-ing with her grandmother for a few days, and when I came in, she exclaimed: "If you are going back to the Côte when you leave here, we might as well go together."

I agreed mechanically; so that I was unable to see Alissa alone. But the presence of this charming girl was, no doubt, a help to us; I no longer felt the intolerable embarrassment of the day before; the conversation among the three of us was soon going smoothly, and was less futile than I had at first feared. Alissa smiled strangely when I said good-bye to her; I had the impression that she had not understood till that moment that I was going away the next morning. But the prospect of my speedy return took any touch of tragedy from my good-bye.

After dinner, however, prompted by a vague uneasiness, I went down to the town, where I wandered about for nearly an hour before I made up my mind to ring at the Bucolins' door. It was my uncle who received me. Alissa, who was not feeling very well, had already gone to her room and, no doubt, straight to bed. I talked to my uncle for a few moments, and then left.

It would be vain for me to blame the perverseness of these incidents, unfortunate though they were. For even if everything had favored us, we should still have invented our embarrassment ourselves. But nothing could have made me more wretched than that Alissa, too, should feel this. This is the letter I received as soon as I got to Paris:

"My friend, what a melancholy meeting! You seemed to lay the blame on other people, but without being able to convince yourself. And now I think—I know—it will be so always. Oh! I beg of you, don't let us see each other again!

"Why this awkwardness, this feeling of being in a false position, this paralysis, this dumbness, when we have everything in the world to say to each other? The first day of your return this very silence made me happy because I believed it would vanish, and that you would tell me the most wonderful things; it was impossible that you should leave me without.

"But when our lugubrious expedition to Orcher came to an end without a word—when, above all, our hands unclasped and fell apart so hopelessly, I thought my heart would faint within me for grief and pain. And what distressed me most was not so much that your hand let go mine, but my feeling that if yours had not, mine would have done so, for my hand too no longer felt happy in yours.

"The next day—yesterday—I expected you madly all the morning. I was too restless to stop indoors, and I left a line for you to tell you where to find me on the jetty. I stayed a long time looking at the stormy sea, but I was too miserable looking at it without you; I imagined suddenly that you were waiting for me in my room, and went in. I knew I shouldn't be free in the afternoon; Madeleine had told me the day before that she meant to come, and as I expected to see you in the morning I did not put her off. But perhaps it was to her presence we owed the only pleasant moments of our meeting. For a few minutes I had the strange illusion that this comfortable conversation was going to last a long, long time. And when you came up to the sofa where I was sitting beside her, and bent down and said 'good-bye,' I could not answer; it seemed as though it was the end of everything: it suddenly dawned upon me that you were going.

"You had no sooner left with Madeleine than it struck me as impossible, unbearable. Will you believe it? I went out! I wanted to speak to you again, to tell you all the things I had not told you; I was already hurrying to the Plantiers'. . . . It was late; I didn't have time, didn't dare. . . . I came in again, des-

perate, to write to you—that I didn't want to write to you any more—a good-bye letter because I felt too much that our correspondence was nothing but a vast mirage, that we were each writing, alas! only to ourselves and that—Jerome! Jerome! Ah! how far apart we were all the time!

"I tore that letter up, it is true; but now I am writing it over again, almost the same. Oh! I do not love you less, my dear! On the contrary, I never before felt so clearly, by my very disturbance, by my embarrassment as soon as you came near me, how deeply I loved you; but hopelessly too, for I must perforce confess it to myself—when you were away, I loved you more. I had already begun to suspect so, alas! This longed-for meeting has finally shown me the truth, and you too, my friend, must needs be convinced of it. Good-bye, my much-loved brother; may God keep and guide you! To Him alone can we draw near with impunity."

And as if this letter was not sufficiently painful, the next day she had added the following postscript:

"I do not wish to let this letter go without asking you to show a little more discretion in regard to what concerns us both. Many a time you have wounded me by talking to Juliette or Abel about things which should have remained private between you and me, and this is, indeed, what made me think—long before you suspected it—that your love was above all intellectual, the beautiful tenacity of a tender, faithful mind."

The fear lest I should show this letter to Abel had doubtless inspired the last lines. What suspicious instinct had put her on her guard? Had she formerly detected in my words some reflection of my friend's advice?

In truth, I felt myself far enough away

from him! The paths we followed were thenceforth divergent; and there was little need of these recommendations to teach me to bear the anxious burden of my grief alone.

The next three days were wholly occupied by my pleading; I wished to reply to Alissa; I was afraid of incurably inflaming the wound by too deliberate a discussion, by too vehement protestations, by the slightest clumsy word; twenty times over I began the letter in which my love struggled for its life. I cannot to this day re-read without weeping the tear-stained paper on which is the copy of the one I at last decided to send:

"Alissa! Have pity on me, on us both! Your letter hurts me. How much I wish I could smile at your fears! Yes, I felt everything you write; but I was afraid to own it to myself. What frightful reality you give to what is merely imaginary, and how you thicken it between us!

"If you feel that you love me less. . . . Ah! let me dismiss this cruel supposition, which your whole letter contradicts! But then, of what importance are your fleeting apprehensions? Alissa! As soon as I begin to argue, my words freeze; I can only hear the weeping of my heart. I love you too much to be skillful, and the more I love you the less I know what to say to you. 'Intellectual love!' . . . What am I to answer to that? When it is with my whole soul that I love you, how can I distinguish between my intellect and my heart? But as our correspondence is the cause of your unkind imputation, as we have been so grievously hurt by our fall into reality from the heights to which that correspondence had raised us, as if you were to write to me now you would think that you were writing only to yourself, since, too, I have not strength to bear another letter like your last—please, for a time, let us stop all communication."

* * *

In the rest of my letter I protested and appealed against her judgment, imploring her to grant us the opportunity of another interview. The last had had everything against it: the scene, the personages, the time of year—and even our correspondence, whose impassioned tone had prepared us for it with so little prudence. This time it should be preceded only by silence. I wished it to take place in the spring, at Fongueusemare, where my uncle would let me stay during the Easter holidays for as long or as short a time as she herself should think fit.

My determination was firmly taken and as soon as my letter had gone, I was able to bury myself in my work.

* * *

I was to see Alissa once more before the end of the year. Miss Ashburton, whose health had been declining for some months, died four days before Christmas. On my return from my military service, I had gone back to stay with her. I left her very little and was present at her last moments. A card from Alissa showed me that our vow of silence lay nearer her heart than my bereavement: she would come up, she said, for the day, just to go to the funeral, which my uncle would not be able to attend.

She and I were almost the only mourners present at the burial service, and afterwards to follow the coffin. We walked side by side and exchanged barely a few sentences; but in church, where she took her seat beside me, I several times felt her eyes resting tenderly upon me.

"It is agreed," said she, as she left me, "nothing before Easter."

"No, but at Easter. . . ."

"I will expect you."

We were at the gate of the cemetery. I suggested taking her to the station; but she called a cab and without a word of farewell, left me.

7.

"Alissa is waiting for you in the garden," my uncle said after having embraced me paternally, when one day at the end of April I arrived at Fongueusemare. If at first I was disappointed at not finding her ready to welcome me, the next moment I was grateful that she had spared us both the first commonplace greetings.

She was at the bottom of the garden. I made my way to the place at the head of the steps, where, at this time of year, the shrubs that set it closely round were all in flower—lilacs, rowan-trees, laburnums, and weigelias; in order not to catch sight of her from too far, or so that she should not see me coming, I took the other side of the garden, along the shady path, where the air was cool beneath the branches.

I advanced slowly; the sky was like my joy—warm, bright, delicately pure. No doubt she was expecting me by the other path. I was close to her, behind her, before she heard me; I stopped . . . and as if time could have stopped with me, "This is the moment," I thought, "the most delicious moment, perhaps, of all, even though it should precede happiness itself —which happiness itself will not equal."

I meant to fall on my knees before her; I took a step that she heard. She got up suddenly, letting the embroidery at which she was working roll to the ground; she stretched out her arms toward me, put her hands on my shoulders. For a few moments we stayed so, she with her arms outstretched, her face smiling and bent toward me, looking at me tenderly without speaking. She was dressed all in white. On her grave face—almost too grave—I recognized her childhood's smile.

"Listen, Alissa," I cried suddenly. "I have twelve days before me. I will not stay one more than you please. Let us

settle on a sign, which shall mean: 'To-morrow you must leave Fongueusemare.' The next day I will go, without recrimination, without complaint. Do you agree?"

As I had not prepared what I was going to say, I spoke more easily. She reflected a moment; then: "The evening that I come down to dinner without wearing the amethyst cross you like . . . will you understand?"

"That it is to be my last evening."

"But will you be able to go without a tear or a sigh?"

"Without a good-bye. I will leave you on that last evening exactly as I shall have done the evening before, so simply that you will wonder whether I have understood. But when you look for me the next morning, I shall just not be there."

"I shall not look for you the next morning."

She held out her hand; as I raised it to my lips, I added: "But from now till the fatal evening, not an allusion to make me feel that it is coming."

"And you, not an allusion to the parting that will follow."

The embarrassment that the solemnity of this meeting was in danger of creating between us had now to be dispelled.

"I should so much like," I went on, "that these few days with you should seem like other days . . . I mean, that we should not feel, either of us, that they are exceptional. And then . . . if we were not to try too hard to talk just at first. . . ."

She began to laugh. I added: "Isn't there anything we could do together?"

Ever since we could remember we had taken great pleasure in gardening. An inexperienced gardener had lately replaced the old one, and there was a great deal to be done in the garden, which had been neglected for two months. Some of the rose trees had been badly pruned; some, luxuriant growers, were encumbered with dead wood; some of the ramblers had come down for want of the necessary props; others were being exhausted by suckers. Most of them had been grafted by us; we recognized our nurslings; the attention of which they were in need took up a large part of our time, and allowed us during the first three days to talk a great deal without saying anything of weight and, when we said nothing, it enabled us not to feel our silence burdensome.

In this way we once more grew accustomed to one another. It was on this familiarity that I counted, rather than on any actual explanation. The very recollection of our separation was already beginning to disappear from between us, and the fearfulness that I had felt in her, the tension of spirit that she used to fear in me, were already beginning to grow less. Alissa seemed younger than during my melancholy visit of the autumn, and I had never thought her prettier. I had not yet kissed her. Every evening I saw sparkling on her bodice the little amethyst cross, which she wore hanging from a gold chain round her neck. Hope sprang up again, confidently, in my breast. Hope, do I say? No! it was already certainty, and I thought I felt it too in Alissa; for I was so little doubtful of myself that I could no longer have any doubts of her. Little by little our talk grew bolder.

"Alissa," I said to her one morning when all the air breathed laughter and delight and our hearts were opening like the flowers, "now that Juliette is happy, won't you let us too. . . ."

I spoke slowly, with my eyes fixed upon her; on a sudden she turned so extraordinarily pale that I could not finish my sentence.

"Dear!" she began, without turning her eyes toward me, "I feel happier with you than I thought it was possible to feel

. . . but, believe me, we were not born for happiness."

"What can the soul prefer to happiness?" I cried, impetuously.

She whispered: "Holiness . . . ," so low that I divined rather than heard the word.

My whole happiness spread its wings and flew away out of my heart and up to Heaven. "I cannot reach it without you," I said, and with my head on her knees, weeping like a child—but for love, not for grief—I repeated again and again: "Not without you; not without you!"

Then that day, too, passed by like the others. But in the evening Alissa came down without the little amethyst ornament. Faithful to my promise, the next morning at daybreak I left.

On the following day I received the strange letter that I give below, with these lines of Shakespeare's as motto:

" 'That strain again,—it had a dying fall:
    Oh, it came o'er my ear like the sweet
        south,
    That breathes upon a bank of violets,
    Stealing and giving odour.—Enough;
        no more,
    'Tis not so sweet now as it was before.'

"Yes! In spite of myself, I looked for you the whole morning, my brother. I could not believe that you had gone. I felt resentful against you for having kept to our agreement. I thought it must be a jest. I expected you to step out from behind every bush. But no! you have really gone. Thank you.

"I spent the rest of the day haunted by the constant presence of thoughts that I should like to communicate to you, and by the peculiar and very definite fear that if I did not, I should have the feeling later on of having failed in my duty toward you, of having deserved your reproaches. . . .

"In the first moments of your stay at Fongueusemare it was astonishment that

I felt—soon after it was uneasiness—at the strange contentment that filled my whole being in your presence; 'a contentment so great,' you said, 'that I desire nothing beyond!' Alas! that is just what makes me uneasy. . . .

"I am afraid, my friend, lest you should misunderstand me. Above all, I am afraid lest you should take for subtlety (Oh, how mistaken a subtlety!) what is merely the expression of the most violent feeling of my soul.

" 'If it did not suffice, it would not be happiness,' you said; do you remember? And I did not know what to answer. No, Jerome, it does not suffice us. Jerome, it must not suffice us. I cannot take this delicious contentment for the true one. Did we not realize last autumn what misery it covered over? . . .

"The true one! Ah! God forbid! We were born for a happiness other than that. . . .

"Just as our correspondence spoiled our meeting last autumn, so now the memory of your presence yesterday disenchants my letter of today. What has happened to the delight I used to take in writing to you? By writing to each other, by being with each other, we have exhausted all that is pure in the joy to which our love dare aspire. And now, in spite of myself, I exclaim, like Orsino in *Twelfth Night:* 'Enough; no more; 'tis not so sweet now as it was before.'

"Good-bye, my friend. *Hic incipit amor Dei.* Ah! will you ever know how much I love you? . . . Until the end I will be your

"ALISSA."

Against the snare of virtue I was defenseless. All heroism attracted and dazzled me, for I could not separate it from love. Alissa's letter inspired me with a rash and intoxicating enthusiasm. God knows that I strove after more virtue only for her sake. Any path, provided it climbed upwards, would lead me to her. Ah! the ground could not too soon narrow enough to hold only her and me! Alas! I did not suspect the subtlety of her feint, and little imagined that it would be by a height where there was room for only one that she might escape me once more.

I replied lengthily. I remember the only passage of my letter that was at all clearsighted.

"I often think," I said, "that my love is the best part of me; that all my virtues are suspended to it; that it raises me above myself, and that without it I should fall back to the mediocre level of a very ordinary disposition. It is the hope of reaching you that will always make me think the steepest path the best."

What did I add which can have induced her to answer as follows:

"But, my friend, holiness is not a choice; it is an obligation [the word was underlined three times in her letter]. If you are what I take you to be, *you* will not be able to evade it either."

That was all. I understood or, rather, I had a foreboding that our correspondence would stop there, and that neither the most cunning counsels nor the most steadfast determination would be of any avail.

I wrote again, however, lengthily, tenderly. After my third letter I received this note:

"My friend,

"Do not imagine that I have made any resolution not to write to you; I merely no longer take any pleasure in writing. And yet your letters still interest me, but I reproach myself more and more for engrossing so much of your thoughts.

"The summer is not far off. I propose that we give up our correspondence for a time, and that you come and spend the last fortnight of September with me at Fongueusemare. Do you accept? If you do, I have no need of a reply. I shall take your silence for consent, and hope, therefore, that you will not answer."

I did not answer. No doubt this silence was only the last trial to which she was subjecting me. When, after a few months' work and a few weeks' travel, I returned to Fongueusemare, it was with the most tranquil assurance.

* * *

How should I, by a simple recital, make clear at once what I myself understood at first so ill? What can I paint here save the occasion of the wretchedness that from that moment overwhelmed me wholly? For if I have no forgiveness in my heart today for my failure to recognize that love that was still throbbing, hidden under a semblance so artificial, it was at first only this semblance that I was able to see; and so, no longer finding my friend, I accused her. . . . No! Even then, Alissa, I did not accuse you, but wept despairingly that I could recognize you no longer. Now that I can gauge the strength of your love by the cunning of its silence and by its cruel workings, must I love you all the more, the more agonizingly you bereft me?

Disdain? Coldness? No; nothing that could be overcome; nothing against which I could even struggle; and sometimes I hesitated, doubting whether I had not invented my misery, so subtle seemed its cause and so skillful was Alissa's pretense of not understanding it. What should I have complained of? Her welcome was more smiling than ever; never had she shown herself more cordial, more attentive; the first day I was almost taken in by it. What did it matter, after all, that she did her hair in a new way, which flattened it and dragged it back from her face so that her features were harshened and their true expression altered—that an

unbecoming dress, dull in color and ugly in texture, turned the delicate rhythm of her body to clumsiness? . . . There was nothing there, I thought blindly, that might not be remedied the very next day, either of her own accord or at my request. I was more unpleasantly affected by the cordiality, by the attentions, which were so foreign to our habits, and in which I was afraid I saw more deliberation than spontaneity and, though I scarcely dare say so, more politeness than love.

That evening, when I went into the drawing-room, I was astonished not to find the piano in its usual place; Alissa answered by exclamation of disappointment in her most tranquil voice: "It has gone to be done up, dear."

"But I repeatedly told you, my child," said my uncle, in a tone of reproach that was almost severe, "that as it had done well enough up till now, you might have waited until Jerome had gone before sending it away; your haste has deprived us of a great pleasure."

"But, Father," said she, turning aside to blush, "I assure you it had got so jingly latterly that Jerome himself wouldn't have been able to get anything out of it."

"When you played it, it didn't seem so bad," said my uncle.

She stayed a few moments in the shadow, stooping down, as if she were engaged in taking the measurements of a chair cover, then left the room abruptly and did not return till later, when she brought in the tray with the cup of *tisane* which my uncle was in the habit of taking every evening.

The next day she changed neither the way of doing her hair nor her dress; seated beside her father on a bench in front of the house, she went on with the mending on which she had already been engaged the evening before. On the bench or the table beside her was a great basket full of stockings and socks into which she dipped. A few days later it was towels and sheets. This work absorbed her, it seemed, to such a pitch that every gleam of expression vanished from her lips and her eyes.

"Alissa!" I exclaimed the first evening, almost terrified by this obliteration of all poetry from her face, which I could hardly recognize, and at which I had been gazing for some moments without her seeming to feel my look.

"What is it?" said she, raising her head.

"I wanted to see if you would hear me. Your thoughts seemed so far away from me."

"No; they are here; but this darning requires a great deal of attention."

"Wouldn't you like me to read to you while you are sewing?"

"I am afraid I shouldn't be able to listen very well."

"Why do you choose such absorbing work to do?"

"Someone must do it."

"There are so many poor women who would be glad to do it for the sake of earning a trifle. It can't be from economy that you undertake such a tedious task?"

She at once assured me that she liked no other kind of sewing so much, that it was the only kind she had done for a long time past, and that she was doubtless out of practice for doing anything else. She smiled as she spoke. Never had her voice been sweeter than now, when she was so grieving me. "I am saying nothing but what is natural," her face seemed to declare; "why should it make you sad?"

And my whole heart's protest no longer even rose to my lips—it choked me.

* * *

A day or two later, as we had been picking roses, she invited me to carry them for her to her room, into which I had not as yet been that year. What flat-tering hopes arose in me at once! For I had not got beyond blaming myself for my sadness; one word from her would have healed my heart.

I never went into this room without emotion; I cannot tell what it was that made up the kind of melodious peace that breathed in it, and in which I recognized Alissa. The blue shadow of the curtains at the windows and around the bed, the furniture of shining mahogany, the order, the spotlessness, the silence, all spoke to my heart of her purity and pensive grace.

I was astonished that morning to see that two large photographs of Masaccios, which I had brought back from Italy, were no longer on the wall beside her bed; I was on the point of asking her what had become of them when my glance fell on the bookshelf close by, where she had formerly kept her bedside books. This little collection had been gradually formed, partly of the books I had given her, partly of others we had read together. I had just noticed that all these books had been removed, and that they had been replaced exclusively by a number of insignificant little works of vulgar piety for which I hoped she had nothing but contempt. Raising my eyes suddenly, I saw that Alissa was laughing —yes, laughing—as she watched me.

"I beg your pardon," she said at once; "your face made me laugh; it fell so abruptly when you saw my bookcase."

I felt very little inclined for pleasantry.

"No, really, Alissa, is that what you read now?"

"Yes, certainly. What is it that surprises you?"

"I should have thought that a mind accustomed to substantial food would have been disgusted by such sickly stuff."

"I don't understand you," she said. "These are humble souls who talk to me simply and express themselves as best they can. I take pleasure in their society. I know beforehand that they will not fall into any snare of fine language and that I, as I read, shall not be tempted by any profane admiration."

"Do you read nothing but that now then?"

"Almost. Yes, for the last few months. But I haven't much time for reading now. And I confess that quite lately, when I tried to re-read one of the great authors whom you taught me to admire, I felt like the man in the Scriptures, who strives to add a cubit to his height."

"Who is this 'great author' who has given you such an odd opinion of yourself?"

"He didn't give it me, but it was while reading him that I got it. . . . It was Pascal. Perhaps I lighted on some passage that was not so good. . . ."

I made an impatient movement. She spoke in a clear, monotonous voice as if she were reciting a lesson, not lifting her eyes from her flowers, which she went on arranging and re-arranging interminably. She stopped for an instant at my movement and then continued in the same tone: "Such surprising grandiloquence and such effort!—and to prove so little! I wonder sometimes whether his pathetic intonation is not the result of doubt rather than of faith. The voice of perfect faith speaks with fewer tears, with fewer tremors."

"It is just those very tremors, those very tears, which make the beauty of his voice," I endeavored to retort, though dispiritedly; for in her words I could recognize nothing of what I loved in Alissa. I write them down as I remember them, and without any addition of either art or logic.

"If he had not first emptied this life of its joy," she went on, "it would weigh heavier in the balance than. . . ."

"Than what?" I asked, for I was amazed at her strange sayings.

"Than the uncertain felicity he holds out."

"Don't you believe in it, then?" I exclaimed.

"No matter!" she answered; "I wish it to remain uncertain so that every suspicion of a bargain may be removed. The soul that loves God steeps itself in virtue out of natural nobility, and not for the hope of reward."

"And that is the reason of the secret skepticism in which nobility such as Pascal's finds a refuge."

"Not skepticism—Jansenism," she said, smiling. "What have I to do with such things? These poor souls, here," she added, turning toward her books, "would be at a loss to say whether they are Jansenist or quietist or what not. They bow down before God like the grass that is bent by the wind, without guile or anxiety or beauty. They consider themselves of little account, and know that their only value lies in their effacement before God."

"Alissa!" I cried, "why do you tear off your wings?"

Her voice remained so calm and natural that my exclamation seemed to me all the more absurdly emphatic.

She smiled again and shook her head. "All that I brought away from my last visit to Pascal. . . ."

"Was what?" I asked, for she had stopped.

"This saying of Christ's: 'Whosoever shall seek to save his life shall lose it.' And as for that," she went on, smiling still more and looking me steadily in the face, "I really hardly understood him any longer. When one has lived any time in the society of such lowly ones as these, it is extraordinary how quickly the sublimity of the great leaves one breathless and exhausted."

Would my discomposure allow me no answer? "If I were obliged to read all these sermons and tracts with you now. . . ."

"But," she interrupted, "I should be

very sorry to see you read them! I agree with you; I think you were meant for much better things than that."

She spoke quite simply and without seeming to suspect that my heart might be rent by these words, which implied the separation of our lives. My head was burning; I should have liked to go on speaking; I should have liked to cry; perhaps my tears would have vanquished her; but I remained without saying a word, my elbows on the mantelpiece, my head buried in my hands. She went on calmly arranging her flowers, seeing nothing—or pretending to see nothing—of my suffering. . . .

At this moment the first bell rang.

"I shall never be ready for lunch," she said. "You must go away now." And as if it had been nothing but play: "We will go on with this conversation another time."

We never went on with the conversation. Alissa continually eluded me; not that she ever appeared to be avoiding me; but every casual occupation became a duty of far more urgent importance. I had to await my turn; I came only after the constantly recurring cares of the household, after she had attended to the alterations that were being carried out in the barn, after her visits to the farmers, and after her visits to the poor, with whom she busied herself more and more. I had the time that was left over, and very little it was; I never saw her but she was in a hurry—though it was still, perhaps, in the midst of these trivial occupations, and when I gave up pursuing her, that I least felt how much I had been dispossessed. The slightest talk showed it me more clearly. When Alissa granted me a few minutes, it was, indeed, for the most laborious conversation, to which she lent herself as one does to playing with a child. She passed beside me swiftly, absentminded and smiling; and I felt she had become more distant than if I had

never known her. It even seemed to me sometimes that there was a kind of challenge in her smile, or at any rate a kind of irony, and that she took amusement in thus eluding my wishes. . . . And at that it was myself that I turned to upbraid, not wishing to give way to reproaches, and, indeed, hardly knowing what might be expected from her now, or with what I could reproach her.

Thus the days from which I had promised myself so much felicity passed by. I contemplated their flight with stupor, but without desiring to increase their number or delay their passage, so greatly each one aggravated my grief. Two days before my departure, however, Alissa came with me to the bench beside the deserted marl-pit; it was a bright autumn evening; as far as the cloudless horizon, every blue-tinted detail of the landscape stood out distinct and clear, and in the past the dimmest of its memories. I could not withhold my lamentations as I showed her my present unhappiness—as I showed her the happiness I had lost.

"But what is it I can do, my friend?" she said at once. "You are in love with a phantom."

"No, not with a phantom, Alissa."

"With a creature of your imagination."

"Alas! I am not inventing. She was once my friend. I call upon her. Alissa! Alissa! it was you I loved. What have you done with yourself? What have you made yourself become?"

She remained a few moments without answering, slowly pulling a flower to pieces and keeping her head down. Then, at last: "Jerome, why don't you simply admit that you love me less?"

"Because it's not true! Because it's not true!" I exclaimed indignantly; "because I never loved you more."

"You love me—and yet you regret me!" she said, trying to smile, and slightly shrugging her shoulders.

"I cannot put my love into the past." The ground was giving way beneath me; and I caught at anything.

"It must pass with the rest."

"A love like mine will pass only with me."

"It will gradually grow less. The Alissa whom you think you still love already exists only in your memory; a day will come when you will remember only that you loved her."

"You speak as if her place might be taken in my heart, or as if my heart were going to stop loving. Do you no longer remember that you once loved me yourself, that you take such pleasure in torturing me?"

I saw her pale lips tremble; in an almost inaudible voice she whispered: "No, no; Alissa has not changed in that."

"Why, then nothing has changed," I said, seizing her arm. . . .

She went on more firmly: "One word would explain everything; why don't you dare say it?"

"What word?"

"I have grown older."

"Hush!" I protested immediately that I myself had grown as much older as she, that the difference of age between us remained the same . . . but she had regained control of herself; the one and only moment had gone by, and by beginning to argue I had let my advantage slip; the ground gave way beneath me.

Two days later I left Fongueusemare, discontented with her and with myself, full of a vague hatred against what I still called "virtue," and of resentment against the habitual occupation of my heart. It seemed as though during this last meeting, and through the very exaggeration of my love, I had come to the end of all my fervor; each one of Alissa's phrases, against which I had at first rebelled, remained alive and triumphant within me after my protestations had died away.

Yes, no doubt, she was right! It was nothing but a phantom that I cared for; the Alissa that I had loved, that I still loved, was no more. . . . Yes, no doubt we had grown old! This frightful obliteration of all poetry, which had chilled my very heart, was nothing, after all, but a return to the natural course of things; if by slow degrees I had exalted her, if out of her I had made myself an idol, and adorned it with all that I was enamored of, what now remained to me as the result of my labors but my fatigue? As soon as she had been left to herself, Alissa had relapsed to her own level—a mediocre level, on which I found myself too, but on which I no longer desired her. Ah! how absurd and fantastic seemed this exhausting effort of virtue in order to reach her there, on the heights where she had been placed by my own sole endeavor. A little less pride and our love would have been easy . . . but what sense was there in persisting in a love without object? This was to be obstinate, not faithful. Faithful to what? To a delusion. Was it not wiser to admit to myself that I had been mistaken?

In the meantime I had been offered a place in the School of Athens; I agreed to take it up at once, with no feeling of either ambition or pleasure, but welcoming the idea of departure as though it had been an escape.

8.

And yet I saw Alissa once more. It was three years later, toward the end of summer. Ten months before, I had heard from her the news of my uncle's death. A fairly long letter, which I had at once written her from Palestine, where I was traveling at the time, had remained unanswered.

I happened to be at Le Havre, on I forget what errand; a natural instinct set me on the road to Fongueusemare. I knew that Alissa was there, but I was afraid she might not be alone. I had not announced my arrival; shrinking from the idea of presenting myself like an ordinary visitor, I went on my way undecided: should I go in? or should I go away without having seen her, without having tried to see her? Yes, without doubt, I would just walk up the avenue, sit on the bench, where sometimes, perhaps, she still went to sit . . . and I was already beginning to wonder what token I could leave behind me, which, after I had gone, would tell her of my coming. . . . Thus reflecting, I walked slowly on; and now that I had resolved not to see her, the sharpness of the sorrow that wrung my heart began to give way to a melancholy that was almost sweet. I had already reached the avenue and, for fear of being taken unawares, was walking on the footpath that ran along the bottom of the bank skirting the farmyard. I knew a place on the bank from which one could look over into the garden; I climbed up; a gardener whom I did not recognize was raking one of the paths and soon disappeared from sight. There was a new gate to the courtyard. A dog barked as I went by. Farther on, where the avenue came to an end, I turned to the right, came again upon the garden wall, and was making my way to the portion of the beech wood parallel to the avenue I had left, when, as I was passing by the little door that led into the kitchen-garden, the idea of going in suddenly seized me.

The door was shut. The inside bolt, however, offered only slight resistance, and I was on the point of forcing it open with my shoulder. . . . At that moment I heard the sound of steps; I drew back around the corner of the wall.

I could not see who it was that came out of the garden; but I heard, I felt, that it was Alissa.

She took three steps forward and called in a weak voice: "Is that you, Jerome?"

My heart, which was beating violently, stopped, and as no word would come from my choking throat, she repeated louder: "Jerome! Is that you?"

At hearing her call me in this way, I was seized by an emotion so great that it forced me to my knees. As I still did not answer, Alissa took a few steps forward and turned the corner of the wall. I suddenly felt her against me—against me, who was kneeling there hiding my face with my arm as if in dread of seeing her too soon. She remained a few moments stooping over me, while I covered her frail hands with kisses.

"Why were you hiding?" she asked, as simply as if those three years of absence had lasted only a few days.

"How did you guess it was I?"

"I was expecting you."

"Expecting me?" I said, so astonished that I could only repeat her words, wondering. . . .

And as I was still on my knees: "Let us go to the bench," she went on. "Yes, I knew I was to see you again once more. For the last three days I have come here every evening and called you, as I did tonight. . . . Why didn't you answer?"

"If you had not come upon me by surprise, I should have gone away without seeing you," I said, steeling myself against the emotion that had at first overmastered me. "I happened to be at Le Havre, and merely meant to walk along the avenue and around the outside of the garden and to rest a few moments on this bench, where I thought you might still come to sit sometimes, and then. . . ."

"Look what I have brought here to read for the last three evenings," she interrupted, and held out to me a packet of letters; I recognized those I had written her from Italy. At that moment I raised my eyes to look at her. She was extraordinarily changed; her thinness, her pale-

ness smote my heart horribly. Leaning heavily upon my arm, she clung to me as though she was frightened or cold. She was still in deep mourning, and no doubt the black lace she had put round her head, and which framed her face, added to her paleness. She was smiling, but her failing limbs seemed hardly to bear her up. I was anxious to know whether she was alone at Fongueusemare. No, Robert was living with her; Juliette, Édouard, and their three children had been spending August with them. . . . We had reached the bench; we sat down, and the conversation for a few minutes longer dragged along in the usual commonplace enquiries. She asked after my work. I replied with bad grace. I should have liked her to feel that my work no longer interested me. I should have liked to disappoint her as she had disappointed me. I do not know whether I succeeded, but if so, she did not show it. As for me, full both of resentment and love, I did my best to speak as curtly as possible, and was angry with myself for the emotion which at times made my voice tremble.

The setting sun, which had been hidden for a few moments by a cloud, reappeared on the edge of the horizon almost opposite us, flooding the empty fields with a shimmering glory and heaping with a sudden profusion of wealth the narrow valley that opened at our feet; then it disappeared. I sat there dazzled and speechless; I felt that I was wrapped round and steeped in a kind of golden ecstasy in which my resentment vanished and nothing survived in me but love. Alissa, who had been leaning, drooping against me, sat up; she took out of her bodice a tiny packet wrapped in tissue paper, made as though she meant to give it me, stopped, seemed to hesitate, and, as I looked at her in surprise: "Listen, Jerome," said she, "this is my amethyst cross that I have here; for the last three evenings I have brought it here because

for a long time past I have been wanting to give it to you."

"What am I to do with it?" I asked, rather brusquely.

"Keep it in memory of me for your daughter."

"What daughter?" I cried, looking at Alissa without understanding her.

"Please, listen to me quite calmly; no, don't look at me so; don't look at me; it's already difficult enough for me to speak to you; but I must, I simply must say this. Listen, Jerome; one day you will marry— no, don't answer; don't interrupt, I implore you. I only want you to remember that I loved you very much, and . . . a long time ago . . . three years ago. I thought that a daughter of yours might one day wear this little cross you liked, in memory of me. Oh! without knowing whose it was . . . and perhaps, too, you might give her . . . my name. . . ."

She stopped, her voice choking; I exclaimed, almost with hostility: "Why not give it her yourself?"

She tried to speak again. Her lips trembled like those of a sobbing child, but she did not cry; the extraordinary light that shone in her eyes flooded her face with an unearthly, an angelic beauty.

"Alissa! whom should I marry? You know I can love no one but you . . . ," and suddenly clasping her wildly, almost brutally in my arms, I crushed my kisses on her lips. An instant I held her unresisting as she half lay back against me.

I saw her look grow dim; then her eyes closed, and in a voice so true and melodious that never, to my mind, will it be equaled: "Have pity on us, my friend!" she said. "Oh! don't spoil our love."

Perhaps she said too: "Don't be cowardly!" or perhaps it was I who said it to myself; I cannot tell now; but suddenly flinging myself on my knees before her, and folding my arms piously round her: "If you loved me so, why have you always repulsed me? Think! I waited first for Juliette to be married; I understood your waiting for her to be happy, too; she *is* happy; you yourself have told me so. I thought for a long time that you didn't want to leave your father; but now we are both alone."

"Oh! don't let us regret the past," she murmured. "I have turned the page now."

"There is still time, Alissa."

"No, my friend, there is not time. There was no longer time from the moment when our love made us foresee for one another something better than love. Thanks to you, my friend, my dream climbed so high that any earthly satisfaction would have been a descent. I have often thought of what our life with each other would have been; as soon as it had been less than perfect, I could not have borne . . . our love."

"Did you ever think what our life would be without each other?"

"No! Never."

"Now you see! For the last three years, without you, I have been drifting miserably about. . . ."

The evening was drawing in.

"I am cold," she said, getting up and wrapping her shawl too closely round her for me to be able to take her arm again. "You remember the Scripture text which troubled us so, and which we were afraid we didn't understand properly: 'These all received not the promise, God having provided some better thing for us'. . . ."

"Do you still believe those words?"

"Indeed I must."

We walked on for a few moments beside each other without saying anything more. She went on: "Can you imagine it, Jerome?—'Some better thing!'" And suddenly the tears started from her eyes, as she repeated once more: "'Some better thing!'"

We had again reached the small garden door through which she had come out a little before. She turned towards me:

"Good-bye!" said she. "No, don't come any farther. Good-bye, my beloved friend. Now . . . the better thing . . . is going to begin."

One moment she looked at me, at once holding me fast and keeping me at arm's length, her hands on my shoulders, her eyes filled with an unspeakable love.

As soon as the door was shut, as soon as I heard the bolt drawn behind her, I fell against the door, a prey to the extremest despair, and stayed for a long time weeping and sobbing in the night.

But to have kept her, to have forced the door, to have entered by any means whatever into the house, which yet would not have been shut against me—no, even today, when I look back to the past and live it over again—no, it was not possible to me, and whoever does not understand me here, has understood nothing of me up till now.

Intolerable anxiety made me write to Juliette a few days later. I told her of my visit to Fongueusemare, and said how much Alissa's paleness and thinness had alarmed me; I implored her to see what could be done and to give me news, which I could no longer expect to get from Alissa herself.

Less than one month later, I received the following letter:

"My dear Jerome,

"This is to give you very sad news: our poor Alissa is no more. Alas! the fears you expressed in your letter were only too well founded. For the last few months, without being ill exactly, she seemed to be wasting away; she yielded, however, to my entreaties and consented to see Dr. A——, who wrote to me that there was nothing serious the matter with her. But three days after the visit you paid her, she suddenly left Fongueusemare. It was from a letter of Robert's that I learned she was gone; she writes to me so seldom that if it had not been for him I should have known nothing of her flight, for I should have been a long time before taking alarm at her silence. I blamed Robert severely for having let her go in this way, and for not having gone with her to Paris. Will you believe that from that moment we were ignorant of her address? You can imagine my sickening anxiety; impossible to see her, impossible even to write to her. Robert, it is true, went to Paris a few days later, but he was unable to discover anything. He is so slack that we could not trust to his taking the proper steps. We had to tell the police; it was not possible to remain in such cruel uncertainty. Édouard then went himself, and at last managed to discover the little nursing home where Alissa had taken refuge. Alas! too late. I received a letter from the head of the home announcing her death, and, at the same time a telegram from Édouard, who was not in time to see her again. On the last day she had written our address on an envelope so that we might be told, and in another envelope she had put the copy of a letter she had sent our lawyer at Le Havre containing her last instructions. I think there is a passage in this letter which concerns you: I will let you know soon. Édouard and Robert were able to be present at the funeral, which took place the day before yesterday. They were not the only persons to follow the bier. Some of the patients of the nursing home wished to be present at the ceremony and to accompany the body to the cemetery. As for me, I am expecting my fifth baby any day now, and unfortunately I was unable to move.

"My dear Jerome, I know the deep sorrow this loss will cause you, and I write to you with a breaking heart. I have been obliged to stay in bed for the last two days, and I write with difficulty, but I would not let anyone else, not even Édouard or Robert, speak to you of her

whom we two, doubtless, were the only persons in the world to know. Now that I am an almost old mother of a family, and that the burning past is covered over with a heap of ashes, I may hope to see you again. If business or pleasure ever takes you to Nîmes, come on to Aigues-Vives. Édouard would be glad to know you, and you and I would be able to talk together of Alissa. Good-bye, my dear Jerome.

"Affectionately and sadly yours . . ."

A few days later, I learned that Alissa had left Fongueusemare to her brother, but had asked that all the things that were in her room and a few pieces of furniture which she mentioned should be sent to Juliette. I was shortly to receive some papers that she had put in a sealed packet addressed to me. I learned, also, that she had asked that the little amethyst cross that I had refused at my last visit should be put round her neck, and I heard from Édouard that this had been done.

The sealed packet that the lawyer sent me contained Alissa's journal. I here transcribe a considerable number of its pages. I transcribe them without commentary. You will imagine well enough the reflections I made as I read, and the commotion of my heart, of which I could give only a too imperfect idea.

Alissa's Journal

Aigues-Vives.

Left Le Havre the day before yesterday; yesterday arrived at Nîmes; my first journey! With no housekeeping to do and no cooking to look after, and consequently with a slight feeling of idleness, today, the 23rd May, 188-, my twenty-fifth birthday, I begin this journal—without much pleasure, a little for the sake of company; for, perhaps for the first time in my life, I feel lonely—in a different, a foreign land almost, one with which I have not yet made acquaintance. It has, no doubt the same things to say to me as Normandy—the same that I listen to untiringly at Fongueusemare—for God is nowhere different from Himself—but this southern land speaks a language I have not yet learned, and to which I listen wondering.

24th May.

Juliette is dozing on a sofa near me—in the open gallery that is the chief charm of the house, built as it is after the Italian fashion. The gallery opens on to the graveled courtyard that is a continuation of the garden. Without leaving her sofa, Juliette can see the lawn sloping down to the piece of water, where a tribe of parti-colored ducks disport themselves and two swans sail. A stream which, they say, never runs dry in the heat of any summer feeds it and then flows through the garden, which merges into a grove of ever-increasing wildness, more and more shut in by the bed of a dried torrent on the one side and the vineyards on the other, and finally strangled altogether between them.

Édouard Teissières yesterday showed my father the garden, the farm, the cellars, and the vineyards, while I stayed behind with Juliette—so that this morning, while it was still very early, I was able to make my first voyage of discovery in the park, by myself. A great many plants and strange trees, whose names, however, I should have liked to know. I pick a twig of each of them so as to be told what they are at lunch. In some of them I recognize the evergreen oaks that Jerome admired in the gardens of the Villa Borghese or Doria-Pamphili—so distantly related to our northern tree, of such a different character! Almost at the farthest end of the park there is a narrow, mysterious glade that they shelter, bending over a

carpet of grass so soft to the feet that it seems an invitation to the choir of nymphs. I wonder—I am almost scared that my feeling for nature, which at Fongueusemare is so profoundly Christian, should here become, in spite of myself, half pagan. And yet the kind of awe which oppressed me more and more was religious too. I whispered the words: *"hic nemus."* The air was crystalline; there was a strange silence. I was thinking of Orpheus, of Armida, when all at once there rose a solitary bird's song, so near me, so pathetic, so pure, that it seemed suddenly as though all nature had been awaiting it. My heart beat violently; I stayed for a moment leaning against a tree, and then came in before anyone was up.

26th May.

Still no letter from Jerome. If he had written to me at Le Havre, his letter would have been forwarded. . . . I can confide my anxiety to no one but this book; for the last three days I have not been distracted from it for an instant, either by our excursion yesterday to Les Baux, or by reading, or by prayer. Today I can write of nothing else; the curious melancholy from which I have been suffering ever since I arrived at Aigues-Vives has, perhaps, no other cause—and yet I feel it at such a depth within me that it seems to me now as if it had been there for a long time past, and as if the joy on which I prided myself did no more than cover it over.

27th May.

Why should I lie to myself? It is by an effort of mind that I rejoice in Juliette's happiness. That happiness which I longed for so much, to the extent of offering my own in sacrifice to it, is painful to me, now that I see that she has obtained it without trouble, and that it is so different from what she and I imagined. How complicated it all is! Yes . . . I see well enough that a horrible revival of egoism in me is offended at her having found her happiness elsewhere than in my sacrifice —at her not having needed my sacrifice in order to be happy.

And now I ask myself, as I feel what uneasiness Jerome's silence causes me: Was that sacrifice really consummated in my heart? I am, as it were, humiliated, to feel that God no longer exacts it. Can it be that I was not equal to it?

28th May.

How dangerous this analysis of my sadness is! I am already growing attached to this book. Is my personal vanity, which I thought I had mastered, reasserting its rights here? No; may my soul never use this journal as a flattering mirror before which to attire itself! It is not out of idleness that I write, as I thought at first, but out of sadness. Sadness is a *state of sin,* which had ceased to be mine, which I hate, from whose *complications* I wish to free my soul. This book must help me to find my happiness in myself once more.

Sadness is a complication. I never used to analyze my happiness.

At Fongueusemare I was alone, too, still more alone—why did I not feel it? And when Jerome wrote to me from Italy, I was willing that he should see without me, that he should live without me; I followed him in thought, and out of his joy I made my own. And now, in spite of myself, I want him; without him, every new thing I see is irksome to me.

10th June.

Long interruption of this journal, which I had scarcely begun; birth of little Lise; long hours of watching beside Juliette; I take no pleasure in writing anything here that I can write to Jerome. I should like to keep myself from the intol-erable fault which is common to so many women—that of writing too much. Let me consider this notebook as a means of perfection.

There followed several pages of notes made in the course of her reading, extracts, etc. Then, dated from Fongueusemare once more:

16th July.

Juliette is happy; she says so, seems so; I have no right, no reason to doubt it. Whence comes this feeling of dissatisfaction, of discomfort, which I have now when I am with her? Perhaps from feeling that such happiness is so practical, so easily obtained, so perfectly "to measure" that it seems to cramp the soul and stifle it. . . .

And I ask myself now whether it is really happiness that I desire so much as the progress toward happiness. Oh, Lord! preserve me from a happiness to which I might too easily attain! Teach me to put off my happiness, to place it as far away from me as Thou art.

Several pages here had been torn out; they referred, no doubt, to our painful meeting at Le Havre. The journal did not begin again till the following year; the pages were not dated, but had certainly been written at the time of my stay at Fongueusemare.

Sometimes as I listen to him talking, I seem to be watching myself think. He explains me and discovers me to myself. Should I exist without him? I *am* only when I am with him. . . .

Sometimes I hesitate as to whether what I feel for him is really what people call love—the picture that is generally drawn of love is so different from that which I should like to draw. I should like nothing to be said about it, and to love him without knowing that I love him. I should like, above all, to love him without his knowing it.

I no longer get any joy out of that part of life which has to be lived without him. My virtue is all only to please him—and yet, when I am with him, I feel my virtue weakening.

I used to like learning the piano, for it seemed to me that I was able to make some progress in it every day. That too, perhaps, is the secret of the pleasure I take in reading a book in a foreign language; not, indeed, that I prefer any other language whatever to our own, or that the writers I admire in it appear to me in any way inferior to those of other countries—but the slight difficulty that lies in the pursuit of their meaning and feeling, the unconscious pride of overcoming this difficulty, and of overcoming it more and more successfully, adds to my intellectual pleasure a certain spiritual contentment, which it seems to me I cannot do without.

However blessed it might be, I cannot desire a state without progress. I imagine Heavenly joy not as a confounding of the spirit with God, but as an infinite, a perpetual drawing near to Him . . . and if I were not afraid of playing upon words I should say that I did not care for any joy that was not *progressive.*

This morning we were sitting on the bench in the avenue; we were not talking and did not feel any need to talk. . . . Suddenly he asked me if I believed in a future life.

"Oh! Jerome!" I cried at once, "it is more than hope I have; it is certainty."

And it seemed to me, on a sudden, that my whole faith had, as it were, been poured into that exclamation.

"I should like to know," he added. He stopped a few moments; then: "Would you act differently without your faith?"

"How can I tell?" I answered; and I added: "And you, my dear, you yourself, and in spite of yourself, can no longer act otherwise than as if you were inspired by the liveliest faith. And I should not love you if you were different."

No, Jerome, no, it is not after a future recompense that our virtue is striving; it is not for recompense that our love is seeking. A generous soul is hurt by the idea of being rewarded for its efforts; nor does it consider virtue an adornment; no, virtue is the form of its beauty.

Papa is not so well again; nothing serious, I hope, but he has been obliged to go back to his milk diet for the last three days.

Yesterday evening, Jerome had just gone up to his room; Papa, who was sitting up with me for a little, left me alone for a few minutes. I was sitting on the sofa, or rather—a thing I hardly ever do —I was lying down, I don't know why. The lampshade was shading my eyes and the upper part of my body from the light; I was mechanically looking at my feet, which showed a little below my dress in the light thrown upon them by the lamp. When Papa came back, he stood for a few moments at the door, staring at me oddly, half smiling, half sad. I got up with a vague feeling of shyness; then he called me: "Come and sit beside me," said he; and, though it was already late, he began speaking to me about my mother, which he had never done since their separation. He told me how he had married her, how much he had loved her, and how much she had at first been to him.

"Papa," I said to him at last, "do, please, say why are you telling me this this evening—what makes you tell me this just this particular evening?"

"Because, just now, when I came into the drawing-room and saw you lying on the sofa, I thought for a moment it was your mother."

The reason I asked this so insistently was because that very evening, Jerome had been reading over my shoulder, standing leaning over me. I could not see him, but I felt his breath and, as it were, the warmth and pulsation of his body. I pretended to go on reading, but my mind had stopped working; I could not even distinguish the lines; so strange a perturbation took possession of me that I was obliged to get up from my chair quickly while I still could; I managed to leave the room for a few minutes, luckily without his noticing anything. But a little later, when I was alone in the drawing-room and lay down on the sofa, where Papa thought I looked like my mother, at that very moment I was thinking of her.

I slept very badly last night; I was disturbed, oppressed, miserable, haunted by the recollection of the past, which came over me like a wave of remorse.

Lord, teach me the horror of all that has any appearance of evil.

Poor Jerome! If he only knew that sometimes he would have but a single sign to make, and that sometimes I wait for him to make it. . . .

When I was a child, even then it was because of him that I wanted to be beautiful. It seems to me now that I have never striven after perfection, except for him. And that this perfection can only be attained without him is of all Thy teachings, my God! the one that is most disconcerting to my soul.

How happy must that soul be for whom virtue is one with love! Sometimes I doubt whether there is any other virtue than love . . . to love as much as possible and continually more and more.

. . . But at other times, alas! virtue appears to me to be nothing but resistance to love. What! shall I dare to call virtue that which is the most natural inclination of my heart? Oh, tempting sophism! Specious allurement! Cunning mirage of happiness!

This morning I read in La Bruyère: "In the course of this life one sometimes meets with pleasures so dear, promises so tender, which are yet forbidden us, that it is natural to desire at least that they might be permitted: charms so great can be surpassed only when virtue teaches us to renounce them."

Why did I invent here that there was anything forbidden? Can it be that I am secretly attracted by a charm more powerful and a sweetness greater still than that of love? Oh! that it were possible to carry our two souls forward together, by force of love, beyond love!

Alas! I understand now only too well: between God and him there is no other obstacle but myself. If perhaps, as he says, his love for me at first inclined him to God, now that very love hinders him; he lingers with me, prefers me, and I am become the idol that keeps him back from making further progress in virtue. One of us two must needs attain to it; and as I despair of overcoming the love in my coward heart, grant me, my God, vouchsafe me strength to teach him to love me no longer, so that at the cost of my merits I may bring Thee his, which are so infinitely preferable . . . and if today my soul sobs with grief at losing him, do I not lose him to find him again hereafter in Thee?

Tell me, oh, my God! what soul ever deserved Thee more? Was he not born for something better than to love me? And should I love him so much if he were to stop short at myself? How much all that might become heroic dwindles in the midst of happiness!

Sunday.

"God having provided some better thing for us."

Monday, 3rd May.

To think that happiness is here, close by, offering itself, and that one only has to put out one's hand to grasp it. . . .

This morning, as I was talking to him, I consummated the sacrifice.

Monday evening.

He leaves tomorrow. . . .

Dear Jerome, I still love you with infinite tenderness; but never more shall I be able to tell you so. The constraint that I lay upon my eyes, upon my lips, upon my soul, is so hard that to leave you is a relief and a bitter satisfaction.

I strive to act according to reason, but at the moment of action the reasons that made me act escape me, or appear foolish; I no longer believe in them.

The reasons that make me fly from him? I no longer believe in them. . . . And yet I fly from him, sadly and without understanding why I fly.

Lord! that we might advance toward Thee, Jerome and I together, each beside the other, each helping the other; that we might walk along the way of life like two pilgrims, of whom one says at times to the other: "Lean on me, brother, if you are weary," and to whom the other replies: "It is enough to feel you near me. . . ." But no! The way Thou teachest, Lord, is a strait way—so strait that two cannot walk in it abreast.

5th July.

More than six weeks have gone by without my opening this book. Last month, as I was rereading some of its pages, I became aware of a foolish, wicked anxiety to write well . . . which I owe to *him*. . . .

As though in this book, which I began

only so as to help myself to do without *him,* I was continuing to write to *him.*

I have torn up all the pages that seemed to me to be *well written.* (I know what I mean by this.) I ought to have torn up all those in which there was any question of him. I ought to have torn them all up. I could not.

And already, because I tore up those few pages, I had a little feeling of pride . . . a pride that I should laugh at if my heart were not so sick.

It really seemed as though I had done something meritorious, and as though what I had destroyed had been of some importance!

6th July.

I have been obliged to banish from my bookshelves. . . .

I fly from him in one book only to find him in another. I hear his voice reading me even those pages which I discover without him. I care only for what interests him, and my mind has taken the form of his to such an extent that I can distinguish one from the other no better than I did at the time when I took pleasure in feeling they were one.

Sometimes I force myself to write badly in order to escape from the rhythm of his phrases; but even to struggle against him is still to be concerned with him. I have made a resolution to read nothing but the Bible (perhaps the *Imitation*) and to write nothing more in this book, except every evening the chief text of my reading.

There followed a kind of diary, in which the date of each day, starting with July 1st, was accompanied by a text. I transcribe only those which are accompanied by some commentary.

20th July.

"Sell all that thou hast and give it to the poor."

I understand that I ought to give to the poor this heart of mine, which belongs only to Jerome. And by so doing should I not teach him at the same time to do likewise? . . . Lord, grant me this courage.

24th July.

I have stopped reading the *Interior Consolation.* The old-fashioned language greatly charmed me, but it was distracting, and the almost pagan joy it gives me is far removed from the edification that I set myself to get from it.

I have taken up the *Imitation* again, and not even in the Latin text, which I was vain of understanding. I am glad that the translation in which I read it should not even be signed. It is true that it is Protestant, but "adapted to the use of all Christian communities," says the title.

"Oh, if thou wert sensible, how much peace thou wouldest procure for thyself and joy for others, by rightly ordering thyself, methinks thou wouldest be more solicitous for thy spiritual progress!"

10th August.

If I were to cry to Thee, my God, with the impulsive faith of a child and with the heavenly tongues of angels. . . .

All this comes to me, I know, not from Jerome, but from Thee.

Why, then, between Thee and me, dost Thou everywhere set his image?

14th August.

Only two months more in which to complete my work. . . . Oh, Lord, grant me Thy help!

20th August.

I feel—I feel by my *unhappiness* that the sacrifice is not consummated in my heart. My God, grant that henceforth I owe to none but Thee the joy that he alone used to give me.

28th August.

How mediocre, and miserable is the virtue to which I attain! Do I then exact too much from myself? . . . To suffer no more.

What cowardice makes me continually implore God for His strength? My prayers now are nothing but complainings.

29th August.

"Consider the lilies of the field. . . ."

This simple saying plunged me this morning into a sadness from which nothing could distract me. I went out into the country and these words, which I kept continually repeating to myself, filled my heart and eyes with tears. I contemplated the vast and empty plain where the laborer was toiling, bent over his plough. . . . "The lilies of the field. . . ." But, Lord, where are they . . . ?

16th September, 10 o'clock at night.

I have seen him again. He is here under this roof. I see the light from his window shining on the grass. He is still up as I write these lines, and perhaps he is thinking of me. He has not changed. He says so, and I feel it. Shall I be able to show myself to him as I have resolved to be, so that his love may disown me?

24th September.

Oh, torturing conversation in which I succeeded in feigning indifference—coldness, when my heart was fainting within me! Up till then I had contented myself with avoiding him. This morning I was able to believe that God would give me strength to be victorious and that to slink forever out of the combat was to prove myself a coward. Did I triumph? Does Jerome love me a little less? Alas! I both hope and fear it together. I have never loved him more.

And if it is Thy Will, Lord, that to save him from me I must compass my own perdition, so be it.

"Enter into my heart and into my soul in order to bear in them my sufferings and to continue to endure in me what remains to Thee to suffer of Thy Passion."

We spoke of Pascal. . . . What did I say? What shameful, foolish words? I suffered even as I uttered them, but tonight I repent them as a blasphemy. I turned again to the heavy volume of the *Pensées,* which opened of itself at this passage in the letters to Mademoiselle de Roannez: "We do not feel our bonds as long as we follow willingly him who leads; but as soon as we begin to resist and to draw away, then indeed we suffer."

These words affected me so personally that I did not have strength to go on reading; but opening the book in another place I came across an admirable passage which I did not know and which I have just copied out.

The first volume of the Journal came to an end here. No doubt the next had been destroyed, for in the papers that Alissa left behind, the Journal did not begin again till three years later—still at Fongueusemare—in September—a short time, that is to say, before our last meeting.

The last volume begins with the sentences that follow.

17th September.

My God, Thou knowest I have need of him to love Thee.

20th September.

My God, give him to me so that I may give Thee my heart.

My God, let me see him only once more.

My God, I engage to give Thee my heart. Grant me what my love beseeches. I will give what remains to me of life to Thee alone.

My God, forgive me this despicable prayer, but I cannot keep his name from my lips nor forget the anguish of my heart.

My God, I cry to Thee. Do not forsake me in my distress.

21st September.

"Whatever ye shall ask the Father in my name. . . ."

Lord, in Thy name, I dare not.

But though I no longer formulate my prayer, wilt Thou be the less aware of the delirious longing of my heart?

27th September.

Ever since the morning a great calm. Spent nearly the whole night in meditation, in prayer. Suddenly I was conscious of a kind of luminous peace like the imagination I had as a child of the Holy Ghost; it seemed to wrap me round, to descend into me. I went to bed at once, fearing that my joy was due only to nervous exaltation. I went to sleep fairly quickly without this felicity leaving me. It is still here this morning in all its completeness. I have the certainty now that he will come.

30th September.

Jerome, my friend! you whom I still call brother, but whom I love infinitely more than a brother. . . . How many times I have cried your name in the beech copse. Every evening toward dusk I go out by the little gate of the kitchen-garden and walk down the avenue where it is already dark. If you were suddenly to answer me, if you were to appear there from behind the stony bank around which I so eagerly seek you, or if I were to see you in the distance, seated on the bench waiting for me, my heart would not leap . . . no! I am astonished at not seeing you.

1st October.

Nothing yet. The sun has set in a sky of incomparable purity. I am waiting. I know that soon I shall be sitting with him on this very bench. I hear his voice already. I like it so much when he says my name. He will be here! I shall put my hand in his hand. I shall let my head lean on his shoulder. I shall breathe beside him. Yesterday I brought out some of his letters with me to reread, but I did not look at them—I was too much taken up with the thought of him. I took with me, too, the amethyst cross he used to like, and which one summer I used to wear every evening as long as I did not want him to go. I should like to give him this cross. For a long time past I have had a dream—that he was married and I god-mother to his first daughter, a little Alissa, to whom I gave this ornament. . . . Why have I never dared tell him?

2nd October.

My soul today is as light and joyful as a bird would be that had made its nest in the sky. For today he will come. I feel it! I know it! I should like to proclaim it aloud to the world. I feel I must write it here. I cannot hide my joy any longer. Even Robert, who is usually so inattentive and indifferent to what concerns me, noticed it. His questions embarrassed me, and I did not know what to answer. How shall I be able to wait till this evening? . . .

Some kind of strange transparent bandage over my eyes seems to show me his image everywhere—his image magnified—and all love's rays are concentrated on a single burning spot in my heart.

Oh! how this waiting tires me!

Lord, unclose for me one moment the wide gateways of gladness.

3rd October.

All is over. Alas! he has slipped out of my arms like a shadow. He was here! He was here! I feel him still. I call him. My hands, my lips seek him in vain in the night. . . .

I can neither pray nor sleep. I went out again into the dark garden. I was afraid —in my room—everywhere in the house —I was afraid. My anguish brought me once more to the door behind which I had left him. I opened it with a mad hope that he might have come back. I called. I groped in the darkness. I have come in again to write to him. I cannot accept my grief.

What has happened? What did I say to him? What did I do? Why do I always want to exaggerate my virtue to him? What can be the worth of a virtue that my whole heart denies? I was secretly false to the words God set upon my lips. In spite of all that my heart was bursting with, I could bring nothing out. Jerome! Jerome, my unhappy friend, in whose presence my heart bleeds and in whose absence I perish, believe nothing of all I said to you just now, but only the words spoken by my love.

Tore up my letter, then wrote again. . . . Here is the dawn, gray, wet with tears, as sad as my thoughts. I hear the first sounds of the farm and everything that was sleeping reawakens to life. . . . "Arise, now. The hour is at hand. . . ."

My letter shall not go.

5th October.

Oh, jealous God, who hast despoiled me, take Thou possession of my heart. All warmth henceforth has forsaken it; nothing will touch it more. Help me to triumph over the melancholy remnant of myself. This house, this garden encourage my love intolerably. I must fly to some place where I shall see none but Thee.

Thou wilt help me to bestow upon Thy poor what fortune I possessed; let me leave Fongueusemare, which I cannot dispose of easily, to Robert. I have made my will, it is true, but I am ignorant of the necessary formalities, and yesterday I could not talk to the lawyer properly, as I was afraid he might suspect the decision I had taken and warn Juliette and Robert. I will finish this business in Paris.

10th October.

Arrived here so tired that I was obliged to stay in bed the first two days. The doctor, who was sent for against my will, speaks of an operation that he considers necessary. What is the use of objecting? But I easily made him believe that I was frightened at the idea of an operation and preferred waiting till I had "regained my strength a little."

I have managed to conceal my name and address. I have deposited enough money with the management of the house for them to make no difficulty about taking me in and keeping me for as long as God shall continue to think it necessary.

I like this room. The walls need no other decoration than their perfect cleanliness. I was quite astonished to feel almost joyful. The reason is that I expect nothing more from life—that I must be content now with God, and His love is sweet only if it fills to completion whatever space there is within us. . . .

The only book I have brought with me is the Bible; but today there sounded in me louder than any words I find there, this wild and passionate sob of Pascal's: "Whatever is not God cannot satisfy my longing."

Oh! too human joy, that my imprudent

heart desired. . . . Was it to wring this cry from me, Lord, that Thou hast thus bereft me?

12th October.

Thy Kingdom come! May it come in me; so that Thou alone mayest reign over me and reign over the whole of me. I will no longer grudge Thee my heart.

Though I am as tired as if I were very old, my soul keeps a strange childishness. I am still the little girl, who could not go to sleep before everything in her room was tidy and the clothes she had taken off were neatly folded beside her bed. . . . That is how I should like to get ready to die.

13th October.

Reread my journal before destroying it. "It is unworthy of noble natures to spread round them the disturbance they feel." It is, I think, Clotilde de Vaux who says this so finely.

Just as I was going to throw this journal into the fire, I felt a kind of warning that held me back. It seemed to me that it no longer belonged to me, that I had no right to deprive Jerome of it, that I had never written it except for him. My anxieties, my doubts, seem to me now so foolish that I can no longer attach any importance to them or believe that they will disturb Jerome. My God, grant that he may at times catch in these lines the unskilled accent of a heart passionately desirous of urging him to those heights of virtue which I myself despaired of reaching.

"My God, lead me to the rock that is higher than I."

15th October.

"Joy, joy, joy, tears of joy. . . ."

Above human joy and beyond all suffering, yes, I foresee that radiant joy. The "rock that is higher than I" bears, I know, the name of happiness . . . I understand that my whole life has been vain, except in so far as it culminates in happiness. . . . Ah! Lord, but Thy promise to the pure and renouncing soul was this: "Blessed *from henceforth*" said Thy holy word, "Blessed are they which die in the Lord from henceforth." Must I wait until I die? This is the point where my faith wavers. Lord! I cry unto Thee with all my strength. I am in the night! I am waiting for the dawn. I cry unto Thee with a crying that wastes me to death. Come and slake the thirst of my heart. It is now, at once, that I thirst for happiness. . . . Or ought I to persuade myself that I have it? And as the pipe of the impatient bird before daybreak calls rather than heralds the light, ought I to sing, without waiting for the night to dwindle?

16th October.

Jerome, I wish I could teach you perfect joy.

This morning I was shattered by a fit of sickness. And afterwards I felt so weak that for a moment I hoped I was going to die. But no; first a great calm fell upon my whole being; then a pang of anguish pierced me, a shudder of my flesh and soul; it was like the sudden and disenchanting *illumination* of my life. It seemed to me that I saw for the first time the walls of my room in their atrocious bareness. I was seized with fear. Even now I am writing to reassure myself, to calm myself. Oh Lord! may I reach the end without blasphemy!

I was able to get up again. I went down on my knees like a child. . . .

I should like to die now, quickly, before again realizing that I am alone.

* * *

I saw Juliette again last year. More than ten years had gone by since her last letter, in which she had told me of Alissa's death. A journey to Provence gave me an opportunity of stopping at Nîmes. The Teissières occupy an important house in the Avenue de Feuchères in a noisy and central part of the town. Although I had written to announce my arrival, it was with considerable emotion that I crossed the threshold.

A maidservant showed me into the drawing-room, where Juliette joined me in a few minutes. I thought I saw Aunt Plantier—the same gait, the same stoutness, the same breathless hospitality. She immediately began plying me with questions (without waiting for my answers) as to my career, my manner of living in Paris, my occupations, my acquaintances; what was my business in the South? Why shouldn't I go on to Aigues-Vives, where Édouard would be so happy to see me? . . . Then she gave me news of all the family, talked of her husband, her children, her brother, of the last vintage, of the fall prices. . . . I learned that Robert had sold Fongueusemare in order to live at Aigues-Vives; that he was now Édouard's partner, which left her husband free to travel, and in particular to look after the commercial side of the business, whilst Robert stayed on the land, improving and increasing the plantations.

In the meantime I was uneasily looking around for anything that might recall the past. I recognized, indeed, among the otherwise new furniture of the drawing-room, certain pieces that came from Fongueusemare; but of the past that was quivering within me, Juliette now seemed to be oblivious, or else to be endeavoring to distract our thoughts from it.

Two boys of twelve and thirteen were playing on the stairs; she called them in to introduce them to me. Lise, the eldest of her children, had gone with her father to Aigues-Vives. Another boy of ten was expected in from his walk; it was he whose advent Juliette had told me of in the letter in which she announced our bereavement. There had been some trouble over this last confinement; Juliette had suffered from its effects for a long time; then last year, as an afterthought, she had given birth to a little girl, whom, to hear her talk, she preferred to all her other children. "My room, where she sleeps, is next door," she said. "Come and see her." And as I was following her: "Jerome, I didn't dare write to you . . . would you consent to be the baby's godfather?"

"Yes, with pleasure, if you would like me to," I said, slightly surprised, as I bent over the cradle. "What is my goddaughter's name?"

"Alissa . . . ," replied Juliette, in a whisper. "She is a little like her, don't you think so?"

I pressed Juliette's hand, without answering. Little Alissa, whom her mother lifted, opened her eyes; I took her in my arms.

"What a good father you would make!" Juliette said, trying to laugh. "What are you waiting for to marry?"

"To have forgotten a great many things," I replied, and watched her blush.

"Which you are hoping to forget soon?"

"Which I do not hope ever to forget."

"Come in here," she said, abruptly, leading the way into a smaller room, which was already dark and of which one door led into her bedroom, and another into the drawing-room. "This is where I take refuge when I have a moment to myself; it is the quietest room in the house; I feel that I am almost sheltered from life in here."

The window of this small drawing-room did not open like the windows of the other rooms, on to the noises of the town, but on to a sort of courtyard planted with trees.

"Let us sit down," she said, dropping into an armchair. "If I understand you rightly, it is to Alissa's memory that you mean to remain faithful."

I stayed a moment without answering. "Rather, perhaps, to her idea of me. No, don't give me any credit for it. I think I couldn't do otherwise. If I married another woman, I could only pretend to love her."

"Ah!" she said, as though indifferently; then turning her face away from me, she bent it toward the ground, as if looking for something she had lost. "Then you think that one can keep a hopeless love in one's heart for as long as that?"

"Yes, Juliette."

"And that life can breathe upon it every day, without extinguishing it?"

The evening came slowly up like a gray tide, reaching and flooding each object, which seemed to come to life again in the gloom and repeat in a whisper the story of its past. Once more I saw Alissa's room, all the furniture of which Juliette had collected together here. And then she turned her face toward me again, but it was too dark for me to distinguish her features, so that I did not know whether her eyes were shut or not. I thought her very beautiful. And we both now remained without speaking.

"Come!" she said at last. "We must wake up."

I saw her rise, take a step forward, and drop again as though she had no strength, into the nearest chair; she put her hands up to her face, and I thought I saw that she was crying.

A servant came in, bringing the lamp.

THE PASTORAL SYMPHONY

By ANDRÉ GIDE

Translated by Dorothy Bussy

FIRST NOTEBOOK

10 February 189—

The snow has been falling continuously for the last three days and all the roads are blocked. It has been impossible for me to go to R—, where I have been in the habit of holding a service twice a month for the last fifteen years. This morning not more than thirty of my flock were gathered together in La Brévine chapel.

I will take advantage of the leisure this enforced confinement affords me to think over the past and to set down how I came to take charge of Gertrude.

I propose to write here the whole history of her formation and development, for I seem to have called up out of the night her sweet and pious soul for no other end but adoration and love. Blessed be the Lord for having entrusted me with this task!

Two years and six months ago I had just driven back one afternoon from La Chaux-de-Fonds when a little girl who was a stranger to me came up in a great hurry to take me to a place about five miles away where she said an old woman lay dying. My horse was still in the shafts, so I made the child get into the carriage and set off at once, after first providing myself with a lantern, as I thought it likely I should not be able to get back before dark.

I had supposed myself to be perfectly acquainted with the whole countryside in the neighborhood of my parish; but when we had passed La Saudraie farm, the child made me take a road that I had never ventured down before. About two miles farther on, however, I recognized on the left-hand side a mysterious little lake where I had sometimes been to skate as a young man. I had not seen it for fifteen years, for none of my pastoral duties take me that way; I could not have said where it lay and it had so entirely dropped out of my mind that when I suddenly recognized it in the golden enchantment of the rose-flecked evening sky, I felt as though I had seen it before only in a dream.

The road ran alongside the stream that falls out of the lake, cut across the extreme end of the forest, and then skirted a peat-bog. I had certainly never been there before.

The sun was setting and for a long time we had been driving in the shade when my young guide pointed out a cottage on the hillside which would have seemed uninhabited but for a tiny thread of smoke that rose from the chimney, looking blue in the shade and brightening as it reached the gold of the sky. I tied the horse up to an apple tree close by and then followed the child into the dark room where the old woman had just died.

The gravity of the landscape, the silence and solemnity of the hour had

[73]

struck me to the heart. A woman still in her youth was kneeling beside the bed. The child, whom I had taken to be the deceased woman's granddaughter, but who was only her servant, lighted a smoky tallow dip and then stood motionless at the foot of the bed. During our long drive I had tried to get her to talk, but had not succeeded in extracting two words from her.

The kneeling woman rose. She was not a relation as I had first supposed, but only a neighbor, a friend, whom the servant girl had brought there when she saw her mistress's strength failing, and who now offered to watch by the dead body. The old woman, she said, had passed away painlessly. We agreed together on the arrangements for the burial and the funeral service. As often before in this out-of-the-world country, it fell to me to settle everything. I was a little uneasy, I admit, at leaving the house, in spite of the poverty of its appearance, in the sole charge of this neighbor and of the little servant girl. But it seemed very unlikely that there was any treasure hidden away in a corner of this wretched dwelling . . . and what else could I do? I inquired nevertheless whether the old woman had left any heirs.

Upon this, the woman took the candle and held it up so as to light the corner of the hearth, and I could make out crouching in the fireplace, and apparently asleep, a nondescript-looking creature, whose face was almost entirely hidden by a thick mass of hair.

"The blind girl there—she's a niece, the servant says. That's all that's left of the family, it seems. She must be sent to the poorhouse; I don't see what else can be done with her."

I was shocked to hear the poor thing's future disposed of in this way in her presence and afraid such rough words might give her pain.

"Don't wake her up," I said softly, as a hint to the woman that she should at any rate lower her voice.

"Oh, I don't think she's asleep. But she's an idiot; she can't speak or understand anything, I'm told. I have been in the room since this morning and she has hardly so much as stirred. I thought at first she was deaf; the servant thinks not, but that the old woman was deaf herself and never uttered a word to her, nor to anyone else; she hadn't opened her mouth for a long time past except to eat and drink."

"How old is she?"

"About fifteen, I suppose. But as to that, I know no more about it than you do. . . ."

It did not immediately occur to me to take charge of the poor, forlorn creature myself; but after I had prayed—or, to be more accurate, while I was still praying on my knees between the woman and the little servant girl, who were both kneeling too—it suddenly came upon me that God had set a kind of obligation in my path and that I could not shirk it without cowardice. When I rose, I had decided to take the girl away that very evening, though I had not actually asked myself what I should do with her afterward, nor into whose charge I should put her. I stayed a few moments longer gazing at the old woman's sleeping face, with its puckered mouth, looking like a miser's purse with strings tightly drawn so as to let nothing escape. Then, turning toward the blind girl, I told the neighbor of my intention.

"Yes, it is better she should not be there tomorrow when they come to take the body away," said she. And that was all.

Many things would be easily accomplished but for the imaginary objections men sometimes take a pleasure in inventing. From our childhood upwards, how often have we been prevented from doing one thing or another we should have liked to do, simply by hearing people about us repeat: "He won't be able to . . ."!

The blind girl allowed herself to be taken away like a lifeless block. The features of her face were regular, rather fine, but utterly expressionless. I took a blanket off the mattress where she must have usually slept, in a corner under a staircase that led from the room to the loft.

The neighbor was obliging and helped me wrap her up carefully, for the night was very clear and chilly; after having lighted the carriage lamp, I started home, taking the girl with me. She sat huddled up against me—a soulless lump of flesh, with no sign of life beyond the communication of an obscure warmth. The whole way home I was thinking: "Is she asleep? And what can this black sleep be like? . . . And in what way do her waking hours differ from her sleeping? But this darkened body is surely tenanted; an immured soul is waiting there for a ray of Thy grace, O Lord, to touch it. Wilt Thou perhaps allow my love to dispel this dreadful darkness? . . ."

I have too much regard for the truth to pass over in silence the unpleasant welcome I had to encounter on my return home. My wife is a garden of virtues; and in the times of trouble we have sometimes gone through I have never for an instant had cause to doubt the stuff of which her heart is made; but it does not do to take her natural charity by surprise. She is an orderly person, careful neither to go beyond nor to fall short of her duty. Even her charity is measured, as though love were not an inexhaustible treasure. This is the only point on which we differ. . . .

Her first thoughts when she saw me bring home the girl that evening broke from her in this exclamation:

"What kind of job have you saddled yourself with now?"

As always happens when we have to come to an understanding, I began by telling the children—who were standing round, open-mouthed and full of curiosity and surprise—to leave the room. Ah, how different this welcome was from what I could have wished! Only my dear little Charlotte began to dance and clap her hands when she understood that something new, something alive, was coming out of the carriage. But the others, who have been well trained by their mother, very soon damped the child's pleasure and made her fall into step.

There was a moment of great confusion. And as neither my wife nor the children yet knew that they had to do with a blind person, they could not understand the extreme care with which I guided her footsteps. I myself was disconcerted by the odd moans the poor afflicted creature began to utter as soon as I let go her hand, which I had held in mine during the whole drive. There was nothing human in the sounds she made; they were more like the plaintive whines of a puppy. Torn away for the first time as she had been from the narrow round of customary sensations that had formed her universe, her knees now failed her; but when I pushed forward a chair, she sank on the floor in a heap, as if she were incapable of sitting down; I then led her up to the fireplace and she regained her calm a little as soon as she was able to crouch down in the same position in which I had first seen her beside the old woman's fire, leaning against the chimney-piece. In the carriage too, she had slipped off the seat and spent the whole drive huddled up at my feet. My wife, however, whose instinctive impulses are always the best, came to my help; it is her reflection that is constantly at odds with her heart and very often gets the better of it.

"What do you mean to do with *that?*" she asked when the girl had settled down.

I shivered in my soul at this use of the word *that,* and had some difficulty in restraining a movement of indignation. As I was still under the spell of my long and peaceful meditation, however, I controlled myself. Turning toward the whole party, who were standing round in a circle again, I placed my hand on the blind girl's head and said as solemnly as I could:

"I have brought back the lost sheep."

But Amélie will not admit that there can be anything unreasonable or super-reasonable in the teaching of the Gospel. I saw she was going to object, and it was then I made a sign to Jacques and Sarah, who, as they are accustomed to our little conjugal differences and have not much natural curiosity (not enough, I often think), led the two younger children out of the room.

Then, as my wife still remained silent and a little irritated, I thought, by the intruder's presence: "You needn't mind speaking before her," I said. "The poor child doesn't understand."

Upon this, Amélie began to protest that she had absolutely nothing to say—which is her usual prelude to the lengthiest explanations—and there was nothing for her to do but to submit, as usual, to all my most unpractical vagaries, however contrary to custom and good sense they might be. I have already said that I had not in the least made up my mind what I was going to do with the child. It had not occurred to me, or only in the vaguest way, that there was any possibility of taking her into our house permanently, and I may almost say it was Amélie herself who first suggested it to me by asking whether I didn't think there were "enough of us in the house already." Then she declared that I always hurried on ahead without taking any thought for those who could not keep up with me, that for her part she considered five children quite enough, and that since the birth of Claude (who at that very moment set up a howl from his cradle, as if he had heard his name) she had as much as she could put up with and that she couldn't stand any more.

At the beginning of her outburst some of Christ's words rose from my heart to my lips; I kept them back, however, for I never think it becoming to allege the authority of the Holy Book as an excuse for my conduct. But when she spoke of her fatigue, I was struck with confusion, for I must admit it has more than once happened to me to let my wife suffer from the consequences of my impulsive and inconsiderate zeal. In the meantime, however, her recriminations had enlightened me as to my duty; I begged Amélie therefore, as mildly as possible, to consider whether she would not have done the same in my place and whether she could have possibly abandoned a creature who had been so obviously left without anyone to help her; I added that I was under no illusion as to the extra fatigue the charge of this new inmate would add to the cares of the household and that I regretted I was not more often able to help her with them. In this way I pacified her as best I could, begging her at the same time not to visit her anger on the innocent girl, who had done nothing to deserve it. Then I pointed out that Sara was now old enough to be more of a help to her and that Jacques was no longer in need of her care. In short, God put into my mouth the right words to help her accept what I am sure she would have undertaken of her own accord if the circumstances had given her time to reflect and if I had not forestalled her decision without consulting her.

I thought the cause was almost gained, and my dear Amélie was already approaching Gertrude with the kindest intentions; but her irritation suddenly blazed up again higher than ever when, on taking up the lamp to look at the child more closely, she discovered her to be in a state of unspeakable dirt.

"Why, she's filthy!" she cried. "Go and brush yourself quickly. No, not here. Go and shake your clothes outside. Oh dear! Oh dear! The children will be covered with them. There's nothing in the world I hate so much as vermin."

It cannot be denied that the poor child was crawling with them; and I could not prevent a feeling of disgust as I thought how close I had kept her to me during our long drive.

When I came back a few minutes later, having cleaned myself as best I could, I found my wife had sunk into an armchair and with her head in her hands was giving way to a fit of sobbing.

"I did not mean to put your fortitude to such a test," I said tenderly. "In any case it is late tonight and too dark to do anything. I will sit up and keep the fire going and the child can sleep beside it. Tomorrow we will cut her hair and wash her properly. You need not attend to her until you have got over your repugnance." And I begged her not to say anything of that to the children.

It was supper time. My protégée, at whom our old Rosalie cast many a scowling glance as she waited on us, greedily devoured the plateful of soup I handed her. The meal was a silent one. I should have liked to relate my adventure, to talk to the children and touch their hearts by making them understand and feel the strangeness of such a condition of total deprivation. I should have liked to rouse their pity, their sympathy for the guest God had sent us; but I was afraid of reviving Amélie's irritation. It seemed as though the word had been passed to take no notice of what had happened and to forget all about it, though certainly not one of us can have been thinking of anything else.

I was extremely touched when, more than an hour after everyone had gone to bed and Amélie had left me, I saw my little Charlotte steal gently through the half-open door in her nightdress and bare feet; she flung her arms round my neck and hugged me fiercely.

"I didn't say good-night to you properly," she murmured.

Then, pointing with her little forefinger to the blind girl, who was now peacefully slumbering and whom she had been curious to see again before going to sleep:

"Why didn't I kiss her too?" she whispered.

"You shall kiss her tomorrow. We must let her be now. She is asleep," I said as I went with her to the door.

Then I sat down again and worked till morning, reading or preparing my next sermon.

"Certainly," I remember thinking, "Charlotte seems much more affectionate than the elder children, but when they were her age, I believe they all got round me too. My big boy Jacques, nowadays so distant and reserved. . . . One thinks them tender-hearted, when really they are only coaxing and wheedling one."

27 February

The snow fell heavily again last night. The children are delighted because they say we shall soon be obliged to go out by the windows. It is a fact that this morning the front door is blocked and the only way out is by the washhouse. Yesterday I made sure the village was sufficiently provisioned, for we shall doubtless remain cut off from the rest of the world for some time to come. This is not the first winter we have been snowbound, but I cannot remember ever having seen so thick a fall. I take advantage of it to go on with the tale I began yesterday.

I have said that when I first brought home this afflicted child I had not clearly thought out what place she would take in our household. I knew the limits of my wife's powers of endurance; I knew the size of our house and the smallness of our income. I had acted, as usual, in the way that was natural to me, quite as much as on principle, and without for a moment calculating the expense into which my impulse might land me—a proceeding I have always thought contrary to the Gospels' teaching. But it is one thing to trust one's cares to God and quite another to shift them onto other people. I soon saw I had laid a heavy burden on Amélie's shoulders—so heavy that at first I felt struck with shame.

I helped her as best I could to cut the little girl's hair, and I saw that she did even that with disgust. But when it came to washing and cleaning her, I was obliged to leave it to my wife; and I realized that I perforce escaped the heaviest and most disagreeable tasks.

For the rest, Amélie ceased to make the slightest objection. She seemed to have thought things over during the night and resigned herself to her new duties; she even seemed to take some pleasure in them and I saw her smile when she had finished washing and dressing Gertrude. After her head had been shaved and I had rubbed it with ointment, a white cap was put on her; some of Sarah's old clothes and some clean linen took the place of the wretched rags Amélie threw into the fire. The name of Gertrude was chosen by Charlotte and immediately adopted by us all, in our ignorance of her real name, which the orphan girl herself was unaware of, and which I did not know how to find out. She must have been a little younger than Sarah, whose last year's clothes fitted her.

I must here confess the profound and overwhelming disappointment I felt during the first days. I had certainly built up a whole romance for myself on the subject of Gertrude's education, and the reality was a cruel disillusion. The indiffer-ence, the apathy of her countenance, or rather its total lack of expression froze my good intentions at their very source. She sat all day long by the fireside, seemingly on the defensive, and as soon as she heard our voices, still more when we came near her, her features appeared to harden; from being expressionless they became hostile; if anyone tried to attract her attention, she began to groan and grunt like an animal. This sulkiness only left her at meal times. I helped her myself and she flung herself on her food with a kind of bestial avidity that was most distressing to witness. And as love responds to love, so a feeling of aversion crept over me at this obstinate withholding of her soul. Yes, truly, I confess that at the end of the first ten days I had begun to despair, and my interest in her was even so far diminished that I almost regretted my first impulse and wished I had never brought her home with me. And the absurd thing was that Amélie, being not unnaturally a little triumphant over feelings I was really unable to hide from her, seemed all the more lavish of care and kindness now that she saw Gertrude was becoming a burden to me, and that I felt her presence among us as a mortification.

This was how matters stood when I received a visit from my friend Dr. Martins, of Val Travers, in the course of one of his rounds. He was very much interested by what I told him of Gertrude's condition and was at first greatly astonished she should be so backward, considering her only infirmity was blindness; but I explained that in addition to this she had had to suffer from the deafness of the old woman who was her sole guardian, and who never spoke to her, so that the poor child had been utterly neglected. He persuaded me that in that case I was wrong to despair, but that I was not employing the proper method.

"You are trying to build," he said, "before making sure of your foundations. You must reflect that her whole mind is in a state of chaos and that even its first lineaments are as yet unformed. The first thing to be done is to make her connect together one or two sensations of touch and taste and attach a sound to them—a word—to serve as a kind of label. This you must repeat over and over again indefatigably and then try to get her to say it after you.

"Above all, don't go too quickly; take her at regular hours and never for very long at a time. . . .

"For the rest, this method," he added, after having described it to me minutely, "has nothing particularly magic about it. I did not invent it and other people have applied it. Don't you remember in the philosophy class at school, our professors told us of an analogous case apropos of Condillac and his animated statue—unless," he corrected himself, "I read it later in a psychological review. . . . Never mind; I was much struck by it and I even remember the name of the poor girl, who was still more afflicted than Gertrude, for she was a deaf-mute as well as blind. She was discovered somewhere in England toward the middle of last century by a doctor who devoted himself to educating her. Her name was Laura Bridgman. The doctor kept a journal, as you ought to do, of the child's progress—or rather, in the first place, of his efforts to instruct her. For days and weeks he went on, first making her feel alternately two little objects, a pin and a pen, and then putting her fingers on the two words *pin* and *pen* printed in a Braille book for the blind. For weeks and weeks there was no result. Her body seemed quite vacant. He did not lose courage, however. 'I felt like a person,' says he, 'leaning over the edge of a deep dark well and desperately dangling a rope in the hope that a hand would catch hold of it.' For he did not for one moment doubt that someone was there at the bottom of the well and that in the end the rope would be caught hold of. And one day, at last, he saw Laura's impassive face light up with a kind of smile. I can well believe that tears of love and gratitude sprang to his eyes and that he straightway fell on his knees and gave thanks to God. Laura had understood at last what it was the doctor wanted. She was saved! From that day forward she was all attention; her progress was rapid; she was soon able to learn by herself and eventually became the head of an institution for the blind—unless that was some other person—for there have been other cases recently that the reviews and newspapers have been full of; they were all astonished—rather foolishly, in my opinion—that such creatures should be happy. For it is a fact that all these walled-up prisoners were happy, and as soon as they were able to express anything, it was their *happiness* they spoke of. The journalists of course went into ecstasies and pointed the 'moral' for people who 'enjoy' all their five senses and yet have the audacity to complain. . . "

Here an argument arose between Martins and me, for I objected to his pessimism and could not allow what he seemed to infer—that our senses serve in the long run only to make us miserable.

"That's not what I meant," he protested; "I merely wanted to say, first, that man's spirit imagines beauty, comfort, and harmony more easily and gladly than it can the disorder and sin that everywhere tarnish, stain, degrade, and mar this world; and further, that this state of things is revealed to us by our five senses, which also help us to contribute to it. So that I feel inclined to put the words '*si sua mala nescient*' after Virgil's '*Fortunatos nimium*,' instead of '*si sua bona norint*' as we are taught. How happy men would be if they knew nothing of evil!"

Then he told me of one of Dickens's

stories—which he thinks was directly inspired by Laura Bridgman's case; he promised to send it to me, and four days later I received *The Cricket on the Hearth,* which I read with the greatest pleasure. It is a rather lengthy but at times very touching tale of a little blind girl, maintained by her father, a poor toymaker, in an illusory world of comfort, wealth, and happiness. Dickens exerts all his art in representing this deception as an act of piety, but, thank Heaven, I shall not have to make use of any such falsehood with Gertrude.

The day after Martins's visit I began to put his method into practice with all the application I was capable of. I am sorry now I did not take notes, as he advised, of Gertrude's first steps along the twilit path where I myself at first was but a groping guide. During the first weeks more patience was needed than can well be believed, not only because of the amount of time an education of this kind requires, but also because of the reproaches it brought me. It is painful for me to have to say that these reproaches came from Amélie; but, for that matter, if I mention this here it is because it has not left in me the slightest trace of animosity or bitterness—I declare this most solemnly, in case these lines should come to her eyes later on. (Does not Christ's teaching of the forgiveness of injuries follow immediately after the parable of the lost sheep?) More than that—at the very moment when I most suffered from her reproaches, I could not feel angry with her for disapproving the length of time I devoted to Gertrude. What I chiefly deplored was that she failed to believe that my efforts would be at all successful. Yes, it was her want of faith that grieved me—without, however, discouraging me. How often I heard her repeat: "If only any good were to come of it all! . . ." And she remained stubbornly convinced that my work was labor lost; so that natu-

rally she thought it wrong of me to devote the time to Gertrude's education which she always declared would have been better employed otherwise. And whenever I was occupied with Gertrude, she managed to make out that I was wanted at that moment for someone or something else, and that I was giving her time that ought to have been given to others. In fact, I think she felt a kind of maternal jealousy, for she more than once said to me: "You never took so much pains with any of your own children"—which was true; for though I am very fond of my children, I have never thought it my business to take much pains with them.

It has often been my experience that the parable of the lost sheep is one of the most difficult of acceptance for certain people, who yet believe themselves to be profoundly Christian at heart. That each single sheep of the flock should be in turn more precious in the eyes of the shepherd than the rest of the flock as a whole is beyond and above their power of conception. And the words: "If a man have a hundred sheep and one of them be gone astray, doth he not leave the ninety and nine and goeth into the mountains and seeketh that which is gone astray?" —words all aglow with charity—such persons would, if they dared speak frankly, declare to be abominably unjust.

Gertrude's first smiles consoled me for everything and repaid me for my pains a hundredfold. For "and if so be that he find it, verily I say unto you, he rejoiceth more of that sheep than of the ninety and nine which went not astray." Yes, verily, the smile that dawned for me one morning on that marble face of hers, when she seemed suddenly touched to understanding and interest by what I had been trying for so many days to teach her, flooded my heart with a more seraphic joy than was ever given me by any child of my own.

5 March

I noted this date as if it had been a birthday. It was not so much a smile as a transfiguration. Her features flashed into life—a sudden illumination, like the crimson glow that precedes dawn in the high Alps, thrilling the snowy peak on which it lights and calling it up out of darkness—such a flood it seemed, of mystic color; and I thought too of the pool of Bethesda at the moment the angel descends to stir the slumbering water. A kind of ecstasy rapt me at sight of the angelic expression that came over Gertrude's face so suddenly, for it was clear to me that this heavenly visitor was not so much intelligence as love. And in a very transport of gratitude I kissed her forehead and felt that I was offering thanks to God.

The progress she made after this was as rapid as the first steps had been slow. It is only with an effort that I can now recall our manner of proceeding; it seemed to me sometimes that Gertrude advanced by leaps and bounds, as though in defiance of all method. I can remember that at first I dwelt more on the qualities of objects than on their variety—hot, cold, sweet, bitter, rough, soft, light—and then on actions: to pick up, to put down, to remove, to approach, to tie, to cross, to assemble, to disperse, etc. And very soon I abandoned all attempt at method and began to talk to her without troubling much whether her mind was always able to follow me; but I went slowly, inviting and provoking her questions as she seemed inclined. Certainly her mind was at work during the hours I left her to herself; for every time I came back to her after an absence, it was to find with fresh surprise that the wall of darkness that separated us had grown less thick. After all, I said to myself, it is so that the warmth of the air and the insistence of spring gradually triumph over winter. How often have I wondered at the melting of the snow! Its white cloak seems to wear thin from underneath, while to all appearance it remains unchanged. Every winter Amélie falls into the trap: "The snow is as thick as ever," she declares. And indeed it still seems so, when all at once there comes a break and suddenly, in patches here and there, life once more shows through.

Fearing that Gertrude might become peaky if she continued to sit beside the fire like an old woman, I had begun to make her go out. But she refused to do this unless she held my arm. I realized from her surprise and fear when she first left the house, and before she was able to tell me so in words, that she had never as yet ventured out of doors. In the cottage where I had found her no one had cared for her further than to give her food and prevent her from dying—for I cannot say that anyone helped her to live. Her little universe of darkness was bounded by the walls of the single room she never left; she scarcely ventured on summer days as far as the threshold, when the door stood open to the great universe of light. She told me later that when she heard the birds' song she used to suppose it was simply the effect of light, like the gentle warmth which she felt on her cheeks and hands, and that, without precisely thinking about it, it seemed to her quite natural that the warm air should begin to sing, just as the water begins to boil on the fire. The truth is she did not trouble to think; she took no interest in anything and lived in a state of frozen numbness till the day I took charge of her. I remember her inexhaustible delight when I told her that the little voices came from living creatures, whose sole function apparently was to express the joy that lies broadcast throughout all nature. (It was from that day that she began to say: "I am as joyful as a bird.") And yet the idea

that these songs proclaim the splendor of
a spectacle she could not behold had begun by making her melancholy.

"Is the world really as beautiful as the
birds say?" she would ask. "Why do
people not tell us so oftener? Why do *you*
never tell me so? Is it for fear of grieving
me because I cannot see it? That would
be wrong. I listen so attentively to the
birds; I think I understand everything
they say."

"People who can see do not hear them
as well as you do, my Gertrude," I said,
hoping to comfort her.

"Why don't other animals sing?" she
went on. Sometimes her questions surprised me and left me perplexed for a
moment, for she forced me to reflect on
things I had hitherto taken for granted. It
was thus it occurred to me for the first
time that the closer an animal lives to the
ground and the heavier its weight, the
duller it is. I tried to make her understand
this; and I told her of the squirrel and its
gambols.

She asked me if the birds were the only
animals that flew.

"There are butterflies too," I told her.

"And do they sing?"

"They have another way of telling their
joy. It is painted on their wings. . . ."
And I described the rainbow colors of the
butterfly.

28 February

Now let me turn back a little, for yesterday I allowed myself to be carried
away.

In order to teach Gertrude, I had had
to learn the Braille alphabet myself; but
she was soon able to read much quicker
than I could; I had some difficulty in de-
ciphering the writing, and besides found
it easier to follow with my eyes than with
my fingers. For that matter, I was not the
only one to give her lessons. And at first I
was glad to be helped in this respect, for I
have a great deal to do in the parish, the
houses being so widely scattered that my
visits to the poor and the sick sometimes
oblige me to go far afield. Jacques had
managed to break his arm while skating
during the Christmas holidays, which he
was spending with us; for during term
time he goes to Lausanne, where he received his early education, and where he
is studying at the theological school. The
fracture was not serious and Martins,
whom I at once sent for, was easily able
to set it without the help of a surgeon;
but it was considered advisable for
Jacques to keep indoors for some time.
He now suddenly began to take an interest in Gertrude, to whom he had hitherto
paid no attention, and occupied himself
with helping me to teach her to read. His
assistance only lasted the time of his con-
valescence—about three weeks—but during those weeks Gertrude's progress was
very marked. She was now fired with extraordinary zeal. Her young intelligence,
but yesterday so benumbed and torpid, its
first steps hardly taken, and scarcely able
to walk, seemed now already preparing to
run. I wondered at the ease with which
she succeeded in formulating her thoughts
and at the rapidity with which she
learned to express herself—not child-
ishly, but at once correctly, conveying
her ideas by the help of images, taken in
the most delightful and unexpected way
from the objects we had just taught her to
recognize, or from others we described to
her, when we could not actually put them
within her grasp; for she always used
things she could touch or feel in order to
explain what was beyond her reach, after
the method of land-surveyors measuring
distances.

But I think it is unnecessary to note
here all the first steps of her education,
doubtless the same in the early education
of all blind people. I suppose too that in
each case the teacher must have been
plunged into a similar perplexity by the

question of colors. (And this subject led me to the reflection that there is nowhere any mention of colors in the Gospels.) I do not know how other people set about it; for my part, I began by naming the colors of the prism to her in the order in which they occur in the rainbow; but then a confusion was immediately set up in her mind between color and brightness; and I realized that her imagination was unable to draw any distinction between the *quality* of the shade and what painters, I believe, call its *"value."* She had the greatest difficulty in understanding that every color in its turn might be more or less dark and that they might be mixed one with another to an unlimited extent. It puzzled her exceedingly, and she came back to the subject again and again.

About this time the opportunity was given me of taking her to a concert at Neuchâtel. The part played by each instrument in the symphony suggested to me the idea of recurring to this question of colors. I bade Gertrude observe the different resonances of the brasses, the strings, and the wood instruments, and that each of them was able in its own way to produce the whole series of sounds, from the lowest to the highest, with varying intensity. I asked her to imagine the colors of nature in the same way—the reds and oranges analogous to the sounds of the horns and trombones; the yellows and greens like those of the violins, cellos, and double basses; the violets and blues suggested by the clarinets and oboes. A sort of inner rapture now took the place of all her doubts and uncertainties.

"How beautiful it must be!" she kept on repeating.

Then suddenly she added: "But the white? I can't understand now what the white can be like."

And I at once saw how insecure my comparison was.

"White," I tried however to explain, "is the extreme treble limit where all the tones are blended into one, just as black is the bass or dark limit."

But this did not satisfy me any more than it did her; and she pointed out at once that the wood instruments, the brasses, and the violins remain distinct in the bass as well as in the treble parts. How often I have been obliged to remain puzzled and silent, as I did then, searching about for some comparison I might appeal to.

"Well," said I at last, "imagine white as something absolutely pure, something in which color no longer exists, but only light; and black, on the contrary, something so full of color that it has become dark. . . ."

I recall this fragment of dialogue merely as an example of the difficulties I encountered only too often. Gertrude had this good point, that she never pretended to understand, as people so often do, thus filling their minds with inaccurate or false statements, which in the end vitiate all their reasoning. So long as she could not form a clear idea of any notion, it remained a cause of anxiety and discomfort to her.

As regards what I have just related, the difficulty was increased by the fact that the notion of light and that of heat began by being closely associated with each other in her mind, and I had the greatest trouble afterward in disconnecting them.

Thus, through these experiments with her, it was constantly brought home to me how greatly the visual world differs from the world of sound, and that any comparison between the two must necessarily be a lame one.

I have been so full of my comparisons that I have not yet said what immense pleasure the Neuchâtel concert gave Gertrude. It was actually the *Pastoral Symphony* that was being played. I say *actually* because, as will be easily understood, there is no work I could have more wished her to hear. For a long time after we had left the concert room, Gertrude remained silent, as though lost in ecstasy.

"Is what you see really as beautiful as that?" she asked at last.

"As beautiful as what, dear child?"

"As that 'scene on the bank of a stream'?"

I did not answer at once, for I was reflecting that those ineffable harmonies painted the world as it might have been, as it would be without evil and without sin, rather than the world as it really was. And I had never yet ventured to speak to Gertrude of evil and sin and death.

"Those who have eyes," I said at last, "do not know their happiness."

"But I who have not," she cried, "*I* know the happiness of hearing."

She pressed up against me as she walked and hung on to my arm in the way small children do.

"Pastor, do you feel how happy I am? No, no, I don't say so to please you. Look at me. Can't you see on people's faces whether they are speaking the truth? I always know by their voices. Do you remember the day you answered me that you weren't crying when my aunt" (that is what she called my wife) "had reproached you with being no help to her? And I cried out: 'Pastor, that's not true!' Oh, I felt at once from your voice that you weren't telling me the truth; there was no need for me to feel your cheeks to know that you had been crying." And she repeated very loud: "No, there was no need for me to feel your cheeks"—which made me turn red, for we were still in the town and the passers-by turned round to look at us. She went on, however:

"You mustn't try to deceive me, you know. First of all, because it would be very mean to try to deceive a blind person . . . and then because you wouldn't succeed," she added, laughing. "Tell me, pastor, you aren't unhappy, are you?"

I put her hand to my lips, as though to make her feel, without having to confess it, that part of my happiness came from her, and answered as I did so.

"No, Gertrude, I am not unhappy. How should I be unhappy?"

"And yet you cry sometimes?"

"I have cried sometimes."

"Not since that time?"

"No, I have not cried again since then."

"And you have not felt inclined to cry?"

"No, Gertrude."

"And tell me—have you felt inclined since then not to speak the truth to me?"

"No, dear child."

"Can you promise never to try to deceive me?"

"I promise."

"Well, tell me quickly, then—am I pretty?"

This sudden question dumbfounded me, all the more because I had studiously avoided up to then taking any notice of Gertrude's undeniable beauty; and moreover I considered it perfectly unnecessary that she should be informed of it herself.

"What can it matter to you?" I said.

"I am anxious," she went on, "I should like to know whether I do not—how shall I put it?—make too much of a discord in the symphony. Whom else should I ask, pastor?"

"It is not a pastor's business to concern himself with the beauty of people's faces," said I, defending myself as best I could.

"Why not?"

"Because the beauty of their souls suffices him."

"You had rather I thought myself ugly," was her reply with a charming pout; so that, giving up the struggle, I exclaimed:

"Gertrude, you know quite well you are pretty."

She was silent and her face took on an

expression of great gravity, which did not leave her until we got home.

On our return Amélie at once managed to make me feel she disapproved of the way I had been spending my day. She might have told me so before; but she had let Gertrude and me start without a word, according to her habit of letting people do things and of reserving to herself the right to blame them afterward. For that matter, she did not actually reproach me; but her very silence was accusing; for surely it would have been natural to have inquired what we had heard, since she knew I was taking Gertrude to the concert. Would not the child's pleasure have been increased if she had felt that the smallest interest had been taken in it? But Amélie did not remain entirely silent— she merely seemed to put a sort of affectation into avoiding any but the most indifferent topics; and it was not till evening, when the little ones had gone to bed, and after I had asked her in private and with some severity if she was vexed with me for taking Gertrude to the concert, that I got the following answer:

"You do things for her you would never have done for any of your own children."

So it was always the same grievance, and the same refusal to understand that the feast is prepared for the child who returns to us, not for those who have stayed at home, as the parable shows us. It grieved me too to see that she took no account of Gertrude's infirmity—poor Gertrude, who could hope for no other kind of pleasure. And if I providentially happened to be free that afternoon—I, who am as a rule so much in request— Amélie's reproach was all the more unfair, because she knew perfectly well that the other children were busy or occupied in one way or other, and that she herself did not care for music, so that even if she had all the time in the world, it would

never enter her head to go to a concert, not even if it were given at our very door.

What distressed me still more was that Amélie had actually said this in front of Gertrude; for though I had taken my wife on one side, she had raised her voice so much that Gertrude heard her. I felt not so much sad as indignant, and a few moments later, when Amélie had left us, I went up to Gertrude and, taking her frail little hand in mine, I lifted it to my face. "You see," I said, "this time I am not crying."

"No," answered she, trying to smile, "this time it is my turn." And as she looked up at me, I suddenly saw her face was flooded with tears.

8 March

The only pleasure I can give Amélie is to refrain from doing the things she dislikes. These very negative signs of love are the only ones she allows me. The degree to which she has already narrowed my life is a thing she cannot realize. Oh, would to Heaven she would demand something difficult of me! How gladly I would undertake a rash, a dangerous task for her! But she seems to have a repugnance for everything that is not usual; so that for her, progress in life consists merely in adding like days to like days. She does not desire—she will not even accept—any new virtue, nor even an increase of the old ones. When it is not with disapproval, it is with mistrust that she views every effort of the soul to find in Christianity something other than the domestication of our instincts.

I must confess that I entirely forgot, that afternoon at Neuchâtel, to go and pay our haberdasher's bill and to bring her back some spools of thread she wanted. But I was more vexed with myself for this than she could have been; especially as I had been quite determined not to forget her commissions, being very well aware that "he that is faithful in that which is least is faithful also in much," and being afraid too of the conclusions she might draw from my forgetfulness. I should even have been glad if she had reproached me with it, for I certainly deserved reproaches. But, as often happens, the imaginary grievance outweighed the definite charge. Ah, how beautiful life would be and how bearable our wretchedness if we were content with real evils without opening the doors to the phantoms and monsters of our imagination! . . . But I am straying here into observations that would do better as the subject of a sermon (Luke xii, 29: "Neither be ye of doubtful mind"). It is the history of Gertrude's intellectual and moral development that I purposed tracing here and I must now return to it.

I had hoped to follow its course step by step in this book and had begun to tell the story in detail. Not only, however, do I lack time to note all its phases with minuteness, but I find it extremely difficult at the present moment to remember their exact sequence. Carried away by my tale, I began by setting down remarks of Gertrude's and conversations with her that are far more recent; a person reading these pages would no doubt be astonished at hearing her express herself so justly and reason so judiciously in such a little while. The fact is her progress was amazingly rapid; I often wondered at the promptness with which her mind fastened on the intellectual food I offered it, and indeed on everything it could catch hold of, absorbing it all by a constant process of assimilation and maturation. The way in which she forestalled my thoughts and outstripped them was a continual surprise to me, and often from one lesson to another I ceased to recognize my pupil.

At the end of a very few months there was no appearance of her intelligence having lain dormant for so long. Even at this early stage she showed more sense and judgment than the generality of young girls, distracted as they are by the outside world and prevented from giving their best attention by a multitude of futile preoccupations. She was moreover a good deal older, I think, than we had at first supposed. Indeed, it seemed as though she were determined to profit by her blindness, so that I actually wondered whether this infirmity was not in many ways an advantage. In spite of myself I compared her with Charlotte, so easily distracted by the veriest trifles, so that many a time while hearing the child say over her lessons, as I sometimes did, I found myself thinking: "Dear me, how much better she would listen if only she could not see!"

Needless to say, Gertrude was a very eager reader, but as I wished as far as possible to keep in touch with the development of her mind, I preferred her not to read too much—or at any rate not much without me—and especially not the Bible—which may seem very strange for a Protestant. I will explain myself; but before touching on a question so important, I wish to relate a small circumstance that is connected with music and should be placed, as far as I can remember, shortly after the concert at Neuchâtel.

Yes, the concert, I think, took place three weeks before the summer vacation, which brought Jacques home. In the meantime I had often sat with Gertrude at the little harmonium of our chapel, which is usually played by Mlle de la M., with whom Gertrude is at present staying. Louise de la M. had not yet begun to give Gertrude music lessons. Notwithstanding my love for music, I do not know much about it, and I felt very little able to teach her anything when I sat beside her at the keyboard.

"No," she had said after the first gropings, "you had better leave me. I had rather try by myself."

And I left her all the more willingly

that the chapel did not seem to me a proper place in which to be shut up alone with her, as much out of respect for the sanctity of the place as for fear of gossip—though as a rule I endeavor to disregard it; in this case, however, it is a matter that concerns not only me but her. So when a round of visits called me in that direction, I would take her to the church and leave her there, often for long hours together, and then would go to fetch her on my return. In this way she spent her time patiently hunting out harmonies, and I would find her again toward evening pondering over some concord of sounds that had plunged her into a long ecstasy.

On one of the first days of August, barely more than six months ago, it so happened that I had gone to visit a poor widow in need of consolation and had not found her in. I therefore returned at once to fetch Gertrude from the church, where I had left her; she was not expecting me back so soon, and I was extremely surprised to find Jacques with her. Neither of them heard me come in, for the little noise I made was covered by the sound of the organ. It is not in my nature to play the spy, but everything that touches Gertrude touches me; so stepping as softly as I could, I stole up the few steps that lead to the gallery—an excellent post of observation. I must say that during the whole time I was there I did not hear a word from either of them that they might not have said before me. But he sat very close to her, and several times I saw him take her hand in order to guide her fingers over the keys. Was it not in itself strange that she should accept instructions and guidance from him when she had previously refused them from me, preferring, she said, to practice by herself? I was more astonished, more pained, than I liked to own and was just on the point of intervening when I saw Jacques suddenly take out his watch.

"I must leave you now," he said; "my father will be coming back in a moment."

I saw him lift her unresisting hand to his lips; then he left. A few moments later I went noiselessly down the stairs and opened the church door so that she might hear me and think I had only just arrived.

"Well, Gertrude! Are you ready to go home? How is the organ getting on?"

"Very well," she answered in the most natural tone; "I have really made some progress today."

A great sadness filled my heart, but we neither of us made any allusion to the episode I have just described.

I was impatient to find myself alone with Jacques. My wife, Gertrude, and the children used as a rule to go to bed rather early after supper, while we two sat on late over our studies. I was waiting for this moment. But before speaking to him I felt my heart bursting with such a mixture of feelings that I could not—or dared not—begin on the subject that was tormenting me. And it was he who abruptly broke the silence by announcing his intention of spending the rest of the vacation with us. Now, a few days earlier he had spoken to us about a tour he wanted to make in the high Alps—a plan my wife and I heartily approved of; I knew his friend T., who was to be his traveling companion, was counting on him; it was therefore quite obvious to me that this sudden change of plan was not unconnected with the scene I had just come upon. I was at first stirred by violent indignation, but was afraid to give way to it lest it should put an end to my son's confidence altogether; I was afraid too of pronouncing words I should afterward regret; so making a great effort over myself, I said as naturally as I could:

"I thought T. was counting on you."

"Oh," he answered, "not absolutely, and besides he will have no difficulty in finding someone else to go with him. I can rest here quite as well as in the Oberland, and I really think I can spend my time better than mountaineering."

"In fact," I said, "you have found something to occupy you at home."

He noticed some irony in the tone of my voice and looked at me, but being unable as yet to guess the motive of it, went on unconcernedly:

"You know I have always liked reading better than climbing."

"Yes, my dear boy," said I, returning his glance with one as searching; "but are not lessons in harmonium-playing even more attractive than reading?"

No doubt he felt himself blush, for he put his hand to his forehead, as though to shade his eyes from the lamplight; but he recovered himself almost immediately and went on in a voice I could have wished less steady:

"Do not blame me too much, Father. I did not mean to hide anything from you and you have only forestalled by a very little the confession I was preparing to make you."

He spoke deliberately, as if he were reading the words out of a book, finishing his sentences with as much calm, it seemed, as if it were a matter in which he had no concern. The extraordinary self-possession he showed brought my exasperation to a climax. Feeling that I was about to interrupt him, he raised his hand, as much as to say: "No, you can speak afterward; let me finish first." But I seized his arm and shook it.

"Oh," I exclaimed impetuously, "I would rather never see you again than have you trouble the purity of Gertrude's soul. I don't want your confessions! To abuse infirmity, innocence, candor— what abominable cowardice! I should never have thought you capable of it. And to speak of it with such cold-blooded unconcern! . . . Understand me: it is I who have charge of Gertrude and I will not suffer you to speak to her, to touch her, to see her for one single day more."

"But, Father," he went on as calmly as ever, driving me almost beside myself, "you may be sure that I respect Gertrude as much as you can. You are making a strange mistake if you think there is anything reprehensible—I don't say in my conduct, but in my intentions and in my secret heart. I love Gertrude and respect her, I tell you, as much as I love her. The idea of troubling her, of abusing her innocence, is as abominable to me as to you."

Then he protested that what he wanted was to be her help, her friend, her husband; that he had thought he ought not to speak to me about it until he had made up his mind to marry her; that Gertrude herself did not know of his intention and that he had wanted to speak to me about it first.

"This is the confession I had to make to you," he wound up; "and I have nothing else to confess, believe me."

These words filled me with stupor. As I listened, I felt my temples throbbing. I had been prepared with nothing but reproaches, and the fewer grounds he gave me for indignation, the more at a loss I felt, so that at the end of his speech I had nothing left to say.

"Let us go to bed," I said at last, after some moments of silence. I got up and put my hand on his shoulder. "Tomorrow I will tell you what I think about it all."

"Tell me at any rate that you aren't still angry with me."

"I must have the night to think it over."

When I saw Jacques again the next morning, I seemed to be looking at him for the first time. I suddenly realized that my son was no longer a child but a young man; so long as I thought of him as a child, the love that I had accidentally discovered might appear monstrous. I had passed the whole night persuading myself that on the contrary it was perfectly natural and normal. Why was it that my dis-satisfaction only became keener still? It was not till later that this became clear to me. In the meantime I had to speak to Jacques and tell him my decision. Now an instinct as sure as the voice of con-science warned me that this marriage must be prevented at all costs.

I took Jacques down to the bottom of the garden.

"Have you said anything to Gertrude?" I began by asking him.

"No," he answered; "perhaps she feels I love her, but I have not yet told her so."

"Then you must promise me not to speak of it yet awhile."

"I am determined to obey you, Father; but may I not know your reasons?"

I hesitated to give them, feeling doubt-ful whether those that first came into my mind were the wisest to put forward. To tell the truth, conscience rather than rea-son dictated my conduct.

"Gertrude is too young," I said at last. "You must reflect that she has not yet been confirmed. You know she was un-happily not like other children and did not begin to develop till very late. She is so trustful that she would no doubt be only too easily touched by the first words of love she heard; that is why it is of im-portance not to say them. To take posses-sion of what is defenseless is cowardice; I know that you are not a coward. Your feelings, you say, are in no way reprehen-sible; I say they are wrong because they are premature. It is our duty to be pru-dent for Gertrude till she is able to be prudent for herself. It is a matter of con-science."

Jacques has one excellent point—that the simple words I often used to him as a child, "I appeal to your conscience," have always been sufficient to check him. Meanwhile, as I looked at him, I thought that if Gertrude were able to see, she could not fail to admire the tall slender figure, so straight and yet so lithe, the smooth forehead, the frank look, the face, so childlike still, though now, as it were, overshadowed by a sudden gravity. He was bareheaded, and his fair hair, which was rather long at that time, curled a little at the temples and half hid his ears.

"There is another thing I want to ask you," I went on, rising from the bench where we had been sitting. "You had in-tended, you said, to go away the day after tomorrow; I beg you not to put off your leaving. You were to remain away a whole month at least; I beg you not to shorten your absence by a single day. Is that agreed?"

"Very well, Father, I will obey."

I thought he turned extremely pale—so pale that the color left even his lips. But I persuaded myself that such prompt sub-mission argued no very great love, and I felt inexpressibly relieved. I was touched besides by his obedience.

"That's the child I love," I said gently. And drawing him to me, I put my lips to his forehead. There was a slight recoil on his part, but I refused to feel hurt by it.

10 March

Our house is so small that we are obliged to live more or less on top of one another, which is sometimes very incon-venient for my work, although I keep a little room for myself upstairs where I can receive my visitors in private—and especially inconvenient when I want to speak to one of the family in private, without such an air of solemnity as would be the case if the interview took place in this little parlor of mine, which the chil-dren call my "sanctum" and into which they are forbidden to enter. On that par-ticular morning, however, Jacques had gone to Neuchâtel to buy a pair of boots for his mountaineering, and as it was very fine, the children had gone out after lunch with Gertrude, whom they take charge of, while she at the same time takes charge of them. (It is a pleasure for me to note that Charlotte is particularly attentive to her.) At tea, then, a meal we always take in the common sitting-room, I was quite naturally left alone with Amélie. This was just what I wanted, for I was longing to speak to her. It happens to me so rarely to have a tête-à-tête with her, that I felt almost shy, and the importance of what I had to say agitated me as much as if it had been a question, not of Jacques's affairs, but of my own. I felt too, before I began to speak, how two people who love each other and live practically the same life can yet remain (or become) as much of an enigma to each other as if they lived behind stone walls. Words in this case—those spoken or those heard—have the pathetic sound of vain knocking against the resistance of that dividing barrier, which, unless watch be kept, will grow more and more impenetrable. . . .

"Jacques was speaking to me last night and again this morning," I began as she poured out the tea; and my voice was as faltering as Jacques's had been steady the day before. "He told me he loved Gertrude."

"It was quite right of him to tell you," said she without looking at me and continuing her housewifely task, as if I had said the most natural thing in the world —or rather as if I had said nothing she did not already know.

"He told me he wanted to marry her; he is resolved to—"

"It was only to be expected," she murmured with a slight shrug of her shoulders.

"Then you suspected it?" I asked in some vexation.

"I've seen it coming on for a long while. But that's the kind of thing men never notice."

It would have been no use to protest, and besides there was perhaps some truth in her rejoinder, so "In that case," I simply objected, "you might have warned me."

She gave me the little crooked smile with which she sometimes accompanies and screens her reticences, and then, with a sideways nod of her head, "If I had to warn you," she said, "of everything you can't see for yourself, I should have my work cut out for me!"

What did she mean by this insinuation? I did not know or care to know, and went on, without attending to it:

"Well, but I want to hear what you think about it."

She sighed. Then: "You know, my dear, that I never approved of that child's staying with us."

I found it difficult not to be irritated by her harking back in this way to the past.

"Gertrude's staying with us is not what we are discussing," I said, but Amélie went on:

"I have always thought it would lead to no good."

With a strong desire to be conciliatory, I caught at her phrase:

"Then you think it would be no good if it led to such a marriage? That's just what I wanted to hear you say. I am glad we are of the same opinion." Then I added that Jacques had submitted quietly to the reasons I had given him, so that there was no need for her to be anxious; that it had been agreed he was to leave the next day for his trip and stay away a whole month.

"As I have no more wish than you that he should find Gertrude here when he comes back," I wound up, "I think the best thing would be to hand her over to the care of Mademoiselle de la M. and I could continue to see her there; for there's no denying that I have very serious obligations to her. I have just been to sound our friend and she is quite ready to oblige us. In this way you will be rid of a presence that is painful to you. Louise de la M. will look after Gertrude; she seemed delighted with the arrangement; she is looking forward already to giving her harmony lessons."

Amélie seemed determined to remain silent, so that I went on:

"As we shall not want Jacques to see Gertrude there, I think it would be a good thing to warn Mademoiselle de la M. of the state of affairs, don't you?"

I hoped by putting this question to get something out of her; but she kept her lips tightly shut, as if she had sworn not to speak. And I went on—not that I had anything more to add, but because I could not endure her silence:

"For that matter, perhaps Jacques will have got over his love by the time he gets back. At his age one hardly knows what one wants."

"And even later one doesn't always know," said she at last, rather oddly.

Her enigmatical and slightly oracular way of speaking irritated me, for I am too frank by nature to put up easily with mystery-making. Turning toward her, I begged her to explain what she meant to imply by that.

"Nothing, my dear," she answered sadly. "I was only thinking that a moment ago you were wishing to be warned of the things you didn't notice yourself."

"Well?"

"Well, I was thinking that it's not always easy to warn people."

I have said that I hate mysteries and I object on principle to hints and double meanings.

"When you want me to understand you, perhaps you will explain yourself more clearly," I replied, rather brutally, perhaps, and I was sorry as soon as I had said it; for I saw her lips tremble a moment. She turned her head aside, then got up and took a few hesitating, almost tottering steps about the room.

"But, Amélie," I cried, "why do you go on being unhappy now that everything is all right again?"

I felt that my eyes embarrassed her, and it was with my back turned and my elbows on the table, resting my head in my hands, that I went on to say:

"I spoke to you unkindly just now. Forgive me."

At that I heard her come up behind me; then I felt her lay her fingers gently on my head as she said tenderly and in a voice trembling with tears:

"My poor dear!"

Then she left the room quickly.

Amélie's words, which I then thought so mysterious, became clear to me soon after this; I have written them down as they struck me at the moment; and that day I only understood that it was time Gertrude should leave.

12 March

I had imposed on myself the duty of devoting a little time daily to Gertrude— a few hours or a few minutes, according to the occupations in hand. The day after this conversation with Amélie, I had some free time, and as the weather was inviting, I took Gertrude with me through the forest to that fold in the Jura where in the clear weather one can see, through a curtain of branches and across an immense stretch of land at one's feet, the wonder of the snowy Alps emerging from a thin veil of mist. The sun was already declining on the left when we reached our customary seat. A meadow of thick, closely cropped grass sloped downwards at our feet; farther off, a few cows were grazing; each of them among these mountain herds wears a bell at its neck.

"They outline the landscape," said Gertrude as she listened to their tinkling.

She asked me, as she does every time we go for a walk, to describe the place where we had stopped.

"But you know it already," I told her; "on the fringe of the forest, where one can see the Alps."

"Can one see them clearly today?"

"Yes, in all their splendor."

"You told me they were a little different every day."

"What shall I compare them to this afternoon? To a thirsty midsummer's day. Before evening they will have melted into the air."

"I should like you to tell me if there are any lilies in the big meadows before us."

"No, Gertrude, lilies do not grow on these heights, or only a few rare species."

"Not even the lilies called the lilies of the field?"

"There are no lilies in the fields."

"Not even in the fields round Neuchâtel?"

"There are no lilies of the field."

"Then why did our Lord say: 'Consider the lilies of the field'?"

"There were some in his day, no doubt, for him to say so; but they have disappeared before men and their plows."

"I remember you have often told me that what this world most needs is confidence and love. Don't you think that with a little more confidence men would see them again? When I listen to His word, I assure you I see them. I will describe them to you, shall I? They are like bells of flame—great bells of azure, filled with the perfume of love and swinging in the evening breeze. Why do you say there are none there before us? I feel them! I see the meadow filled with them."

"They are not more beautiful than you see them, my Gertrude."

"Say they are not less beautiful."

"They are as beautiful as you see them."

" 'And yet I say unto you that even Solomon in all his glory was not arrayed like one of these,' " said she, quoting Christ's words; and when I heard her melodious voice, I felt I was listening to them for the first time. " 'In all his glory,' " she repeated thoughtfully, and was silent for a time. I went on:

"I have told you, Gertrude, that it is those who have eyes who cannot see." And a prayer rose from the bottom of my heart: "I thank Thee, O Lord, that Thou revealest to the humble what Thou hidest from the wise."

"If you knew," she exclaimed in a rapture of delight, "if you knew how easily I imagine it all! Would you like me to describe the landscape to you? . . . Behind us, above us, and around us are the great fir trees, with their scent of resin and ruddy trunks, stretching out their long dark horizontal branches and groaning as the wind tries to bend them. At our feet, like an open book on the sloping desk of the mountain, lies the broad green meadow, shot with shifting colors —blue in the shade, golden in the sun, and speaking in clear words of flowers— gentians, pulsatillas, ranunculus, and Solomon's beautiful lilies; the cows come and spell them out with their bells; and the angels come and read them—for you say that the eyes of men are closed. Below the book I see a great smoky, misty river of milk, hiding abysses of mystery— an immense river, whose only shore is the beautiful, dazzling Alps far, far away in the distance. . . . That's where Jacques is going. Tell me, is he really starting tomorrow?"

"He is to start tomorrow. Did he tell you so?"

"He didn't tell me so, but I guessed it. Will he be away long?"

"A month. . . . Gertrude, I want to ask you something. Why didn't you tell me that he used to meet you in the church?"

"He came twice. Oh, I don't want to hide anything from you; but I was afraid of making you unhappy."

"It would make me unhappy if you didn't tell me."

Her hand sought mine.

"He was sad at leaving."

"Tell me, Gertrude—did he say he loved you?"

"He didn't say so, but I can feel it without being told. He doesn't love me as much as you do."

"And you, Gertrude, does it make you unhappy that he should go away?"

"I think it is better he should go. I couldn't respond."

"But tell me, does it make you unhappy that he should go?"

"You know, pastor, that it's you I love. . . . Oh, why do you take your hand away? I shouldn't speak so if you weren't married. But no one marries a blind girl. Then why shouldn't we love each other? Tell me, pastor, do you think there's anything wrong in it?"

"It's never in love that the wrong lies."

"I feel there is nothing but good in my heart. I don't want to make Jacques suffer. I don't want to make anyone suffer. . . . I only want to give happiness."

"Jacques was thinking of asking you to marry him."

"Will you let me speak to him before he goes? I should like to make him understand that he must give up loving me. Pastor, you understand, don't you, that I can't marry anyone? You'll let me speak to him, won't you?"

"This evening."

"No, tomorrow; just before he leaves. . . ."

The sun was setting in majestic splendor. The evening air was warm. We had risen and, talking as we went, we turned back along the somber homeward path.

SECOND NOTEBOOK

25 April

I have been obliged to put this book aside for some time.

The snow melted at last, and as soon as the roads were passable, there were a great many things to be done that I had been obliged to put off all the long while our village was isolated from the outer world. It was only yesterday I was able for the first time to find a few moments' leisure again.

Last night I read over everything I had written here. . . .

Now that I dare call by its name the feeling that so long lay unacknowledged in my heart, it seems almost incomprehensible that I should have mistaken it until this very day—incomprehensible that those words of Amélie's that I recorded should have appeared mysterious —that even after Gertrude's naïve declarations, I could still have doubted that I loved her. The fact is that I would not then allow that any love outside marriage could be permissible, nor at the same time would I allow that there could be anything whatever forbidden in the feeling that drew me so passionately to Gertrude.

The innocence of her avowals, their very frankness, reassured me. I told myself she was only a child. Real love would not go without confusion and blushes. As far as I was concerned, I persuaded myself I loved her as one loves an afflicted child. I tended her as one tends a sick person—and so I made a moral obligation, a duty, of what was really a passionate inclination. Yes, truly, on the very evening she spoke to me in the way I have described, so happy was I, so light of heart, that I misunderstood my real feelings, and even as I transcribed our talk, I misunderstood them still. For I should have considered love reprehensible, and my conviction was that everything reprehensible must lie heavy on the soul; therefore, as I felt no weight on my soul, I had no thought of love.

These conversations not only were set down just as they occurred, but were also written while I was in the same frame of mind as when they took place; to tell the truth, it was only when I reread them last night that I understood. . . .

As soon as Jacques had gone (I had allowed Gertrude to speak to him before he left, and when he returned for the last few days of his vacation, he affected either to avoid her altogether or to speak to her only in my presence), our life slipped back into its usual peaceful course. Gertrude, as had been arranged, went to stay at Mlle Louise's, where I visited her every day. But, again in my fear of love, I made a point of not talking to her of anything likely to agitate us. I spoke to her only as a pastor and for the most part in Louise's presence, occupying myself chiefly with her religious instruction and with preparing her for Holy Communion, which she has just partaken of this Easter.

I too communicated on Easter Day.

This was a fortnight ago. To my surprise, Jacques, who was spending a week's holiday with us, did not accompany us to the Lord's Table. And I greatly regret having to say that Amélie also abstained—for the first time since our marriage. It seemed as though the two of them had come to an understanding and resolved by their abstention from this solemn celebration to throw a shadow over my joy. Here again I congratulated myself that Gertrude could not see and that I was left to bear the weight of this shadow alone. I know Amélie too well not to be aware of all the blame she wished indirectly to convey by her conduct. She never openly disapproves of me, but she makes a point of showing her displeasure by leaving me in a sort of isolation.

I was profoundly distressed that a grievance of this kind—such a one, I mean, as I shrink from contemplating—

should have so affected Amélie's soul as to turn her aside from her higher interests. And when I came home I prayed for her in all sincerity of heart.

As for Jacques's abstention, it was due to quite another motive, as a conversation I had with him a little later on made clear.

3 May

Gertrude's religious instruction has led me to reread the Gospels with a fresh eye. It seems to me more and more that many of the notions that constitute our Christian faith originate not from Christ's own words but from St. Paul's commentaries.

This was, in fact, the subject of the discussion I have just had with Jacques. By disposition he is somewhat hard and rigid, and his mind is not sufficiently nourished by his heart; he is becoming traditionalist and dogmatic. He reproaches me with choosing out of the Christian doctrine "what pleases me." But I do not pick and choose among Christ's words. I simply, between Christ and St. Paul, choose Christ. He, on the contrary, for fear of finding them in opposition, refuses to dissociate them, refuses to feel any difference of inspiration between them, and makes objections when I say that in one case it is a man I hear, while in the other it is God. The more he argues, the more persuaded I am he does not feel that Christ's slightest word has a divine accent that is unique.

I search the Gospels, I search in vain for commands, threats, prohibitions. . . . All of these come from St. Paul. And it is precisely because they are not to be found in the words of Christ that Jacques is disturbed. Souls like his think themselves lost as soon as they are deprived of their props, their handrails, their fences. And besides they cannot endure others to enjoy a liberty they have resigned, and want to obtain by compulsion what would readily be granted by love.

"But, Father," he said, "I too desire the soul's happiness."

"No, my friend, you desire its submission."

"It is in submission that happiness lies."

I leave him the last word because I dislike arguing; but I know that happiness is endangered when one seeks to obtain it by what should on the contrary be the effect of happiness—and if it is true that the loving soul rejoices in a willing submission, nothing is farther from happiness than submission without love.

For the rest, Jacques reasons well, and if I were not distressed at seeing so much doctrinal harshness in so young a mind, I should no doubt admire the quality of his arguments and his unbending logic. It often seems to me that I am younger than he is—younger today than I was yesterday—and I repeat to myself the words:

"Except ye become as little children, ye shall not enter into the kingdom of heaven."

Do I betray Christ, do I slight, do I profane the Gospels when I see in them above all a *method for attaining the life of blessedness*? The state of joy, which our doubt and the hardness of our hearts prevent, is an obligation laid upon every Christian. Every living creature is more or less capable of joy. Every living creature ought to tend to joy. Gertrude's smile alone teaches me more in this respect than all my lessons teach her.

And these words of Christ's stood out before my eyes in letters of light: "If ye were blind ye should have no sin." Sin is that which darkens the soul—which prevents its joy. Gertrude's perfect happiness, which shines forth from her whole being, comes from the fact that she does not know sin. There is nothing in her but light and love.

I have put into her vigilant hands the four Gospels, the Psalms, the Apocalypse, and the three Epistles of St. John, so that she may read: "God is light, and in him is no darkness at all," as in the Gospel she has already heard the Saviour say: "I am the light of the world." I will not give her the Epistles of St. Paul, for if, being blind, she knows not sin, what is the use of troubling her by letting her read: "sin by the commandment might become exceeding sinful" (Romans vii, 13) and the whole of the dialectic that follows, admirable as it may be.

8 May

Dr. Martins came over yesterday from Chaux-de-Fonds. He examined Gertrude's eyes for a long time with the ophthalmoscope. He told me he had spoken about Gertrude to Dr. Roux, the Lausanne specialist, and is to report his observations to him. They both have an idea that Gertrude might be operated on with success. But we have agreed to say nothing about it to her as long as things are not more certain. Martins is to come and let me know what they think after they have consulted. What would be the good of raising Gertrude's hopes if there is any risk of their being immediately extinguished? And besides, is she not happy as she is? . . .

10 May

At Easter Jacques and Gertrude saw each other again in my presence—at least, Jacques saw Gertrude and spoke to her, but only about trifles. He seemed less agitated than I feared; and I persuade myself afresh that if his love had really been very ardent, he would not have got over it so easily, even though Gertrude had told him last year before he went away that it was hopeless. I noticed that he no longer says "thou" to Gertrude, but calls her "you," which is certainly preferable; however, I had not asked him to do so and I am glad it was his own idea. There is undoubtedly a great deal of good in him.

I suspect, however, that this submission of Jacques's was not arrived at without a struggle. The unfortunate thing is that the constraint he has been obliged to impose on his feelings now seems to him good in itself; he would like to see it imposed on everyone; I felt this in the discussion I had with him that I have recorded farther back. Is it not La Rochefoucauld who says that the mind is often the dupe of the heart? I need not say that, knowing Jacques as I do, I did not venture to point this out to him there and then, for I take him to be one of those people who are only made more obstinate by argument; but the very same evening I found what furnished me with a reply— and from St. Paul himself (I could only beat him with his own weapons)—and left a little note in his room, in which I wrote out the text: "Let not him which eateth not judge him that eateth: for God hath received him" (Romans xiv, 3).

I might as well have copied out what follows: "I know, and am persuaded by the Lord Jesus, that there is nothing unclean of itself: but to him that esteemeth any thing to be unclean, to him it is unclean." But I did not dare to, for I was afraid that Jacques might proceed to suspect me of some wrongful interpretation with regard to Gertrude—a suspicion that must not so much as cross his imagination for a second. Evidently it is here a question of food; but in how many passages of the Scriptures are we not called on to give the words a double and triple meaning? ("If thine eye . . ." and the multiplication of the loaves, the miracle of Cana, etc.) This is not a matter of logic-chopping; the meaning of this text is wide and deep: the restriction must not be dictated by the law but by love, and St. Paul exclaims immediately afterward:

"But if thy brother be grieved with thy meat, now walkest thou not charitably." It is where love fails that the chink in our armor lies. That is where the Evil One attacks us. Lord, remove from my heart all that does not belong to love. . . . For I was wrong to provoke Jacques: the next morning I found on my table the same note on which I had written out the text; Jacques had simply written on the back of it another text from the same chapter: "Destroy not him with thy meat for whom Christ died" (Romans xiv, 15).

I have reread the whole chapter. It is the starting-point for endless discussion. And is Gertrude to be tormented with these perplexities? Is the brightness of her sky to be darkened with these clouds? Am I not nearer Christ, do I not keep her nearer to Him, when I teach her, when I let her believe, that the only sin is that which hurts the happiness of others or endangers our own?

Alas! There are some souls to whom happiness is uncongenial; they cannot, they do not know how to avail themselves of it. . . . I am thinking of my poor Amélie. I never cease imploring her, urging her—I wish I could force her to be happy. Yes, I wish I could lift everyone up to God. But she will none of it; she curls up like certain flowers that never open to the sun. Everything she sees causes her uneasiness and distress.

"What's the good, my dear?" she answered me the other day, "we can't all be blind."

Ah, how her irony grieves me! And what courage I need not to be disturbed by it! And yet it seems to me she ought to understand that this allusion to Gertrude's infirmity is particularly painful to me. She makes me feel, indeed, that what I admire above all in Gertrude is her infinite mildness; I have never heard her express the slightest resentment against anyone. It is true I do not allow her to hear anything that might hurt her.

And as the soul that is happy diffuses happiness around it by the radiation of love, so everything in Amélie's neighborhood becomes gloomy and morose. Amiel would say that her soul gives out black rays. When, after a harassing day of toil—visits to the sick, the poor, the afflicted—I come in at nightfall, tired out and with a heart longing for rest, affection, warmth, it is to find, more often than not, worries, recriminations and quarrels, which I dread a thousand times more than the cold, the wind, and the rain out of doors. I know well enough that our old Rosalie invariably wants her own way, but she is not always in the wrong, nor Amélie always in the right when she tries to make her give in. I know that Gaspard and Charlotte are horribly unruly; but would not Amélie get better results if she scolded them less loudly and less constantly? So much nagging, so many reprimands and expostulations, lose their edge like pebbles on the seashore; they are far less disturbing to the children than to me. I know that Claude is teething (at least that is what his mother declares every time he sets up a howl), but does it not encourage him to howl for her or Sarah to run and pick him up and be forever petting him? I am convinced he would not howl so often if he was left to howl once or twice to his heart's content when I am not there. But I know that is the very time they spoil him most.

Sarah is like her mother, and for that reason I should have wished to send her to school. She is not, alas, what her mother was at her age, when we were first engaged, but what the material cares of life have made her—I was going to say the *cultivation* of the cares of life, for Amélie certainly does cultivate them. I find it indeed very difficult to recognize in her today the angel of those early times who smiled encouragement on every highminded impulse of my heart, who I dreamed would be the sharer of my every hope and fear, and whom I looked on as my guide and leader along the path to heaven—or did love blind me in those days? . . . I cannot see that Sarah has any interests that are not vulgar; like her mother, she allows herself to be entirely taken up with paltry household matters; the very features of her face, unilluminated as they are by any inward flame, look dull and almost hard. She has no taste for poetry or for reading in general; I never overhear any conversation between her and her mother in which I have any inclination to take part, and I feel my isolation even more painfully when I am with them than when I retire to my study, as it is becoming my custom to do more and more often.

And I have also fallen into the habit this autumn, encouraged by the shortness of the days, of taking tea at Mlle de la M.'s whenever my rounds permit it—that is, whenever I can get back early enough. I have not yet mentioned that since last November Louise de la M. has extended her hospitality to three little blind girls, entrusted to her care by Martins. Gertrude is teaching them to read and to work at sundry little tasks over which they have already begun to be quite clever.

How restful, how comforting I find its warm friendly atmosphere every time I re-enter the Grange, and how much I miss it if I am obliged to let two or three days pass without going there. Mlle de la M., it is hardly necessary to say, has sufficient means to take in and provide for Gertrude and the three little boarders without putting herself out in any way; three maidservants help her with the greatest devotion and save her all fatigue. Can one imagine fortune and leisure better bestowed? Louise de la M. has always interested herself in the poor; she is a profoundly religious woman and seems hardly to belong to this earth or to live for anything but love; though her hair is already silvery under its lace cap, nothing can be more childlike than her laugh, nothing more harmonious than her movements, nothing more musical than her voice. Gertrude has caught her manners, her way of speaking, almost the intonation, not only of her voice, but of her mind, of her whole being—a likeness upon which I tease them both, but which neither of them will admit. How sweet it is, when I can find the time, to linger in their company, to see them sitting beside each other, Gertrude either leaning her head on her friend's shoulder or clasping one of her hands in hers, while I read them some lines out of Lamartine or Hugo; how sweet to behold the beauties of such poetry reflected in the mirror of their limpid souls! Even the little pupils are touched by it. These children, in this atmosphere of peace and love, develop astonishingly and make remarkable progress. I smiled at first when Mlle Louise spoke of teaching them to dance—for their health's sake as much as for their amusement—but now I admire the rhythmic grace to which they have attained, though they themselves, alas, are unable to appreciate it. And yet Louise de la M. has persuaded me that though they cannot see, they do physically perceive the harmony of their movements. Gertrude takes part in their dances with the most charming grace and sweetness, and moreover seems to take the keenest pleasure in them. Or sometimes it is Louise de la M. who directs the little girls' movements, and then Gertrude seats herself at the piano. Her progress in music has been astonishing; she plays the organ in chapel now every Sunday and preludes short improvisations to the singing of the hymns. Every Sunday she comes to lunch with us; my children are delighted to see her, notwithstanding that their tastes are growing more and more divergent. Amélie is not too irritable and we get through

the meal without a hitch. After lunch the whole family goes back with Gertrude to the Grange and has tea there. It is a treat for my children, and Louise enjoys spoiling them and loading them with delicacies. Amélie, who is far from being insensible to attentions of this kind, unbends at last and looks ten years younger. I think she would find it difficult now to do without this halt in the wearisome round of her daily life.

18 May

Now that the fine weather has returned, I have been able to go out again with Gertrude—a thing I had not done for a long time (for there have been fresh falls of snow quite recently and the roads have been in a terrible state until only a few days ago), and it is a long time too since I have found myself alone with her.

We walked quickly; the sharp air colored her cheeks and kept blowing her fair hair over her face. As we passed alongside a peat-bog, I picked one or two rushes that were in flower and slipped their stalks under her béret; then I twined them into her hair so as to keep them in place.

We had scarcely spoken to each other as yet in the astonishment of finding ourselves alone together, when Gertrude turned her sightless face toward me and asked abruptly:

"Do you think Jacques still loves me?"

"He has made up his mind to give you up," I replied at once.

"But do you think he knows you love me?" she went on.

Since the conversation I have related above, more than six months had gone by without (strange to say) the slightest word of love having passed between us. We were never alone, as I have said, and it was better so. . . . Gertrude's question made my heart beat so fast that I was obliged to slacken our pace a little.

"My dear Gertrude, everyone knows I love you," I cried. But she was not to be put off.

"No, no; you have not answered my question."

And after a moment's silence she went on, with lowered head:

"Aunt Amélie knows it; and *I* know it makes her sad."

"She would be sad anyway," I protested with an unsteady voice. "It is her nature to be sad."

"Oh, you always try to reassure me," she answered with some impatience. "But I don't want to be reassured. There are a great many things, I feel sure, you don't tell me about for fear of troubling or grieving me; a great many things I don't know, so that sometimes—"

Her voice dropped lower and lower; she stopped as if for want of breath. And when, taking up her last words, I asked:

"So that sometimes—?"

"So that sometimes," she continued sadly, "I think all the happiness I owe you is founded upon ignorance."

"But, Gertrude—"

"No, let me say this: I don't want a happiness of that kind. You must understand that I don't—I don't care about being happy. I would rather know. There are a great many things—sad things assuredly—that I can't see, but you have no right to keep them from me. I have reflected a great deal during these winter months; I am afraid, you know, that the whole world is not as beautiful as you have made me believe, pastor—and, in fact, that it is very far from it."

"It is true that man has often defaced it," I argued timidly, for the rush of her thoughts frightened me and I tried to turn it aside, though without daring to hope I should succeed. She seemed to be waiting for these words, for she seized on them at once as though they were the missing link in the chain.

"Exactly!" she cried; "I want to be sure of not adding to the evil."

For a long time we walked on very quickly and in silence. Everything I might have said was checked beforehand by what I felt she was thinking; I dreaded to provoke some sentence that might set both our fates trembling in the balance. And as I thought of what Martins had said about the possibility of her regaining her sight, a dreadful anxiety gripped my heart.

"I wanted to ask you," she went on at last, "—but I don't know how to say it. . . ."

Certainly she needed all her courage to speak, just as I needed all mine to listen. But how could I have foreseen the question that was tormenting her?

"Are the children of a blind woman necessarily born blind?"

I don't know which of us this conversation weighed down more, but it was necessary for us to go on.

"No, Gertrude," I said, "except in very special cases. There is in fact no reason why they should be."

She seemed extremely reassured. I should have liked in my turn to ask her why she wanted to know this; I had not the courage and went on clumsily:

"But, Gertrude, to have children, one must be married."

"Don't tell me that, pastor. I know it's not true."

"I have told you what it was proper for me to tell you," I protested. "But it is true, the laws of nature do allow what is forbidden by the laws of man and of God."

"You have often told me the laws of God were the laws of love."

"But such love as that is not the same that also goes by the name of charity."

"Is it out of charity you love me?"

"No, my Gertrude, you know it is not."

"Then you admit our love is outside the laws of God?"

"What do you mean?"

"Oh, you know well enough, and I ought not to be the one to say so."

I sought in vain for some way of evasion; the beating of my heart set all my arguments flying in confusion.

"Gertrude," I exclaimed wildly, "— you think your love wrong?"

She corrected me:

"*Our* love. . . . I say to myself I ought to think so."

"And then—?"

I heard what sounded like a note of supplication in my voice, while without waiting to take breath she went on:

"But that I cannot stop loving you."

All this happened yesterday. I hesitated at first to write it down. . . . I have no idea how our walk came to an end. We hurried along as if we were being pursued, while I held her arm tightly pressed against me. My soul was so absent from my body that I felt as if the smallest pebble in the path might send us both rolling to the ground.

19 May

Martins came back this morning. Gertrude's is a case for operation. Roux is certain of it and wishes to have her under his care for a time. I cannot refuse and yet, such is my cowardice, that I asked to be allowed to reflect. I asked to have time to prepare her gently. . . . My heart should leap for joy, but it feels inexpressibly heavy, weighed down by a sick misgiving. At the thought of having to tell Gertrude her sight may be restored to her, my heart fails me altogether.

19 May. Night

I have seen Gertrude and I have not told her. At the Grange this evening there was no one in the drawing-room; I went upstairs to her room. We were alone.

I held her long in my arms pressed to my heart. She made no attempt to resist, and as she raised her face to mine our lips met. . . .

21 May

O Lord, is it for us Thou hast clothed the night with such depth and such beauty? Is it for me? The air is warm and the moon shines in at my open window as I sit listening to the vast silence of the skies. Oh, from all creation rises a blended adoration that bears my heart along, lost in an ecstasy that knows no words. I cannot—I cannot pray with calm. If there is any limitation to love, it is set by man and not by Thee, my God. However guilty my love may appear in the eyes of men, oh, tell me that in Thine it is sacred.

I try to rise above the idea of sin; but sin seems to me intolerable, and I will not give up Christ. No, I will not admit that I sin in loving Gertrude. I could only succeed in tearing this love from my heart if I tore my heart out with it, and for what? If I did not already love her, it would be my duty to love her for pity's sake; to cease to love her would be to betray her; she needs my love. . . .

Lord, I know not. . . . I know nothing now but Thee. Be Thou my guide. Sometimes I feel that darkness is closing round me and that it is I who have been deprived of the sight that is to be restored to her.

Gertrude went into the Lausanne nursing-home yesterday and is not to come out for three weeks. I am expecting her return with extreme apprehension. Martins is to bring her back. She has made me promise not to try to see her before then.

22 May

A letter from Martins: the operation has been successful. God be thanked!

24 May

The idea that she who loved me without seeing me must now see me causes me intolerable discomfort. Will she know me? For the first time in my life I consult the mirror. If I feel her eyes are less indulgent than her heart and less loving, what will become of me? O Lord, I sometimes think I have need of her love in order to love Thee!

8 June

An unusual amount of work has enabled me to get through these last days with tolerable patience. Every occupation that takes me out of myself is a merciful one; but all day long and through all that happens her image is with me.

She is coming back tomorrow. Amélie, who during these last weeks has shown only the best side of herself and seems endeavoring to distract my thoughts, is preparing a little festivity with the children to welcome her return.

9 June

Gaspard and Charlotte have picked what flowers they could find in the woods and fields. Old Rosalie has manufactured a monumental cake, which Sarah is decorating with gilt paper ornaments. We are expecting her this morning for lunch.

I am writing to fill in the time of waiting. It is eleven o'clock. Every moment I raise my head and look out at the road along which Martins's carriage will come. I resist the temptation to go and meet them; it is better—especially for Amélie's sake—that I should not welcome her apart from the others. My heart leaps. . . . Ah, here they are!

9 June. Evening

Oh, in what abominable darkness I am plunged!

Pity, Lord, pity! I renounce loving her, but do Thou not let her die!

How right my fears were! What has she done? What did she want to do? Amélie and Sarah tell me they went with her as far as the door of the Grange, where Mlle de la M. was expecting her. So she must have gone out again. . . . What happened?

I try to put my thoughts into some sort of order. The accounts they give are incomprehensible or contradictory. My mind is utterly confused . . . Mlle de la M.'s gardener has just brought her back to the Grange unconscious; he says he saw her walking by the river, then she crossed the garden bridge, then stooped and disappeared; but as he did not at first realize that she had fallen, he did not run to her help as he should have done; he found her at the little sluice, where she had been carried by the stream. When I saw her soon afterward, she had not recovered consciousness; or at least had lost it again, for she came to for a moment, thanks to the prompt measures that were taken. Martins, who, thank Heaven, had not yet left, cannot understand the kind of stupor and lassitude in which she is now sunk. He has questioned her in vain; she seems either not to hear or else to be determined not to speak. Her breathing is very labored and Martins is afraid of pneumonia; he has ordered sinapisms and cupping and has promised to come again tomorrow. The mistake was leaving her too long in her wet clothes while they were trying to bring her round; the water of the river is icy. Mlle de la M., who is the only person who has succeeded in getting a few words from her, declares she wanted to pick some of the forget-me-nots that grow in abundance on this side of the river, and that, being still unaccustomed to measure distances, or else mistaking the floating carpet of flowers for solid ground, she suddenly lost her footing. . . . If I could only believe it! If I could only persuade myself it was nothing but an accident, what a dreadful load would be lifted from my heart! During the whole meal, though it was so gay, the strange smile that never left her face made me uneasy; a forced smile, which I had never seen her wear before, but which I tried my utmost to believe was the smile of her newly born sight; a smile that seemed to stream from her eyes onto her face like tears, and beside which the vulgar mirth of the others seemed to me offensive. She did not join in the mirth; I felt as if she had discovered a secret she would surely have confided to me if we had been alone. She hardly spoke; but no one was surprised at that, because she is often silent when she is with others, and all the more so when their merriment grows noisy.

Lord, I beseech Thee, let me speak to her. I must know or how can I continue to live? . . . And yet if she really wished to end her life, is it just because she knew? Knew what? Dear, what horrible thing can you have learned? What did I hide from you that was so deadly? What can you so suddenly have seen?

I have been spending two hours at her bedside, my eyes never leaving her forehead, her pale cheeks, her delicate eyelids, shut down over some unspeakable sorrow, her hair still wet and like seaweed as it lies spread round her on the pillow—listening to her difficult, irregular breathing.

10 June

Mlle Louise sent for me this morning just as I was starting to go to the Grange. After a fairly quiet night Gertrude has at last emerged from her torpor. She smiled when I went into the room and motioned to me to come and sit by her bedside. I did not dare question her, and no doubt she was dreading my questions, for she said immediately, as though to forestall anything emotional:

"What do you call those little blue flowers that I wanted to pick by the river? Flowers the color of the sky. Will you be cleverer than I and pick me a bunch of them? I should like to have them here beside my bed. . . ."

The false cheerfulness of her voice was dreadful to me; and no doubt she was aware of it, for she added more gravely:

"I can't speak to you this morning; I am too tired. Go and pick those flowers for me, will you? You can come back again later."

And when an hour later I brought her the bunch of forget-me-nots, Mlle Louise told me that Gertrude was resting and could not see me before evening.

I saw her again this evening. She was lying—almost sitting up in bed—propped against a pile of pillows. Her hair was now fastened up, with the forget-me-nots I had brought her twisted into the plaits above her forehead.

She was obviously very feverish and drew her breath with great difficulty. She kept the hand I put out to her in her burning hand; I remained standing beside her.

"I must confess something to you, pastor; because this evening I am afraid of dying," she said. "What I told you this morning was a lie. It was not to pick flowers. . . . Will you forgive me if I say I wanted to kill myself?"

I fell on my knees beside the bed, still keeping her frail hand in mine; but she disengaged it and began to stroke my forehead, while I buried my face in the sheets so as to hide my tears and stifle my sobs.

"Do you think it was very wrong?" she went on tenderly; then, as I answered nothing:

"My friend, my friend," she said, "you must see that I take up too much room in your heart and in your life. When I came back to you, that was what struck me at once—or, at any rate, that the place I took belonged to another and that it made her unhappy. My crime is that I did not feel it sooner; or rather—for indeed I knew it all along—that I allowed you to love me in spite of it. But when her face suddenly appeared to me, when I saw such unhappiness on her poor face, I could not bear the idea that that unhappiness was my work. . . . No, no, don't blame yourself for anything; but let me go, and give her back her joy."

The hand ceased stroking my forehead; I seized it and covered it with kisses and tears. But she drew it away impatiently and began to toss in the throes of some fresh emotion.

"That is not what I wanted to say to you; no, it's not that I want to say," she kept repeating, and I saw the sweat on her damp forehead. Then she closed her eyes and kept them shut for a time, as though to concentrate her thoughts or to recover her former state of blindness; and in a voice that at first was trailing and mournful, but that soon, as she reopened her eyes, grew louder, grew at last animated even to vehemence:

"When you gave me back my sight," she began, "my eyes opened on a world more beautiful than I had ever dreamed it could be; yes, truly, I had never imagined the daylight so bright, the air so brilliant, the sky so vast. But I had never imagined men's faces so full of care either; and when I went into your house, do you know what it was that struck me first? . . . Oh, it can't be helped, I must tell you: what I saw first of all was our fault, our sin. No, don't protest. You remember Christ's words: 'If ye were blind ye should have no sin.' But now I see. . . . Get up, pastor. Sit there, beside me. Listen to me without interrupting. During the time I spent in the nursing-home I read—or rather I had read to me some verses of the Bible I did not know—some

you had never read me. I remember a text of St. Paul's which I repeated to myself all one day: 'For I was alive without the law once; but when the commandment came, sin revived, and I died.' "

She spoke in a state of extreme excitement and in a very loud voice, almost shouting the last words, so that I was made uncomfortable by the idea that they might be heard outside the room; then she shut her eyes and repeated in a whisper, as though for herself alone:

"Sin revived—and *I* died."

I shivered and my heart froze in a kind of terror. I tried to turn aside her thoughts.

"Who read you those texts?" I asked.

"Jacques," she said, opening her eyes and looking at me fixedly. "Did you know he was converted?"

It was more than I could bear; I was going to implore her to stop, but she had already gone on:

"My friend, I am going to grieve you very much; but there must be no falsehood between us now. When I saw Jacques, I suddenly realized it was not you I loved—but him. He had your face —I mean the face I imagined you had. . . . Ah! why did you make me refuse him? I might have married him. . . ."

"But, Gertrude, you still can," I cried with despair in my heart.

"He is entering the priesthood," she said impetuously. Then, shaken by sobs: "Oh, I want to confess to him," she moaned in a kind of ecstasy. . . . "You see for yourself there's nothing left me but to die. I am thirsty. Please call someone. I can't breathe. Leave me. I want to be alone. Ah! I had hoped that speaking to you would have brought me more relief. You must say good-by. We must say good-by. I cannot bear to be with you any more."

I left her. I called Mlle de la M. to take my place beside her; her extreme agitation made me fear the worst, but I could not help seeing that my presence did her harm. I begged that I might be sent for if there was a change for the worse.

11 June

Alas! I was never to see her again alive. She died this morning after a night of delirium and exhaustion. Jacques, who at Gertrude's dying request was telegraphed for by Mlle de la M., arrived a few hours after the end. He reproached me cruelly for not having called in a priest while there was yet time. But how could I have done so when I was still unaware that during her stay at Lausanne, and evidently urged by him, Gertrude had abjured the Protestant faith? He told me in the same breath of his own conversion and Gertrude's. And so they both left me at the same time; it seemed as if, separated by me during their lifetime, they had planned to escape me here and be united to each other in God. But I tell myself that Jacques's conversion is more a matter of the head than the heart.

"Father," he said, "it is not fitting for me to make accusations against you; but it was the example of your error that guided me."

After Jacques had left again, I knelt down beside Amélie and asked her to pray for me, as I was in need of help. She simply repeated "Our Father . . ." but after each sentence she left long pauses, which we filled with our supplication.

I would have wept, but I felt my heart more arid than the desert.

THE LIFE AND WORKS
OF ANDRÉ GIDE

By MARC BEIGBEDER

THE WORKS OF André Gide, more than most literary productions, are inseparable from the man's life. Gide understood this, and talked a great deal about himself to others, right up until his death. Stories about him abound, often contradictory in what they seem to reveal of the man. But Gide's life, like his works, embraced ambiguities. The question is, what final image of the man emerges from it all?

In a life at once open and discreet, Gide was motivated by nothing so much as his own literary genius. André Gide decided in childhood to become a writer, and he unerringly pursued his chosen course.

In the modern world, the vocation of the writer often has a threefold aim: first, to escape from a set of circumstances; second, to do so in an indirect, sublimated way; and, finally, to reach out from one's particular situation to embrace the universal. Gide's particular set of circumstances was shaped almost entirely by family background and his Protestant upbringing. The Protestantism of the late nineteenth century instilled a personal dedication, a need for commitment, and a constant scrutiny of oneself and one's feelings. In Gide, this influence led to those examinations of conscience in which he indulged to the end of his days.

Gide's father died when the boy was quite young, and his life at home was largely influenced by the women of the family. They allowed him great freedom and he did practically anything he wanted. His sense of individuality, indeed of fantasy, was encouraged by such circumstances. So was his passion for nature and his sense of pleasure, of innocent enchantment, almost of intoxication, in discovering the beauties of the countryside. "I was passionately fond of the country around Uzès, of the valley of the Fontaine d'Ure and above all of the *garrigue*," he recalled. At first, Marie, the family's maid, went with him on long walks. Like every true Swiss woman, she loved flowers and they carried them home by the armful. The aridity and bareness of the *garrigue* made the flower gathering more difficult, but added to Gide's delight in it.

As the family traveled, young Gide explored nature in new settings, still sharing his discoveries with approving women. In *Si le Grain ne Meurt* (*If It Die* . . . , 1924) we have Gide's impressions of seeing eucalyptus trees in flower during a visit to the Côte d'Azur with his mother and Anna Shackleton, a friend of the family: "The first one I saw sent me into transports; I was alone, but I ran off at once to announce the event to my mother and Anna and I did not rest satisfied till I had dragged Anna to the spot where the tree of wonders grew." He also went to the islands of Lérins, where he discovered the submarine flora and fauna in the crannies of the rocks displaying "their splendor with oriental magnificence."

These impressions were shaped by the mature writer, but with age he neither invented nor distorted the boy's sensations. His reaction to natural beauty was never passive; it involved all of his sensibility and intelligence.

Gide craved novelty, change, and surprise for the pleasure they gave, but he did not let his experience overwhelm him. He took them apart, mastered them, and played with them—like the kaleidoscope he once took to pieces, to make it yield its secret. His passion for analysis, his need to know more, his unaggressive tenacity —traits derived directly from his Protestantism—were freely cultivated at home, in the company of women. Yet at the École Alsatienne, he gave the impression of being stupid and uncouth. Asked by his teacher to repeat the observation that the words *coudrier* and *noisetier* designated the same tree, he would not—indeed, could not—answer. Sent out to the playground, then told to come back and repeat the few words required, he was just as tongue-tied as before, to the great delight of the whole class.

Was he clowning or simply being obstinate? Neither. School was all rules, conventions, and habit; organized, monotonous, impersonal, bearing no relation to the natural life. It was not that Gide was lazy. What he needed, would always need, was to be swept up in enthusiasm. Gide wrote in *If It Die:* "I experienced an unspeakable distaste for everything we did in class, for the class itself, for the whole system of lectures and examinations, even for the play hours; nor could I endure the sitting still, the lack of interest, the stagnation. One would like to believe that in the age of innocence the soul

is all sweetness, light, and purity, but I can remember nothing in mine that is not all ugly, dark, and deceitful. . . . A photograph of myself, taken at that time . . . represents me half-hidden in my mother's skirts, frightfully dressed in a ridiculous check frock, with a sickly ill-tempered face and a crooked look in my eyes."

At the École Alsatienne he did master the art of recitation but his manner of reciting and his teacher's compliments only earned him the jealousy and derision of his schoolmates, who used to set upon him after school. Fortunately, he was a good runner and often managed to elude them. Not always, however—he was bullied and beaten and finally had a dead cat rubbed against his face. At last he found a way out: illness. While convalescing from smallpox, he had dizzy spells which he deliberately tried to exacerbate: "Ha! I said to myself, suppose I were to imitate what I imagine!" And he would let himself collapse, after making sure that it was in a place where the fall would not hurt too much. Was he sly? There are all sorts of slyness and his was of a childish, even open kind, without malice or falsehood, a means of defense rather than attack. A weakling's way out? Rather that of a child terrified of being sent back to the slaughter. He liked doing it, too, not only because it was a source of relief, but because he was taking an unknown path, making new feelings conceivable by miming them. These traits would recur in Gide's later life.

At school, he had been unfairly excluded from the company of others and had felt their hatred. As an only child, he adored having friends, for he was of an eminently sociable, friendly disposition. He wanted to be liked, but was rejected. It was the fault of the others, but, instead of hating them for it, he tried to win them over. With his neurotic make-believe he did not mean to shut himself off, to become aloof and embittered; dislodged from one branch, he simply perched himself on another, to see and be seen, to charm others and himself. For his make-believe was as much social as it was neurotic. He threw himself into a role full of refinements, surprises, and subtle effects —a double role, a creation.

Thus we find him on the threshold of his career: an esthete and an individualist. He wanted not only to live apart from the crowd, to be true to himself—but also to be liked. He sought to be sincere, but at the same time sought to please by his sincerity, which inevitably became suspect. It was this conflict, this peculiar set of circumstances from which Gide sought to escape by becoming a writer.

When he returned home from school, the question of his future arose. Gide loved nature, and his mother suggested he make a career in forestry or something similar. But he did not want a profession, since his real interests lay elsewhere—exactly where, it would have been difficult to say. He only knew that he did not, and would never, want an official function. How, at the age of fifteen, could he admit to this evasion? Inflating his esthetic leanings and his feeling of being "different" into a sense of moral purpose, he thought up, innocently enough, another role—one with mystical tenets. He became a religious enthusiast.

At the same time, he was also awakening to the mysteries of sex. As he had been taught, or at least allowed, to let things take their course, he offered no resistance to his desires and cravings. He was fully prepared to give in to them, provided they made no real demands on him and were intense and exciting—like a game. There were two possibilities: either the game could be a solitary one—he took to masturbation with alacrity—or it could be played with partners, inevitably children. In *If It Die . . .* Gide describes an episode of this kind with the concierge's son, both of them hidden under the family table. Not just any children would do; only those who were most instinctive and natural. And even with them, things should not get too serious. The game also needed a proper setting—preferably the open air with the complicity of nature. In playing the game, Gide could embrace and escape several experiences at the same time.

His religious "awakening" was also, in its way, a game. He plunged into mysticism with the same enthusiasm, dash, goodwill, and tenacity that he put into everything. He carried a New Testament, which he pulled from his pocket on any pretext. He mortified his flesh by sleeping on a board and getting up to pray in the middle of the night and then plunging into icy water. Was he really a believer or was he just putting on an act? The second supposition, even in his own eyes, was probably the correct one. Imagination, a craving for the unreal or for art, played an important part in his fervor, as it would later in his love life.

But Gide was unable—and never would be able—to find the flesh displeasing. So, in his twentieth year, his religious fervor failed, or rather came to a halt. Enthusiasm is an unreliable motive force, and when, as in Gide's case, it is not the object of the enthusiasm that counts but the enthusiasm itself, it soon finds a new outlet. This is particularly so when the enthusiasm is accompanied by a critical eye that, while delighting in the game one is playing, also sees through it.

On coming of age, Gide acquired a certain amount of money. He never became attached to money for its own sake, but it always ensured his independence. With his school days at an end, he came under the influence of Pierre Louÿs (a Protestant only in name), who introduced Gide to the Parisian literary avant-garde. Among the writers he met was Mallarmé, and the effects of this encounter were far-reaching for Gide. Gide felt reassured and justified when he found that Mallarmé shared his own estheticism and concern for verbal music. Gide's problems of soul and style were resolved—provisionally at least—by Mallarmé and his mystic devotion to the word. There remained, however, more burning problems touching on Gide's life, personal and beyond the understanding of his contemporaries.

Where would he find a circle in which he would be at home? He had, in fact, to form and foster it himself. Eventually, in 1909, he brought together a series of patiently acquired friendships that had been cultivated separately and were based as much on the bestowal and acceptance of differences as on a common fastidiousness—a circle, but one of individuals. The *Nouvelle Revue Française* was established and in its circle Gide was, at last, at home.

By now, the demands of the flesh could no longer be ignored. To give them their due, Gide left for North Africa with the similarly minded Paul Laurens. Health was the object of the trip, but how was it to be found? "Our predominant feeling," he wrote in his *Journal,* "was one of horror for anything peculiar, odd, morbid, and abnormal." He did not even set out as a "heretic," sexually speaking; his Protestant conscience made him sleep dutifully with various women during his stay. But in vain: the only one who found favor in his eyes was "Miriem," to whom Paul Louÿs would later be attracted as a result of Gide's enthusiastic descriptions. But what he really liked in her was her urchinlike quality and her resemblance to her brother.

In *If It Die . . .* he relates the famous episode with Ali in the sandhills and the rapture it brought him. Once released, this rapture burst forth in laughter and high spirits, as might have been expected. But, from his silence on his return, it was

clear that he had not finished with it: later he would have to tell and justify everything. This became one of the aims of an increasingly large part of his work, work that from now on would be indistinguishable from his life. The need for self-justification became all the more acute and embarrassing (not to say enriching) when, with the rashness of youth, he complicated his problem by marrying his pure-minded cousin Madeleine, known as "Em." Almost all his work, as he said himself, was to be a long attempt to come to terms with an essential contradiction, a tenacious and unremitting dialogue between the levity that was part of his nature and the serious-mindedness—also part of it—that was entirely characteristic of Em.

Everything in Gide is ego-oriented. A large part of his work is in the form of confidences that, like most confidences, were intended for the ears of those closest to his own life. The fact that Gide was his own subject matter did not preclude objectivity—far from it. Indeed, for quite a time he was as preoccupied with language as with himself. It did not take him long to realize that he would never be a poet. (It is to Gide's credit that, relying solely on his own taste, he discovered this very early in his career.) Nevertheless, he was influenced by the Symbolists—especially Mallarmé—for some time. While confining himself to prose, he wanted it to derive life and substance from its form alone. He would have scorned to put a "story" into it. His first works were prose poems, whose underlying thought is expressed only indirectly with artistic reticence. Nothing could be more modern, more contemporary. Perhaps it is because of this that Gide is still in favor with today's avant-garde, just as he was—though for other qualities as well—briefly in favor with the Surrealists.

Gide's first book *Les Cahiers d'André Walter* (*The Notebooks of André Wal-*

ter) appeared anonymously in 1891, and it reveals a Gide still unconsciously fettered by the rigors of Puritanism. The journal of a poet and moral philosopher, it prefigures later works such as *La Porte Étroite* (*Strait is the Gate*) and *If It Die*. . . . The same year Gide also published *La Traité du Narcisse* (*The Treatise of the Narcissus*)—which has the subtitle "Theory of the Symbol" and is dedicated to Paul Valéry. These works, and his next book, *La Tentative Amoureuse* (*The Attempt at Love*, 1893), were, as the author knew, slight, ephemeral efforts. "Our books," he wrote in his preface to the latter, "are never very veracious accounts of ourselves—but rather our wistful desires, our craving for other lives eternally denied us, for every impossible gesture. Here I have written down a dream that was troubling my thoughts too much and demanded an existence. And every book is only a different temptation."

Somewhat less evanescent, a little more substantial and virile, are *Le Voyage d'Urien* (*Travels of Urien*, 1893) and *Paludes* (*Marshlands*, 1895), which may be linked with *Saül*, written in 1896, but not published until 1903. In these two works, purity, austerity, and abstraction rise to a peak, but they are protected and hedged round by irony. *Le Voyage d'Urien* (which could justly have been titled *Voyage de Rien* or "*Journey of Nothing*") and *Marshlands* may, on the whole, be considered satirical works in which routine, depersonalization, apathy, repose, resignation—as represented by a colorless group of men and women of letters—are taken to task. *Marshlands* is the story of a bachelor in a tower surrounded by marshes, a man who is content with his restricted little world and makes no attempt to escape from it, and is thereby doomed to inertia.

Les Nourritures terrestres (*Fruits of the Earth*, 1897), like the preceding works, was published at the author's own expense. It is the most extreme and meticulous example of Gide's early predilection for poetic prose. But it was also a breakthrough for Gide. Here he gave up irony and indirection for a positive celebration of the senses, of self-indulgence in beauty. He stopped putting off temptation, or being ashamed of it, and celebrated its savor, its liberating qualities, no longer in a tone of lamentation but with a hymnlike fervor.

It is easy to see how such exaltation disconcerted the public and the critics, who—for the moment at least, a moment that was to extend beyond World War I—remained unimpressed. Gide's expressions did not fit into any of the accepted conventions, yet did not lash out against them. Apart from Nietzsche, who certainly had some influence on Gide, there were few precedents for a didactic work of so personal and lyrical a nature.

The apparent detachment of *Prométhée mal enchainé* (*Prometheus Unchained*, 1899) might tempt one to link it with the works preceding *Fruits of the Earth* if it were not even more deft and lighthearted, more perfect in its virtuosity, and if it did not mark a further advance in Gide's thought. Here, for the first time, Gide equates freedom with the gratuitous, with chance. By acting gratuitously, he asserts, the individual is liberated from himself, leaving self-interest, the routine, and the commonplace behind.

While *Fruits of the Earth* represented a vital breakthrough, it was with *L'Immoraliste* (*The Immoralist*, 1902) that the real change in Gide seems to have occurred. To write a novel was a betrayal, a capitulation to middlebrow standards. But the need for escape, for self-examination combined with concealment (confession without giving too much away), gave Gide the needed courage. *The Immoralist* is, in fact, barely more than a laborious travesty of the author's own history. What is important, however, is that Gide employed the narrative form in this book in defiance of his own circle. He can only be admired for doing so, despite the outcry from the purists and the book's failure with the public, while continuing to produce and publish the critical writings expected of him. Gide sees his characters as embodiments of certain problems, but it is the problems themselves that most interest him.

Through Alissa, whose devotion to duty is like that of a Sister of Charity to the lepers, and her antagonist Jerome—smitten, vacillating, frustrated, shattered—the idea of moral obligation is attacked from the inside in *Strait is the Gate*. Not only incompatible with happiness, it excludes sincerity, or at least genuine feeling. Needless to say, although André, Em, and their childhood background are drawn upon, the book belongs to the realm of fiction in that everything is heightened, transformed, and embroidered.

In *The Immoralist,* Gide's sexual problem is only secondary. It was not until *Strait is the Gate* that Gide started dealing with sex more or less directly instead of obliquely. One of his aims in writing *Strait is the Gate* was to convince Em, his wife, of his error; to establish by a sort of *reductio ad absurdum* the inimical truth before which he was still hesitating and which—hence his use of the novel form —he was reluctant to state outright.

Isabelle (1911) is a rather cold and austere tale seemingly concerned with abortive revolt, but in *Les Caves du Vatican (Lafcadio's Adventures,* 1914), Gide really casts off his shackles and breathes the intoxicating air of freedom. It is perhaps his most free-and-easy work and certainly his most picaresque, with an air of fantasy that led him to call it a *sotie,* or satirical farce, rather than a novel. There is an amusing anticlerical element, a marked irreverence toward religion and moralistic cant, and the hero Lafcadio is a young man endowed with every charm. Motiveless action, which Gide had treated with a certain ambiguity in *Prometheus Unchained,* he now openly acclaimed. This book briefly linked Gide with the Surrealist movement, which was then in its infancy.

Gide's most authentic and penetrating work—excepting his *Journals,* which did not begin publication until 1931—is *Le Symphonie pastorale (Pastoral Symphony,* 1919), which appeared after an apparent hiatus in his work between 1914 and 1918. Of all his books, this is the least self-conscious. It brings all his experience of faith into play, to heap humiliation, touched with a certain sublimity, on a naive and unfortunate Swiss pastor who is subjected to the temptations of a neophyte. We can see how much of himself Gide put into it—unstintingly for once. We can also see that the book is more than a stinging satire, for it arbitrates the conflict between nature and moral obligation.

It is obvious that Gide's inspiration is bound up with Christianity (or what is called Christianity). This element is, however, almost completely missing from the background of *Les Faux Monnayeurs (The Counterfeiters,* 1926). It may well be this lack that prevents the book, which Gide took pains to term a "novel," from being more than an attractive fresco. On *The Counterfeiters* Gide attached the highest importance to the opinions of others, and I should not be surprised if he divided his critics, friends, and enemies into two categories—those who thought it a masterpiece and those who did not. For once, he had set out to produce something like a professional piece of work. He wanted to be accepted as a novelist, to prove himself, and in a sense he succeeded. Though written in the spirit of a wager, the book is by no means contrived. It gives the impression, however, of an assemblage of exact, vivid, sometimes penetrating observations, brought together with a purpose that is less than profound and that only rarely captures the imagination.

What had deprived Gide of substance, or rather of roots, though at the same time brought him balance, was the termination of the conflict between his private experiences and their literary expression. The open publication of his most candid, personal works, *Corydon* (1923) and *If It Die* . . . , occurred after both books had first been privately circulated. There is something touching about this deferred public confession. While the reticences, qualifications, and evasions that hedge it round may be irritating, it is largely this hesitant, embarrassed, constrained approach that—as Sartre has justly observed—gives it its special quality.

If It Die . . . provided lucid, disarmingly discursive memoirs, in contrast to *Corydon,* which is a bland, rather superficial and arbitrary exercise. But with their appearance, Gide closed that long period of his identity-seeking and self-torment, of which *Dostoevsky* (1923) had marked yet another stage, and in which most of his writings had been motivated by irresolution. Since he no longer had much to question in himself, it was natural that he should turn to social problems.

Now the time had come to exteriorize the values he had gradually assimilated. After *The Counterfeiters,* he turned to social criticism in a series of works—*Le Voyage au Congo* (*Travels in the Congo,* 1927), *Le Retour du Tchad* (*Back from the Chad,*[*] 1928), and *L'École des femmes* (*Girl's School,* 1929). The most militant of Gide's crusading works—apart from certain scattered notes (*Feuillets*)—began to appear with *Oedipe* (1931), in which rejection of a divinity and faith in man are presented with great assurance and delightful humor. Gide's crusade gained momentum almost imme-

diately afterward, when he started his flirtation with Communism.

Believing, not altogether wrongly, that his own personal values (sexual freedom, social equality, atheism) were, or would become, social values, Gide made his offering—indeed, practically gave himself as an offering—to the Communist creed. There were many reasons for this move. He was motivated, in part, by a sense of guilt (this time, over being rich) with which he had always lived. In Communism, too, he could see the opportunity of renewing contact (against established Christianity) with the evangelical spirit that was still very close to his heart, thus demonstrating that there was some continuity in his life. Finally, and perhaps primarily, he was inspired by a need for personal renewal, for rejuvenation. But like his earlier enthusiasms, this one did not survive his own critical view.

In his cooling-off, seen in *Retour de l'U.R.S.S.* (*Back from Russia,* 1936), Gide demonstrated a great deal more acuteness and prudence than he had in the first flush of enthusiasm. He withdrew, in sorrow and confusion at first, into the shell from which, undoubtedly, he should never have emerged. Through the hostilities of World War II and the French Liberation that was, for Gide, also a personal one, he kept himself in form, as was his habit, by critical reflections and adaptations such as *Interviews imaginaires* (*Imaginary Interviews,* 1942), *Le Procès* (*The Process,* 1947), and *Anthologie de la poésie française* (*Anthology of French Poetry,* 1949). He was aware, though he had succeeded in staving off the wrinkles, that the end was near, and he had only one concern: to finish his life well.

First of all came the modestly triumphant smile of *Thésée* (*Theseus,* 1946). Then he exercised that gift for self-examination, which he had continued to cultivate in the *Journals* and *Feuillets* and which was now more concerned with God than with the sinner, in *Et nunc manet in te* (*Madelaine*) and the posthumous *Ainsi soit-il* or *Les Jeux sont faits* (*So Be It*), which complete and elaborate, with their fitful grace, the interrupted confessions of *If It Die*. . . .

From a man who followed such a tortuous path through life, it would be foolish to expect any one metaphysical or moral thesis. However, Gide persistently made a fundamental distinction between the Gospels proper—to which he subscribed, insofar as it can be summed up in terms of joy and love—and the additions of St. Paul and the Church, which he rejected. "The Gospel as it stands is enough for me," he wrote in *Un Esprit non prévenu*. "As soon as I come face to face with it again, everything becomes glowingly clear to me. Human explanations obscure it; when I look for Christ, I find the priest instead and, behind the priest, St. Paul."

The following lines from the *Feuillets* are also worth quoting in this regard: "How extraordinary that they should reproach me for interpreting the words of the Gospel to suit my own ends. On the contrary, it is they who interpret and explain. I take those words as they are given to me in that little book which confounds the wisdom of men."

This opposition to authority is freely expressed in the anticlerical passages of such books as *Lafcadio's Adventures, Isabelle,* and *Oedipe.* Theologically, the great interpolation of St. Paul (and of the Church) is, in Gide's opinion, the Cross. Since the Crucifixion was a complete failure in the eyes of the world, an attempt had to be made to salvage everything possible from the wreckage. Gide noted in his *Journals:* "It was essential to show that the end had been foreseen, to show that it was necessary to the accomplishment of the Scriptures and likewise to the

salvation of humanity. Once that doctrine had mastered minds and hearts it was too late: it was Christ crucified that people continued to see and to teach." He abided by this strict evangelism even when he was tempted by Catholicism, and it served him as an emotional armor.

For a long time, Gide associated this "primitive Christianity," which he then considered the only true kind, with the identification of God with nature and love, but he seems to have gone back on this opinion: "I recognize that I have long used the word 'God' as a sort of dumping-ground for the most woolly concepts. This has ended up in something quite different from Francis Jammes' benevolent white-bearded God, but scarcely more real. For some time yet, this divine residue, shedding personal attributes, tried to take refuge in the esthetic, the harmony of numbers, the *conatus vivendi* of nature. At present I don't even see the point of talking about it any more."

The question is more squarely tackled in Gide's 1949 *Journal:* "I believe that there are not two separate worlds, the spiritual and the material, and that it is useless to set them apart. They are two aspects of one and the same universe; as it is useless to oppose the soul and the body. It is in their identification that I have found calm."

Gide is aware not only of the taboos Christianity places on the senses but, even more, of how much it can detract from the human personality and its natural, genuine development. In Gide's opinion, religious faith may spring solely from within, which obviously deprives it of the authority it claims, indeed of any authority at all. "There is not one of these conversions in which I do not find some inadmissible secret motivation: fatigue, fear, disappointment, sexual or emotional impotence."

As for the idea of an afterlife, he seems in the end to have rejected it completely:

"That the life of the *soul* should continue beyond the dissolution of the flesh, I find inadmissible, unthinkable, and against all reason. I do not believe in the soul separated from the body. I believe that body and soul are one and the same thing and that, when life has withdrawn from the body, it is all over with both of them at once." Thus, even from his evangelism, he retained only the moral teaching.

It is obvious that Gide's work is already of historic interest. There are two main reasons for this: the place that Gide held in the awareness of the public, that is, his identification with a certain attitude to life, and the place he held in art itself. But it remains to be seen whether André Gide is simply a respectable library author or if he still has something to say to the world of today.

The survival of, say, Corneille or Racine, is not merely academic. We do not read or go to see their plays just to learn about the past; we are stirred by them. An even more striking example is the Beaumarchais of *The Marriage of Figaro*. It is the same with Balzac: his portrait of society is fantastically exact but, though it contains much to interest us, this is not —or at least not primarily—what keeps *Eugénie Grandet* or *Father Goriot* alive. It is the power and the art of the portrayal. Thus, to a large extent, it is the art they continue to radiate that gives life to the works of dead authors and it would be quite wrong to attribute their survival simply to interest in the period.

With André Gide, this fact is attested not only by the frequent new editions of his books, but also by the manner in which he is read. There can be little doubt that he holds his readers primarily by his way of expressing himself, by his style rather than his imagination. He attracts us not as a lyrical, creative writer but as an ironist, a critic, a stylist. This is why his seemingly most casual works have the greatest survival value, why

Gide the writer is identified with a *Journal,* and, even more, with a kind of taste —perhaps with taste itself.

But it is also worth considering why his literary definitions and his "human values" are likely to survive. For the most part, his definitions of art are so shrewd that they could never become mere museum pieces; they are still relevant and shall continue to be so. No doubt they contain some excesses, half-truths, presumptions, and even errors. But the essential remains intact, lively, and permanent. Once the prejudices have been trimmed away, there remains the sound sentiment that art is a personal, difficult domain for the use of what is best in man and for his pleasure. In the future Gide's "human values" will probably cease to be associated with his own personality so much. The hundred-and-one twists and turns of his spiritual and moral itinerary, as well as his confessions and his parade of his day-to-day existence, have already lost their attraction. This is not to say that his image will be entirely obliterated, but it will become more like a face behind a curtain, a rustle, a breath—in short, it too will eventually become stylized.

It was not against the man himself— kindly and worthy of respect—but against his personal values that his opponents had a grudge. After his death they continued to tilt at them, thus showing, even at his graveside, that Gide's ideas were still very much alive and that he had kept faith with himself right to the end. "André Gide's death was well received" —Jean Paulhan's witticism is quite true. Gide survives because he continues to make the same friends and the same enemies: Those who—without necessarily having discovered them through Gide himself—share his values and those who reject them, who are scandalized by or indifferent to them.

What has been called his humanism

was not, and could not be, a doctrine: a doctrine is too rigid. He was a humanist only in wishing that nothing should be alien to him. This is what justified his shrewd and disconcerting "crises," his sexual conflicts, his fugitive yet sincere conversions: it is also what makes us concerned about them.

He would have belonged to the Académie Française if this would not have prevented him from being something other than an Academician. For fear of having strings attached, of being classified, he accepted only one prize, the one that classifies without classifying: the Nobel Prize for Literature.

Marc Beigbeder is a professor of philosophy and literature at the Lycée de Carthage. Translated by Helga Harrison.

THE 1947 PRIZE

By KJELL STRÖMBERG

The award of the Nobel Prize to André Gide in 1947 caused a worldwide sensation. The choice in itself, as courageous as it was wise, was not particularly a target for criticism—quite the contrary—but for ten years no first-rate writer of world fame had attracted the favor of the Swedish Academy. There was a distinct impression that the Academy had been going to special lengths to ferret out and reward local talents.

At the time, Gide was still a highly controversial writer in his own country. Although no one ever denied the originality of this mercurial, perturbing mind or the great artistic value of his work, he was in a certain sense in disgrace because some of the more unusual expressions of his art were viewed as an outrage against decency. By the end of World War II, however, the battles that had raged around both his person and his books during the twenties and thirties had diminished considerably. During the war, at least politically, his attitudes had been estimable. He had, moreover, just published his *Journal,* a lengthy work which is remarkable as a faithful portrait of both the author and his times. This balance sheet of half a century of literary activity was generally hailed as his masterpiece, a worthy companion to Montaigne's *Essays* and Rousseau's *Confessions.*

Indeed, after the death of Paul Valéry, Gide, by then nearly eighty, enjoyed a national and international prestige such that many—and not necessarily his most fervent admirers—were led to see in him something of a reincarnated Goethe.

The Nobel Prize was neither the first nor the only public award offered to and accepted by Gide. In 1945, the city of Frankfurt had given him its Goethe Medal, and in 1947 Oxford University had granted him an honorary doctor's degree. Gide even journeyed to Oxford to accept it personally. At the same time, however, he had refused to submit his candidacy to the Académie Française although, according to Gide himself, several influential Academicians had repeatedly invited him to do so.

Gide had already been proposed for the Nobel Prize in 1946, but it was not until 1947 that a proper report was submitted to the Swedish Academy on his behalf. Written by Holger Ahlenius, a specialist in French literature, the report ended in a veritable deification of the writer as a climax to a detailed analysis of the chief works. Ahlenius paid enthusiastic homage to the author, qualifying him as a "unique complicated personality, who is certainly less distinguished by his creative power than by his analytical and dialectical genius, his intransigent logic, his extraordinary ingeniousness in formulating problems and stirring up men's minds." Precisely for these reasons, he recognized Gide as "one of the greatest European writers of his age and, especially, the one modern French writer who has come closest to the Goethean ideal." In spite of Gide's extreme (and often contradictory) positions on many topics, Ahlenius saw him as "a classic writer for his limpid, balanced style, well chiseled, precise, and subtle, a style directly descended from the seventeenth century." No modern French writer had published less reticent confessions, none had cast a more revealing light on the human soul. Thus Gide struck a responsive chord in young European intellectuals of several generations.

Ahlenius recalled how an entire literary school had grown up around the *Nouvelle Revue Française,* the monthly journal founded and edited for many years by Gide. In its pages he was the first to introduce the psychologies of Freud and Dostoevsky into French literature. In his variations on the ambiguous theme of the *acte gratuit* (the wholly disinterested act), he became one of the instigators of Surrealism. It was high time, Ahlenius concluded, for the Swedish Academy to cheat death by honoring this "aged poet," as he called him, with the Nobel Prize which he deserved above all other living writers.

The Academy did not wait to hear these extraordinarily warm recommendations a second time. No doubt the Academicians remembered the mistake they had made in waiting too long to honor another French author of equally universal fame—Valéry, who had died the very year that he was almost certain to receive the award. It is true that Gide had competitors, including several French writers, who might well have proved more acceptable to some of the Academicians. There were Georges Duhamel, Jules Romains, and for the first time, André Mal-

raux. Two future Prizewinners, the Swedish poet Pär Lagerkvist and the American novelist Ernest Hemingway, also figured in the list of thirty-five candidates. Many highly regarded "perennials" were also competing, including T. S. Eliot, who was just a year away from his award. Gide had just passed his seventy-eighth birthday, and his health was seriously impaired. Men of letters not only in Sweden but all over the world were eager for the Prize to go, at last, to this venerable snake charmer.

No doubt, the Academy responded to the insistence of public opinion, which was increasingly pressing; but apparently not without considerable resistance, for week after week passed with no decision forthcoming. The final scruples were doubtless overcome by the highly favorable report submitted by the Academy's expert. An attenuated echo of the report is found in the published motivation, which declared that the Nobel Prize for 1947 was awarded to André Gide "for his comprehensive and artistically significant writings, in which human problems and conditions have been presented with a fearless love of truth and keen psychological insight."

On November 13, when the prize was announced, Gide was at Neuchâtel with his daughter and her husband, Jean Lambert. In his brief book of reminiscences of Gide, Lambert tells us that, unlike most, Gide considered the number 13 lucky. Except for his publishers and his immediate family, no one knew his hideaway. Reporters assaulted his house at 1-bis, rue Vaneau in Paris. They were received, then courteously dismissed by his friend Pierre Herbart and his neighbor, Madame Théo van Rysselberghe, who was also the mother of his wife. Mum was the word, to the point where Gide could go that very evening to see a film featuring Fernandel (he liked it very much). He had already sent his thanks to the Swedish

Academy, together with his regrets, since his health would almost certainly not allow him to go to Stockholm to accept the Prize. He was even obliged at the last minute to turn down a formal dinner given in his honor by the Swedish ambassador to France on December 10, the day the prizes were distributed.

As a matter of fact, Gide was deeply depressed at the time. He confided in his friend Jean Delay, who was later to write his biography. "Now that my heart is weakening, nothing I write is of value. I am waiting to get better, but so far it has been in vain. Simply not to get any worse is a great thing. I have turned my lamp down low, it burns slowly, but I can accept this, perhaps for a long time." Delay, an eminent physician and psychiatrist, observed that the Nobel Prize represented a real satisfaction for Gide, but he also recalled that it was "the occasion for a sudden buildup of nervous tension." Gide himself confirmed this. "An old man and tired, I am finished off by honors."

In an open letter to several leading Swedish newspapers which had sought interviews, Gide confessed that he had received the Nobel Prize "with deep emotion, with tears in my eyes, like a schoolboy who has won a prize." Then he added, begging pardon for his presumption, "However, the child's joy would not have been so full had he not found himself worthy of this recompense."

On this point, the entire press, Swedish and French alike, were in agreement. Rarely, perhaps never, has a Nobel Prize for literature been welcomed so joyously in France. All the Paris papers (except the Communist *L'Humanité*) agreed that the new Prizewinner, so long misunder-stood, had appeared in recent years to an increasingly wider public as the one truly great figure of contemporary French literature. The Swedish Academy had definitely rehabilitated him, and in exemplary fashion, without bothering to wait for posterity's verdict.

In his address in honor of the laureate for 1947, Mr. Osterling noted that the Swedish Academy was not seeking to crown vice in the person of André Gide, as had been maintained in the Paris salons by, among others, a great Catholic writer who had been his friend for many years and who, between appointments as French Ambassador, would have been delighted to serve as his spiritual director. The award, we learn, celebrated a work of genius and even "of idealistic tendencies," as the donor had hoped when he entrusted to the Academy the delicate task of awarding literary prizes. It is true that the Supreme Sacred Congregation of the Holy Office lost no time in reacting— it put the entire body of Gide's work on the *Index librorum prohibitorum*. Gide himself was certainly not greatly upset by this event, for it was made public only after his death. Indeed, he loved being called "the first Nobel Prizewinner who cannot be read by everyone."

At the traditional banquet held at the Stockholm City Hall after the awarding of the Prizes, Gabriel Puaux, the French Ambassador, read a brief message from Gide, expressing his gratitude and his regrets at having been obliged to abandon "a trip that promised to be both pleasant and instructive." He had made a point of reminding his public that he had always refused honors, "at least those which as a Frenchman I could expect from France."

Translated by Dale McAdoo.

Karl Gjellerup

1917

"For his varied and rich poetry,

which is inspired by lofty ideals"

Illustrated by MAY NEAMA

BECAUSE OF WORLD WAR I, NO NOBEL

PRIZE CEREMONIES WERE HELD IN 1917

MINNA

A NOVEL

By KARL GJELLERUP

Translated from the Danish by C. L. Nielsen

As I perused a copy of Thomas Moore's "Irish Melodies," bequeathed to me, with some more favorite books (English and German classics), by my late friend Harald Fenger, I found this "exquisite inscription" strongly underlined with pencil. So I thought it fit to place it as a motto at the head of these recollections of his love-story, the manuscript of which he confided to my care before he died in London. His death, I am half-happy, half-sorry to say, took place not many years after he had lost his beloved Minna. Indeed the fear which she mentioned in her letter to Stephensen, that Fenger's chest was not strong, proved to be less unfounded than he himself supposed. It was also thought probable by his doctor that the heart-wound, of which these pages tell, added fuel to the complaint from which he was already suffering.

KARL GJELLERUP.

Dresden, August 1912.

BOOK I

CHAPTER I

The term at the Polytechnic had been rather tiring. Dresden had begun to grow unbearably hot, and, to make matters worse, I was living at the time in one of the smaller streets of the "old city," which was not exactly airy, though clean and well-kept. I often felt a home-sick longing for the Danish "Sund." The evenings by the Elbe, though beautiful, brought hardly any refreshing coolness, and the thermometer still showed some eighty-eight degrees, even as late as between nine and ten P.M., when I dragged myself, gasping for a breath of air, up the steps of old Brühl's famous terrace. In a way it was consoling, as it proved that I had an undoubted right to feel hot, and that it was an excusable luxury to take an ice-cream outside the Café Torniamenti, while I sat between the columns and listened to snatches of the concert in the "Wienergarten," on the opposite side of the river.

It was on such an evening that I made the bold decision to go into the country during the approaching summer holidays. To myself, at any rate, this decision appeared rather daring, as I was both obliged and accustomed to live very economically. The thought occurred to me that I would go to Saxon-Switzerland, and the last morsel of ice-cream had not melted in my mouth when I had decided upon the little hamlet of Rathen. Dear, tiny nook that it was, it had left upon me the impression of a rarely tender idyl, though, like most travelers, I had only seen it in passing, and then in the twilight, when coming down from the Bastei.

Towards noon, a few days later, I alighted at the little railway station, and walked past the fruit gardens down to the ferry. In this part the Elbe goes winding round cultivated land, which gradually rises into undulating country, dark with pine woods and overhung by rocks, while gently sloping down towards the river. Here lies Upper-Rathen with its substantial, if somewhat scattered farms, and a thin network of fruit trees spreads over the cornfields and green meadows. The opposite side is one long chain of mountains with but a single break in the middle, a small valley disclosing the unimportant village of Lower-Rathen, of which scarcely anything is to be seen but the two inns—the bare new one, and the overgrown old one—lying one on each side of the brook which runs sparkling into the river as it glides swiftly by. To the left of this valley rise the bluish-gray towering rocks of the Bastei, covered down towards the base with woods of pine and beech; these are succeeded by shining sandstone quarries, the most beautiful in the whole country, a series of lofty, yellow walls, some of which rise to a height of several hundred feet. In contrast to these, the quarries on the farther side of the village lie along the base of the hills like one unbroken wall of rock, above which rolls a sea of forests with Lilienstein floating therein—a gigantic man-of-war.

The ferry boat went slantingly, just like a dog, across the current that propelled it forward. It was fixed to a chain, with a barrel midway as float, the farther end of the chain being anchored far up the stream, and in order to obtain the desired motion and direction the ferryman only needed once or twice to tighten the connection chain which ran through a pulley in the little mast. The downward force of the current, acting on the broadside of the boat, did all the work.

Notwithstanding this, the man constantly wiped the perspiration with his shirt sleeve from his face, which was so sunburnt that he seemed to me to be more like a Red Indian than the Sioux Indians themselves, whom I had seen the evening before in the Zoological Gardens. But here, in the middle of his domain, one could not wonder at his appearance, as the glittering water around seemed rather to shed heat than coolness, and the whole curved bank of the river with its rocky walls opened to the south like a concave mirror, whose point of focus lay in front of Rathen. The ferryman and I agreed that I had not chosen a cool spot. But it was not far to the shaded, well-wooded glens; besides which I do not easily change my mind when it is once made up. Perchance, on this occasion, the finger of destiny also played a

part. The event proved of sufficient importance for Fate to have intervened. At any rate, if I afterwards regretted that I did not allow myself to be frightened away, it was not on account of the heat. And have I ever regretted it? Even to this very day—it is now five years ago—I am unable to answer this question.

Some author or other—I should even say, were I asked, a very famous one—has said, that in hours of sorrow nothing is so sad as the remembrance of happy days. Of course I have not the courage to dispute the truth of his words, especially as they have been so often repeated that they are almost proverbial, otherwise I should have thought that, in such hours, it would be still sadder if one had no happy moments upon which to look back. And in this frame of mind I will recall, as well as I can, the days of Rathen and those which followed.

To find a lodging was the first difficulty that presented itself. The two inns had only the most inferior rooms left, and these at rather high terms. I was driven from pillar to post, and had many times to cross the little brook and ascend the tiny wooden steps, from the shoemaker's on the one side to the baker's on the other, back again to the watchman, and then again over to the grocer's; but either the lodging was let or else two rooms went together, and to pay for two rooms was more than I could afford. In the end the schoolhouse, which lay far back on the outskirts of the pine woods, remained as my last hope.

As it was not school time, I knocked boldly at the door of the master's private apartments. A small boy answered the knock. He did not know, he said, whether the master was at home, and having vanished for a moment he suddenly flew past me up the stairs, to appear almost instantaneously with a pair of boots in his hand; then again he darted away, to return triumphantly with a coat. Soon

afterwards the schoolmaster appeared, equipped in this outfit, with a half-sleepy and half-comical smile on his open, good-natured face. Quite right, he had two rooms to let, but they were only let together and at the rent of two guineas a month. I apologized for having given him useless trouble, and he consoled me with the hope that I might get a single room in the new *Pension-Villa* next door.

The villa, which I now approached, looked very smart; the green shutters were thrown back from the windows, creepers covered the walls, and the verandah was well shaded by foliage. It stood on high ground, and the garden, which I had already entered, consisted of a series of terraces connected by graveled pathways between flowering shrubs. But notwithstanding that the very attractions of the place made it somewhat alarming to a poor, Polytechnic student, I still determined to accept the smallest of the attics, regardless of cost, if this palace would take me in at all; for I was heartily disgusted with running about, as I had been doing, and knocking at all doors.

Then, however, a party of ladies and gentlemen appeared on the verandah, and the house looked to me less and less like a *Pension*. Indeed, I felt relieved when a maid, who, at a turn of the path, nearly ran into me, rescued me from my dilemma, though in a very superior and mocking way, by saying—

"No, indeed, we do not let rooms here; the house you are seeking can be seen at the very top of the hill."

So far it had been hidden by the house before me, and I was by no means enchanted when I caught sight of it, for it stood out with a certain bold nakedness against the blue sky, and, as a matter of fact, with hardly so much as a bush to shelter it. Altogether it looked so brand new that I felt convinced that it could never have been inhabited.

I had again to pass down the valley, to

cross over the stream, and crawl about a hundred and fifty feet up an arrangement of paths and stone steps to the edge of the hill. The house did not look more habitable on a nearer view; heaps of gravel, pieces of stone and planks were scattered about, and most of the windows had still to be finished. On entering I encountered a horrible draft, the door banged to, and from the basement I heard a coarse woman's voice hurling forth the many-worded curses and oaths used in vulgar German. A man was hearthstoning the steps, evidently for the first time. A young girl, who was scrubbing the floor in a passage, turned her head at my entrance and showed a pretty pale face with a red spot on one cheek, as if she had just received a smart slap. On my asking for the landlord or landlady, she ran quickly away and disappeared into the basement, leaving the marks of her bare feet upon the sawdust which covered the floor. Soon afterwards she returned, and was following by a portly-looking woman, whose wide mouth had evidently been the outlet for the oaths I had heard, and whose clumsy palms, which she was wiping in her apron, had, I suspected, been in all too close contact with the girl's cheek. Her turned-up skirt showed her bare bow-legs and flat, sprawling feet.

"You want a room, sir?" she said. "Well, you're just in time, if it has to be a single one. Get along with your scrubbing, you young drab, you, it isn't you who has to show the gentleman about, is it? It's on the second floor, please."

We came into a rather spacious room, light and airy enough, for as yet no glass had been placed in the windows. Even the frames were not painted; and the walls, though covered with gray paper, still showed patches of damp, and, in spite of the airiness, I thought the place smelt more than a little fusty.

But before I could make any remark about this she began to praise the perfec-tion of the room, speaking of the satisfaction of former lodgers, notwithstanding that both of us knew perfectly well the house had never been inhabited. I asked for the terms, which were ten shillings more than I had intended to give. She protested that it was a bargain, and that her house was both better and less expensive than anyone else's. There was none of the mist from the river with which the people down by the Elbe were troubled, and one also avoided the closeness of the valley. At such a height I should breathe pure Swiss air and have the best view in the village; lastly, there were the shady promenades belonging to the house, where the lodgers might walk when they did not care to go farther. She always returned to "them shady promenades," and in so doing spread out her dirty arms to indicate their extent, always repeating the words *"da'rim und dort'nim"* (over here and over there).

In the end we split the difference, and she promised that everything should be quite ready in a week, when my holidays began. I gave her half a crown as deposit, and, very happy to have settled matters, I left her.

As I walked away from the house I was bound to admit that the woman's praise of the view was correct. On the right one saw a richly wooded stretch of valley surrounded by mountains; straight ahead lay a by-path leading from the town to the cozy saw-mill, at the entrance to the "Blackbirds' Glen," which, with its green fir trees and gray rocks, soon hid the clear water. To the left, the bend of the Elbe valley opened out under the sun-scorched stone quarries, which cast their reflection over the river, where several rafts and a couple of boats were slowly gliding down with the current. Below lay all the cottages, either built entirely of wood or at least timber-framed, with thatched roofs, and for the most part overgrown with vines. Luckily there was only one other villa to be seen besides the two already mentioned, and it was modestly hidden away. The blue smoke rose from all the chimneys in curling wreaths, forming a thin veil right across the valley, through which glittered the brook between silvery willow trees and somber alders. How idyllic and how very German it all was! I felt so indescribably happy at the prospect of being able to live for a whole month surrounded by this loveliness, that unconsciously I began to sing—

"Guten Morgen, schöne Müllerin."

With the same lack of consciousness I stopped again so that I might take deep breaths of this fresh and fragrant air— "Swiss air"—as the woman had called it, and then I laughed when I thought of "them wonderful shady promenades," for from the spot on which I was standing, I could only see scattered fruit trees on the high-lying fields, and close to the incline a couple of birch trees, the long trailing branches of which caused the leaves to quiver and glitter in the sunshine.

After taking a small meal at the "Erbgericht" on the terrace overlooking the Elbe, I sought the waiter and discovered him talking to my acquaintance, the schoolmaster. The latter was smoking a pipe ornamented with big tassels and a couple of burrs of a deer's horn, evidently his pride, and of which no student need have been ashamed. The tobacco smelt very good and it was, as he afterwards told me, the real old Alstädter; and he drank Münchener-beer, altogether sure signs of a man with refined tastes and habits. He at once greeted me and congratulated me on having found a lodging. I couldn't, he said, have chosen a better spot in the whole of Saxon-Switzerland; there were plenty of unexplored nooks, and I had only to apply to him for advice. He then asked me to what country I belonged, and when he heard that I was a

Dane, he remarked that he also had been in Denmark in 1864, evidently without intending to make himself disagreeable, but only with the object of finding a common subject of interest, in which he succeeded, as I was well acquainted with the surroundings of Kolding, where for a long time he had been quartered. He now became quite excited, questioning me as to whether I remembered this farm and that house, this forest and those hills, and with the mouthpiece of his pipe he pointed out on the colored tablecloth the position of the different places. He was most anxious to know whether the stout Ole Larsen was still in possession of the farm with the outbuildings of stone and the green fence, or whether his son Hans had succeeded to the property—for he and the son had been together in the hospital at Flensburg.

He then talked of the battle in which he had been wounded.

I cannot say that this conversation was either pleasant or unpleasant, but there was something both attractive and straightforward in the way the German spoke of bygone days. It was agreeable to feel how little personal animosity such a war had left, though all the same I had a feeling that everything was not as it ought to be.

I therefore took advantage of a short pause to ask who owned the smart villa, into the grounds of which I had wandered.

"It belongs to the Kammerherr von Zedlitz. He lives here every summer, when he is not with the King at Pillnitz. A distinguished family who live in a rather secluded manner, but who give a considerable amount to the school fund. But, my word, they have a governess; well, you will see for yourself, she *is* a pretty girl. Slightly related to me—not that I know much about her. In fact she is very retiring, and I only wish she was less so."

Just then the whistle from the river steamer sounded; and, having said good-bye to the schoolmaster, I hurried down to the bridge.

CHAPTER II

A week later, at eight o'clock in the morning, I set out.

As usual I came on board at the last minute, and we had already reached the Albert Bridge when, after getting rid of my luggage, I began to look around. The town showed its characteristic profile; the beautiful towers over Brühls Terrace stood out well against the clear sky, while overhead it was misty, and in front of us rather dark. The air was chilly, so I unfastened my traveling plaid. As we steamed past the three castles the town could scarcely be seen, and on reaching Loschwitz, rain began to fall. That is to say, it did not exactly rain, but . . .

"Well, it is just drizzling a bit," said a stout "Dräsener" to his better half, who put her head out of the cabin door with an inquiring look.

When we stopped nearly opposite, at Blasewitz, the newcomers at once went down into the saloon, and the ladies disappeared from the soaked deck. The men also soon left, one after another. The dismal truth could not be hidden any longer —it was pouring!

I lit a cigar and went to the smoking-saloon, which was filled with people and fumes of tobacco. The weather was the only topic of conversation. A long-haired professor, who was taking his *Früh-schoppen,* held forth, saying that when, after such heat, rain began to fall at this period of the year, it would not be fine again until September. All this time the rain was pattering on the roof, and when it ceased to patter it began to splash. It became so gloomy that one felt almost blinded in the unnatural darkness. Through the cabin windows, over which the water was running, one could scarcely see the vine-terraces and gardens on the banks of the river.

When I had finished my cigar I went to the saloon, in which not a seat was to be found, and it was so stuffy that I did not feel inclined to bring a campstool there, but went out into the lobby, where the stairs led up to the deck. A young lady, with two little girls, had seated herself here. I took down a campstool from the pile and, well wrapped up in my plaid, placed myself just opposite the stairs.

The fresh, damp air coming down was pleasant, though it often brought a showerbath, the drops of which remained clinging to the woolen plaid. The upper steps were dripping with water; a pool had collected in a corner of a black tarpaulin which was spread over some luggage on deck, and a miniature fountain kept spurting up from it.

The young lady, seated on the other side of the saloon door, took a little book from her bag, and was soon lost to all around her.

She did not, however, have much peace, for the smaller child, an over-dressed little girl, with flaxen curls, began to cry, and though, in a way, it was appropriate to the situation, the governess had to pacify her. "Lisbeth wants to hear more," the bigger girl said, and the little one confirmed this suggestion by tearfully saying. "More about Peter! More about Peter!"

"Oh, for shame, to let the strange gentleman see you like this, Lisbeth!" the lady whispered. "Do you think *he* cares to hear about Peter?"

The little one sobbed, sucked her forefinger, and looked at me with large, discontented eyes. The look, which so clearly said, "Why can't he go away?" made me very uncomfortable. I felt an intruder, and feared to make matters difficult for the fair young governess, who very likely wished to be alone with her pupils.

I had just made up my mind to move, when she gave me a most humorous look —*how* humorous I suppose she hardly realized herself—a look which clearly said that my company was agreeable to her, though the reason was not a flattering one for me: she did not wish to tell "more about Peter." I smiled back in a way intended to tell her that I had grasped the situation. Then I made myself still more comfortable, and endured with great calmness the angry eyes of the disappointed little one. It was very pleasing to me to be able to do my pretty neighbor a service in so simple a manner.

For pretty, nay, even beautiful, she was, as I had meanwhile had opportunity to realize. Her face belonged to the square type; it was clearly cut, and, as she was a brunette, at first sight she had rather a southern appearance. But the nose was quite German, short, straight, and modest. The lips possessed a rare charm, for the outline and coloring— from nature's hand, of course—were in perfect harmony. It is often the case that lips are either only perfect in color or in outline, or the two are not in harmony and therefore spoil one another; here they were perfection itself. As to the little round chin and the curve of the cheek, I had never seen anything so delicately molded.

She appeared to be of middle height, and rather thin than otherwise. Her dress was not in the latest fashion, which pleased me, but what especially took my fancy was her headgear. Horribly high-peaked hats, trimmed with artificial flowers, were in vogue that year, and in the saloon I had just had the opportunity of wondering at the lack of taste shown in this respect. She, however, wore a small, toque-shaped, straw hat, bound with blue velvet, and a silver-gray veil.

To wear a nice veil at a time when veils are out of fashion always shows good taste on the part of the lady, and a pardonable desire to please. I cannot imagine *the* adored one without a veil, this festive streamer on life's billows, always pointing the direction one is to follow, and always making the heart beat, though sometimes leading astray. Well, I am speaking as if I had already fallen in love, which I had not at the time, though when is one not liable to do so? The world of women is for us divided into two classes: the one with whom it is more or less possible to fall in love, and the other in which one feels as if in the society of men. This time I was surely enough in the society of the former class.

We had gone some distance before I had come to this conclusion, for I only now and then dared to glance at her. All the same, I looked perhaps more often than would be considered correct; at any rate I noticed that she blushed deeply, and bent still farther down over the book, which was by no means of a size to shield her.

This little dumpy book began to make me inquisitive, with the real, traveling, rainy-weather inquisitiveness, that may be aroused by any casual circumstance. Old German translations of Cooper and Walter Scott are usually of a similar size, and I had already judged her literature to belong to this respectable type, when a sudden turning of the leaves revealed that it belonged to an even more serious order —it was a pocket dictionary.

This discovery increased still more my interest in the girl, and I looked at her with a certain emotion, picturing how the stress of life must have forced her to accept one of those trying situations as governess, which require more accomplishments than have ever been found in one human being, and perhaps had obliged her to use every spare moment to add to her knowledge in the quickest and driest manner, forcing her daily to swallow a dose of vocabulary *in natura,* a bitter but strengthening mixture on her thorny path.

When so pretty an image of youthful maidenhood has hardship as a somber background, it can but gain in brightness and relief. Had she been a spoilt young lady of fashion, who passed her time reading the usual library novel, she would not have been half so interesting to me.

Though this interest ought to have been unselfish enough to prevent me from disturbing her, I could not resist doing so in order to start a conversation. I am ashamed to confess that I could not accomplish my purpose any better than by walking twice up the cabin stairs in the hope that she would ask if the weather was clearing—which it was not at all. She never spoke, however, and so I was at my wit's end.

I had thought of and rejected several forms of introduction, when the smaller girl began to complain of the cold. The poor governess had no choice but to wrap her up in her own shawl. As I am myself sensitive to cold, I could sympathize with her in parting with the wrap, especially as I had noticed how contented she had looked when tightening it round her arms and pushing her little chin between the soft folds.

I felt that my time had now come, and courteously offered her my plaid.

As I expected, she politely refused it. "You will need it yourself," she said, "and may catch cold."

I could not possibly deny this, as I was already troubled with a cold in my head, which had made me sneeze twice so furiously that the little girl had been frightened, and the bigger one had, only with an effort, restrained herself from laughing. So I had no other way out of the difficulty than to say I was going to the smoking-saloon and should not require the plaid.

Then the governess expressed a hope that she was not preventing me from smoking, to which I replied that I would on no account annoy her by doing so. On this point I remained obdurate, and thus affected a consideration that was foreign to me. I added that I wanted to move because the air had become rather chilly; and so I succeeded in retiring, leaving behind me my plaid as—*sans comparaison* —Joseph his coat.

Seated again on the oilcloth-covered bench in the little stuffy smoking-saloon, where I had lit my cigar and ordered a glass of beer, I could not hide from myself the fact that my first attempt at an introduction had not been very successful, inasmuch as it had forced me to retire. Had I been bolder I might have managed so that we had shared the plaid, or, if this was impossible, I might have put the little girl next to me and covered her up with my own plaid. In short, I had acted like a fool, and was the more annoyed as my former place was much more agreeable, and I already began to feel symptoms of a headache.

The boat gave a bump and then came to a standstill. Overhead they were dragging along boxes and trunks. We had reached Pirna. I looked apathetically at the small houses of the town, with the many green trees, and the tent-like roof of the lofty church, but with more interest at its Acropolis, Sonnenstein, which had at one time been a fortress, and was now a large lunatic asylum. The brush of Canaletto has often glorified this picture, but always in a better light. As if nature wished to relieve the gloom, a gleam of light suddenly fell on the turrets of the castle.

Now when I recall the scene, it appears to me as if a finger from Heaven had pointed out the building in order to attract my attention and to fix in my heart a foreboding of the feelings with which I should afterwards regard it, and with which I, at this moment, see it with my spiritual eye until my bodily eye grows dim with tears, and I am forced to lay down my pen. At that time nothing suggested itself to me but the glad sign of clearing weather. Gradually the light increased and spread, as walls and turrets began apparently to move and slowly glide to the right; I even faintly saw a patch of blue sky, and before the roof of the church down in the town entirely disappeared, I could see a dull, leaden hue on its steep slope. But again the rain washed down the window.

As we gradually came into the sandstone region, the rain abated. The smoking-saloon's puffing inhabitants disappeared, one by one, and were heard tramping overhead.

I went up also. It was raining rather heavily, the drops glittering like pearls in the hazy light, but as the clouds overhead were beginning to disappear, it was difficult to understand why the rain continued.

The stone walls of the old lower quarries, which here are a reddish-brown, seemed to be varnished, and, from the undulating bank on the right, the tree-tops of a pale green forest shone through the rainy mist. The rain, that for a moment had stopped, grew heavier again, though blue sky could be seen through the clouds.

I went down the cabin stairs and found my little party still in the lobby. The governess was no longer reading, nor was she telling tales, for her little tormentor was sleeping peacefully. This time I did not wait for the question, "Is it clearing?" but said at once that it was likely to be fine. In reply she smiled cheerfully, and thanked me for the use of the plaid, which she began carefully to fold up, and, as it was a large one, I had to help her, and succeeded in making her laugh at my awkwardness. There was just room enough to put it out to its full length,

after which we manœuvred towards each other in the accustomed manner until our hands met. Before I could say a word, she had, with a hurried "thank you," rushed up the stairs, leaving the bigger child to wake up the smaller one.

The moist, shining deck, where one could not yet sit on the benches, was soon overcrowded with passengers. A few drops only glittered through the air, which was quite damp and warm; above, the sky was blue, the river valley was still filled with a light moisture, and the woods on the rocky terraces steamed, as if each pine-top was a little chimney, from which a blue smoke curled up and dissolved itself in the sunshine.

Ahead the glare of the river was almost blinding. At the foot of the perpendicular rocks of the Bastei, a few houses of Rathen could already be seen, and behind them a strange mass of wildly torn crags —the Gamrig-stone, which I had noticed from my window.

I looked for my small piece of luggage, and found that it had been kept quite dry by a tarpaulin. Being thus occupied, I had not had time to look for my beautiful travelling companion, before I heard the shout—"Rathen, *am steuer absteigen*," and I was busy forcing my way sternwards with my baggage. But when I had arrived there I saw, to my great delight, the gray veil flying foremost in the row of people, and soon after the governess passed over the gangway with her little pupils.

Before I could engage a porter, both she and the children had disappeared from view.

CHAPTER III

If I had my wish, a monument to the obloquy of the man who gave this part of the country the name of "Saxon-Switzerland" would be erected in a most prominent spot. Visitors now come here, either with a remembrance of Switzerland, or with a fantastic delusion as to size; comparing, disapproving, and saying, with a sneer, that they had seen or imagined something much grander—a treatment for which the poor little country has never asked.

But if one comes without expectations, and accepts the country as it is, especially not trying to *do* it in tourist fashion, but quietly settling down to live and enjoy— what richness of beautiful nature does it not offer you, and how filled it is with striking contrasts, which are harmonized in its own idyllic, rustic way! Barrenness and prolific growth, wild ruggedness and cultivated land are lying side by side, or one above another; from bright burning heat one suddenly plunges into cool, humid shade. Where do the lungs expand in a fresher and more exhilarating air than in that which sweeps over these heights, and fills the woods and rocky valleys?

Rightly to understand the peculiar nature of this country, a study must be made of it in order to discover that it is not a mountainous district, but a plateau which, by the action of floods, has been rent, hewn, and washed out, revealing the stone, sometimes as sides of the fissures and sometimes as ruins in them, so that in this way the rocks form more of the excavated than of the elevated part. For this reason one is at first astonished to find a stretch of rich verdure winding up over the uneven, stony surface of a steep rock, as a velvet saddle on an elephant, and still more astonished when, after having passed through waving cornfields, and on looking down a precipice, one suddenly sees a wild tract of rugged rocks with numerous crags and pinnacles, and sandstone columns a hundred feet high.

At first these contrasts are almost irritating, but as time goes on they grow upon one. On the top of this plateau, with the mountainous land beneath, one finds, again, these solitary, towering rocks that give the land its characteristic physiognomy, which is, to tell the truth at the expense of the aesthetic, a rather warty one. For, seen at some distance, these stones, whether called Kingstone, Popestone, Lilystone, or what not, are really more like gigantic warts than anything else, not even excepting the Schneeberg with its two thousand feet and its far-reaching crest. A few, as for instance the Winter Mountains, vary from this type, but they are just on the frontier, and as one comes into Bohemia a more ordinary mountain aspect is to be seen. To be quite correct, the Schneeberg is situated in Bohemia, and the boundary is not altogether so sharply defined as is the quality of the coffee, which is so excellent in the first Bohemian hamlets that one might imagine oneself already at Carlsbad; while, on the Saxonian side, one drinks the famous "Bliemchen-Kaffee," a decoction which has taken its name from the fact that through it one can see the little flower painted at the bottom of the cup.

Only that afternoon I had partaken of the usual quantity of this beverage, which is by no means dangerous to the heart. The day before I had tasted the Bohemian coffee in Prebischthor, and two days previously—in short, I had moved about a good deal and did not feel fit for any long excursion. I was now sitting dozing in my window, considering whether I had the energy to go down to the Blackbirds' Glen. It was very hot and perfectly calm. The filmy clouds, which seemed to be half-absorbed by the gray-blue sky, had a rosy hue. The grass and foliage did not glitter in the sunlight, but were of a more than usually intensified green color; the shadows between the rocks were not transparent, and those cast from one on to another had no sharp outlines. From the Glen the notes of the cuckoo were constantly heard, as they had been for hours, this monotonous sound adding greatly to the drowsy effect which all nature was producing. . . . I certainly did not feel inclined to walk many yards; I could not sleep, did not care to read, and, as to writing a letter, such an idea was out of the question.

In this state of indecision "them shady promenades" came into my mind. So far I had not thought of them, but now I wished them to serve a better purpose than simply that of a trump-card for the landlady. Just then my eye fell on a small avenue of young birches that faced my window and was about fifty feet from it. This avenue soon made an abrupt turn and disappeared behind the shrub-covered margin of the hill, which sloped down rather steeply towards a little kettle-shaped valley. I had imagined that the birch avenue belonged to the smart neighboring villa, but it now struck me that it was not in any way separated from the ground on which stood the house I lived in. This ground was used for grow-ing potatoes, lettuces, some rows of peas, and included a grass plot. The plot brought the avenue suddenly to an end, and, farther on, stretched uninterruptedly up to the shrubs at the margin of the hill. It was, therefore, just possible that the beginning of the slope might belong to my landlady, and that the suddenly broken avenue only waited for the finish-ing touches, which, when the ground had been fully laid out, would join it to the pathway leading to the house; conse-quently I thought that "the shady prome-nade" might be down there.

In my own mind I apologized to the woman for having made fun of her and for having been so unbelieving, and I de-cided at once to make use of my highly valued privilege as a lodger to walk *"da'rim und dort'nim."*

I did not go towards the birch avenue, but went across to the coppice of hazel and may. The grass, filled with daisies and buttercups, peeped through all the openings of the scattered bushes, and ex-tended up to a gravelled path. On the other side of this path the grass-covered slope led, rather precipitously, down to the small valley that was covered with fir and birch wood, while to the right the gravelled path was soon transformed into a modest foot-track which lost itself amongst the fir trees. I turned to the left so that I might make myself acquainted with the grounds.

I had hardly walked more than a few steps before I stood in front of a small grotto. Here the underlying stone was ap-parent, but for the most part one only saw turf and sand on this hill; the rock was overhanging as if it had run its head through the soil, and the sides were bent forward like two prominent shoulders, in this way forming, nearly all day, a natu-ral shelter from the sun. A table and a couple of garden seats were placed here, and in the middle of the wall was painted "Sophien Ruhe."

For a moment I stood quite impressed; I could not have believed that Mother Richter held such a trump-card in her hand. I then sat down on one of the com-fortable seats, but did not feel quite at home, as I was more and more doubtful whether I had the smallest right to be where I was. While this reflection was troubling me, I caught sight of a little book lying on the seat. I took up the book, and as I turned over the leaves I discovered, to my astonishment, that it was a *German-Danish Dictionary*. I was not aware that any countryman of mine was in the *Pension*, which this barrack of a villa was called, in spite of the fact that it was only able to accommodate lodgers. Who, in these parts, could be interested in studying Danish, an interest so rarely found in Germany? The worn cover was in some way familiar to me.

The gravel crunched under light, quick footsteps. As I raised my head a girl approached along the path, and I saw the beautiful governess of the steamer.

Since my arrival I had been so busy touring about the country, that I had not had time to long for a renewal of our short acquaintance, and during these last few days I had not thought of her at all. Now I suddenly recollected that the schoolmaster had spoken of a pretty little governess living at the smart villa.

She had evidently not expected to find anybody there, for, involuntarily, she gave a tiny scream. I had, of course, scrambled to my feet and blurted out several excuses and apologies, saying that my landlady, having spoken of "the shady promenades," had made me think of coming to the place. I added that I feared I was accidentally trespassing, and regretted it all the more as I seemed to have frightened her.

She smiled shyly.

"Your mistake is quite intelligible, so you really have nothing to apologize for nor anything to regret on my account."

Her glance now fell on the little book, which I, in my confusion, kept twirling between my fingers. The color mounted to her face.

"Perhaps this is your book?"

"I had just come to fetch it."

"Then I must apologize again for being so bold as to open it. . . . It was a strange surprise to me, for I am a Dane."

"I was quite sure of that," she answered. "I recognized it from the first words you spoke to me on board the steamer."

This remark of hers was not very flattering to me, as I secretly hoped my pronunciation to be so good that a German might take me for a fellow-countryman living in a distant part.

"I suppose you have associated a good deal with Danes?" I asked.

"I have known a few countrymen of yours," she said, and suddenly her gaiety vanished.

"And these acquaintances have led to your studying a language so little used?"

"Yes," she answered hesitatingly, as if considering how she could bring the conversation to an end.

"Perhaps in some way I might be of help to you . . ."

"No, thank you—unfortunately. That is to say, there was some talk of my going as a governess to a family in Denmark, but the idea has now been given up."

These details about things which were no concern of mine rather surprised me, and I was expecting her to continue the conversation when she said in a reserved tone—

"I should be very sorry to drive you away from this comfortable seat. It is not at all necessary for you to go. I know the customs of the house, and nobody ever comes in the grounds or the garden at this hour. That is why I was so frightened when I saw somebody sitting here; I am rather nervous. Good-bye!"

I was just going to try and persuade her to remain, as I knew that we should be undisturbed, when I became aware of tears glittering in her eyes, which withdrew their glance from mine. And this, combined with a trembling at the corner of her lips, proved to me that she was on the point of bursting into tears, a discovery which made me utterly confused. I stammered something about her great kindness, of which I should not like to take advantage; at any rate, I had the courage to add, when her society no longer . . .

But she had vanished.

Bewildered by this unexpected meeting, I, however, did not move, but tried to retain the image of the young girl who, on this second occasion, had made a still deeper impression on me. It was now quite clear to me that she was the prettiest girl I had ever seen. She had been wearing a garden hat encircling her face like an old-fashioned hood, which had given me the opportunity to see that her forehead was unusually high and well-shaped. But it was especially the eyes, rather deeply set under this arch, which had struck me. When she opened them wide there was hardly any distance between the lashes and eyebrows, neither of which riveted my attention as much as the clear-cut setting of her eyes. The eyes themselves were striking rather for their brilliance than their size, and were apt to dart quickly from one object to another in a curious way of their own. Their irises, in which yellow and green were blended with brown, made the same impression on one as when, in a shady wooded cleft, one looks down into a stream, at the bottom of which soft sunbeams play; and the expression of them changed as rapidly as that of the rippling water under the movements of the foliage and the clouds.

I felt that they were impressed upon my memory forever.

This coincidence of the *Danish Dictionary* was very striking. It appeared to me as an omen, the finger of fate, or, in short, something that had a meaning, and could not remain as an isolated fact. I did not quite believe her assertion that she might have gone as a governess to Denmark; but then, why should she have said so? More than all, why had she been on the point of crying without any apparent reason?

All this kept on working in my mind, whilst I lost myself in the valley and walked through the big fir wood right across to Polenzgrund, where I took my supper in the Walthersdorfer-Mill. The intense heat had given place to a most pleasant afternoon.

I still enjoyed nature, not, however, with my accustomed calmness, but with a spiritual elation, which resembled the bodily sensation one has after drinking freely of wine. This sensation is by no means disagreeable, for in rendering one's senses readily open to external influences, it at the same time makes things appear less distinct. Therefore it is easier for this "sweet lingering thought" to mingle with other impressions.

If I looked down into the sometimes quickly, sometimes slowly gliding Polenz, its green and brown shimmer in the golden rays of the afternoon sun reminded me of *her* peculiar eyes. I discovered some beautiful flowers, and at once I thought, "If only I were now on such terms with her, that she would accept a nosegay from me." Then I lay on a steep slope listening to the soughing of the wind in the fir trees, and I said to myself, "Supposing I were a poet, then surely this moment would inspire me to create a poem which would meet with *her* admiration, and through which my feelings might speak." Yes, I even found a theme. She was a problem that continually puzzled me, and "it seemeth to me"—this expression I found very poetical—that if I could only discover the solution, I might find "Life's Treasure." However, I could not get my words to rhyme, nor could I make any sort of rhythmic connection.

Darkness had fallen before I returned to Rathen. Only a small portion of the moon appeared dimly over the hill on which the villa was situated. Between the bushes and the garden, and in the shrubs near the brook, the fireflies were swarming. The little sparks peacefully floated to and fro, ascending and descending, as if they were tiny lamps carried by invisible elves. Sometimes a few leaves of a bush were lit up by a hidden firefly; now and again one flew up so high that against the sky it looked like a moving star. No other stars appeared; it was again sultry and calm.

On the previous evening also I had enjoyed this wonderfully ethereal phenomenon of the erotic of nature, and it was not only because of its being richer on this night that it touched me in quite a different manner, and put me into a most inde-scribable mood. And to be honest, what meaning is there in these everlasting examinations of moods, which modern authors feel obliged to make? As if, for instance, anyone could form an idea of water by being told that it consists of hydrogen and oxygen in a proportion of one to two, even if one were well acquainted with both of them. Surely it would take God Himself to do so, and then he *eo ipso* has created it, so that would be nothing to boast of. I can only say this much, that my heart was beating fast when I came up the hill, and I often stopped to look down into the valley, in which the little lights moved about, and where, in some places, a small shining lattice lit up the surrounding foliage, while around I felt rather than saw the steep rocks, all of which seemed to be the same distance from me.

On the stone step, leading up to the door, I saw one more lonely little spark, spreading its phosphorescent light. I lit a match and discovered a small gray, hairy insect, which was again turned into a spark as the match went out. However, I was afraid to disturb it, as I had a mysterious feeling for this glow-worm, which now, for three nights in succession, had been in the same place, in the inner corner of the step near the cellar window; and I had made sure that it was not there during the day. What was stirring in such a tiny creature, that, night after night, it found its way to this enchanted spot? Had it, perchance, been disappointed each time and still patiently returned with its erotic lantern of Diogenes, not searching for what it had found now—a human being—but a mate? and did it stay there in the hope that its burning love, in this conspicuous position, would attract its object? . . . Has, perhaps, a secret constant passion, such as this, an irresistible power in us also, though in our case hidden, while in the case of the glow-

worm one can literally "see the heart burning through the waistcoat"?

One would think that I must have been in especial need of such an unusual power, for while I tossed to and fro on my bed (which always felt a little damp), I continually thought of the little light-giver, and, as far as I remember, it also played a prominent part in my rather bewildered dreams.

CHAPTER IV

When I went out on the following morning, I carefully examined not only the stone steps, but also the little recess of the window. But the glow-worm had gone. I made up my mind, that if it was there again in the evening, I would take it as an omen that a closer relationship would be established between me and my beautiful neighbor.

I went straight to the schoolmaster, who had asked me to call for advice with regard to nice excursions, and who was a distant relation of hers.

It was holiday-time, and I found him in the kitchen-garden in front of the house, where he was working with an enormous rush-hat on his head. He was evidently pleased to see me. After having exchanged the usual remarks about the weather, which looked fairly settled, he asked me where I had been, and soon mentioned a walk I did not know of, and that I could not take by myself. I therefore willingly accepted his offer to accompany me directly after midday.

On the way he was—well, there is no other expression for it but the German *kreuzfidel* (wound up). It transpired that he had studied for a considerable time—very likely more in the public-houses than in college—and the recollections of those days were the pride of his life. He sang one ditty after another from *The Stu-*

dents' *Songbook;* many of his songs showing a remarkable lack of sense, as, for instance—

"On the wall
In the hall
Sits an ancient bug;
See how well this bug can prance,
See him gaily lead the dance."

Later on he took the opportunity to sing some ditties from the years of the war. For, when I walked quickly uphill and left him behind, he always blurted out the Saxonian mocking verse from 1813—

"Be slow in advance,
Be slow in advance,
Let the Austrians' attack this time have
a chance."

But if I loitered, he said—

"You Hannemann,
You go in front;
Your boots so high will bear the brunt."

That this souvenir from '64, and especi-ally the name "Hannemann," could not be pleasing to a Danish ear, the thick-skinned German did not take into consid-eration; but at the same time he looked so good-natured that, in spite of some patri-otic struggles, I could not be offended with him. When we were resting he usu-ally related tales of his student life or of the war, which latter, however, were mostly of a rather peaceful order.

"Yes, there you are perfectly right, it is an excellent tobacco," he said, when he was lighting his pipe after supper. "What do you think of the strange coincidence which happened to me in connection with this tobacco? But in those days it was of a better quality than at present; it was fa-mous throughout almost the whole of Germany—the Altstädter-Ziegel tobacco. Well, it was in those days, I think I have already told you, that I was in the Laza-retto at Flensburg after having received a bullet in my shoulder, and, as I was get-ting on well, they gave me permission to

smoke just one small pipe. Before pro-ceeding I really ought also to say that I was born in Altstadt, and that my mother, who lived there, frequently sent me some good things; there was no freight to pay, and she always put a packet of this excellent tobacco in the hamper. To return to my story, I get the pipe lit, and hardly has the tobacco begun to burn, before the man next to me (he was a Dane who had been taken prisoner at Düppel, where he had come too close to a bayonet) lifts his head a wee bit from the pillow, and starts sniffing; and I quite understood that the smell was not disagreeable to him, for he hugged him-self with delight. I am puffing with all my might. He goes on sniffing and inhaling. 'My word,' he says. 'Why,' I reply, 'does it perhaps smell of sulphur?' 'Nothing of the kind,' he says in fairly good German; 'but I'll be hanged if it isn't Altstädter-Ziegel tobacco you are smoking.' 'Then you won't be hanged this time,' I tell him. 'By the way, how do you know Altstädter-Ziegel tobacco?' 'Well, I should think I ought to know it,' he answers, 'for I was two years in Altstadt when I travelled for my trade—I am a watchmaker. Since then I have not tasted that tobacco, and now, when smelling it once more, I feel again as if I were with my kind Master Storch at the corner of Goose Square and Smith Street.' 'Well, I never!' I say, nearly dropping the pipe. 'You can take my word for what I've told you,' he answers. 'Why, then, you were working under my own father!'—What do you think of that? And as we came to talk about it, I was able to recall him, though he had grown a big beard, a real Hannemann-beard. . . . Finally I gave him a pipe of tobacco, but it might have chanced that I had given him a hot bullet instead."

When this story came to an end, I took the opportunity—if it could be said to exist—of asking him about his relations, and, after having endured pages of family history, I was at last rewarded by hearing the name of Minna Jagemann—"that pretty little governess living with the von Zedlitzses, whom I suppose you have seen."

At first the information about her was of a very ordinary and uninteresting character.

Her father had been a teacher in one of the large public schools, and had died a year ago. Her mother took in lodgers, and the girl earned a little money by giving German lessons to foreigners, conversational classes, etc. She had for the present, contrary to her usual custom, accepted this situation as governess, which was very well paid; otherwise she lived with her mother in one of the smaller streets of Dresden.

All this sounded very commonplace to me, because I had conjured up a romantic history for her.

"At any rate, it is not always advisable for such an innocent girl to associate with these foreigners," he remarked, pushing down the ash in his pipe.

"Why not?" I asked with interest. "What do you mean?"

"Well, one doesn't always know with what kind of persons one may have to do, and it might lead to things that are not quite pleasant."

"Has Miss Jagemann had such an experience?"

"Indeed she has. There was a young painter, a countryman of yours, an unsteady sort of chap. He threw her over, and surely she did not deserve that."

"Is that so? Then they were engaged?"

"I don't know for certain whether they were really engaged. I haven't sufficiently inquired into the matter, but I got my information from Aunt Sophie; perhaps you remember I spoke of her, she was not all she ought to have been. . . . Anyhow, there was some sort of love-affair between them. Every one thought they were going to be married; but he went

away, and has not written since. I am not in the least surprised, for he had taken painting lessons in Paris, which is a real Sodom. Not that Dresden is quite . . . well, I suppose you have already noticed it yourself. But Paris, good gracious! It's something awful; and we are so hated that a German can hardly live there. In spite of this, they have to send for our beer; they can't even imitate it, much as they would like to! The other day the French again closed a factory near the frontier, because it belonged to a German. It will never work! Just you see, it won't take many years before we have to go there again. Mark my words, did you notice what Bismarck said the other day?"

He now became immersed in politics.

To tell the truth, I was at the moment much more anxious to hear what happened to the pretty little girl from Dresden, and her Danish painter, than to get the most authentic information of the day and hour on which the Germans were to enter Paris. But I asked in vain if he could remember the name of the painter.

I remained rather silent on our homeward journey, for I was very disturbed by what the schoolmaster had told me. In one way I was content to have satisfied my curiosity, and to have had my suspicions confirmed, but in another I did not like this episode, though it had nothing to do with me, not in the least—and still . . . I now thought of the strange little incident of the pocket dictionary, which seemed to be Miss Jagemann's favorite literature, accompanying her both travelling and walking. I surmised that it was a *Postillon d'amour* which drove this little linguistic omnibus, where the noblest and simplest words are to be found side by side. Did she faithfully cling to a dear remembrance when learning words of the language which was this painter's mother-tongue, or had she not yet given up the hope that it also might become hers by adoption? Perhaps she did not know herself.

I thought of the little glow-worm keeping its faithful watch evening after evening on the same spot, and throwing its light out into the night for companionship.

As I came close to the stairs its spark met me from the corner of the stone steps.

CHAPTER V

To one who loves German music—and who does not love it?—these shady and well-watered valleys possess a wealth of suggestion which can only be described by music. Men's choruses by Schumann seem to pour forth and meet one from the fir-trunk columns, when evening peacefully falls over the mountain woods; the clear mill-stream, in which trout glide swiftly by, trills out a Schubert melody, and the hunting-horn of Weber echoes in the wild labyrinth of rocks from its "Wolf-pits" to its "Hawk-pinnacles," which seem to be ideal scenery for *Der Freischütz*. But Wagner requires the grander scenery of the Rhine country.

Notwithstanding this, I stopped one fine day outside a small cave in which was placed a primitive bench, consisting of a plank, a hand's-breadth in width, supported on a couple of thin poles; and on the uneven stone-wall I found that the imposing name "Wotans Ruhe" was painted.

Had this inscription been put by a too naïve Wagnerian, or, perhaps, by a malicious anti-Wagnerian?

This question I addressed to no less a person than Miss Jagemann.

She was not seated on the bench, on which, in fact, no human being could sit, though maybe a god might, for I suppose they are made of a lighter material. She had chosen a more solid seat, a large block of stone, which projected far over the turbulent brook on the other side of the path.

There was a narrow fissure between this block and the path, so it almost formed a little island, and as a shrub was growing in front of it, I might easily have passed without seeing her, especially as I had been turning my back towards her while looking at the "Wotans Ruhe."

But she revealed herself, whether intentionally or not, by mingling her fresh youthful laughter with my involuntary outburst.

"Never mind," she said; "anyway he deserves to be laughed at!"

She sat on the grass, resting on one arm with the other lying in her lap, and in her hand she held a bunch of the lovely flowers that are so plentiful in these parts.

The sleeves of her pink morning dress were tucked up over the elbows, either for the sake of comfort or coolness. The arm in her lap looked milk-white, while the other one against the rich green grass showed a brownish outer side, and was overspread by a fine down which shone in the rays of the sun, its plump soft form giving the impression of childishness which is so touching in a woman.

The two little girls sat next her, making chains of straw; the juice of the bilberries, which they had been enjoying on the way, was smeared all over their faces. Miss Jagemann's lips also showed traces of the bilberries, and when she laughed her teeth did not shine as usual.

"It is rather incautious of you to speak in that way, Miss Jagemann," I answered, "as you cannot be sure that *I* am not an anti-Wagnerian."

"In that case you would not mind being laughed at by a girl. But, besides, you are from Denmark, and there they do not know much about Wagner, or so I was told."

As she spoke her gay expression disappeared, and I fancied that I was able to trace the thought which was passing through her mind, and casting a shadow over her face.

This secret thought, which she of course could not guess that I had fathomed, gave me a feeling of depression, and I became as silent as she was.

Suddenly I noticed that she was looking at me with an astonished glance which clearly said: "Why has he also nothing to talk about, and why does he look so sulky and disagreeable?" And at the same time I felt that my lips showed annoyance or mockery. It was indeed that telltale look of hers that made me conscious of my own mood; and this mood greatly surprised me, for I could not disguise from myself that it was caused by jealousy. And could anything be more foolish, than to be jealous for the sake of a girl with whom I had hardly spoken, and should very likely never become well acquainted?

During these meditations I had begun to be talkative. I told her I had been long enough in Dresden to gain some knowledge of the works of Wagner, and that they had a special interest for a Dane, as in the *Niebelungen-Ring* he had used a subject from our own sagas.

Then I passed on to Danish literature, and hastened to ask if she had been getting on well enough with the language to read any of our authors.

"Yes, I have read *Aladdin,* by Oehlenschläger," she answered. "I spelt my way through it when I only knew a few words and a little grammar."

"Then, I suppose, you did not enjoy it much?"

"Indeed I did; I read it over several times, especially parts of it, which I found quite beautiful. But in the end I was rather annoyed because I could not feel any interest in this loafer who is always favored by good luck."

I made some remarks about the Aladdin and Faust types, and about the Danish and German national characteristics —a part of which I borrowed from something I had read years before in a magazine; but the other part consisted of ideas which came to me on the spur of the moment, and which could not have been of any value.

"What you have just said," she remarked, "is not very flattering to your countrymen."

I looked at her in surprise, for it had not occurred to me that my words could bear such a meaning.

"Well, to be perfectly candid, do you really find that Faust is so much to be admired? I mean, if one looks at him with the sober eye of a moralist? To give up one's soul to the devil, to seduce a young, innocent girl, to kill her brother in a very doubtful duel . . ."

"I know that, but all the same . . . You are a Protestant, aren't you?" she suddenly asked with a triumphant smile, as if she had thought of something very much to the point.

"Yes?"

"Then you know that human beings are not judged by their actions only."

"By what, then? I really do not consider Faust an orthodox saint, in spite of the fact that he translated the Bible."

"Perhaps you are right, but Faust is anyhow worth more than this Mr. Aladdin," she said, evidently pleased at having used this mocking "Mister" instead of an argument—though no argument was really needed, as, at the bottom of my heart, I shared her opinion.

"In the same way as Marguerite is worth more than Gulnare," I remarked.

Naturally, in speaking of Marguerite, I thought of *her,* though in appearance, anyhow, she did not answer to the traditional notion of this German maiden, much less to a foreigner's conception of her. I could not help smiling as my thoughts reverted to a little Frenchman at the Polytechnic, who, whenever we passed a fair girl, used to nudge me and say, "Gretchen!" without troubling to notice whether she was nearly a dwarf or a giantess, a bold minx or an overdressed girl with a self-assertive air. Always, "Voilà Gretchen," with the impossible *ch!*

If *she* did not resemble Marguerite, neither could I in the least be compared with Faust—a fact which I at once made evident, by lacking the courage to offer myself as her escort.

For her part she seemed quite content to remain where she was. But I was in a difficulty, for although to converse across a chasm on such elevated topics appeared to be absurd, yet I could not persuade myself that I had the right to join her. Indeed, to propose such a thing was quickly made impossible by the smaller child exclaiming—

"Why doesn't he come over here, when he so much wants to speak to you?"

After this remark there seemed nothing else to do but to pretend that it was time for me to go home. So I wished her a pleasant walk, and consoled myself with a hope that I should soon have another chance to meet her.

This hope, however, was not realized. Day after day I wandered about, looking and listening like a hunter—coming again and again to "Wotans Ruhe." But all in vain.

I also fruitlessly taxed my poor brain to find an excuse, a way, any means—it did not matter what—to establish a communication between us. Impossible!—I might as well have tried to write a novel.

CHAPTER VI

When I was not going for a long expedition, I took my dinner every day about one o'clock at the "Erbgericht," on a beautiful terrace by the river, shaded by glorious maples; the lower parts of these trees were clipped straight, forming a pretty green shelter, which gave a pleasant light and allowed the sun spots to play on the table-cloth, and sparkle on the lids of the glasses.

One day, when I arrived a little later than usual, every place seemed to be occupied. I was looking around inquiringly, when, to my surprise, I heard someone calling me by name. An old couple, who had a table to themselves, were beckoning to me. They were two of my Dresden acquaintances, and, in addition to that, favorite ones. I was very pleased to have escaped from my difficulty in such an agreeable manner, and was soon seated with, so far, only a glass of beer in front of me, beside the homely pair.

At first glance one saw that the old man was a Jew. The shape of the very hooked nose was unmistakable, and the sparse, rather bristly moustache and beard did not hide the thick lips, the lower one of which was underhung, and, when he was talking, gave the impression that he was sucking something in. It seemed also to affect his speech, which was slow and lisping. The eyes were overshadowed by strongly marked gray brows, and under them hung big wrinkled bags. Their expression was lively, clear, and quite unusually good-natured. His wife was a stately old lady, of a more Southern than Jewish type; her fresh face, which was constantly smiling—with the smile that one sees in paintings of the Empire period—was decked on both sides by a bunch of gray curls, in the old-fashioned style, and so tight were they that they looked as if they were made of wire.

I had been introduced to this venerable pair by their son, to whom I had become attached at the Polytechnic, though he was my senior by several years. He now had an appointment in a factory at Leipzig. I had at once won the favor of the old man by my unfeigned interest in his hobby. He was a bibliophile, but his greatest passion was for the autographs of famous men, of which he had a large collection, from Luther to our time—I should think that if Hermann the Cherusk had left any writings he would surely have got hold of them. The documents were arranged in portfolios, each of which was numbered, and to each portfolio was added a protocol of handmade paper, (written with goose-quill and specially prepared ink for the sake of eternity), containing proofs of authenticity, as well as reference to biographical works and letter collections, and to these were added his own notes. This precise man was not content to collect only, but when he had got hold of a little manuscript he had no peace until he had found out to what period it belonged; and in cases in which this problem had already been solved, there were still commentaries to be written regarding the persons named, the circumstances referred to in the manuscript, and finally all the conclusions which he had drawn from his research had to be tabulated.

In this way his passion flowed back and contributed, as it were, to the source from which it had sprung, namely, the history of literature. To gratify this passion, it was necessary to acquire a great fund of knowledge, but this fund, having been acquired, paid an excellent rate of interest. With him it was far from being an unprofitable hobby—as hobbies so often are—it was rather a living expression of his inner self, satisfying at the same time his highest spiritual aims and his orderly business instincts.

Old Hertz had retired from business some ten years or more, and at this time was living in Dresden, in the "Rentier Corner," as it was, not without reason, called. He had been a merchant in Königsberg, where he was born, and had belonged, so to speak, to the merchant nobility. This home had left a lasting impression on his nature and development.

Königsberg is a commercial town which has obtained its peculiar character from the master-mind of one great man —a fortunate circumstance which sometimes happens in small towns that do not produce many celebrities; for people whose interests might be given to some less worthy object can cling with pride to the memory of the man who made their town famous. What Erasmus is for Rotterdam, this, and still more, is Kant for Königsberg; partly because he is a greater personality, and partly because, being of later date, the present older generation in Königsberg are the children of those whom he used to visit.

This was the case with Hertz. The great philosopher had willingly associated with members of the large commercial firms of his native town. These formed a powerful stock which guarded as a precious legacy the spiritual and literary interests he had grafted upon it. As a class they possessed the breadth of mind and versatility characteristic of business men, and they afforded him welcome shelter from the dripping sky which masked the darker days of pietism. It followed naturally that Kant, more than any one else, was the old man's hero. How deeply he had penetrated the philosophy of Kant, of course, I could not judge; but an almost touching tone of profound reverence was noticeable whenever he uttered the name of his great fellow-citizen.

He had chosen Dresden as the spot in which to spend his old age, partly on account of his relations and acquaintances, partly for the sake of the well-known Polytechnic, where his son studied, and lastly, I suppose, because it is the most beautiful town in Germany. But its spiritual atmosphere did not please him. Both from a commercial and literary point of view he looked down on this unscientific and unenterprising residential city, where an unimportant aristocracy ruled. He often remarked that Schiller had already called Dresden a spiritual desert, and in those days Körner resided there—but now? Therefore the old Königsberger lived in great isolation, and associated mostly with the already infirm Gustav Kühne, a veteran from "the young Germany" of which Hertz had known almost all the Coryphæuses. This was nearly all I knew of this quaint old man, who now saluted me as with the kindness of a friend. It was a nice trait in this couple that they were very fond of young people. I also noticed that the youth of both sexes almost involuntarily showed them more respect than the younger generation of our day are in the habit of showing to elderly people. Perhaps they gained this respect by their own very modest manners, which even had the appearance of a certain fear lest they might be a trouble or an inconvenience to others.

They were not at Rathen upon a trip, as I imagined, but had taken a small house by the Elbe for six weeks, where they had already spent three days.

It so happened that I had been out on excursions, or taken my meal at a different hour, so had not met them before; but now I had to promise to look them up and take coffee with them on that same day.

"And you shall not feel the hour hang heavily upon you with no other society than that of two old people."

"No, you shall not feel the time long at all."

"But you must not speak like that."

"Indeed, we should not like to encroach on your time, especially when there is so much for your young legs to do. But a young lady is coming, and it would please us very much to give her more youthful companionship than we ourselves can offer."

"You will not regret making her acquaintance—at least I hope not." These last words the old lady added with an arch glance.

"From this place?" escaped my lips.

Mrs. Hertz misunderstood my question, and laughed.

"No, you need not be afraid of a too rustic naïveté. She is not a Rathener."

"Nor is she a Königsberger."

"Perhaps she knows but little of Kant? Tell me, Mr. Hertz, do you really think that all ladies from Königsberg have read *The Critique of Pure Reason?*"

"Unfortunately, my young friend, they have not even read *The Critique of Judgment,* which they need so much. As we are on the subject, I have in my day given lectures for women. . . ."

I had put my rather satirical question in order to affect a great indifference to the present topic, and also to gain time; as in a way I feared to be robbed too quickly of the hope which I had suddenly begun to cherish. But the old lady had read my thoughts.

"Be honest, Mr. Fenger, and admit that you are burning with curiosity, and would much prefer to know something about the young lady, than about my husband's lecture."

The old gentleman laughed.

"Look at him; see how he is blushing! Yes, my wife knows something of human nature; she is quite a Lavater."

To hide my confusion I drained my glass of beer.

"Well; is she pretty?" I asked.

"Pretty? My dear fellow, she is quite a beauty! Yes, but not exactly what one ordinarily means by a beauty. Don't misunderstand me, she is a Thekla from the bourgeoisie, a Lotte, a Fredericka Brion, though perhaps not quite that; she is not a clergyman's daughter from the country either, however idyllic that may be. She is a Kätchen, more than anything a Kätchen!"

"But, dear husband, do you need the whole range of German poetry to aid you? In this way you will raise too great expectations."

"On the contrary! Not even German poetry is sufficient! There is only one thing that is better than German poetry——"

"Kant's *Critique,* I suppose you mean?"

"No, I mean German women—when they are charming. But, joking apart, she is an excellent girl."

"Well, you will see for yourself. She is a relation of mine, rather a distant one. I think I told you that I am from Dresden."

These last words made me lose all my interest. Then, after all, it was not Miss Jagemann of whom they had been speaking. In the first place, she did not look like a Jewess; and secondly, from what the schoolmaster had told, I was convinced that she was not one. I listened with a polite smile, but without attention to Mrs. Hertz's recital of the family pedigree.

Suddenly, as if in a dream, I heard her say, "But I quite forgot that you may have already seen her, for after what you have told me, she must be your neighbor. She is at present a governess——"

A cold shudder ran down my back. Strangely enough, at that moment I was not so much conscious of joy as of a certain conviction. Then, after all, it must be the finger of Fate! In my confusion I answered that I did not think I had seen her, supposing this to be the best diplomacy. But hardly had the words escaped my lips, when I realized that this untruth was sure to be found out, and would put me in a ridiculous and rather doubtful position. I wished to take back my words, but could not make up my mind to do so, which made me so distrait that I quite misunderstood a question of Mr. Hertz's.

Luckily, the waiter just then brought me the bill, and in my bewilderment I gave him twenty-five pfennig as a tip, which gained for me a polite bow from the man, and a fatherly reproach from Mr. Hertz, who advised me to be more economical in my dealings with such people.

CHAPTER VII

What was to be done? Would it be wiser to confide the circumstances of the case to Miss Jagemann, and ask her to pretend not to know me at all? At first this idea seemed quite impossible, but as time went on it grew upon me, until finally it seemed to be so attractive that I no longer regretted my foolishness.

It was quite an easy matter to meet her on the way, and, when greeting her, I added that I believed we were bound for the same destination. On hearing that I was invited to the Hertzes', she said gaily—

"Well, then at last we are going to be introduced to one another."

"Yes," I answered, "it is just for that reason that I have a rather queer favor to ask of you. Will you pretend not to know me? I mean, will you appear as if we had not met before."

"I can easily do that, but why?"

I told her what had happened, and my explanation was received with laughter.

"Are you always so absent-minded?"

"Not always. But I got so confused when suddenly it became clear to me that I was going to meet *you.*"

She looked at me in a naïve inquiring way, then suddenly blushed and withdrew her eyes, with all of which I was more than satisfied.

"Au revoir, then. I must go up the hill again to fetch my keys; it would not do for us to arrive together," I said.

The old couple had taken the middle house of the three small ones which had been built close to the rock by the Elbe.

As I went up the many little stone steps leading up from the bank, I saw the party sitting in the summerhouse, the top of which, like the greater part of the white-washed, timber-built house, was covered by a vine. The afternoon sun was blazing upon it, but over this corner the fruit trees cast a deep shadow, in which the white table-cloth and the shining kettle formed a bright center to the little company. Minna was busily making the coffee.

We went through the ceremony of introduction with the usual stiffness; but, in offering me a cup of coffee, her half-hidden smile told me that she, as well as I, enjoyed the harmless way in which we had deceived our host and hostess. This slight confidence between us appeared to me, and possibly also to her, of exaggerated importance; it seemed to whisper the promise that we should also be able to keep a greater and sweeter secret than this acquaintanceship from those around us, and the hope that it would be so.

"By the way, you, too, know some Danish. Why not practice now?" Mrs. Hertz said.

I received this surprising news with as much astonishment as, at the moment, I could muster.

Minna told again the tale about the Danish family in which "there had been an idea" of her being the governess. But her gaiety was suddenly mingled with nervousness, and this confirmed my suspicion that she was concealing something. At the same time I guessed that Mrs. Hertz knew the true state of affairs.

"Then perhaps, Miss Jagemann, you have made yourself acquainted with our literature?" I asked.

To this opening she replied very readily, and we then—almost word for word—reproduced the whole of our conversation at "Wotans Ruhe" about Faust and Aladdin. Only it ran more fluently, as a well-studied scene, and was urged on by an undercurrent of youthful hilarity which now and then brought forth a new and happy idea. Such an improvisation in the rôle on the part of one speaker, gave at once an incentive to the other, who did not care to be surpassed, but also, with a smile expressive of "I'll give you tit for tat," showed a new side to the question. And in this way the discussion got fuller and deeper, though the subject now was indifferent to us, and only a means for coquetry. We, however, made such an impression upon our audience, that Mr. Hertz said to me: "How talkative you have made the little Minna; she is not generally so communicative." And, later on, Minna herself confided in me that Mrs. Hertz had said to her: "There, now you have found one with whom you can talk."

These remarks seemed to breathe a real satisfaction, and I think that the old people, after this meeting, came to the rather hurried conclusion that we were well-matched. As they had taken us both to their hearts, it was easy to understand that they wished us to become better acquainted, and so much the more because they thought that Minna needed to have some sweet, though only too painful, remembrance banished by the awakening of another and fresh interest. This idea, even in those days, I had already grasped, and afterwards it was still further proved to me. And so it came to pass that several times a week we met each other at the little house by the Elbe. Minna could, without difficulty, get off from her duties in the evening, and, with regard to myself, I, of course, never had anything better to do than to be in the place where I could meet her.

Apart from the fact that Minna and I were daily becoming more intimate, each of these meetings was almost the same as the first one, the only variation being that the heat sometimes drew us to one of "the cool glens." As a rule we remained near the river, this being most convenient for Mr. and Mrs. Hertz. When the sun began to steal into the summer-house, it was the signal to take a walk. The shadows from the plateau of Lilienstein gradually grew deeper, and the edges of the stones stood out in high relief, throwing long quivering streaks over the river. Underneath, in the long yellow slates of the quarries, all the cracks and crevices showed violet and purple, like a cuneiform writing relating to industrial achievements. The reflection in the river grew clearer and more distinct. In the middle of it a long raft might be gliding, winding in and out, following the bend of the river, while its oars, four or five in a row, both fore and aft, moved glitteringly. Or a couple of "Ziller," heavily laden barges about the size of a schooner, would come down the stream with the current, their coal-blackened hulls looking like enormous beetles, or with large outspread sails, which shone far away over the fields long after the boat itself was out of sight. Then a chain steamer might come puffing and blowing, and tugging half a dozen of these barges up against the current; while the submarine chain would wind itself round its flat bows with a deafening rattle, which made, however, in the distance an agreeable tinkling sound.

When dusk came, the rafts carried small blazing fires, which seemed to float on the water and would light up a couple of hairy faces, or would silhouette a strong figure which bent forward and thrust the slanting pole against its shoulder. Afterwards the tug flotilla would appear like a grand illumination, winding round the point, close under the dark Bastei rock, like a procession of perpendicular staves with large golden knobs on the top led by a ruby and an emerald one.

Nor did life stand still on the other bank of the river, as a train now and then passed from one side or the other, stopping and whistling at the little station.

This would continue until about half-past nine, when the express for Prague and Vienna flew by like lightning among the trees, without so much as slackening speed, and always reminded us that it was time to go home. We needed this reminder, because "in the house of the happy the clock does not strike," as Schiller has it.

Moreover, I was not the only one who was happy. The sadness, which had at first overshadowed Minna, gradually wore off and gave place to a youthful gaiety. That some sorrow still remained in the depths of her soul one could only guess from the strange shadows which, now and again, would fall upon her brightest moods. I might, without being too conceited, ascribe to my own influence some part of this change in her. The kindness of the benevolent old couple towards both of us did Minna good; it took the character of the caressing sympathy with which one encourages the convalescent to enjoy life. To me it was rather irritating, but she seemed only to feel comfort in it.

Thus we watched the big stream, with its quaint life passing by, in the same manner that one allows life to drift along in happy days without desiring anything more.

It also gave a topic for our talk. She told me all about the raftsmen's life, especially up in the mountain rivers, where the men have such a constant fight with the currents that until they land in the evening they have no time to snatch a meal. In return I had, as well as I could, to give her a description of the big ships, of the busy traffic in the sea-ports, or the peaceful life of the fishing villages on the coast. Then the quarries, which on both sides were reflected in the river, and sent their blocks down stream in shiploads, made us talk about what the sandstone town of Dresden owed to this little stone region. It struck me that the cut stone used in its beautiful edifices seemed to impart to them some characteristics of their own rock life, so that the rococo town suited the sandstone land, in the same way as the Greek architecture goes with the noble gable-shaped marble mountains, and Egypt's colossal temples with the vast plains and heavily-terraced rocks. Such reflections were of course new to her, for her knowledge of architecture was rather primitive, while I have always been specially attracted by this art, to which, probably, I should have devoted myself, if circumstances had permitted.

CHAPTER VIII

One day as we were sitting in the summerhouse after coffee, Minna handed me a note-book and asked me to draw the capitals of the Doric and Ionic columns with the entablature appertaining, and add the names, all of which she thought most peculiar. While I was sharpening a pencil, the wind turned over a page, and I saw an unsuccessful attempt at the same thing on the page before me.

"No, you must not," she said, her face quite flushed and imploring, as she tore the book from my hands; "you will only laugh at me! I will see myself if it is rightly done. Of course it isn't, and the names I could not remember at all."

I promised not to look at her attempt, and started on my own, which, I assured her, would seem very poor in the eyes of an architect. It did not indeed take long before I began to get muddled; for it is simple enough to know what architrave, triglyph, and metope mean; but when one has, for the first time, to express oneself on paper, many minor difficulties arise which are not easily overcome. It was therefore a welcome suggestion when Mrs. Hertz asked Minna to help her to clear away and to wash up the cups. She

was sitting near me, evidently to watch, and had not anticipated being called away before the drawing was finished. Hesitatingly she responded to this summons, and before she went she seemed more than once to have something on her lips, which she could not bring herself to say; her anxious glance also clearly told me not to examine this mysterious book, on the homely linen cover of which was printed, in very clumsy golden letters, "Poesy," and I reassured her with a smile.

I sat alone gnawing my pencil, wondering whether the architrave in the Doric order was parted or not, when the draught again turned the leaves, and on this occasion to written pages farther back. Both prose and poetry revealed themselves. I did not imagine for a moment that Minna was the author of these compositions, but that made me wish all the more to see what favorite sentences and extracts she had liked to preserve, and in this way to gain an insight into her character and knowledge. Twice I resisted the temptation; but a longer piece of prose remained open before me until, half against my will, I caught sight of a few words which whetted my curiosity too much.

I made sure that I was not watched, and read in German the following extracts, written in a fine, rather sloping Gothic handwriting:—

"Between a young couple, who by nature are in harmony with one another, nothing can add more to a pleasant intercourse than for the girl to be anxious to learn, and the young man willing to teach. It produces a profound and agreeable relationship between them. She sees in him the creator of her spiritual existence, and he in her a creation, which owes its perfection not to nature, accident, or a single will, but to a union of wills; and the interchange of thought is so beautiful, that from such a meeting of two natures, the strongest passions, bringing as much happiness as misfortune, have sprung, at which we cannot wonder. So it has been since the old and the new Abelard."

In reading these last words I heard a door being closed upstairs and quick steps coming down. I hastily turned the leaves, and resolutely drew an architrave with one division with the triglyph over; the lines were not very clear, for my hand was shaky, and the guttae I forgot altogether. But whether the palpitation of my heart came from what I had read, or from fear of having been discovered, I cannot tell.

Minna sat down next to me with her needlework, and seemed very satisfied to find me so engrossed in my drawing. The air had been sultry all day, and clouds had gathered. Hardly had I finished my two sketches before we heard loud thunder, and big dark spots soon appeared on the stone steps. I helped to take off the table-cloth, and then we went up to the old people. We but seldom occupied their sitting-room before tea-time, for being a corner one, facing south and west with two windows on each side, it was, on sunny days, unbearable during the afternoon.

Between two of the windows stood a small, hard, upholstered sofa, and between the other two windows, a table. Over this hung a common oleograph of the Kaiser and the Crown Prince, and under them Hertz had hung one of his special treasures, which followed him after the fashion of the Penates; it was a small portrait of Kant, a Königsberger print, faintly colored, and from his own time. The whole figure of the philosopher was shown standing near a long-legged writing desk, and so stooping and hump-backed, that one would say an invisible hand was pushing his face down to the paper; while from the little gray wig protruded a bit of pigtail, over the high coffee-colored coat collar. This quaint

and old-fashioned picture, with its mildew, spots that came from old age, and flat mahogany frame, gave a certain cosiness to the low room, which was increased by the small window-panes, and by an enormous fire-clay stove that occupied, I should think, an eighth part of the room.

Near this latter Minna soon seated herself, with her back turned towards the window so that she could not see the lightning, which constantly lit up the reddish brown bend of the river. When the blinding reflection came into the room, or the thunder roared so furiously that the house shook and the window-panes rattled, she gave a start, and sometimes even a little scream, though she evidently tried her utmost to control herself. Mrs. Hertz got up from the sofa and calmed her with motherly kindness, and Minna smiled as courageously as she could, though with the fear of the next shock always written on her pale face. Old Hertz looked sympathetically up from his newspaper, which the constant flashes nearly prevented him from reading.

As for myself, I sat near the little window, down which the rain was washing like a shower-bath. My thoughts were constantly occupied by what I had read in *The Poesy-Book*. I did not know the extract, but the style reminded me of Goethe. When recently I read his autobiography and, in the lovely episode with Gretchen, suddenly came across these well-known words, what a storm of feelings overwhelmed my soul! In *Wahrheit und Dichtung* I did not get further, but tried to calm my painfully sweet emotion by writing down these memories, which can only lay claim to the first word of this famous title.

The question as to the authorship did not trouble me much in those days, but the application of it distressed me considerably. I had noticed that Minna, in our conversations, sometimes betrayed artistic knowledge which she could not have gained in school or college, nor by herself. Besides, I knew quite well from whom I suspected that she had obtained her information. Were those reflections written now, or then? There was no date to them, and they were separated, by a considerable interval, from the leaf upon which I had been asked to draw, but it had not escaped my notice that this piece of prose was written with fresher ink than the preceding extract, dated a couple of years before. This, I thought, might be in my favor, but on the other hand my hopes might be built upon the sand.

It was nearly tea-time before the storm was over. Then Minna, who in the reaction from her nervousness had become quite jubilant, took a gray stone jar and went down to fetch water, and I followed her. The way of obtaining water at this spot was very romantic; there was neither well nor pump, but all the water had to be fetched from the spring close to the banks of the Elbe below the house. Just where the meadow-grass ended, and only separated from the running stream by three or four yards of stone and gravel, lay the little basin with clear water, that constantly bubbled up from the small stones and sand, which later moved as if it was full of small living animalcules. We jokingly called it the spring of youth, after a fairy tale that old Hertz had told us one evening.

The breeze which met us was fresh and pure, with a healthy smell of wet earth mingled with the odor of moist foliage and grass, and spiced with the scent of flowers, especially of honeysuckle; in air which the lungs drink in deep draughts, in the same way that one enjoys a pure wine. The heavy clouds had parted; here they were rolling away in murky, smoke-like masses; there dissolving into fleecy vapor or vanishing like thin mist. Overhead, the sky shone a lilac blue; farther on there were patches of pale green, and

golden rays were appearing in the west. Between the low-hanging clouds with their deep leaden or reddish stone color, high ones, standing out with glowing tops, could be seen. On the side of Lilienstein appeared a broad rainbow column which rapidly grew more vivid. At the very top of the longish plateau of this isolated mountain lay a small detached cloud which remained suspended in the fir wood, in the same way as tobacco smoke might remain when blown into a child's curly hair. Only a dull light from the sun lit up the hills over the long quarries; and all the steep crags around lay in a cool bluish haze. The river was still an opaque reddish brown in the curve, but farther on it again resumed its mirror-like appearance. Now and then faint flashes of lightning were to be seen over the open country, and long drawn-out rolls of thunder were heard echoing in the mountains.

"Look," Minna exclaimed, "what coloring! It is quite a Poussin!"

These words of hers stabbed me to the heart. My God! what young girl knows Poussin, and still more has him ready to hand to quote? All the same, the resemblance was quite striking. Now, if she had only said: "It looks like a picture of Poussin in the gallery." But this: "It is quite a Poussin," made me furious! I longed to seize her, as "Carl Moor" seizes "Roller," and cry out: "Who inspired thee with that *word*? That human soul of thine did not produce it, but that of a *painter* did."

But she had already run down the long row of shiny wet stones. Whether my face had betrayed my feelings, or whether she was ashamed of having borrowed another's phrase, I do not know, but evidently she had run away from her Poussin.

She did not at once start bailing out the water, but placed the stone jar on the lower step near the spring, and turned to a pretty little twelve-year-old boy who sat close by. He was the son of the landlord, who had a partnership in one of the big quarries, the rows of which start under the Bastei rocks. The farthest and largest of the quarries stood out against the bright sky-line like a promontory split up to its summit, where a thin line of weather-beaten pines seemed to touch the copper-colored edge of the low-hanging clouds. The boy pointed out to us the quarry which was his father's property.

He was very busy over an ingenious toy: a water-mill, which he had constructed at the outlet of the spring. Through a little unripe apple he had stuck a stick as an axle, and round it he had fixed, in a circle of incisions, large wings cut out of wood. He had dammed up the water-course, so that a tiny mill-pond was formed from which there was sufficient fall; and there the wheel whirled and whirled, without, however, accomplishing any work. From the summer-house, and also from the window, I had seen this funny little thing continually turning round and round. The powerful storm of rain had broken through the dam, and the boy was occupied in trying to repair it, but he found it difficult to get the axle to rest in such a way that it could not get stuck.

"I should so much like to make it go by the time father comes home from work," said the boy, looking earnestly at Minna. "For father is always amused when I find out a thing like that, and I should like him to be in a good temper to-night, for then I will ask him if I may go to see the blasting to-morrow."

"Are they going to blast in the quarry?"

"Oh yes! A whole wall."

"Do you think we might be allowed to see it?" Minna asked.

"You might ask my father."

"To-morrow would suit me admirably; my pupils are going with their mother to see an aunt at Pirna. Wouldn't you also like to see this performance?"

Naturally I had nothing whatever to say against such a proposal.

A long "Oh," into which the little boy suddenly burst, made us look away from the quarries and turn round. The rainbow column had grown to a perfect arch, a reflection of which was just forming, but the lower part only stood clear, while the arch itself was very faint and broken in places. Soon afterwards this also became perfect, and the two bows formed the outer and inner brilliant edge of a broad violet band. Under this bridge the encircled sky-ground was darker than that above it, where the blue soon shone through; in the middle of this dark ground, under the glorious arch, and lit up by the sun, which shed its rays under the clouds through the whole valley, stood Lilienstein, like a smoking stone altar, with the little cloud still resting on its surface. This image had also formed itself in the little boy's imagination, for quite lost in wonder he said: "It's just like in master's picture-bible, where Noah makes his offering."

In perfect harmony with this patriarchal impression, Minna took her stone jar, the plain homely shape of which no old German painter would have hesitated to put into a Rebecca's hand; but her blue skirt, which she lifted with her left hand, might perhaps have been scarcely suitable as a dress for that nomadic lady though it was neither draped nor trimmed. Bending down over the spring, in order to press the obstinate jar into the water, her one shoe with its non-nomadic heel slipped on the wet stones, and she would have got a cold bath, if I had not caught her round the waist and kept her steady. She let go the jar, which floated upon the water; the mirror on the surface of the pool reflected a smile on her face, which seemed more arch than displeased, but in the same moment the jar had filled, and, in going to the bottom, produced a whirlpool that obliterated the image in the water. She had now recovered her balance, but I was far too careful of her, as if the little pool was a precipice, to hasten to release her; yes, I even felt that in this favorable moment I might have permitted myself more than this lingering pressure, which was excusable, had the surroundings only been more secluded. But a few yards away we had the youthful observer, and the windows were not far off.

"Thank you, I shan't fall any more now," she said, and jumped up to the path. "By the way, the water?"

I took the full jar out of the spring, and carried it after her.

When, after tea, we heard the landlord's voice, we went down to ask about the blasting. It was to take place the next day, surely enough, and we should be welcome to see it. Accordingly we arranged that little Hans, whose request had been granted, should show us the way to the quarries.

The moon had risen over the woodcovered heights on the other side of the river. It reflected itself in the middle of the stream, and between the stones close to the bank. The sky was almost clear, save that behind Lilienstein, which was but dimly visible, a dark mist was hanging. On the other side the contour of the rocks was clearly defined against the pale sky, but presently their masses also assumed life; the projections stood out, while the fissures were in deep shadow, and the surface of the quarries was but faintly lighted. On the terrace of "Erbgericht" many lamps shone amongst the foliage; and on the top of the Bastei a bonfire burned in changing colors, and scattered notes from a waltz tune came down from the heights.

The beautiful evening soon tempted Mr. and Mrs. Hertz to come down, though it was too wet to walk on the grass. We remained on the steps in front of the house, and entertained ourselves with the landlord and landlady. The handsome, rather square-built woman rocked a baby on her arm; Hans sat on one of the steps and cut new wings for his water-mill; the landlord, meanwhile, perched himself astride on the railing and puffed at his pipe, delighted over the storm and the coolness it had brought. Well might they need coolness up in the stone quarries, where, although the sun at midday sent the temperature up to a hundred and thirty degrees, hard work had still to continue. Old Hertz inquired about the profit and the prices. The landlady told him of the difficulties during high water in the spring, and of some years when the river had come up almost to the foot of the steps.

A sudden whistle, which rang through the valley, and a passing light between the trees on the other bank, gave the signal for dispersing. As usual I accompanied Minna to her home.

To tell the truth, during the whole evening I had looked forward to this little moonlight walk with a certain nervous expectation. It seemed as if, from the moment near the spring, something was due to me, but if so the vital hour had evidently not come. In spite of the moon, the brook with the alder shrubs, the mountain valley, the loneliness, all undoubted sentimental ingredients, nothing would bring Minna into a sentimental mood. Had she only been silent! But she chattered in the sweetest way about many things that were not in the least connected with love. She would not understand anything: I delicately alluded to the well, but this only caused her to discuss the difficulties of the inhabitants when the river overflowed in spring, and to wonder what would then be the nearest spot from which to fetch water. "Very likely 'Erbgericht'; but perhaps there would be a well on higher ground in the old inn 'Zum Rosengarten,'—surely there must be!"

In short, we talked as sensibly, and parted as formally, as if no such things as slippery steps nor springs of youth had ever existed.

CHAPTER IX

After many warnings to be careful, we went out on the following afternoon with the jubilant Hans, who both acted as our guide and carried our basket of provisions.

Our path, which followed the Elbe, soon ran on the right-hand side, by long slopes of stone, rubble, and gravel which, like a bastion, rose fifty feet or more up to the plateau of the quarries, and downwards was bordered by a wall of more than a man's height. Here and there, in front of each quarry, this gave place to wooden rails, leading from the high-lying works to the bank, where the cut stones are sent down on a species of sledge. Near one of these loading places lay a barge, already half-filled with its heavy cargo; and close by, some very muscular navvies were unloading a trolley, while the next in order stood ready to follow on the top of the rails near the winch.

I suppose we had walked more than a mile, when Hans stopped near a ladder leaning against the wall. We climbed up to the foot of the slope without difficulty. Here, however, we halted, examining, with distrustful eyes, the path which was to lead us up, and which could only be dimly perceived, like a pale zigzag line on the steep grayish surface. On closer examination we discovered steps of a sort, formed by projecting stones, or simply dug out with a single stroke of the spade, but these looked as if they might give way under one. Hans, who had already

climbed a good way up, turned round in astonishment, wondering why we were not following him.

"But you must go first," Minna said, turning red.

"No, Miss Jagemann, it won't do. If you slip in such a place there is nothing for you to catch hold of. I can manage to steady myself and support you if you stumble; you need not be afraid of pulling me down, and anyhow——"

"If only you would go on now," she interrupted.

"Dear me, do let us give up being so ridiculously particular. Would you, for the sake of such trifles, risk breaking your neck? Bother it all, there must be another way up. These stupid people! But in any case there is no danger if only you will do as I tell you. Please do not be so squeamish!"

In saying these words I pretended to be much more impatient and irritable than I really was, and I did it designedly. It gave me a delicious satisfaction to play the part of mentor, and to tyrannize over her for the sake of her welfare.

"I know you mean well, and so I won't be offended at your peremptory tone," she said, and looked at me earnestly. "In a way you are right. Indeed you would be quite so, if it were pretense or affectation on my part. But, unfortunately, I have this feeling, and to such an extent, that my movements would be like those of the dolls which used to be fashionable and whose boots were attached to one another by chains; and we should both, in the end, turn somersaults down the slope, which seems admirably adapted for such a performance. If, however, you go in front and allow me to help myself, and climb as ungracefully as I like, then, I promise you, the worst misfortune which can happen will be that I may scrape my knees a little, and if you find that I am an obstinate person now, then console yourself with the idea that I shall certainly not be otherwise when I reach the top."

The decided manner, mixed with pleasant humor, with which she said this, suddenly dragged me down from my pedestal, and, to tell the truth, made me feel so small, that I might have crept into a mouse-hole. In default of such, I crept up the slope, and bore the deadly fear that something might happen to my companion, as a just punishment.

Both of us, however, reached the summit in safety.

The white surface, which stretched in front of us right up to the blasted rock, suggested to me the ruins of a temple. Mill-stones were lying about in long rows, like enormous portions of fallen columns. We also saw regularly cut stone blocks and curb-stones, which together gave the idea of partial foundations. Heaps of sand, rubble, and larger broken stones had here and there formed banks intersecting the ground, some of which were covered with miniature woods, consisting of the American elder, the scarlet-colored berries of which stood flaring against the shiny white masses of stone. On one side appeared a tiled roof with a smoking chimney; it was a smithy, a thing which each quarry possessed.

After having passed over one of the banks we found ourselves in the hindermost part of the quarry, just in front of the rock itself. Here stood the owner and two workmen. Our landlord took his wooden pipe from his mouth, and welcomed us by saying that we had just come in the nick of time; they were quite ready. A big man, in neat check trousers and a fairly clean shirt, stood with his back bent towards the stone surface, where he seemed to be examining something; he turned his red-bearded face for a moment with a familiar nod, while a smaller man of a gnome-like appearance, and covered with dirty rags, scowled fur-

tively at us as he moved away some tools. A few yards away a couple of workmen were hammering small wedge-shaped iron poles into a big stone which was to be split. Farther away one heard the sound of pick-axes and crow-bars.

The man in the check trousers stepped back from the stone; then we noticed a thick cord, hanging like the tail of an animal which had crept into a hole. It hung hardly four feet from the ground on a projecting part of the blasting surface, some twenty feet in height. The projection had already, by a narrow rent, loosened itself from the rock wall. This ascended bare and yellow-tinted for some hundred feet or so, until dark, rough shapes of rock appeared with shrubs and fir trees on all prominent points and in every fissure, giving the mountain the appearance of an enormous moss-grown tree which had been stripped of its bark and split at the base.

The landlord recommended us to go up the nearest stone bank, which lay on the side of the blasting operations. He waved away a man, who came from the smithy with a couple of pick-axes on his shoulder, and having put his hands to his mouth, he shouted: "Beware!" After this he knocked some ashes out of his pipe, puffing vigorously as he went towards the stone, where he put the end of the slow-match into the bowl of his pipe, which he did not take out of his mouth, and then sauntered quietly towards us, still smoking, and with his hands tucked under his leather apron. The spark of the slow-match that for one moment had been visible, disappeared; a thin smoke oozed out of the stone. Minna and I looked at each other with a strange smile of nervous anxiety, expecting a terrific explosion. At last we heard a rather faint muffled report; pieces of stone were thrown out, a small cloud of dust and smoke spread; the solid mass still stood, though very much undermined. The owner swore, the man with the check trousers scraped some loosened bits out with his pick-axe. In the gash of the stone wound I could see the black trace of the mine.

"We shall have to bore again," he shouted to the owner.

While we were inspecting the spot at close quarters, and the men were looking for the best place to bore, I had taken a pick-axe and chipped one of the pieces, which had come off by blasting, and which easily broke into regular flat bits under my tool. Suddenly I found myself caught and tied up with a piece of the fiber which they used as a wad, while a roar of laughter burst upon my ears, and a red-bearded face bent over my shoulder. I also laughed, of course, but in the unnatural way which is always a clear proof that one does not altogether appreciate the joke. The gay captor, it is true, did give some sort of explanation, evidently under the impression that I understood the whole thing, but he spoke in such broad Saxonian dialect that I was none the wiser.

Minna laughed heartily at seeing me in the arms of the giant, and still more, I suppose, at the funny expression on my face, which said clearly that "I was not in it," but should like to be. At last she controlled her merriment, which, against my will, had annoyed me a good deal.

"He expects you to pay a ransom for your liberty, and he has the right to do so," she said. "It is one of our traditions that if any one trespasses on a workman's preserves, the latter has the right to handcuff him just as you have been."

She had said this in Danish, slowly and with faltering accents, sometimes using a German expression. It was the first time I had heard her speak my mother tongue, and it both surprised and flattered me, because we Danes are always pleasantly astonished when a stranger can make himself understood in a language so little known. And besides, I suspected her of having recently made a special study of it, though she had not said anything to me about it.

I willingly paid my ransom with interest, so that besides the toll exacted by the red-bearded man, there was a tip for the others, but it is not unlikely that the presence of Minna had something to do with my generosity. Then my humorous captor, having pocketed the money with a polite "Thank you," released me, and, after this encouragement, he started with the fresh boring, while the poor gnome, whose rags might, one feared, at any moment fall off completely, drove his iron pole into the stone with the help of a heavy hammer.

As it seemed to be a long business, we went round the quarry to look at the traces of former blastings, and to enjoy the sight of these brittle and gritty stones being so easily shaped by such clever workmen. After this we took to the less serious pastime of gathering some of the beautiful flowers which grew between the blocks; but when Minna came upon some colored, almost transparent, pebbles, she turned her attention to them, and in her enthusiasm lay down on the ground, thinking she had found a mine of wealth. I lit a cigar, and took a seat on a stone close by in the scanty shade of some bushes.

"Are they not sweet?" said Minna, holding towards me a sea-green and lilac pebble, and, blinded by the white glare of the quarry, she looked at me with blinking eyes.

"Indeed, awfully pretty. But what are you going to do with them?"

"Oh, I shall give them to little Amelia. Though, to be quite honest, I should like to keep them myself. . . . You think me rather childish? Well, it is just because they remind me of my childhood, though there is not much worth remembering in it. And yet I like to recall it. It is strange how it is; but time softens everything, even what lies but a short distance off seems glorified. Isn't it always a comfort that the hour will come when a halo will be shed over all memories and make them beautiful?"

"Yes," I replied, "you are right. And this present time, this very day, perhaps a time will come when one will find it almost painfully beautiful, and reproach oneself for not having appreciated it enough at the moment; still, as far as I am concerned, that would be unjust."

Minna bent her head lower, and added some fresh stones to the collection in her handkerchief.

"As a child I adored these clear stones, I had plenty of them, and imagined myself to be a Princess, and that they were my jewels. I said that I would give them to little Amelia, but it is quite likely she might be offended by such a present, and her father silly enough to give her real ones instead of them."

"It cannot be an easy task for you to be a governess to such spoilt children. I daresay you have had a more sensible bringing up."

"Honor to whom honor is due," she said a little bitterly, and shook the stray hairs away from her eyes. "Sense! There was not much of that."

"Was your home very simple?"

"Had it been simple only, I should not have minded, but it lacked joy and homeliness. Certainly we were poor, but that alone was not the cause of the discomfort. Can you imagine, I was fourteen years old before I had ever been to Loschwitz? Of course we came now and then on to the terrace. It was a gala day for my brother and me when father took us to Plauen, where he sometimes had his glass of beer. In those days most of the factories had not been built; it was lovely in the small valley by Weisseritz, and we so enjoyed clambering about the rocks. It was there I found just such beautiful pebbles as these. In the evenings he also sometimes took mother with him to the beer-house; it was a reminiscence of the early days of their married life, when she used to accompany him every evening. And if you, when you go back to town, look in at 'Zur Katze' in Castle Street about eight o'clock you will see, in the inner room, an old woman, who is supposed to be like me, sitting with her glass of beer; and if she has a friend with her, she will spin a long sentimental yarn about the many cozy hours she has spent in this very room with her late dear husband. When the remembrance of home-comfort lodges in 'Zur Katze,' you can imagine what remained for my brother and myself! We attended a good school, but that was our whole education. Father never troubled about us, and that was a great pity, for he was not only a well-educated man, but also right-minded and very honorable. This, however, I only recognized as I grew older; it was quite in a fragmentary way that I got to understand anything about him, for he was most reserved. He never spoke to mother about anything but the weather, and sometimes after reading the newspaper they quarrelled a little about politics. Father was an Imperialist, but mother was on the Saxonian side and hated the Prussians; she could not understand the good of the great Union, and insisted that it only brought heavy taxation. In that respect I am my mother's daughter; I can never forgive the Prussians, because in sixty-six they cut down all the trees in Ostra Avenue; and I can never see those stiff-backed military figures strutting along our streets without feeling irritated. Otherwise they had no subject for discussion, as I have already told you. As time went on I understood better how they felt towards each other, and I am convinced that with another wife he would have been a different man, and also a better father; and that, in a way, it was just his best qualities which, during the years he lived with mother, caused him to grow more and more reserved, and which finally turned him into an oddity. Odd, he really was beyond all description, and his peculiarities especially recoiled upon us children. Most annoying was his fury if he encountered any strangers in the house. It was an impossibility for me to have a friend with me if he was at home. Once, it was my birthday—I was eleven years old—my mother had given me permission to have a small party down in the garden, at an hour when we knew that my father was giving lessons. For some reason or another the school closed that day. Mother, who saw him coming down the street, flew out to us with a terrified face, and the whole party had to take to their heels through the next garden. You will understand that in this way he became quite an ogre to us, and that we took the part of mother, who really showed more feeling for us. Unfortunately this state of affairs led to our hating everything about him, and we hid much from him, with mother's knowledge and at her instigation, which his disapprobation might have stopped us from doing; while, as it was, his disapproval only seemed to us another proof of his bad temper, from which we had to escape. But why do I tire you with these reminiscences?"

"Surely you are telling me this because you know that it does not tire me at all, and that at the present moment nothing has more interest for me. I am very grateful to you. I have had a happy childhood myself, and can possibly, for that reason, sympathize with you all the more fully in what you have missed. But you will have to make up for it by enjoying the brighter side of life, and I am sure you will not miss the opportunity."

Minna did not answer, but examined carefully a new heap of pebbles which she had scraped together.

"You spoke of a brother. I have never heard him mentioned before. Has he, perhaps, left Dresden?"

"He died two years ago."

"Poor you, to have had that sorrow also. It must have been a very bitter one."

Minna shook her head.

"No, I did not care much for him. While only a boy he was not kind to me, and made my childhood still worse; and later on, when he was grown up—well, I suppose he was eager 'to make up for what he had missed of the lighter side of life.' I am afraid he would never have given us anything but sorrow."

She looked at me with a defiant expression as much as to say, "I can quite imagine that you think me hard-hearted. Well, do as you like! Should I love him only because he was my brother, when he did not otherwise deserve it? . . . For the rest, do not imagine that I am so good and kind."

"Were there no other relations who might have helped you?" I asked, in order to change the painful subject.

"I had a great-aunt who was my godmother, and who for that reason felt a sort of call to look after me. She even cared for me in her way, but I am sorry to say it was a very disagreeable way, which repelled me. She always grumbled and complained of everything, even to the dressing of my hair. In those days I wore heaps of curls, so she was right in that as in most other things. It was with her the same as with father, except that she really did take trouble with me. It was only much later that I understood the value of their intentions, which in her was hidden under severity, and in him under indifference. She was an oddity, as well as he, and was very fond of him; but she looked down upon my mother, and therefore regarded with suspicion everything in me which might possibly be inherited from her. When she gave me a present it was as a rule with a threat; for instance, she allowed me to subscribe to a classical periodical, and gave me, in advance, the money for binding—she never did anything by halves. It is quite a small library, containing about a hundred volumes, and when she gave me the money she said: 'If you ever, even in the greatest need, part with your classics, though I am dead, my spirit will return and torment you,' and I am perfectly certain that she would keep her word. I have, however, no cause for fear, and I have not allowed the books to stand idle on the shelf; if only for this gift I have great reason to be thankful to her. I had always good literature to my hand, and as I didn't have so much recreation as other young girls, or rather none at all, to take up my time, I was enabled to read a good deal, an opportunity which most young girls do not get. Indeed, I read some things which would have been better deferred. Funnily enough, it never struck my otherwise pedagogic aunt that the good classics contain some things that are not fit for a fourteen-year-old girl to read. I was not older when the subscription started; but either her literary memory was rather faulty, or the immaculate 'German Classics' were for her something so elevated that such an idea could not enter her mind. At that age I read *Oberon*. Well, probably you have not read it. After all, I don't think there was much harm done. And these evenings, when I sat and read the great authors, long after mother had gone to sleep, were the first happy hours I experienced. They were more than happy, but also thereby less so, for while they opened out many beautiful visions, they at the same time brought with them the dark shadow of self-recognition. I understood that there existed quite a different world. I do not mean the world of outer circumstances, but of thoughts and feelings, quite different methods of judgment as to what has value and what has not, which had been obscured by the web

mother had spun around me of doubtful and elastic rules of life, and to these were added many specious and sentimental phrases which, apparently, only served to cast a sort of veil over them.

"Perhaps you wonder that I had to gain this experience from the authors, as I had received Christian teaching. It was indeed not precepts I needed, but life itself, which in our little circle had nothing which might be called, I will not say elevated, but noble and pure. Of course we saw only mother's relations, sisters, aunts, and cousins, and of them she was the best; they were scarcely tolerated by father, and only came when he was out, or they crept into the kitchen and held a gossiping conclave. Oh, how it disgusts me to think of all this! The fact that the clergyman who confirmed me, and over whose sermons mother cried, had not the best of reputations socially, must also, I suppose, have been a bad influence. Goethe and Schiller had to preach for me, and they were not the worst of prophets. But this brought, of course, a violent revolution in me, with many struggles and doubts, which greatly affected me. As I had to get up early in order to help with the household duties, this evening-reading, which often developed into night-reading, was very exhausting. To this was added the fact that we always lived too frugally, and, still worse, unwholesomely; so that without knowing it I had, in a way, been starving all through the years of my growing up. I suffered from anæmia and nervousness, and these circumstances combined had the result that, in those days, I was never really well. I would suddenly turn giddy when walking in the street, and I used to be overcome by unreasonable fears. At times it seemed as if I was no good to anyone, and I was terrified lest my reason should go. With regard to my spiritual development, I felt that I might have had some help from my father, but reserve had then become his second nature, and, at the time, infirmity was added to this barrier. He died about a year ago, without my coming nearer to him; and some of the blame was mine, I suppose. That he never troubled about my inner life made me haughty, and I felt that I shut myself off from him. I frequently made up my mind to approach him with confidence and affection, but when it came to the point, it annoyed me to think that there should be any difficulty, and that such an effort was necessary between father and daughter, and I remained silent at the critical moment. The last time I went in to see him he kissed me and said: 'Always continue to be a brave girl.' Giving way to the feelings of the moment I nearly burst out crying, but the old voice within me whispered: 'What have *you* done to help me to be so? And how do you know that I am one at all?' It ended with a formal promise and a cold embrace. When a few hours later I returned from giving some lessons, my father was dead."

Minna remained quiet for a long time, with downcast eyes; the corners of her mouth twitched, and I expected every moment that she would burst into tears. Suddenly she lifted her eyes and looked at me with a tearless, but singularly earnest and piercing look, as if wondering what effect her narrative had produced on me. Surely she was saying to herself: "No doubt you now think me very nasty! I sincerely wish I was better, but anyhow I will not make myself out to be better than I am." Her face was very sorrowful, and I was convinced that it was more this thought than the painful recollections that caused her troubled expression.

I myself was strangely moved, and would willingly have pressed her hand; but we were seated a few paces apart, and the workmen were close to us. A pressure of my hand would have made her understand the whole depth of my feelings for her better than any words, which on such an occasion are enshrouded in shame at their own feebleness. I told her I had long suspected that something sad in her past lay heavily upon her, but that I had no idea it was so deeply rooted in the whole of her childhood and development.

At this remark her face assumed a peculiar, suspicious and almost ironical expression, which I well knew.

"But you have only dwelt on the dark side of your life," I said, to change the subject. "How is it you have not mentioned Mr. and Mrs. Hertz? They were already in Dresden in those days, I suppose?"

"Yes, but I only made their acquaintance at that time, just at my father's funeral. . . . The relationship with Aunt Thea was so distant, really none at all . . . so much the better, perhaps! . . . Their house became another home to me: no, I ought not to call it 'Home,' something much better, but that you know. . . . And after what I have told you, you can realize better what these excellent people have been to me. . . ."

She said this slowly, and as if she was distrait, perhaps tired of talking, and maybe regretting that she had been so confiding.

Our landlord now interrupted us with a request that we should go back to our former safe seats, as everything was ready for the fresh blasting.

I had almost forgotten where we were, and why. Some of her words, with their melancholy and often bitter tone, kept sounding in my ear, as they do even now. Regarding the account, it has, of course, formed itself in my memory into a more continuous whole than at the time when it came from her lips, and it is very likely that, in reality, some of the incidents were only told during the following days; but such small inaccuracies cannot affect the main impression. What especially struck me was the clear reflective way in which she spoke of and judged her life; it was evident that she had frequently thought over all the details and their connection with one another, examining both cause and effect. I saw in this the proof that she was of a more melancholy nature than I had thought. For I had lately been misled by the youthful gaiety that so often broke forth.

The fresh blasting passed off just like the first; the stone mass still stood, though now it was almost entirely undermined, and hung free like a shelf. The red-bearded workman approached carefully, and scraped out with his axe the loose bits which the explosion had not removed. At the corners in the background some half-split blocks still gave a little support. While the owner and the ragged workman kept an eye on the mass of stone in order to give the alarm at the smallest movement, the courageous man struck heavy blows on those places. In the beginning he paused between each blow, ready to jump away, but little by little he became too excited to be cautious. The pickaxe made its way, blow followed blow, and small bits flew about him; he seemed enraged at the stubborn resistance. It looked terribly dangerous; the eyes, which were tired of gazing on this blinding surface and hardly dared to blink, seemed each moment to see movement in the edge of the colossal block. Twice was the alarm given, and after each disappointing pause the attack commenced afresh, more furiously and with growing danger.

Minna was quite pale, and pressed her lips together. I, for my part, my feelings blunted by the long suspense, went a few steps nearer, the better to see the effect of these giant strokes; then she jumped after me, and with an impetuous grip on my arm dragged me back. Simultaneously a shout was heard; I saw a huge glare moving overhead and on the side, and heard a heavy thud. The whole stone mass lay

some distance off, and loose blocks fell a few yards from us. My first thought was for the clever workman; he stood safe and sound on the side of the stone monster which he had overcome, and nodded to us with a smile as if to say, "It was a near shave." I supported Minna, who was trembling violently, and made her sit down on a stone.

CHAPTER X

The afternoon sun shed its full glare on the rocks, but over them dark clouds were hanging, and the rain suddenly began to fall in such big drops that its stormy character could not be mistaken. We were obliged to hurry over the shrub-covered bank to the smithy of the quarry. This effort gave Minna back her strength, and she, who a minute before had hardly been able to support herself, now ran the last few steps through the pouring rain, as if her nerves had not been in the least shaken.

It was a great change to come from the vast, bright space, with its white, sunlit rocks, into a small room overcrowded with workmen, and enveloped in a sooty and black obscurity which was only relieved by red-glowing flames. A strikingly handsome young man stood by the forge; he stretched up his muscular arm, caught a rope, and pulled the long bent pole which worked the bellows. The heap of coal flared brightly, he poked it, threw on another shovelful, put a pickaxe with a blunt end into it, and took out another one with a red-hot point; then he spat on one of his fingers, with which he skimmed the hot metal, and dipped it into a trough of water, causing it to frizzle and send up a white steam.

Minna laughed.

"Just now we saw Siegfried fighting

with the dragon, and here we have him alive in the forest smithy."

She had again been speaking Danish to me, and the workmen looked at us wonderingly, astonished at this gibberish. The smith did not seem to pay any attention to it; just at that moment he laid the smoldering pick, which was beginning to turn gray, onto the anvil, and worked it with his hammer, so that the sparks flew about, and we stepped back a few yards out of the way. Minna looked at him with an admiration which did not please me.

"Don't you think him handsome?" she asked. "As he stands there at his work, one cannot imagine anything more picturesque. If only Gudehus[1] looked like that!"

"Of course he is good-looking, but you will spoil him by admiring him so openly. He will be so conceited, that the poor little village maidens will never be able to please him again."

"He is occupied with his work, surely he does not notice it."

"Then the others will tell him."

"But, really it is so delightful to see something absolutely perfect!"

However justifiable this might have been, I did not like it.

"I wonder if he is a Saxon?" she said, a little while after.

"No, miss, I am from Schleswig," the workman answered quite calmly in Danish, throwing the pick aside, and occupying himself by blowing the bellows.

One would have thought that he blew the flush onto her cheek, so red did she turn. The workmen about chuckled a little, and seemed to have understood the situation. At first I enjoyed her confusion, as a fitting punishment, but soon I began to pity her, for she did not seem to have the courage to lift her eyes from the ground. Fortunately the rain had nearly

ceased. We bade good-bye to our kind landlord and the red-bearded giant; the gnome scowled from a corner, and the Adonis of the smithy sent a gay "Farvel" after us.

We were, of course, not inclined to risk going down the same way up which we had crawled. So the little Hans was ordered to show us the way through the neighboring quarries, but I soon told our youthful guide that I could manage for myself, and eventually succeeded in escaping from him.

Most of the quarries were deserted by the workmen. One saw everywhere the same white ground and walls, shrub-covered banks, rows of hewn stone, gigantic masses of rough blocks, which had the appearance of ruins, and here and there parts of rocks that had fallen over, remains of the much more extensive winter-blasting by which, at times, the river gets blocked. By keeping as close as possible to the rock-wall, we had little difficulty in finding a fairly good pathway. The quarries were separated from one another by waste ground covered with chips of stone, that moved and gave way under one's feet, for which reason there was often an opportunity to support Minna, who screamed and laughed on the unsafe ground, stretching out her arms to me either to find support, or when she thought that I was slipping. The sad recollections on which she had dwelt, the nervous excitement while the blasting was going on, and, lastly, her confusion in the smithy, seemed but to have dammed her stream of gaiety, which now burst forth with still greater force. Once we both fell, she on the top of me—fortunately I was the only one at all hurt; Minna got up laughing, and helped me without any sign of shyness. Perhaps at this moment she would even have forgotten to send me on in front if we had been obliged to climb

---

[1] Famous Wagner singer (Siegfried) in Dresden.

up the mountain; really she appeared to have no thought for anything but her exuberant mood, and perhaps also for mine, and for Nature's, which with scent and twitter met us from the mountain wood we now entered.

The strong, incense-like perfume, which the sun had drawn out from the slope, was refreshed by the rain; and, intoxicated by the sweetness, the birds sang as if it were spring-time. The evening sun cast its rays between the firs, the bent, fringed branches of which glittered as if hung with stars. Underneath, between the trunks, one saw the river as a gliding light, and above, the gently nodding treetops were surmounted by a bark-colored, grooved and cleft rock, bounded by a bluish rim of weather-beaten firs mounting upwards towards the cloudless sky.

Now and then the soughing of the wind, like a wave approaching us, was heard from above, big drops fell on us, and Minna's skirt fluttered aside. It was of a soft pale chamois-colored material, which hung in loose folds from her leather belt. She walked cautiously on the sloping ground, which, wherever it had remained dry, was made very slippery by the fir needles and the cone shells; she often slid, stretching out her right arm with a little scream, so that the wide sleeve was caught up over the dimple of the elbow, while the other one, with its ungloved and sunburnt hand, seized hold of the moss.

Suddenly I burst out laughing, and as she turned with a questioning smile, I pointed to her shadow, which, in a stout unshapely form, showed itself on the perpendicular stone surface next to her; she answered with an even heartier laugh, and pointed out mine, which, longer legged than a stork, stretched up a height. For a long while we could not get away from this place, as by the smallest movement the two shadows cut a more and

more ridiculous figure. When at last we moved on, and came to a place where the incline grew less steep and the wood had been allowed to spread, the shadows again began to play their funny tricks; now lying over the green turf, then jumping from trunk to trunk, and bounding directly from a tree close to us to one lit up far away in the density.

"Do you know?" said Minna, "what a good thing it is that you are not Peter Schlemihl, for in that case you would now be discovered!"

"Without doubt I should be, and what then?"

"Well, then—? Anyhow, I should not like it at all."

Her little ear had turned quite red, and this could not have been due to transparency, as the sun was behind us. My heart danced with joy, for I could not doubt that she thought of the place in the immortal book, where the poor shadowless man, Schlemihl, walks at night in the garden with his beloved, and suddenly comes to a spot where the moon shines, and where only *her* shadow is to be seen stretching out before their feet. She had also instantly understood that my—apparently—very simple "and what then?" was more bold than stupid, for she herself had lately lent me the book—a volume of those classical periodicals of which she had spoken.

Yes, suppose my shadow had not been visible, then she would have fallen into a faint, and I should have been obliged to leave her forever; but now, being perfectly alive and playing hide-and-seek with her shadow in the forest, suffused by the evening glow, what obstacle was there in my way? Sure enough, I had no inexhaustible purse in my pocket, but my shadow was complete enough. Did it not stand just now on the sloping stone surface, black and white, as an indisputable proof that I was an honest fellow with no devilry about me? And the little lobe of the ear in front, which was so rosy red, did it not say that it belonged to a woman who loved me just a little? Why then should not my heart jump for joy?

"Do tell me, are you as thirsty as I am?" Minna suddenly asked.

"That's a question I cannot answer, but I am *very* thirsty."

"Well, over there I see lots of bilberries, and I do not know why we should let them dry up and be of no use."

I was quite of her opinion, and we began to plunder the small bushes as quickly as we could. As it was too uncomfortable to stand for long in a bending position, we went down on our knees and crept from bush to bush on all-fours. Soon it became too much trouble to pluck off the berries one by one, so we tore off stalks and pulled them through our mouths, and in thus satisfying our thirst we for the first time realized how great it had been. Minna almost hugged herself, and even began to make a purring sound like a contented little animal. Seeing that this amused me, she carried the joke further, and snapped the berries from the bushes with her lips, not using her hands, which were spread out, like paws, upon the ground. Then she glanced up at me with a very humorous expression, at the same time purring and shaking her head, with some little curls dancing round her brow. Her lips were dark blue, and her smile showed a row of bluish teeth. Whether it was this rustic *négligé* which rendered her mouth less unapproachable than my respect had previously found it, or whether this color, as a sign of our childish mood, aided my natural diffidence, I know not; but it is certain that it gave me an irresistible desire to kiss her. At this moment we both discovered a berry as big as a small cherry, and our heads collided; while I still laughed and rubbed mine, she snatched the berry, and, immediately afterwards, my lips pressed a long kiss on

hers, and my glance pierced her eyes, which grew quite small and in their depths had a gleam of the last golden sunbeam. Only our lips met, our arms rested on the ground like fore-legs; and just as I wanted to make a more human use of them, and place them round her shoulders, half unconscious and intoxicated as I was by the heavenliness of the first kiss, she jumped to her feet and ran down the path. Before I could overtake her, she had already reached a spot where I could not walk by her side, as the path was only a foot in breadth, and the slope was steep. Aware of this, she walked quietly.

"Minna!" I called softly and diffidently.

She did not seem to hear me.

"Were you unable to find my shadow?" I asked, trying to make a joke of it, "since you so suddenly ran away from me. Just look behind, and you will see that I still have it, though it has turned much paler, but so has yours."

Still no answer.

"Are you angry with me?"

She shook her head, but neither stopped nor looked back. The manner of her answer had, however, calmed me; I did not know what to say, nor did I wish to bother her, though this silent march, one behind the other, was dreadfully painful to me. At last we came near the place where the tiny mountain-path, between the outer firs, sloped down to the meadow near the river, only a few minutes' walk from Rathen. There I should, at any rate, be able to see the expression on her face.

Like a deer which is brought to bay, she turned to face me.

"I will now say good-bye. We are near home, and you are not to come any farther with me."

"But why not? What do you mean?"

"Let me alone! Do let me go by myself this time, it is the only thing I ask of you, because I let you, because you . . ."

"But, anyway, tell me . . ."

"Good-bye, good-bye!"

She ran rather than walked down the stones, and over the meadow, where her steps grew noiseless; only the leather belt round her waist creaked with her quick movement, just like the girth of a horse's saddle. It had creaked like that whilst she crept amongst the bilberries. I grew quite sad when I could not hear it any longer.

There I remained on the same spot, gazing after her as long as I could see her light dress.

BOOK II

CHAPTER I

More in a dream than awake I wandered near the river bank for a long time. One reflection alone continually recurred to my mind with ever-increasing joy: she was not only free now, but had apparently always been so, and perhaps knew no more of heartache than I did. It was absurd of me to have been jealous of the good-looking workman in the smithy, but still more absurd to have indulged in the same feeling towards the visionary person called "The Danish Painter." No doubt the whole of this story was only family gossip gathered from an old aunt who, according to the schoolmaster, "was not quite what she ought to have been." In addition to which Minna herself had spoken often about these aunts and their foolish tittle-tattle.

She was to be mine. Was she not mine already? I still felt her kiss on my lips. But why had she left me so suddenly? Why did she not allow me to take her home? Girlish fancies! Who can comprehend them, and who would be without them?

It was already growing dusk. The afterglow of the evening sky dazzled the eye to such an extent that one could hardly judge the distances in the somber foreground. A faint gleam of light still fell on the edges of the rocks above, and a gray cobweb seemed to stretch over the green meadows on the other side of the water.

I heard voices ahead, and saw a man and a boy coming towards me. The landlord and his son were returning from the quarry. When we were close to each other the boy ran towards me with something white in his hand.

"Here is your letter," he called out.

"My letter?"

"Yes, I suppose it is one you wanted to post," said the owner of the quarry, "for it is addressed to Denmark."

"I found it where you sat so long while the boring was going on," said Hans.

With an uncomfortable feeling I took the letter, which was quite moist.

In the fading twilight I had some difficulty in discovering that the blurred address on the letter was to "Axel Stephensen, Esq., Artist." I wanted to see once more if my suspicions of the handwriting were correct, but the light dazzled my eyes.

"Yes, it is all right, thank you. Good-bye."

There stood the name of "The Danish Painter." If I had suddenly seen a ghost my back could not have felt more icily cold.

Axel Stephensen, indeed! Of course I knew him. Who does not know our young artists, even the least famous of the celebrities! It was some small consolation to me that, at any rate, I had not to cope with a genius. I knew him, that is to say, I had met him once at a café; I also remembered a rather nice landscape of his in the academy; and I had from time to time heard him mentioned, though not always in the most flattering terms, for he was considered rather fast. But what struck me as a most remarkable coincidence was the fact that on this very day I had received a letter, in which a cousin of mine had made some slangy insinuations about Axel Stephensen himself, to the effect that this Paris dandy was persistently carrying on with a young lady of our acquaintance, whose purse was more attractive than her looks, and whose portrait he had painted in so flattering a manner that both the object of his attentions and her family were quite delighted. Unfortunately for the painter, the one to whom the portrait gave especial pleasure was its destined owner—a fully-fledged naval officer whose successful examination was now to be rewarded by the announcement of the engagement.

So Stephensen was the man who had played a not unimportant part in Minna's life! From what the schoolmaster had said, I understood that a couple of years must have passed since Minna had known him in Dresden, and yet they still wrote to each other. What could it mean but a kind of love, a secret understanding, or something of that sort? But on the other hand her confidence in me, her innocent coquetry, this kiss, which she willingly enough had allowed me to steal; how could one reconcile this with such an intimacy, except in a girl of a frivolous nature? The more I thought of these contradictions the more incomprehensible they appeared.

My reverie was at last interrupted by the bell-like sound of a chain-worked steamer.

It was quite dark.

The moon was indistinctly seen behind the fir-tops on a height on the other side of the river; its light did not yet reach down upon the water, and one could not see the ships, but the line of lanterns with their long reflections in the water moved on slowly, again reminding me of a procession of golden staves with big knobs, led by a ruby and emerald one.

This sight, which recalled so vividly our happy life by the river, made me still more depressed.

I went slowly home with the fatal letter in my hand.

As soon as I had lighted the lamp I began to look at it more closely. The moisture had loosened the gum so much that the envelope was only fastened in one single spot.

It would be the easiest thing in the world to open and to close it without being discovered.

This thought made me turn hot and cold; I threw it on the table in terror, and kept on walking round the room and glancing at it as I walked.

Suddenly I had the letter in my hand and was picking with my nail at the closed spot; but, as if it had only been done in a fit of abstraction, I quickly turned the letter over and eagerly examined the address.

If I had so far been able to doubt whether the handwriting was Minna's, my uncertainty quickly vanished.

But a certain circumstance occurred to me; both the address and the piece of prose by Goethe in the poetry book had been written in the same reddish and rather muddy ink which I thought was very probably to be obtained from the Rathen grocer. If this was the case, I was, without doubt, the cause of the insertion of that lovely fragment, and this thought made me regard the tiresome letter with greater equanimity.

I took a piece of notepaper and wrote to Minna that this letter, which evidently she had lost, had been found and brought to me, but that I did not like to post it without her consent, as the address seemed to have suffered a good deal from the damp, and was so illegible that I thought she might prefer to have the letter returned to her.

I then put a big wrapper round the whole thing, addressed it, and went out at once to take it to the post-box at "Erbgericht." Thus I got rid of both temptation and annoyance.

Clear moonlight lay on the heights over the sleeping hamlet, of which only the roofs of a few houses were high enough for the moonbeams to shed their rays over the small window-panes. Far above these stood the crown of steep rocks, appearing closer and more than usually blended together in vague, shadowy shapes. The quarries shone in the distance, away over the bend of the river, and I could distinguish the spot where we had spent the day together.

This quiet, cool beauty calmed me, and its effect was soon enhanced by a deadly weariness which suddenly overtook me as I again began to climb up to my mountain-home.

More quickly than I had thought to be possible I went to sleep in expectation of "the things which were to come."

CHAPTER II

The next morning I ran down at once to the grocer, and brought back a bottle of the only sort of ink that he had in stock, as likely to be the presumed *corpus delicti.* My investigation gave the wished-for result: both the letter and the transcription in the poetry book had been written with this *instrumento,* and I quickly began to look at things in a more cheerful light.

I began to consider "the things which were to come." She would by now have received what I had forwarded, and I did not doubt that an explanation on her part

would follow. It seemed to me that most likely she would choose to answer in writing. Would she send me a letter by hand? But that might easily give rise to gossip. Perhaps, however, she might not have time to write early enough in the day to make this mode of despatch of any avail, and the post might bring the letter as quickly. This day would have to be dedicated to the exercise of patience.

How was I to wile away the dreadful time? First I thought of taking a long trip, but I shivered at the idea of letting my own thoughts have sway, and being doomed to turn and twist the same question over and over again in my mind. I preferred, therefore, to give myself up to the perusal of a German novel of the domestic type, with the purest aims, and with contents which mercifully time has blotted from my memory. I then ordered my dinner to be sent for.

By and by it grew dreadfully hot and no air came through the open window. I threw off one garment after another until I lay on the bed in my shirt, which was hardly considerate to the figures depicted in the novel, who were the essence of propriety. I did not think there was any risk of other visitors, the old Hertzes could not possibly venture so far up. Suddenly an idea dawned upon me: Suppose she herself came to see me! It seemed impossible, but in such cases one must be prepared for any emergency.

At once I began to dress with the greatest care. Yes, I would even have shaved had not the sun been so blinding. As my eye caught sight of the little birch avenue, I was possessed by a new idea— the grotto "Sophien-Ruhe"! She had said that at this time the people of the house never came there; what if, trusting to my memory and shrewdness, she expected to see me there! Surely she would do so. It was like a revelation! And off I darted.

A few yards from the place I paused in order to gain control over my feelings, and at the same moment a tall gentleman, with moustache and beard *à la Kaiser Wilhelm,* came out of the grotto with an aggrieved air.

"I beg your pardon," I stuttered; "I am afraid . . . perhaps this is private ground——"

"Strictly private, sir," answered the Kaiser-bearded gentleman in a most majestic tone, and I disappeared from his lordly and offended gaze.

Not in the best of humors, I returned to the house and plunged into the second volume of the novel. Just at the most critical point, another idea occurred to me. Might she be with the Hertzes? Why had I not thought of that before? No—she had said yesterday that she would be unable to be there. Again the wave from the waters of Lethe was borne upon my bewildered brain by the sentimentality of the novel, until the candle had burnt down in the socket and sleep wafted me away from noble Counts and still more noble clergymen's daughters.

The hour of the post next morning came and passed by.

"The post for thee no letter brings,
My heart, my heart." [1]

I attacked the third volume of the novel, which, like the others, contained five hundred pages. When that was finished and I noticed that the sun had already passed the one window frame, I hurried my preparations for shaving, taking into consideration that it is advisable to be well-shaved when a scene of a delicate description is imminent. The time for the second and last postal delivery approached rapidly; I did not care to contemplate what I should do in case of disappointment, and still I was almost sure that it awaited me. I had cleared the stubbly field of the right cheek, when my hand shook so much that I had to put

down the razor, the reason being that I saw, coming up the zigzag path of the hill, the long, thin postman, who, in his uniform jacket and military cap, resembled badly-drawn pictures of Moltke. I remained at the window in breathless expectation and, as I saw him disappear round the corner of the house, I listened for the steps on the staircase, and was still listening in vain when his figure became visible marching down the steep slope.

A dreadful disappointment overcame me and, exasperated beyond endurance, I threw myself upon the bed. Clattering steps of bare feet were then heard on the landing, and there was a knock at my door, that was locked on account of the *négligé* attire which I had assumed during the reading of the novel. As soon as I had opened the door a big, wet hand thrust a thick letter into the room.

CHAPTER III

It really was from her! I tore open the envelope and pulled out several closely-written pages of note-paper, from which fell a smaller letter—the one to Mr. Stephensen—in an open envelope. This confidence astonished me, but seemed to be a good omen; naturally I did not at first stay to examine it more closely.

Her letter, which, woman-like, was undated, read as follows:—

"DEAR MR. FENGER,—I wonder what you really think of me, though, I am sure, that you positively do not know what to think. I quite understood that the reason why you did not post my letter was not because it was wet, but because you wished to ask me 'What does it mean?' Such an explanation I think you have a right to demand or, at all events,

---

[1] Schubert, *Die Post.*

to expect. Even without this incident I should have taken the first suitable opportunity to let you know, at any rate, most of the contents of this letter. I have been in doubt whether it would not be better to speak to you—there are plenty of lonely walks and the children could always be with us—but, after all, I thought writing would be best, for really I am going to make a sort of confession. When it is over, you will not think so well of me as you do now. But just for that reason it is a necessity to me that you should come to know me, however sad it may be to destroy pleasant illusions.

"It was a lucky coincidence that I had given you a rather detailed account of my home and my bringing up. Not altogether a coincidence, however, as I had previously decided to let you know what I had experienced, and my former confidences had to be the introduction. I therefore ask you to call to mind as much as you can remember; the main points will, I suppose, have given you a distinct impression, even if my description was rather confused, and without it you might judge me much more harshly than I perhaps deserve.

"But let me begin. Ah! I wish you were sitting opposite to me, it is so difficult to write about it.

"I do not know if I told you that my mother had six sisters. They were daughters of a wealthy inn-keeper, whose hostel was chiefly patronized by country people. They all had to take their part in the household duties, and consequently did not get much education. Of family life there was hardly any, as the mother was occupied in the housekeeping, and the father in the business. He sometimes flogged his daughters with the stick, it was nearly their whole education, and it did not bear good fruit. (I am thankful I am *writing* now.) Five of them had children before they were married, my mother and her younger sister alone

being of the opinion that everything was permitted so long as one did not commit that error.

"By such a mother I was brought up, and I clung to her with a great love; for while only a little child I was made her confidante and shared her sorrows, while father never spoke to me. When quite a little girl, I heard her tell her love stories, and I grew up with the idea that one rose in the eyes of other people in proportion to the number of admirers one had.

"Shortly after my confirmation, I renewed acquaintance with a former school-friend, who was some years older than I. Our gardens joined and she often called me over to her. I soon remarked that, when we walked out, Emily sent many covert glances towards the house in the neighboring garden, and she soon confided in me that 'her darling' lived there, but I was not to tell her mother. One day two young men looked out of the window, the 'darling' and a friend of his, and I could hardly believe my eyes when the friend nodded to me. I told it all to mother, who was very much amused. How it happened I don't remember now, but a meeting was arranged to which my mother accompanied me, and I can still distinctly call to mind the mingled feelings of disgust and pride which filled my mind as I walked with this stranger. After this he came to see us; I was then not more than fourteen years old. He sat beside me and also kissed me, and we took walks together. Oh, dear friend, it was dreadful! Imagine, I believed that this was quite correct, and yet this individual was so unsympathetic to me. He went away, and we wrote occasionally to each other—God knows what about! I always lived with a vague feeling that things were not as they ought to be, especially as this introduction was deceitfully hidden from my father.

"It must have been shortly after this that a young musician came to live with us. I had to wait on him as I did on the other lodgers. He was more intimate with us than any of the others had been, and, unfortunately, I grew very fond of him, but quite—I must now ask you, dear Mr. Fenger, to give me your absolute trust —in an innocent way. When, through the door, I could hear that he was preparing to go out, I quickly put on my hat and jacket, pretending I had a commission to do for my mother, but really with the hope that I could walk down the street with him. One day a picnic was arranged by my cousins, and I asked if the musician could be of the party, but as the others objected to a stranger, I stayed at home. He then invited me to go alone with him to Loschwitz, which my mother did not object to, and, as usual, an untruth was told to my father.

"After this we one evening played a game of forfeits, and he was deputed to kiss me, which I distinctly refused to allow. He went into his room, and my mother, by some ruse or another, sent me to him. He repeatedly asked me for the kiss, and got it, and from that day I really loved him so much that, according to my fifteen-year-old ideas, I thought that I could never love another so well. The previous intimacy now began to worry me dreadfully, but I did not see any way out of it. However, the correspondence soon came to an end.

"The young musician asked my mother for my hand, but she told him I was far too young to think of a serious engagement. Soon afterwards I heard that he was on the point of being engaged to someone else—which report, however, turned out eventually to be untrue—and my despair was beyond everything. Anyhow he left us, and, a fortnight later, Mr. Stephensen took the room. The day the musician departed, I knelt on the floor and tore off some dead twigs of a garland which he had won at a shooting competition, and kept it as a souvenir.

"Mr. Stephensen then came. Later on he assured me that he had only engaged the lodging for my sake, as in reality he did not care for it. He was thus already attracted by me, and, as he afterwards told me, looked upon me as a superior and unapproachable being. For the sake of both these men's honor, I must remark that they were never unduly familiar towards me. Therefore I could afterwards understand the passion of Mignon, which is also so perfectly innocent.

"When Mr. Stephensen had lived with us a fortnight, the musician came one evening to say good-bye. I went with him to the door. There he asked me to kiss him at parting, which I did, Stephensen" —(a commenced "Axel" was here crossed out)—"in his jealousy, listening at the door. Since then he has told me that from that minute he looked upon me as in no way different to others, and began to want me to be his according to his own 'views.'

"Oh, dear friend, it was hard to learn that in a moment, when I was so little conscious of doing anything wrong, I had lost a man's respect and love, and in his eyes lowered myself to the level of a worthless woman. Never shall I forget the feelings which overwhelmed me when I came to realize how low I had fallen in the eyes of one who, though he had known me so little, thought so highly of me, and whom I afterwards came to love! Thousands of times I cried bitter, despairing tears. My only consolation was that I knew myself to be innocent. Often, when I have pondered over it, it has appeared to me that when a man has formed so pure and beautiful an impression, which after all must be intuitive, he ought not, through an accidental circumstance, to change his opinion so that it becomes entirely different, but should wait until he is calm again and is able to judge dispassionately. I think that a real lover ought not to have thrust me away, but have made allowances for a childish indiscretion, considering that, after all, my faults were those of my bringing up and surroundings, and that he would be able to shield me from harm and raise me to the ideal he had formed. But perhaps this was too much to expect, and very likely it is only ignorance of feelings which makes me reason thus. Maybe that in reading this you will understand Mr. Stephensen better than you do me, and feel that in his place you would have reasoned in the same way.

"It was this recollection which so strongly overcame me after I had allowed you to kiss me. If you had known whom you had kissed, and that it was far from —oh, so far, from being my first kiss! And did not even this kiss prove that he had been right in considering me flighty? Perhaps you also had discovered it, and therefore took advantage of the knowledge. But no, I could not think *that* of you after our innocent intercourse. Such a kiss would not have been in accordance with it; perhaps it was a childish, thoughtless, or playful kiss, but certainly it was not one of love's Judas kisses. However, I understood neither, you nor myself, and I was afraid for both of us. When I came home, I cried as if my heart would break, without really knowing why I was crying.

"But I must return to the old days. Mr. Stephensen spoke much to me about what I have told you, pointing out how wrong it all was, and correcting the objectionable views in which my mother had brought me up, and gradually he opened my eyes to many things to which I had previously been blind. He also discussed his art with me, and found that I had a good deal of natural taste for it (the painter Jagemann from the Weimar period, a friend of Schiller, about whom perhaps you have read, was one of my ancestors, and my father had, as a young man, painted a little himself). I often

went with Mr. Stephensen round our glorious gallery, where he was copying two pictures. During this time he grew more and more demonstrative, to which I strongly objected, and I only put up with it because I was so fond of him. Besides, I had the hope that he would marry me, but he always tried to talk me out of it. He had no means, and his art, he said, would suffer under domestic troubles, and when I promised to be so good a housewife that it would not cost him more than when he was single, he replied that such a tie was not good for an artist, who had to travel about and give himself up completely to his work and ideas. He kept on trying to convince me that the suggestion of a closer bond was mere Philistinism and selfishness on my part, and that free intercourse between man and woman, under such circumstances, was a quite worthy, nay, even, ideal relation. I have never been able to agree with this, and while he, with good reason, had begun to find my moral education very unsatisfactory, I ended by finding his own morals rather loose—perhaps it was prejudice on my part, but, anyhow, I could not adopt his views. So much I know, that it was not calculation or worldly wisdom in me, but an unconquerable feeling, accompanied by the painful knowledge that his love for me was far from being so tender as mine for him; of course he also had his art, while I only had my love.

"When his time in Dresden was over, we parted with the understanding that we should remain good friends and write to one another. I was to try and marry well and be sure to tell him all my experiences, so that I might not again take a false step.

"This was my position. Can you imagine how very lonely I was? For my mother I felt an aversion. The dearest in this world, the only one with whom I could converse, had left me, and I had not even the right to long for him. I tried to take up my piano-playing again, but every beautiful melody made me so indescribably sad that I had to give it up.

"It was at this time that my father died (about which I think I told you) and I came to know Mr. and Mrs. Hertz, with whom I found an atmosphere as totally different from the one in my home as—on the other hand—from the artistic one which I came to know through your countryman; and this helped, more than I can say, to bring me peace. But I can never forget that it was Mr. Stephensen who, by his sympathy and interest for me, first of all awoke my feeling of pride and prevented me from being ruined by the unhealthy atmosphere which surely bid fair to destroy me.

"With regard to our correspondence, it has continued ever since, with longer or shorter intervals, for a year and a half. He has always answered my letters rather quickly and asked me to write again soon; sometimes he has sent a leaf of his sketch-book, and last Christmas a beautiful painting. In order to make you understand this kind of correspondence, I beg you to read the enclosed letter, which has already been through your hands. Not that I think you have any suspicion from which I could, by this means, clear myself; but you will not misunderstand my fancy, even if you do not understand it. Perhaps I do not understand it myself, but only feel that I want you to know it; it even seems to me as if the circumstances have given you a sort of right to do so, and as if by simply tearing the letter up I should deprive you of it. Send it off I will not, for, as you will see by the date, it will soon be a fortnight old; I was sure that I had posted it, and rather expected the case to be reversed, and that the post would bring me a letter from him.

"And now, good-bye! I have been writing half the night and am dreadfully

tired. My hope is that you will not judge me too harshly after this communication, but, anyhow, you must tell me quite candidly what impression this letter has made on you, and not out of kindness be too lenient. Unless this confidence is frankly answered, how shall I benefit by it? That I value your judgment you know beforehand, and you will also see it by my letter to Mr. Stephensen.—Your friend,

MINNA JAGEMANN."

Confused though I was by the many conflicting emotions caused by the reading of this letter, I did not at first try to come to any clear comprehension of it, but at once opened the letter with which two days before I had been tempted to tamper. I did not doubt that it would contain observations about myself.

I quickly ran through the opening sentences, with the usual excuses for not having written for so long, and the remarks about the weather and the country. A little more attention was bestowed upon a short, not very complimentary, description of the honorable family with whom she was living, and I noticed that she did not try to play the novelist, a part which young letter-writing ladies—especially in the governess line—are apt to indulge in on such occasions. After this I read with a palpitating heart the following lines—

"I have made acquaintance with a young student by the name of Fenger, a countryman of yours. It was, as you will understand, this fact which first recommended him to me, and made us more quickly acquainted than is usually the case. I very often meet him at the Hertzes. He is not exactly handsome, but has one of those frank fair faces which please one, especially when he smiles. He

is very tall, but stoops a little, and sometimes it seems to me that his chest is not
very strong. I should be very grieved if
such was the case. He shows me so much
attention that I cannot hide from myself
that he appreciates me. Time will show,
however, if this is anything more than a
fleeting summer-holiday fancy. He is still
very young, his age is only twenty-four,
but really he seems much younger, as if
he was still untouched by life. With regard to myself, I hardly know what position I should take in case things took a
serious turn, and I cannot make myself
reflect over this and take up a position
accordingly; such a course being against
my nature. Of course, when one can be
accused of having 'encouraged' a young
man—I think that is the expression—or
even of having 'flirted' with him, which
often only means having been gay, natural, and having given way to moods, and
then when it comes to the point drawing
back, which means not being willing to
follow him to the ends of the earth; well,
then, of course, one is a horror, or, at any
rate, a rather contemptible person. For
my part, I think it would be extremely
foolish and stupid if two people dare not
so much as look at each other because
their acquaintance might culminate in
love, which, after all, is not bound to be
unhappy. Then again, mere friendship
can exist between man and woman, and
the greatest possible advantages may result from such companionship. No, if I
started such calculating considerations I
should always feel both conceited and
foolish. In short, I very much like this
Mr. Fenger, and to talk with him is both
pleasant and in many ways instructive.
But perhaps you now think that I am, if
not actually taking a false step, nevertheless upon a dangerous path?"

After this followed the finishing remarks, and the signature, "Your friend."

CHAPTER IV

I once more took up Minna's letter, in
order to read it carefully word by word.
On the first reading I had been overwhelmed by a dreadful fear that, in truth,
as she had warned me, something would
be revealed that would lower her in my
estimation, a terror which restlessly
haunted me from line to line, my eyes always running on in advance. This fear diminished as I proceeded; her almost exaggerated repentance because of these
innocent entanglements made me smile
half pitifully, and when my brows were
knitted it was with indignation against
this Stephensen; and yet I could not help
feeling a sort of gratitude towards him
for not having bound her.

An exultant joy at the same time grew
upon me: the consciousness that with this
letter she laid her fate in my hands.
Throughout it was instinct with the feeling that we stood in front of a decisive
step, and with the honest resolution that
nothing in the past was to be left un-
cleared. She wanted to be able to say to
herself: "I have told him everything, before I allowed things to go further."

And if I now said—and how deeply I
felt that I could and had to say so!—
"Well, after having heard all this, I think
as before, only that you are more precious to me, because I know and understand you better," how could she then
draw back? Was not this confidence a
permission to speak the language of
love?

The letter to Stephensen showed that
she herself had thought of a union between us, though her expressions on this
point were not quite satisfactory. But it
was only during the last two weeks that
we had been growing daily more intimate, and by her pointing out that the letter was a fortnight old, I saw a hint that

these remarks were no longer to be considered valid.

I wanted to write to her at once.

I had, however, the self-control to take time to shave the left cheek, on which the dried-up lather was still visible, for the sun was already striking the window-post and would soon have made this necessary operation quite impossible. During this performance I collected my thoughts, and managed with flying pen to write the following letter—

RATHEN, *14th August 188–*

"DEAREST FRIEND,—To what extent your sweet letter has moved me, and how far it is from having by its confidence revealed anything save that which but finishes and deepens the beautiful picture I had already formed, I have only one means of convincing you.

"You say you will send Mr. Stephensen a new letter. Now I propose that you should copy the old one up to the remark where you fear my chest is weak, which I can assure you is quite without foundation.

"After this you should then—according to my idea—continue—

" 'He has already shown me so much attention that I could not very well doubt his feelings for me. It therefore did not come as a surprise, when he today asked for my hand. He has no private means of his own, but will certainly in a year or so have a respectable income, very likely in England, where he has a well-to-do uncle who will help him. I do not doubt for a moment that I ought to link my fate with his,' etc. etc.

"If you are able to send off such a letter, then come to the Hertzes today at the usual hour. If I do not see you there when I come, I shall look upon it as a sign that I shall miss you forever, and that my friendship, instead of being the beginning of an everlasting happiness, was only a passing but blessed dream.

"In that case, farewell, and may you be happy!—Yours affectionately,

HARALD FENGER."

I put this letter, together with the one to Mr. Stephensen, in an envelope and sent it down to the villa by a little boy.

CHAPTER V

The afternoon was beautifully still and warm when the time came for me to go down the hill. I ran rather than walked along the path, which passed cottages and hedges, and through the little lane between the garden walls that opened to the glorious, bright Elbe valley. But as every stride brought me nearer to my fate, and altogether I had only a short distance to go, my pace slackened, and I came to a complete standstill when I saw the lower stone-step leading from the narrow meadow up to the cottage. The smallest movement would now have enabled me to see its corner, with the projecting summer-house appearing behind the foliage of a fruit tree in the neighboring garden. It was as if somebody had caught hold of my throat, and my legs seemed to have disappeared from under me.

There was the sunlit lime wall under the shining tiles, the vine creeper, the shadow projected by the tree, enveloping the summer-house, where the gray-green table-cloth had a crooked sun-streak of yellow—I looked for a long time at this streak so that the critical moment might be delayed; some leaves of the fruit tree hid the corner of the table-cloth, and over them came the steam of the coffee-machine. A white-bearded man I had already discovered, now also the old lady, but no one else was there.

I continued to stare, hoping that I might after all be able to see *her*. In spite of the intense heat of the sun I shivered

as if I was standing in an evening mist, but I was again master of myself, which, until then, I had hardly been. My first idea was to creep away, for I did not doubt that, if she had wanted to come, she would already have been there. But perhaps she had gone up to fetch something for the coffee-table, or she had been prevented from coming, and a message was waiting for me. This explanation of her absence I offered to myself, and then refused it as a weakness of my poor soul, which dared not look matters straight in the face.

A rattling stone, or an indistinct vision of something which moved, made me look in the opposite direction, down towards the river. There, at the little well, hardly fifty yards from me, a figure rose into view. . . .

It was Minna.

I wanted to run to meet her, but Hertz had already discovered me and called out, "Mr. Fenger, do hurry up, do hurry up!" I also saw that he waved his hand, and though I did not understand the meaning of all this excitement, I obeyed willingly. When, running at top speed, I had reached the verandah, I nearly knocked over a long, bony woman, who rushed out of the door with a bag and a plaid in her hands.

"At last! What a good thing that you came!" Mr. Hertz said.

"We nearly sent for you, but Minna insisted that you were sure to come."

"Just imagine, we are off to Prague this evening! Yes, in a minute."

"But we are not going to drive you away for that reason. On the contrary, we hope you will accompany us for a little way. The express does not stop here, so we are obliged to go on to Schandau, and we will do that by boat. The weather is beautiful now, so you might as well take that trip with us. There is a train back at nine o'clock. Minna has already promised to come."

Of course I hastened to do the same.

My fertile, self-tortured brain had for a minute whispered to me the possibility that my letter had not been delivered, and that Minna's presence was without meaning, and that everything might still end in disappointment. But Mr. Hertz's remark that Minna had insisted that I was sure to come calmed me.

She herself now came up the steps, dressed in the same light chamois-colored frock which she had worn during our expedition to the quarry. In giving me an unusually long and firm shake of the hand—her way of shaking hands was individual and sincere—she smiled, but only with her eyes, that looked straight into my soul, with a glance as different from all former ones as "my love" is from "my friend." All the blood flew to my head; and when she let go my hand, it trembled, and my knees shook. Now, for the first time, when I had certainty and felt quite calm and happy, I could physically feel how much the dreadful strain and fear had affected me.

Minna had felt it, and could not help smiling secretly with a rather flattered air, while she poured out the glass of cold-well water for Mr. Hertz, which he always appreciated so much with his coffee —it was just as if we were in a café. And while he was sipping first the coffee and then the water, he talked in his excited way—

"For you must know, yes, it is sure to interest you, perhaps it will tempt you to follow us to Prague. Well, you will not? But indeed it is better so, for then Minna will have company on her return, and to you we dare trust her. Well, in Prague a manuscript has been found of *Faust,* OF FAUST, my dear boy, that is to say, a part of the first scenes—which differs, of course, only in details, but, all the same, *there* lies the interest. It is supposed to be stronger in expressions, and is very likely one of the first sketches. A queer old man, he is a pensioned colonel, inherited it, God knows how long ago, from a great-aunt or some one like that, who, at the Court in Weimar, was—well, how intimate with Goethe I really cannot say! And it doesn't very much matter. By the way, there you have our modern military Germany! He inherits a chest with letters and papers in which, if he had not been an ignoramus, he might have guessed there were things from Goethe; but contempt for everything literary prevents him from even opening the chest. He is in want of money, a spendthrift of course, and must throw himself into the arms of the moneylender, though all the time he has a treasure in his loft, with which he could buy a castle. And it is not as though no hint had been given him, for we had an idea that something might be there, perhaps not a manuscript, but letters and information—I have written to him myself. But no, family papers, defamatory secrets perhaps, and he would see that they were not given into the hands of those damned literary fellows, of course he reasoned like this. So he contents himself with Johannisberger-Dorf in his cellar; it is notorious that he was a skilled connoisseur of wine. And all the time a castle in his loft. That is Nemesis! Oh, how this fellow has annoyed us! Well, he is dead now, thank goodness, and the manuscript has been found. That I should not be there! But today, dear friend, I received a letter calling me in, so to speak, as an authority, and you can imagine . . ."

Just as no smile of Minna's escaped me, nor any of her movements, so no word of his account was lost upon me. I felt a vastness and elasticity of mind, as if at the same time it could hold all sorts of impressions, so long as they were pleasing and pure. The old man had never had a more sympathetic and attentive listener, indeed some of his exaltation even communicated itself to me. My condition was like a slight opium intoxication, which makes music sound still more wonderful. While I congratulated him on this interesting journey, which conferred so much honor upon him, and questioned him and answered his lively outbursts, I drank my cup of coffee which Minna had poured out and given me. But far from finding the "brown nectar," prepared by my beloved's hands, incomparable, I decided in my own mind that Minna, true to her Saxonian origin, made "Bliemchen-Kaffee," and that time would come when she would have to grow accustomed to be less economical with the coffee-beans.

I do not think, however, that I should have had the heart to refuse another cup, if I had not heard from the river the dull sound of the steamer's propeller. The others insisted that it was too early, but soon afterwards we saw the funnel of the ship over the green fields, like a black line coming forward on the white background of the waste slope under the quarries.

We were soon seated on the deck under the awning, and saw the house gliding by, the greenish table-cloth still shining in the shadow of the summer-house. We sailed towards Lilienstein and its twin brother Königstein, which now appeared opposite the former, with sunlight on the margin of its wall and on the small watch-towers. The glare of the yellow quarries flickered over the water, in which each red spot, or violet-shaded line above, here grew into a long, quivering streak. Along the banks, the fields, bushes, and fruit trees dipped their green reflections in the river. From the plowing prow, long mussel-shaped waves slid out to the sides, and as they came towards the bank the reflecting colors flowed into their blue, shining valleys just like a fluid which suddenly finds a canal and draws out the picture in an elongated distortion, until everything was jumbled up in a vibrating mixture of tongue-shaped and twisted spiral colors, all light and clear as glass.

Old Hertz was very lively, and talked untiringly about the wonders of Prague; about the peculiar Teyn Church, where my famous countryman Tycho Brahe was buried, about the dirty Jewish quarter with its gloomy Synagogue, and the overgrown churchyard, where the plain Oriental grave-stones stood slanting and leaning, and crowded so closely together that they looked as if they would push one another out of the ground. About Hradschin, the Bohemian Acropolis, and its terrace-shaped Palace-gardens climbing up the side of the rock. Of all those wonders which I should be able to admire the next day, if I allowed myself to be persuaded to go on with them tonight. For he pretended all the time to hope that I would eventually give way, and good-naturedly enjoyed listening to the many feeble excuses I made to his reiterated invitations.

But he always wound up by saying, "Yes, yes, it is also a good thing that Minna gets company, though I am quite sure that she would not be afraid to return alone." Then of course she began to assure us how willing she was to do this daring act, and that I was "on no account to give up this enjoyable trip for her sake, when there was such a good chance to take it with pleasant companions." While teasing me in this way she laughed with her half-closed blinking eyes, so that in the end I did not know what to answer. We, in our turn, amused ourselves heartily over the fact that the good-natured man, while meaning to make fun of us, was in reality himself deceived, as he could not have any notion of how on this, of all evenings, it was really impossible for me to leave her. Mrs. Hertz, however, who sat on the bench opposite us, sometimes shook her gray curls and smiled while she looked at us, as if this talk tired her, but at the same time with a question-

ing look, as if searching a secret under this play of words.

In Schandau we scarcely had time for anything except to have supper in the garden of an hotel near the river. Dusk closed in quickly. Hertz reminded us about the home-journey. But Minna assured us that the steamboat, in connection with the train service, started regularly a quarter of an hour before the departure of the train, a fact which we must surely know from the time-table. As the station is situated on the other side of the river and a good half-mile from the center of the town and the landing-place, the communication is kept up by means of a little steamboat. This combination made old Hertz feel uneasy; he began to get travelling fever, and every minute pulled out his gold watch with its face cover.

Minna admitted at last that it was now time for us to be moving.

There was no boat visible at the little bridge. The black water, which had a shimmer over it from the light of the lanterns that collected in the whirlpools, flowed freely past its empty planks, where there was not so much as a portmanteau or handbag to be seen.

"Surely we have come to the wrong bridge, it must be the steamer bridge," Mrs. Hertz said.

"Not at all, we are only too early," Minna answered, and she seemed to be a little hurt at this want of confidence.

We dawdled up and down for a few minutes, without seeing anybody or anything. Hertz went into the open shed, which served as a waiting-room, and sat down. In one corner there was a working-man sleeping, with the brim of his hat pulled down over his forehead, for the smoking oil-lamp gave just sufficient light to dazzle one's eyes. Hertz stood up after having consulted his watch two or three times, approached the stranger, sauntered round him, coughed, and at last cautiously asked whether the gentleman also waited for the steam-launch going to meet the Dresden train.

"Nach Brag!" the stranger muttered mechanically, without looking up, and almost without waking.

A faint hope began to break upon me. When I saw a porter slouching down to the bridge I went up to him and asked for information. "The steam-launch for the Dresden train left ten minutes ago," he replied. Inwardly beaming with joy, and outwardly as annoyed as possible, I went up to the ladies with my news. They stood close to the little lamp, and I could see that Minna's annoyance at being disgraced over her assurance was struggling with a joy which, fortunately, was not imcomprehensible to me. She seemed purposely to avoid meeting my eyes.

"There is plenty of time, it is sure to come, he has not had proper information. . . . Look, is it not the one out there?"

A red lantern approached from the other side of the river, near the spot where the station was. A couple of ropes were soon faintly to be seen, and the steam, driven ahead by the wind over the launch, which slowly came up against the current, floated above like a little rosy cloud. The stroke of the propeller could be heard.

I felt rather mortified, and looked impatiently at old Hertz, who uttered a heart-felt "Thank goodness," and hurried down the bridge, as if there was no time to be wasted, and as if he himself was going to Dresden.

The boat came out of the darkness, the whistle sounded, a shout from the launch was answered by the porter, and past the bridge-lantern flew a lasso, that nearly caught the good Hertz, and landed a few yards behind him. The little steamboat lay beside the bridge with its coal-smeared hull still quivering; on the low, dirty cabin wall fell the glare from the machine-room, where the slow puff-puff still continued; and nauseating fumes of burnt oil, mixed with coal smoke, streamed into the fresh night air.

"For Dresden train?"

"No, the express for Vienna. There's plenty of time, for we stay here nearly half an hour."

"Yes, but the train for Dresden?"

"We have just taken the people across for that."

"But there's still time enough. Can't we get a boat to take us across?"

"I don't think you will get any boat at this time of night. I say, Heinrich, is there any boat to be got?"

"No, of course there's no boat to be got," answered the porter, and spat in the water. "People ought to be here in time for the launch."

A load fell from my heart, and it seemed to me that Minna also breathed more freely. But Hertz looked quite terrified; evidently he felt that he was solely responsible for having put us in this predicament, and for being compelled to leave us in it.

"But it was also your fault, Minna! Why were you so positive? One ought never to rely upon one's memory in such a case, and the time-table may be altered from one year to another. I ought to have thought of that myself. It really is very annoying."

"Oh dear me!" said Mrs. Hertz soothingly, "after all, it is nothing so very dreadful. You will be obliged to remain here for the night, but anyhow there are plenty of hotels in Schandau; the town contains hardly anything else."

This practical remark quieted him down.

"Luckily there is an early train to-morrow. But perhaps you will be missed," Hertz said to Minna.

"Oh, I shall be back before anybody is up," she replied.

We walked up and down for a few minutes, and then Hertz took me aside.

"Tell me, dear Mr. Fenger, you came

on this expedition so unprepared, and besides you did not think of staying the night here—I mean have you, by accident, not enough money with you?"

I hastily reassured him, as I, really "by accident," had more than sufficient with me.

The old man looked at me in astonishment and hesitatingly put his purse, which he had already taken out, back into his enormous deep pocket, while he moved his lower lip as if he was going to speak.

"The ladies and gentlemen will be obliged to stay overnight," shouted the mate of the steamboat; "there are no more trains northwards."

"No, but we are going southwards. We are bound for Prague."

"But you were asking for the Dresden train."

Hertz began to explain the situation.

A steam whistle sounded on the other side of the river, and like a shining centipede the train glided past hissing and squeaking. It was the one that was to have taken us back to Rathen. I stood alone next to Minna and, as I thought nobody noticed us, I gave way to my gaiety and made a face at the passing train. Minna burst out laughing, and a rather coarse bass, a little to the side of us, joined in. I turned round, almost alarmed, and discovered the porter, who seemed to understand the situation.

"But what in the world are you laughing at?" asked Mrs. Hertz.

Hertz now busied himself with getting on board, as if there was danger of the launch leaving them behind. They remained near the railing, and for a quarter of an hour we kept up a spasmodic conversation, searching for something to say, all of us tired of waiting. Hertz recommended an hotel which was good and "moderate." At last the signal bell rang. Hertz remembered the man in the waiting-room.

"Let him come if he cares to," said the mate.

But the old man got excited. I ran and woke up the phlegmatic stranger, who followed me grumpily. As soon as he had passed over the gangway, it was hauled in, and the steamer glided away, turned slowly, and disappeared in the darkness. Minna kept on waving her handkerchief.

I was on the point of embracing her, when I remembered that perhaps we might still be visible from the boat. Besides, the porter was sitting a few yards away, astride on the railing.

CHAPTER VI

We walked slowly back. At the corner of the shed was a big, blue letter-box. Minna smiled, pulled a letter out of her pocket, and held it in front of me so that I might read the address, which was, as I had guessed, Stephensen's. Then, having looked at me with a questioning glance, which said, "Shall I?" she stretched out her hand and put it under the flap. The letter fell with a dull sound into the empty box. Though this sound gave me the answer I longed for, it, at the same time, raised in me a faint feeling of uneasiness, as of a bad omen. This passing and apparently quite uncalled-for feeling I remember most distinctly, though not for a moment did I yield to it. For I had already drawn her to me, and soon felt my embrace returned with a fervor which had not so much the character of passion as of deep tenderness. Her strong maiden-arms in thus clinging to me seemed to seek to bind us so closely together that nothing could part us. When she noticed that I gasped for breath, she suddenly let me go.

"Have I hurt you? I am so violent."

She looked so terrified, as if I really might have broken to pieces in her arms, that involuntarily I burst out laughing, and covered her face with kisses, until she hushed me with a still startled, yet roguish, look peeping out of wide-open eyes, and whispered from half-parted lips on which she laid her finger. But nobody was near, and the corner of the shed hid us in a three-cornered shadow.

We left it at last. I wanted to take her farther out along the river, but she did not like the darkness, and wanted to go towards the town. "We can be reasonable," she said. But our words were not so much talk as translated caresses.

We walked slowly arm-in-arm on the broad quay towards the lights of the town, which, like scattered sparks, mounted towards the stars, and some distance ahead of us, against the bend of the river, culminated in a golden border inlaid with the green enamel of the hotel gardens. On the opposite bank nothing was to be seen but two colored signal lamps, and the dark mass of rock only showed as a starless part of the sky.

The express tore past on the other side of the river, and reminded us of the time. But just now the light in front of us began to brighten with a mother-of-pearl-like shade and under the clearing the dark bend of a mountain appeared. The masts of a couple of Elbe rafts showed against the sky. The glare quickly became redder, as if from a fire; had one been near the Rhine, one would have imagined it to be Brünhilde's rock ablaze, mounting like a glowing dome over Winterberg's even wood-stretches, just where the depression midway silhouetted itself. A few minutes afterwards the moon floated free, growing ever less golden and more crystalline over the mountain landscape with its river band, a scene which it seemed to create out of the chaos of the night and gradually bring to perfection.

It was too beautiful for us to think of parting. We kept on going backwards and forwards along the river, from the little lonely waiting-shed until we came so close to the garden of the first hotel that we could see the black coats and the many-colored hats of the ladies moving under the foliage.

Alone in this strange spot we seemed to be a newly-married couple on their honeymoon, and I blessed the happy incident which had forced us to stay over-night.

"I was in reality also pleased at first," said Minna, "but soon afterwards I felt anxious, for in a way I had it on my conscience. I ought not to have been so positive. I myself had only a few marks in my pocket. If you had not had any more, my recklessness would have brought us into a nice dilemma. I *did* feel relieved when I saw you talking to Hertz and understood that you did not need to borrow anything from him. I was already quite alarmed. . . . Oh, the money, Harald! Perhaps it was a reminder how one always has to think of it when planning out anything."

We soon lost ourselves in plans for the future and calculations as to how little, with the help of economy, would be enough; apparently a very prosaic subject, but one that for a young couple (just as poor as loving) in reality possesses a greater attraction than even the most elevated romance. Notwithstanding our enthusiasm, I doubt whether the gold that the moon shed over the darkness of the river appeared to us more poetical than that with which our household needs were to be paid in due time. And I must admit that the one was just as unreal and fantastic as the other.

CHAPTER VII

We had, at last, to make up our minds to look for our hotel. It was not one of those which faced the river, but lay with its front towards the same square on which their nobler brothers turned their backs, an oblong place, half overshadowed by the church on the short eastward side. Twelve strokes had just boomed from its tower, the small tiles of which shone like wet scales.

The porch was lighted by a dim lantern, and the stairs were in darkness. A waiter, whose ears projected and whose face was covered with pimples, scowled at us, and seemed to be looking both for a tip and for our luggage, the latter of which was, of course, entirely lacking. Then he scratched his carrot-colored hair and answered, while he winked one of his pig-eyes in an especially impertinent way—

"Two rooms? And I suppose they must join? Well, I'm not quite sure—"

"Then make sure, on different floors, it does not matter; but be quick, there are plenty of other hotels in Schandau," I said roughly, controlling a violent desire to pull one of his ears. Minna had turned quite crimson at his rudeness, and looked terrified.

A woman's face, in Rembrandt light, peered over the second landing. We heard the woman on the landing calling out various numbers to the waiter; and then the man suddenly took up a diplomatic position and invited us, with a gracious wave of the hand, to go up the stairs which were covered with well-worn cocoa-matting. Then he handed us over to the woman-genius with the light, who dropped big streaks of candle grease down upon the somewhat red-gray shoulder of his tailcoat, while in a deep guttural voice he announced the numbers of the rooms which had been chosen for us. And, after peremptory orders to wake us in time to catch the first train in the morning, we obeyed his summons.

The rooms were next to each other, and even communicated, and though I had so promptly declared that they might be on different floors, I must admit that I was well pleased to be Minna's immediate neighbor. I do not know if it was by accident that we at the same moment put our shoes out into the corridor, which was empty and dark, and only lighted by a distant lamp. Silently we crept out to the neutral ground, and gave each other a long good-night kiss.

When I was again in my room, and was pulling off my coat and waistcoat, I noticed that the key was in the door on her side. This discovery put me at once into a pleasantly agitated state, but brought at the same time annoyance and anger when I recollected the nasty leer of the waiter with the winking pig-eye. And then I called to remembrance how crimson Minna had turned at the time, and saw quite distinctly her dignified and alarmed air, and this picture gave me intense delight. I fell into a reverie, with my waistcoat hanging over one arm, and continued to stare at the important keyhole. Was the key turned or not? Creeping towards the door I touched the handle, but dared not turn it, for fear of frightening her.

Then I went back into the room and continued to undress; still, however, peeping at the key in the same way that I had peeped at her letter two evenings before. But I had left that untouched, and this very day I had received it with the right to read it. Such a clear proof of the reward of virtue strengthened my conscience. "This barrier also will some day fall away, if only I have patience, and we shall have nothing with which to reproach ourselves."

Just as I had put out the light and laid my head on the pillow, a gentle rapping startled me. I was on the point of jumping out of bed, when it struck me that the tapping was on the wall just by my head, and I remembered that her bed stood by the same wall. I quickly answered, and she responded, alternately in softer and stronger tones, with the knuckles and the palms. Through all tempos and in different rhythms the telegraph was continued, as if two "rapping spirits" were communicating with one another; and this conversation without words, which expressed clearer than any words could have done our separated nearness, our longing and our hope, left me in a quiet, happy frame of mind.

I knew that on both sides of this wall, which was under no conventual scrutiny, had moved the same moods, feelings, and thoughts,—even if they had not in her taken such a tempting and decided form. This hour seemed to me in a mysterious way to have brought us closer to each other; and while my joy so far had been the consciousness of being allowed to love, I now was overcome by the blessed feeling of being loved, of being myself the object of another's longing and secret wishes.

CHAPTER VIII

I found Minna waiting for me in the little sitting-room of the hotel. She poured out the coffee from a tarnished pot, and we sat down at the table just like a newly married couple, as if, indeed, the bowl of honey on the tray was a symbol of honeymoon days. The room was rather gloomy, for the mist, like a blind, obscured the windows. The unusually early hour at which I had been obliged to rise affected my head, and also made me feel rather nervous.

As we stepped outside we could not see the church, and the houses on the other side of the square appeared but dimly, as an indistinct mass. The pavement was greasy; Minna slipped and took my arm. Two street-sweepers moved grotesquely in the milk-white atmosphere. Under the

barber's signboard, which seemed to be a free floating moon, a glass door clinked, and was opened with a kick. Near the grocer's, at the corner, a variously mingled and rather spicy smell impregnated the air for a certain distance; we suddenly stepped into it, and just as suddenly out of it.

We arrived in good time for the steam launch.

Hardly had it left the bridge before the bank had disappeared, and we might easily have imagined ourselves at sea. We only saw the little waves shining like scales close to us, with the mist passing over them like steam. The sooty coal-smoke from the funnel struck down over the deck. The whistle sounded continually, sometimes with long hissing sounds, sometimes in short staccato shrieks and sighs. At times another whistle or a long shout replied to our warnings, and a big dark shape glided by like a phantom.

Minna drew closer to me and pressed my arm.

"I hope a collision will not take place."

"Surely not!" I assured her.

But why, I asked myself, should this little steamer not be run down? One drowns as easily in the middle of the Elbe as in the Atlantic.

This feeling of danger united us more closely than all the dreams of the future. But the same mist that had created the danger soon dispelled it by chilling us through and through. Fear of colds and coughs drowned the romantic terror, and with it the hope of being united in a sudden death.

So confusing was this journey in the bewildering mist that when a bump announced that we had landed, we were in such a state of perplexity that we thought that we had returned to Schandau. When we stood on the platform and the Dresden train puffed in, we imagined that it was the one going to Bodenbach.

We quickly, however, discovered that

it was really our train, and, thanks to a well-invested tip, we were soon by ourselves in a second-class compartment. Over the misty white pane of the window flew gray shadows of leaves, branches, and bushes, and one drop after another rolled slowly down it.

The train shook so much that our shoulders constantly met, but Minna hardly responded to the pressure of my hand, and she spoke very little. I wanted to draw her to me, but she moved away and pointed with a shy look to the window, which was darkened by the figure of the conductor.

When our tickets had been collected and I, after having closed the window, turned round, pleased by the idea that we were now to be undisturbed, Minna got up. A sudden jerk of the train threw me down on the soft cushion, and immediately Minna was kneeling at my feet. I laughingly wanted to lift her up, but was stopped by a frightened and imploring expression in her face.

"Harald! I have something I must tell you. But promise me not to be angry. . . . No, no, you must not promise anything; perhaps you won't be able to help it."

"But, Minna, what does all this mean? Do get up, my dear!"

"No, no, you must first listen. I was so nasty yesterday. . . . I have deceived you all, and also told lies to you."

"But what do you mean? When?"

"Have you no idea? Can't you guess?"

"No, I assure you."

"Just think of it!" she continued, with a heart-broken expression upon her face, "you cannot imagine that I can be so false. . . . And when you hear it you will perhaps fear that I am always so."

"But what is it, then? So far you have told me nothing."

"Well, it was yesterday evening. It was my fault that we were too late for the ferry steamer. I knew quite well that the steamer for the train went earlier than I said it did, and I pretended——"

"But is that all?" I interrupted laughingly.

"You are making fun of me! It would be much better if you would beat me! Is it nice to get a wife who can tell lies and deceive you like that? . . . Don't you think that it was at all wrong?"

I made some kind of explanation, but she continued rapidly—

"And the good old Hertz who was so troubled, evidently he felt the responsibility of having drawn us into the adventure. I also forgot that I, without permission, must make use of your purse, and that perhaps you had not money enough, and might be put into a most awkward position. All this was very wrong. But the worst of all was, when you yourself began to talk about the fortunate mistake and I had not the courage to confess, but continued telling lies to my own dear friend. Then I was quite disgusted with myself."

"But why did you not dare 'to confess,' as you call it?"

"At that time I could not possibly dare to do so, but now I cannot do anything else. Though I had really made up my mind never to tell, or at any rate not until much, much later. . . . Oh, perhaps you cannot understand it at all! But isn't it true that we enjoyed being alone together —for so far we really had not been able to speak in private—more than being ferried in a boat filled with people, and stuffed into a nasty train. That train is always overcrowded, horrid, you know! And then"—her voice sank to a whisper, and she rested her face on my knees— "was it not also a little—just a little— sweet to be so near to each other in the night?"

I bent over her.

"And when you tapped the wall."

"Hush!" she exclaimed, putting her forefinger to her lips, and looking at me with a queer and somewhat terrified face. But suddenly her expression became almost sulky.

"But you calmly said that it did not matter whether the rooms were on the same floor or not."

"Before the waiter, dearest."

She jumped to her feet and suddenly gave me an eager kiss; it was as if I had been hit in the face by a soft ball.

"Then you are not angry any longer?"

I lifted her to the seat by my side.

"Any longer? But I assure you, Minna, I have not been angry at all."

"But you really might have been; yes, you ought to have been."

"Oh, nonsense! I only think it much sweeter now that I know that it was not an accident but your wish."

"There is nothing to be done with you; you will absolutely spoil me, and I can't imagine what the end of it will be!" Minna exclaimed, and pressed me tenderly to her. "But look how the weather is clearing. We shall have a fine day after all."

Outside, on the white sheet of mist which was stretched in front of the window, appeared dusky crowns of fruit trees, pointed fir-tops, and the margin of a roof with a tiny shining skylight, everything becoming indistinct as it approached the ground, just like the pictures of a magic-lantern that are beginning to take shape.

And above all this appeared a dark mass; it was the rock plateau of Lilienstein, floating like an island in the air with the mist stream gliding round its rough stone sides, with long dark purple clefts, and with myriads of little fir-tops pointing up twoards the sky, which shone through with the bluish tint of an opal.

"And what shall we do today?" I asked. "Tomorrow afternoon we are going to

meet at the Hertzes', but I really must see you before then."

"Yes, indeed, we must use the time— 'Our pleasant sojourn in Aranjuez is coming to an end.' [1] So you really go away the day after to-morrow?"

"Yes, my sweet Minna; it is after all for the best. The holidays are over, and my landlady has let my room."

"Well, in a week I am also as free as a bird. . . . Let me see, I will take the children out for a walk. If your many engagements do not prevent, you can expect me on the forest path, the one turning off to the left, you know, just beyond the school-house. I will walk on until I meet you."

The train whistled and stopped. We had already reached Rathen.

As we went down to the ferry, the mist only fluttered, like torn bits of cobweb, over the wet grass which was glittering in the sun.

CHAPTER IX

Needless to say that I was on the appointed path in more than good time.

It was my first tryst. I do not know whether my delight was greater than my wonder when I thought of how, hardly four weeks ago, I had strolled about here and on other pathways in the vain hope of meeting Minna. And now! Even in those days the sun had laughed and smiled through the air, the shadows had refreshed me, the woods had been filled with perfume, the song of the birds had made everything joyous, and the fresh, light breeze had rustled through the high crowns of the trees. But now, with how much more intensity did the same nature, that was as radiant and summerlike as ever, fascinate my overwrought senses! I

[1] Schiller, *Don Carlos.*

threw my hat into the air; I meant it to have flown up into the sky as a salute, but it scarcely reached the lower branch of one of the gigantic pine trees. I boldly cried out to a little robin redbreast which twittered on a dry twig of one of the trunks: "Ah, ah! you little one, are you also waiting for some one? I am waiting for my beloved one, for my darling, my little Minna."

Thereupon I peeped round, frightened that some one might have witnessed my childishness. At the same moment Minna appeared at the turn of the path with her little pupils, and with as much calmness as I could muster I hurried to meet her.

"Here I am with my chaperones," said Minna. And she quickly added: "Remember to call me Miss Jagemann, and if you feel tempted to say something which they are not to hear, then speak Danish; I shall manage to understand it."

"Little pitchers have long ears," I remarked.

Minna laughed heartily, and pointed in front to the eldest of the little girls, who happened to be endowed with large projecting ears which glowed transparently in the sunshine.

How gay and full of spirits Minna was! Though generally she looked older than her age, now she seemed so childlike that I involuntarily said to myself: "Is it possible that this is the girl who loves me as a woman loves, and who, unfortunately, has even loved before?" She wore the hood-shaped garden hat made of black straw, which I knew from 'Sophien Ruhe,' a practical head-gear, as it shaded her face down to the middle of the cheek. From this calm shadow, which caught a green light from the wood, the clear, deep-set eyes looked without a cloud, at nature and at me. Her dress was of some light material, in blue and white stripes, falling in long pleats from the waist, which was tightened by a light-blue silk ribbon, instead of the usual belt.

I had already, for several minutes, expressed myself in Danish upon rather indifferent topics, when the catastrophe foreseen by her occurred. I became so overwhelmed by my feelings that I exclaimed: "But, Minna, how well that dress suits you, how sweet you look in it!" As I had already accustomed myself to express my love in German, this little Cupid, on leaving my lips, put on that becoming linguistic garment. Of this I first became aware when Minna violently caught hold of my arm, and I saw that one of the projecting ears in front had disappeared, while the other one was turned towards us.

Minna bit her lip. At the same time the smallest girl turned round and held her doll towards her.

"Miss Jagemann, shall we soon be in the shade? Otherwise Caroline will get freckles."

We were only too glad of the chance to laugh, but the child was very much insulted by our outburst.

"Then I will say it is your fault, and mother will have to give Caroline some of her toilet water."

"Good-day, Cousin Minna," suddenly sounded behind us. "I say, how jolly! Good-day, Mr.—Mr. Fenger!" The schoolmaster, marching along in shirt-sleeves, with his jacket hanging on a stick over his shoulder, had come up behind us, and Minna replied a little stiffly to his greeting.

"Ah, is it you, Mr. Storch," I exclaimed, feeling as if he had caught me in a trap.

"Yes, indeed," he answered, with a wink which clearly said: "Well, so you have discovered her, the little governess, my beautiful Cousin Minna! Now, did I not say so?"

"Nice weather, but warm—pouf! It is the last day of my holiday," he added with a sigh.

"Where are you going?"

"I am bound for Hohenstein; will you come with me?"

"Thanks, not this time."

"Do not mind for my sake, Mr. Fenger——" Minna began.

"My goodness! An engagement is an engagement, and what is best is best. In your case, neither would I go—'Why gaze into the distance, look here—the good lies near.' Thank goodness one knows one's classics. As long as one can quote Goethe, drink München beer, smoke Altstädter-Ziegel tobacco, climb up and down the mountains, and one more thing, which I dare not mention before Cousin Minna, so long Poland is not lost, even if one has to ram knowledge into the heads of stupid youngsters six hours a day; or, to use a more stylish expression, to work in the noble service of the education of the people. Well, good-morning!"

He disappeared quickly, humming a gay ditty—

> "We make a night of it,
> We make a day of it,
> We make a whole life of it. . . ."

"What a funny fellow!" exclaimed the smallest of the girls; "and he called you cousin!"

"The baker's Tinka says that he gives them so many slaps," the eldest one added. "A nice cousin! What a dirty shirt he was wearing!"

"Mother always tells us to say 'chemise.' "

"Not about that sort, Sophy!"

Minna threw a look, not of the kindest, after the sleeves of the garment mentioned, which shone between the trunks of the trees, and asked with a little annoyance—

"How is it that you are on such intimate terms with my honored relation?"

I told her about our acquaintance, the reason why I had taken a walk with him,

and how my expectations had been rewarded.

"So already in those days you made inquiries about me," she said, shaking her finger, and at the same time smiling quite gaily. "If only I had known that!"

"What then?"

Minna laughed, and having put down her parasol she pointed with it to a shady road which almost seemed to breathe out coolness in the heat of the sun.

"Let us go down here, then Caroline will avoid freckles, and we, very likely, tourists."

The road was so overgrown with long grass that the wheel tracks were obliterated. A fine moss of tiny green stars, in which drops of the morning dew were still sparkling, covered the ditches, and a whole hedge of different kinds of ferns bent over the olive-brown moss-cushions, which swelled out on the margin of the other side.

"Just look how pretty!" Minna exclaimed, and pointed to some ferns that only consisted of one single stem with lancet-shaped fronds. As a rule they were not higher than a span's length, but some of these were quite a foot high. "I wish I could have one or two of those, roots and all. I have already got several ferns. Here, too, is a beautiful one."

She pulled off her silk gloves and knelt down. In the meantime I succeeded in jumping over to the other side.

"If only we can get them properly! Have you got a knife?"

"No, but we say in Danish: 'Five fingers are just as good as a boat hook.' "

She laughed and shook the loose hair from her face; then we began to dig and scratch away the earth. At last we got the plants out of the ground, and as I re-crossed the ditch I succeeded in wetting one of my feet. Minna carefully bound her handkerchief round the ferns, so that she should not lose any of the mould that was hanging to the roots. We showed our earth-begrimed hands to each other and laughed like a couple of children as we hurried after the little girls, who had nearly gone out of sight and were now beginning to call for us.

Above the tops of the dark fir-trees the arched sky was of a reddish blue. Into the deep brown shadows between the gray trunks, keen slanting rays of the sun penetrated like golden spears, while dim lights quivered, glittering like silver, on the huge ferns that resembled the out-stretched wings of an enormous bird; and bright yellow flames of the sulphur-like saxifrage shone along the edge of a bit of rock, which lay between the trees, like a little house with a garden of ferns and young beeches on its flat and slightly sloping roof. The air was fragrant with the scent of firs and the fresh smell of fungi.

I do not remember what the subject was on which I began to talk, but even if the theme had been interesting, I at any rate wasted my breath, for I noticed that Minna constantly stared at me with a pe-culiar, inattentive smile which had some-thing almost teasing in it, and increased just like a spreading light.

"Why do you smile?" I asked, a little mortified. "Do you not think so?"

"What?"

"Oh—of course——"

"I do not know. I have not heard any-thing. I have not the faintest idea what you have been speaking about, and I do not care about it at all"—(the words came hurriedly)—"but continue, please do. I am listening to your voice, to your voice alone. I have no mind to understand with; I look at your mouth and your pro-file. Do you know, Harald, you have a nice profile? And your mouth is so funny when you speak. Your lower lip pro-trudes—like this—with every pause. But it suits you, and the dimple in the chin gets deeper, and the nose bends right at the point, and that is the best of all. It is a Schiller nose, and you are an idealist like him—you are indeed, darling."

Quickly glancing ahead to see whether the children were out of sight she kissed me impetuously.

"But, Minna, you cannot mean what you say!"

I was quite intoxicated by this sweet flattery. It was the first time in my life that my physical vanity had been tickled. Formerly, on the contrary, I had always had to hear about my "beak of a nose," and about being a little underhung—really not much, it seemed to me—and now! That this pretty girl should find something attractive in me, and just in these peculiarities—it was like a fairy tale. I felt myself in the seventh heaven, and God only knows how foolishly I should have behaved, had not the chil-dren come running to tell us that beauti-ful ripe raspberries were to be found—in this seventh heaven!

The wood became less dense, with low shrubs between big moss-covered stones. The road we had followed now narrowed down to a path, at the side of which we stopped beneath the shadow of a baby rock, while the little girls crawled about between the bushes. Minna took off her hat, lay down on her back, and looked up into the deep sky. Suddenly she burst out into brief laughter.

"What is it?"

She half got up, and, supporting her-self on one arm, said—

"Do you remember, Harald, there are on the Zwinger some tiny children—fauns I think they are called—with goat-legs, quite plump, you know; they also have a small tail?"

"Well?"

"It struck me if such a little chap came jumping along how sweet it would be. I would take him on my lap and pet him."

"Yes, I should like to see that. How funny you are!"

"Am *I?*" she asked with a comical little stress on the "I."

At the same instant something living moved with big bounds within the bushes. The smallest girl began to shriek, and the good-natured head of a pointer appeared, his long tongue hanging out on one side of his dry mouth. The next moment a bearded forester with a gun over his shoulder stood on the path a few yards from us, and scrutinized us with a most sullen look. Surely this man could have no human feeling in that broad breast of his since he could scowl at Minna in such a way, as she sat there with her bodice tightened by the uplifted half-bare arms, which she had raised to put straight her hair and hat. A veritable forest ogre!

"What are you doing here?" he asked sternly. "This is not a road for tourists."

"Well, you must excuse us, but there was no notice-board with 'Trespassers will be prosecuted' at the entrance."

"As if you couldn't see that it was only a wood-road! . . . Hang it all, there are pathways enough made for the public."

"So one is not allowed to take a step beyond the laid-out pathways? Upon my word, it is too bad!" I shouted, and began to lose my temper.

"No, damn it, you are not allowed!" he yelled, his face extremely red and angry.

"We really did not know, otherwise we should not have come here," Minna said politely but firmly. "But I do not think we have done any harm."

"Then it's not your fault," he mumbled, a little less irritably. "A few yards farther on there are plenty of fir trees about the size of a nail, and anyhow the kids don't think where they are stepping. You too, I suppose, have also something else to think of." And annoyed at having allowed himself to be smoothed down so far as to give an explanation, he added, "Well, now you know what you have to do."

He then whistled the dog, spat contemptuously, and marched off by a side-path into the wood, at the same time looking occasionally over his shoulder to see whether we were also returning.

We did so, with that crestfallen feeling which, whether reasonably or not, one has after such an encounter.

"That was a fine old Pan who came and drove us away, instead of the little one you had dreamt of."

"What a bear!" she said sulkily, and imitated mockingly his hoarse bass.

The children laughed boisterously.

"Well, I suppose he was right after all, though a notice-board ought to have been put up," she said. "If I were a forester, I should also be annoyed with all these people who come running about in the woods. But you really ought to feel it more than I, being the son of a ranger. Was your father like that, Harald?"

"My father was a Royal Forester, this one was only an impolite steward."

"Aristocrat!"

"Well, you yourself do not speak exactly like a democrat about people who roam about the woods."

"That is quite a different matter."

"No, not at all."

In this way we argued gently and joked for the rest of the way. Indeed, in the end we even played tag with the children, and came home hot and out of breath and in the best humor in the world.

CHAPTER X

The following day, when Mrs. Hertz had spread the table-cloth in the summer-house and her husband was just sitting down with his newspaper, we appeared on the scene arm-in-arm, and in this manner betrayed our secret from afar.

This could not have been received with more hearty joy, even had Minna been their own daughter, and I a millionaire. A bottle of Rhenish wine was sent for from the hotel, and our healths were drunk in the little arbor, where the evening sun stole in between the foliage, and sparkled like gold in the brownish-green glasses. Hertz spoke much about the interesting Faust manuscript, the authenticity of which he did not doubt; the discrepancies, however, were fewer and of less importance than he had expected. This led quite naturally to a discussion as to whether it was right to publish such an early and, according to the author's own judgment, unfinished sketch of a famous piece of poetry; and the old man brought forward many good and striking arguments against those who, for the sake of a great feeling of veneration towards perfected works, insist upon suppressing the founts from which they sprang, which are, after all, of deep human interest and of great value for all artistic psychology.

But he spoke more slowly and with more effort than usual, and was often interrupted by a troublesome cough, that evidently distressed his wife. The fog, which near the Elbe had been so unusually thick that it resembled the famous Rhine mist, had also not spared the Moldau Valley; and in the narrow-built town of Prague it had lasted till far on in the day, penetrating everything with its wet cold. In addition to this, Hertz had for hours been in a loft, where this dampness had been accompanied by a dreadful draught.

Nobody had shown sufficient forethought to have the contents of this extraordinary chest removed to more habitable rooms, and besides there were also many bookcases and boxes which had not allowed Hertz any peace, and in which he had also succeeded in discovering one thing and another. Notes from Carl August and Archduchess Amalia, original copies of a couple of books by Wieland and Herder with dedications, theatre pro-

grammes, etc. A few of these things he had managed to buy, and he showed them to us with great joy when, a little before sunset, we went into the house. But we could not hear this cough, which constantly interrupted his gay remarks, without the fear that he might have bought his treasures too dearly.

When we were going homewards, a little earlier than usual, Minna gave way to her distress—

"Hertz is weak, and he cannot stand much."

"It may be so, but that is no reason to fear the worst."

"Well, I am like that, Harald! Your cheerful disposition will be thoroughly tried by me. I always meet troubles halfway, and it seems to me it does not make the way shorter. Just look at me, I am now in reality as depressed as if the dear old man had gone already."

"Indeed it would be a hard trial, not only for his good wife, but also for my friend Immanuel. I have never seen so charming an intimacy between father and son. It reminds me of the patriarchs."

"Ah well! It might well touch me, as it was so different from what I experienced in my own home."

"Aren't you fond of Immaneul? He really is such a nice fellow."

"Yes, indeed—very nice——"

It struck me that she had never much to say about Hertz's son, and it also surprised me that *he* had never spoken to me about Minna, and that I had never seen her when I had visited him. Very likely in those days she had come less frequently, or at fixed hours of the day. As a matter of fact it was only in the last part of the year, before he left for Leipzig, that our acquaintance had grown so intimate.

I would willingly have continued this subject, but Minna had already put it on one side.

"By the way, when you come to town you will call to see mother—I have written to her. And listen—do not judge her too harshly."

"But, dearest girl, how can you fear——"

"Well, well, I have not myself raised your expectations too highly. But there is any amount of good in her; truly she does not of her own free will harm anybody, and she is so fond of me—she really is."

"The last is enough for me."

"Do you know, Harald, there is one thing which pleases me."

"Well?"

"But you must not be so delighted, it is not at all nice of me, but very selfish. Do you know, I am so pleased that you have no parents alive."

"Oh, why? They would have been so fond of you."

"No, no," she exclaimed, in an almost frightened tone.

"How could they have been? They would have expected quite a different daughter-in-law, and they would have been right. But as it is, there is no one but you who has any claim on me, if only you will be satisfied with me as I am."

"My own beloved wife! But you are crying?" I exclaimed, as my lips met tears on her cheek.

"Never mind! But it sounded so sweet, do say it again!"

"My wife!"

Already we had more than once walked backwards and forwards through the little village. The night was pitch dark.

The lights of the solitary windows, which were scattered on both sides of the dark valley, added more to the coziness than to the brightness of the place. Above the obscurity of the heights and rocks sparkled the stars, keen and restless, and now and again a falling star darted over our heads. Besides our own footsteps we only heard the little brook babbling between the stones, and from time to time a passing movement in the willows on its bank, as if an enormous animal was suddenly shaking itself.

As we, for the third time, came near to the lights that beckoned us from the Zedlitz Villa, our steps grew gradually slower.

"You sigh?" said Minna when, against our will, we had at last stopped walking.

"I have something like a presentiment, I cannot help it. It seems to me so sad to part from Rathen, I feel depressed—I fear something, I think."

"We have been so happy here. But it is my own dear town we are going to, I am looking forward also to our walks there."

"It is only this. Our love is just like a plant that has grown up here, and now has to be transplanted."

Minna laughed, a subdued and wise laugh.

"No, it is only going to be removed. For it is a plant which has its root in the heart and not in any especial locality."

After a long, long embrace she glided away from me and disappeared in the darkness, while the tiny twigs still crackled under her steps, which tripped on the gravel path. Suddenly they stopped.

"Good-night, love!" sounded her high, clear voice, surprisingly near.

"Good-night, little soul!"

And again it sounded, but this time far away, as a voice from beyond—

"Good-night!"

BOOK III

CHAPTER I

By five o'clock on the following day I was in Dresden. As soon as I had unpacked my things, and dined in my usual restaurant, I thought of going to see my prospective mother-in-law—not so much on account of politeness or inquisitiveness, as for the reason that I was thus indirectly communicating with Minna.

It was not many minutes' walk to "Seilergasse," where Mrs. Jagemann lived. The house was exactly like the neighboring and opposite ones. Through the open front door one entered an arched, whitewashed passage that at the other end led into the garden, and in the center had the usual winding stone staircase whitened with hearthstone, leading up to the upper floors. On the first landing I stopped at an open window and looked out. Just as the interior had already pleased me by its familiarity, so also did the view, which reminded me of the few places where I had lived, and of the homes of my friends. It was, in short, a commonplace Dresden home of the regulation citizen type.

The garden was joined on all three sides to other gardens, and these again to neighboring ones, so that they formed a big garden square, surrounded by rather low two-storeyed houses. By this plan the Dresdeners gained air and light, even in the old, narrow parts of the town. The sinking afternoon sun beamed over the various trees, while the pathways and small lawns lay in monotonous shadow. In a neighboring garden some young boys were running to and fro, in another several little girls were playing; in one place some drying clothes waved gently. The little garden beneath was empty. In a bed, in front of the vine-covered summer-house, roses were flowering; an acacia and a pretty cherry-tree stretched their branches over almost the whole space, and the elder-tree was not missing, "der Hollunder," in the absence of which, since the days of Kleist, one cannot imagine German love-scenes, and in the presence of which one cannot avoid thinking of them. It is true that the tree was not in flower, but at the end of August it could scarcely be blamed for that.

On the first floor a faded visiting-card in a small frame announced that College-teacher Jagemann lived there. I rang the bell time after time, but in vain. As I could not decide to leave this place, the only one in the beautiful town where I could find anything that was associated with Minna, I went into the garden and sat down in the summer-house.

It was almost as quiet as if one had been in the country, for only now and then did the heavy rumble of a cart remind me that I was in a town. From the garden in which the small girls were playing, voices could be heard constantly singing—

"Here we go round the mulberry bush,
Here we go round the mulberry bush,
Here we go round the mulberry bush,
So early in the morning."

This childish play made me think of what had happened in these gardens ten years before.

One of these voices was Minna's, and it was her pink dress which, through the bushes, I saw turning round like a top. She was visiting a friend of hers, for here, on account of her father, she did not dare to play with the other children. But once he nearly caught her in this crime, and I began to wonder into which of the two adjoining gardens she might have escaped. Behind me was some wooden boarding—that way was fairly barred; to the left was a hedge of hawthorn behind a paling, but it didn't look sufficiently old; opposite me the paling was a little higher, but in the corner the ground sloped upwards, so that it was easier to climb over; and also this was the place most hidden from any one who came through the entrance door. All this I examined just as carefully as an historian would inspect the localities at Pharsalia in order to get a clear idea of the plan of Cæsar's battle; and it cost me just as much head-work to decide upon the neighboring house and the window from which her friend's beloved and his friend, her first adorer, had made their salutations.

In the end the elder tree occupied all my attention. It stood in a corner against the neighboring garden, and overshadowed a little bench which was made of two or three boards and looked extremely old. I moved from my seat in the summerhouse to this one. It was not exactly a comfortable seat for an old man who wished to take a nap in the mid-day heat, but it was very suitable for a young couple who didn't demand much comfort. And then this romantic "Hollunder"! It was not in flower now, but it had flowered—for him! Like the shadow from this bush jealousy filled my soul, the jealousy which my feeling of happiness and Minna's presence had so far kept away. I wanted to own her altogether, would like to have seen her as a child; in imagination I could picture her leaving her play-fellows in order to put her little plump arms round my neck. If there were a pre-existence, it seemed to me that this also should have been mine. But not even her first youth had belonged to me! Another had possessed this beautiful fragment of her life, and had kept it as a jewel with which to deck his vanity. In the end, however, it was I who had won the treasure, while he had been blind enough to be satisfied with a few baubles.

This thought consoled me the more because it flattered my sense of self-esteem.

I got up and went out into the street. The twilight had deepened. On the one side some dark tree-tops over a garden wall had caught the roseate glow of evening, on the other it was quite dark between the houses, the upper windows of which sparkled like gold, while the lanterns were lighted at their feet. As I had no particular aim in view I went towards the bright side.

At the corner was, of course, the inevitable beer-shop.

A little old woman, who, in spite of the heat, was wrapped up in a thick woollen shawl, toddled in. This reminded me that Minna had said that her mother, towards evening, usually took her beer in "Zur Katze." The site of this restaurant I recollected well, for I had always noticed its very humorous sign.

So I directed my steps to the center of the town and soon reached the brilliantly lit-up Schloss Strasse, which was crowded with people. Several oldish men were sitting in the restaurant. I saw directly that it was not a place that would tempt many casual visitors, but depended chiefly upon regular customers. One of the men, who had a bundle of newspapers and a portfolio in front of him, scowled at me furiously as I approached, just like a dog which growls when one goes too near its dish of bones. A well-preserved, clean-shaven gentleman sat in a corner and rather loudly entertained a couple of decayed Philistines with the last scandal from the Court Theatre.

An open door led into a smaller room. I peeped in, and saw an old woman seated close to the door; just opposite to her, in the big room, an old-fashioned mirror was hanging. As I wished to be undisturbed while I looked at her reflection in the mirror, I quickly retired, and once more seriously terrified the newspaper reader by sitting down next to him.

By way of pretense I took up the paper he had laid aside; but even against this he protested with a discontented murmur. The waiter placed a glass of beer in front of me.

I could not, however, imagine that the old woman in the inner room could be my future mother-in-law. Minna had said that there was some resemblance between them, and it was impossible for me to find any trace of such a thing. The forehead was not at all high, but strongly arched, the eyes were not deeply set, and the lips were thick and shapeless, as was the rest of her grayish face. It looked like a thing which had been so long in water that it had become soaked and puffy, and such a condition might—to be sure—have effaced any resemblance which had ever existed.

I called the waiter, so that I could pay him, and asked if he knew a widow of the name of Jagemann who was often supposed to come there. "She sits in the small room," he answered, and I got up immediately and went to her. She moved uneasily on her sofa-corner, and, as I stepped up to her with a greeting, she looked so terrified that one would at least have thought that she was alone with me in a railway compartment.

I told her who I was, and supposed that she through a letter—

"Yes, indeed, to be sure, Minna has written—that dear child, oh dear me! . . . Well, I am glad. . . . So you have come up to town, Mr. Tenger—"

"Fenger."

"Ah! certainly, Fenger, of course, you really must be kind enough to excuse me. It was in a letter, and the capitals are so much alike, my eyes also are not very good, and Minna writes rather indistinctly . . . don't you think so? My good husband wrote such a clear hand, he also gave writing lessons, you know, and Latin as well. Oh dear me, yes, he really was very learned. . . . Minna,

too, was well educated, it was quite different in my time, but the young people nowadays. . . . Won't you take a seat? You really must sit down."

I placed a chair close to the table, and when I saw that she thought of offering me some refreshment, I hastened to anticipate her.

"You really are too kind. Indeed I don't know, perhaps for company's sake, but only a small glass, please. I suppose you drink many glasses. Young people! Dear Jagemann was also a heavy beer drinker . . . from the student days, you know. Do you drink much beer in Denmark?"

I tried in vain to start a sensible conversation while we drank our beer. Sometimes she became limp and stared stupidly at me, not answering anything but "Oh dear me, yes." Then, directly afterwards, she would start, as the Germans say, "to talk the blue off the sky"; evidently not for the pleasure of talking, but from nervousness, and especially from a fear of being obliged to speak of the relationship between Minna and myself. It seemed to me that she had not much belief in it, and I thought that very likely she was judging her daughter by the standard of her own flighty youth. Sometimes, when she thought that I was not noticing, she looked at me critically, as if she was thinking, "What kind of fellow is this that Minna has now got hold of?" Then if I looked at her she put her glass to her lips so quickly that she spilt drops of beer down her black shawl, which showed signs of having been dyed.

When we left, I wanted to take her home, but on no account would she allow me to go out of my way; and, when I insisted, she told me that she had some shopping to do. She disappeared down the first dark turning, not, however, before I had given the promise, or the threat —I do not know which she considered it —to visit her the next day.

I went straight from the Polytechnic to her flat.

When I rang for the second time I noticed that in a window, which opened on to the stairs, a dirty little curtain moved slightly in one corner, and from the darkness behind, an eye peeped out at me, after which the curtain fell back in its place. Having waited for some time I heard shuffling footsteps, and at last the door was opened by Mrs. Jagemann, who, had I been the tax-collector, could not have looked more alarmed. I was on the point of asking her why in the world she was so frightened, when it struck me that very likely I myself was the cause of the trouble. She seemed to have forgotten that I was to call, or she had regarded what I had said as merely an empty form of politeness. The dyed black shawl, which I had seen on the previous evening, enveloped her and seemed to be thrown over her chemise, while her skirt bore a marked resemblance to a petticoat. She took me to the sitting-room with many apologies, and then disappeared for half an hour, "so that she could offer me a cup of coffee."

The rather small room, facing the garden square which I have mentioned, was bright and cheerful, and got plenty of sun. The furniture, however, was not only plain, and even partly broken, but everything showed symptoms of an entire want of order. The lid of the upright piano was quite gray with dust, and on the top of it, on a bundle of music, stood a plate containing half a smoked herring. It has always been a mystery to me how it ever arrived there, for I soon discovered that Mrs. Jagemann never inhabited this room, but muddled about the whole day long in the almost dark kitchen, where she prepared and ate her meals, slept, and read *Dresdener-Nachrichten*. In a corner stood a bookcase almost entirely filled with green-bound volumes which I at once recognized as Minna's classical treasures,

the gift from that severe aunt who would haunt her as a spirit, if she ever parted with them. A door in the middle of one of the walls was covered with a green rug, and a sofa had been placed in front of it. With this rug as a background, an oil-painting was hanging, on which I saw part of a fishing village under low dunes, near a bay. In the foreground sat a couple of young girls netting, while they at the same time carried on a flirtation with a town dandy who was conspicuous by the addition of a paint-box and had an unmistakable likeness to Stephensen. His pointing finger and the laughing expression of the girls evidently suggested that a deeper meaning was signified in this netting. While the figures were as conventionally painted as they were tastelessly thought out, there was a good deal of freshness and nature-study in the beach and the sunlight on the sand-dunes, and the picture with its powerful bright colors beamed in the little room, to the more than plain furniture of which it stood out in striking contrast. Everyone was bound to wonder how it had come there. And to me, for whom this question was answered beforehand, it spoke in a forcible manner of all that I would fain forget. Surely he appreciated her and their friendship, since, years after, he had sent her such a finished picture. But, at the same time, what indelicate coquetry, to suggest himself flirting with two young fishermaidens in a gift to *her!* What feelings would it not awaken in a German girl, whose heart was full of love for the Danish painter, and whose fancy was full of poems by Heine! *"Du schönes Fischermädchen"* and *"Das Meer erglänzte weit hinaus"* would constantly sing out to her from this canvas, both awakening in her an intense longing after the unknown romantic charm of his fatherland, and creating a perpetual jealous unrestfulness. A refined self-love and a stupid heartlessness seemed to me to have drawn this bragging monogram on the stone on which the dandy put his boot, a boot, by-the-bye, that was so shiny that it could not possibly have trodden even a few steps on the dusty road.

Besides this picture there were two others in the room done by the same hand. They hung under one another between the window and the bureau: A pastel portrait of Minna and a pencil drawing of a middle-aged man with a high forehead, a straight nose and small, compressed lips—which combined with overhanging brows and deep-set eyes gave him a discontented and bitter look—thin hair and big whiskers, that did not conceal a small but firmly shaped and clean-shaven chin. Especially in the chin and forehead there was a striking likeness to Minna, and when I examined it closely, the shape of the lips also was the same; but her nose was broader and shorter. This drawing was cleverly done and showed a good solid training.

But I could on no account reconcile myself to the pastel portrait. It was a head and shoulder picture in three-quarter size. She was in a black dress without the slightest relief, which rendered her much exaggerated paleness still more striking, and the whole thing floated away in a blue mist so that one would think it was a young tobacco-smoking woman who had just enveloped herself in smoke; only that this did not seem to stream out of her compressed bloodless lips but rather from her indistinct, expressionless eyes—an art which, as everybody knows, is not yet discovered. This kind of misty picture had in those days just come into vogue. And this was a man who had painted his beloved! Where was the love that goes into all details, the jealous care that preserves even the smallest of them, because it sees that which is greatest behind, the self-forgetting losing of oneself in the object, the love's realism in which there is only room for a loving

idealism, which far from hiding the individuality only wants to put it in the clearest and truest light? Nothing of all this; everything here was sketchy, and the whole thing done in a careless sort of way in order to blur it in the indistinct fashion of the moment, affecting an artistic "vue" rather than giving a human aspect. The more I looked at this portrait the stronger became my disgust and fury against this man, who had painted Minna in such a way, this artist, who so boldly had prepared a picture after the last recipe, who had taken his beloved as a "subject" and had dodged all the difficulties, and indeed everything that should have been made clear. It seemed to me that, if he came into the room, I should take him by the collar, drag him in front of this sinful work, shake him soundly and shout into his ear, "What a beastly modern and artistically decayed ass you really are! Look there, you knight of the palette, what a disgusting scarecrow of a lie in colors you have made, with the most beautiful of God's creation imaged in your eyes, nay, in your heart, too, if one could only believe you!" And I heard him answer: "And what kind of fellow are *you,* and what can *you* do? *I* have at least been able to paint a portrait of her, that anyhow can be recognized, and which every one will see represents a pretty girl, and in which an artist would see talent. . . . *Maintenant à vous, monsieur.* Take color and canvas and place yourself, with your 'self-forgetting,' losing of yourself in the object, 'your love realism,' and then see what kind of a fright you will get out of it! But never mind, try all the same: they are very agreeable hours, I assure you; you have the sweet girl sitting in front of you, and can look at her to your heart's content; she will blush, therefore you must moderate the color a little. I recommend you to tone the shades a little cooler than one usually does. . . ." In this manner I worked myself up to such a degree of jealous fury, that I very likely should have seized the picture and thrown it on the floor, had not Mrs. Jagemann at last appeared with the coffee.

It gave her a great fright to find me on my feet, and she hurried to get me seated on the little sofa behind the rather shabby mahogany table, on which she served the Saxon drink. An important change had taken place in her, and she had now quite a dignified matronly appearance in a dark blue, white-spotted delaine dress, and a big cap with lilac ribbons. She herself sat on the edge of a chair just opposite me and sipped her coffee slowly, putting her head right down to the cup. I had already for some time noticed a sweet sickly smell which now constantly grew stronger, and I realized that on the other side of this covered door a very common tobacco was being smoked. Mrs. Jagemann seemed to guess my thoughts; and presently she began to cough—

"Oh dear me, yes . . . it's this tobacco smoke, it *will* make its way in here. Our lodger lives in there, a very pleasant young man, but he smokes all day long. Do you also smoke? Please don't hesitate to do so on my account; it tastes so well with the coffee, they say. We have lodgers, otherwise we could not keep the flat going, you know, and when one is accustomed to good living. . . . But it has its disadvantages, as now, this tobacco smoke. Of course one can get lodgers who smoke less, or who are not so much at home . . . there are even those who do not smoke at all, but there might be other objections. Dear me, Mr. Fenger, there are so many bad men in the world! As, for instance, this lodger, there is not much to say against him. He always pays me, even if he is sometimes a month late, but, good gracious, there are also those who do not pay at all. I have had plenty of them; they clear out suddenly, with promises, of course, that they will come

and pay. . . . Oh, dear me, bad people, Mr. Fenger!"

I again began to stare at the irritating portrait, and suddenly burst out with— "What a beastly modern artistically decayed ass!" And Mrs. Jagemann, who saw what I was looking at, began at once to praise the portrait.

"Yes, that's a portrait of my Minna, as you can see. It is really very good, almost as good as a photograph. Oh dear me, yes! What wonderful skill! What they can do nowadays, Mr. Fenger! In America they can now take photographs in colors, so the papers say. My goodness, what will happen to the poor painters? What are they to do? Art moves on, the one flies higher than the other, one's death is the other's bread, as the saying is. By the way, it was painted by a countryman of yours; he was also one of our lodgers. . . . Mr. Stephensen was his name; he lived here for six months."

She spoke slowly, with constant pauses between her jerky sentences, and she looked at me as craftily as she could with those dull eyes of hers.

"Yes, I know all about Stephensen. Minna has told me. She does not keep any secrets from me," I replied.

"No, of course not! Yes, he is a countryman of yours, and even an artist, of course you have heard of that," she said quickly, evidently satisfied to know that I understood what she was talking about, but at the same time anxious not to pursue the subject.

"Oh yes, such talent," she prattled, "you are quite right in that!" (I had not referred in any way to his talent.) "And a nice man, so pleasant to have dealings with! He always paid me punctually, sometimes even before the time; not because I asked him to do so, but times were hard, and he was very considerate. He only smoked cigarettes . . . very different to our present lodger. By the way, he is also a painter, that is to say, he

comes from Holstein. It's houses he deco-
rates, ceilings and walls. . . . But Mr.
Stephensen only smoked cigarettes. Oh,
when in those days one came into the
room, it was just like smelling the incense
in the Catholic Church. Yes, you have
been there? Dear me, so lofty, isn't it, and
all the candles on the altar? Yes, and how
they sing! It's just as if one heard the angels. I've been there with Minna. She said
it was Latin they sang; my good husband
was an excellent Latin scholar. Otherwise, I go to the Anna Church near here.
It's a wonderful parson we have; he
shook hands with me the other day and
asked for Minna. He confirmed her, but
for some reason she doesn't like him. She
easily takes fancies . . . and of course
she's right in a way, there are so many
bad people. Good gracious, it is a trouble
to know what to do among them all,
therefore we have religion. What should
we be without religion, Mr. Fenger?"

"Well, I am sorry to say I am not very
churchy, but I think that Minna and I
also in that respect——"

"Oh, dear me, yes, young people, you
see! When I was young . . . it was just
the same . . . then one only thought of
amusing oneself. And, upon my word,
why not, as long as one doesn't do anything bad!"

"Anyhow, I think also about earning
something, and hope soon to be in a position to marry. I have an uncle who is a
factory-owner in England, and he wants
me to go over there."

"To England, oh, I say! I had a sister
who was several years in England. Oh
dear, what tales she could tell! It must be
an awful town, London! All the fog and
smoke! There also they live on several
storeys, and the whole family take their
dinner in the kitchen."

When at last it was clear to me that it
was hopeless to try to lead the conversation into a sensible track, I let her babble
on to her heart's content, and made no
attempt to stop her. She had at first
spoken fairly correctly, but as she got excited her provincial accent became apparent; she said "m'r" for "wir" and
"sein" for "sind," and interlarded her talk
with many slang expressions and terms;
and it then amused me to remark that
Minna, when she sometimes jokingly
chattered her Dresden dialect, resembled
her mother very strikingly, even in countenance and features. Consequently, I
was as patient and attentive a listener as
the old woman could have desired.

When I at last took my leave, she did
not make any attempt to detain me, but
accompanied me to the door with many
curtsies and salutations.

Well, I had made acquaintance with
my future mother-in-law, and was in a
way not at all discontented with the result, however far it was from being brilliant. The reason was, that when I had
pictured the future and imagined the
happiness of bringing a beloved woman
home as bride, I had always shuddered at
the thought of a mother-in-law, and had
been terrified by the prospect of marrying
into a family which might provide me
with a tail of brothers-in-law and sisters-
in-law, and a new outfit of aunts and
uncles, and so forth. Now in this case
there was evidently no idea whatever of a
family; if Minna did not bring me any
dowry in money, she did not bring me
any superfluous relations. As far as the
mother was concerned, of whom, I knew,
that Minna had in her own mind formed
an unusual but sound judgment, she
seemed to be a rather modest being, who
would certainly prefer to toddle about in
peace in her kitchen, and take a nap in
"Zur Katze," and who was so wrapped up
in her Dresden customs that there could
hardly be any idea of bringing her to
England. Supposing that I had got a
stately lady as "mamma" who embraced
me in a motherly way, criticized my habits, was discontented with my prospects,

mixed herself up in the household affairs, put the daughter against me as much as possible, insisted upon visiting on regular evenings! My goodness, how easily I had got out of it with this homely motherly soul!

If I had written a diary, I should, that day, have put down: "At ease on one point, mother-in-law harmless."

CHAPTER II

Two days later, at five o'clock, Minna arrived by the steamer. I was, of course, on the landing-stage to receive her. As we walked together through the streets, it seemed to me there was something that weighed heavily on her mind, but I determined to ask no questions before we reached her home. Besides, I thought it was Hertz's condition that had grown worse.

When Minna had finished her dinner, and her mother had left us alone, my dear one became more and more silent. Sometimes she gave me a long sad look which almost brought tears to my eyes; soon after she began gazing, as if her thoughts were far off, and I felt very distressed.

"Do you fear that it is serious with Hertz?" I asked at last.

"Yes, I think so; you will see that he is going to die. And why not? It was searching for Goethe's manuscript in Prague that made him so ill. It is his hobby that kills him—there is something beautiful in that."

"But his poor wife!"

Minna rose with a sigh, and went to the window.

There she stood for a long time, looking down into the little garden. The setting sun cast its beams on her face, that with its air of seriousness and depression seemed to belong to a much older woman. The front folds of her light blouse rose and fell forcibly and irregularly. The right hand, hanging by her side, grasped tightly a small handkerchief; once or twice she lifted the other hand, shading her eyes as if she was looking for something definite, but just as quickly she forgot it, and either stroked the hair away from her forehead, or drummed upon the window frame.

I went quietly up to her and laid my arm round her shoulder.

"Has anything else troubled you, darling?"

"I have received a letter—from him, an answer to the one I sent off the other evening."

"Well?"

"It has given me pain, it was not at all what I had expected. He does not think of me as a good friend. It is as if he wanted to hurt me. I don't understand it."

"What has he written, Minna?"

"Well, you shall see for yourself."

She went back into the room and knelt down by the little handbag that stood open in the middle of the floor. Taking a letter from a blotter she gave it to me. It was written on very elegant notepaper and had only some unimportant lines as introduction to a poem by Heine, which I did not know. It read as follows:—

"Once more from that fond heart I'm driven
  That I so dearly love, so madly;
Once more from that fond heart I'm driven—
  Beside it would I linger gladly.

The chariot rolls, the bridge is quaking,
  The stream beneath it flows so sadly;
Once more the joys am I forsaking
  Of that fond heart I love so madly.

In heaven rush on the starry legions,
  As though before my sorrow flying—
Sweet one, farewell! in distant regions
  My heart for thee will still be sighing."

"Silly nonsense!" I exclaimed, and involuntarily crumpled the paper between my hands. But Minna, who had again been looking out of the window, turned quickly, and snatching it from my hands began at once to smooth it out.

"I fancy it is a treasure!" I said, with a bitterness which I could not possibly conceal.

She looked at me reproachfully.

"If you ever leave me, even with far bitterer words, I would do as much for your letter, Harald." And she put back the letter in the blotter.

The touching faithfulness to all her heart's remembrances, that breathed from her words and manner, disarmed me, but a sting of ill-feeling was left behind.

"I was wrong, forgive me—but it is a letter which might make an angel swear, there is neither meaning nor sound sense in it."

"No; I do not understand him. It was he, after all, who wished that our intercourse should be friendship only, and who advised me to marry an honest man, and now he reproaches me for doing so."

"And in such a foolish way! Why does he not express his own feelings? A poem by Heine! It would be foolish even if it was appropriate, which it is not, by any means."

"Just so; it was that which also struck me so strangely as a false note. Otherwise, it would have hurt me much more, or perhaps it might have reconciled me. But at this I could not help feeling annoyed."

"His vanity has been hurt by your forgetting him for another, that is all. Therefore, he has nothing to say himself. Most men would have sought refuge in 'The Complete Letter-writer,' being an artist he betook himself to Heine."

"And yet, if he still loved me and suffered!" she exclaimed and clenched her hands.

"Loved? There are so many different ways of loving. Why did he leave you?"

"For the sake of his art. And is not that worth more than I?"

"No, a thousand times no! For the sake of his art? A silly phrase. Such a miserable fellow! How does he think he can produce art worth anything, when he is such a chicken-hearted fool, who does not dare to face life, and how can he expect to put real feeling into his pictures, when he plays with himself and with you?"

"But suppose he had only *said* so. If for a time he had been obliged to work alone, and therefore wouldn't bind me, but trusted that my love was firm and constant enough to last, and he himself had waited faithfully, and worked, and now had been disappointed?"

I walked irritably up and down the little room. The thought of Mr. Axel Stephensen as a faithful lover, sitting in Denmark, and working in order to be able to unite his life with hers, seemed to me, after all I had heard of him, to be so very far apart from the truth, that I was on the point of laughing ironically; but a look at the beloved girl, whose misplaced belief did so much honor to her soul, disarmed by bitterness, and only a deep painful sigh escaped me.

Minna still stood close to the window with her back turned towards it, leaning on an old-fashioned chest of drawers that was covered with cheap knick-knacks and faded and soiled photographs. She supported herself on the edge with both hands and looked down on the floor.

"I am to be unhappy and to make others unhappy, too," she murmured, as if she was speaking to herself.

"Minna, Minna!" I exclaimed in despair, stopping in front of her and stretching out my arms towards her, "you must not say that, with me and to me you cannot possibly say that."

Without looking up she shook her head very gently.

"But he thinks it is flightiness on my

part, and I cannot allow him to think that. He must be able to understand that——"

"But you are not going to write to him after this?" I interrupted.

"Indeed, Harald, I shall do so."

"But why, dearest friend? Nothing but pain for all of us can come out of it. Put an end to this correspondence, it has already lasted too long."

"Then one more letter would not hurt, it will be the last one."

"I beg this much of you, Minna! Leave it off for my sake. I cannot explain to you, I myself don't know why, but it alarms me."

"I must," she answered, in a tone of fatalistic assurance. . . . "He and I cannot part like that."

"I wish you had never met," I exclaimed.

She looked at me for some moments with a strangely puzzled expression, as if she was unable to realize the vastness of this idea. Then she came close to me and put her arms round my neck.

"Yes, I wish to God he and I had never met. Why did you not come in those days? Why did we not come to know each other first? Then everything would have been right."

"It is going to be right all the same, my love," I said, and kissed her forehead.

We sat down at the open window and talked about that dear Rathen. Minna teased me by saying that, in a letter which I had sent to her two or three days before, I had confused one view of the country with another. This I denied, and demanded that we should examine the letter itself.

"Oh, it is not worth the trouble, anybody might make a mistake in writing," she said, and it seemed to me she was rather confused.

"But I am sure that I have not done it. Do let me see the letter."

"Then we will say that I made a mis-take in reading it, I do not mind," she said, and turned crimson. It was evident she had a reason for not showing the letter.

The irritation which, during the whole of this conversation, had been lurking within me because she had kept his letter so carefully, now burst out with a jealous suspicion that she had handled *mine* more carelessly and did not know where to find it. I was not sufficiently generous to spare her, though I knew well enough that even the most precious letter can easily be lost, especially when one travels.

"You cannot possibly be so lazy as that. Your blotter lies there on the table."

"No, it is not there," she answered, getting up. "Obstinate! I must take the trouble to go out in the passage to fetch my travelling-bag."

"No, I brought it in; it hangs there, near the door."

She looked in the bag.

"Then I suppose it is in the trunk," she remarked, with a shrug of her shoulder. " 'Tant de bruit pour une omelette.' "

"Thanks!" I said, with an ironical intonation of which she took no notice, for she laughed gaily while she went down upon her knees and started to turn over the things in her trunk. To me this laughter sounded a little unnatural, as the situation was obviously painful.

"You must not look, Harald, do you understand? My trunk is so untidy."

"Very well," I said, and stared irritably out of the window. At last I heard her get up and come towards me. She handed me the letter. The rather stiff paper was crumpled and twisted and bent in a strange way.

"I suppose you have used it for packing," I remarked bitterly, and held it up to her.

She did not answer, but smiled in a very peculiar way, which suited her admirably and both irritated me and made me madly in love.

"It does not seem that you handle my letters with the same care, or keep them as well, as those of Mr. Stephensen!"

Minna bit her lip, and peeped up at me with a teasing but still caressing look. I did not understand how she could take this matter in such a way, and should surely have been as angry as a Turk, had I not had a feeling of uncertainty and a suspicion that I was making a fool of myself.

"But you are quite forgetting to examine it, Harald," she said, as I continued to hold the letter towards her.

"Oh, you are quite right," I decided, without deigning to look at the letter, which I threw upon the floor.

Minna bent down very quietly and picked it up.

She gave me a reproachful glance, which made me ashamed, and I looked away, though I still thought myself right. Then, without withdrawing her eyes from me, but with a more and more tender smile, she unbuttoned the upper part of her blouse, loosened her bodice at the top, and let the letter slide down into her bosom, where it disappeared with the rosy shimmer of the last sunbeams which were glowing through the little room. I took her eagerly into my arms and covered her face and neck with kisses, while I stammered forth excuses for my uncalled-for behavior, my jealousy, and my foolish suspicion, of which she, in such a touching manner, had made me ashamed. This repentance, and still more the happy feeling of being so sincerely and sweetly loved, caused my tears to flow so freely that Minna jokingly said she feared they would obliterate the writing on the precious letter. Her eyes were also moist as we laughed and cried at the same time, and kissed away the tears from each other's cheeks.

But before we could look round, her mother had entered the room. Then we awkwardly released each other, and

Minna tried, by a quick turn, to hide her rather disordered toilet. The old woman coughed apologetically, and even her careful steps in her almost worn-out slippers seemed quietly to whisper, as she crept out with the coffee cups: "It doesn't matter, my children, I'm no nun myself. I have also been young. Go on billing and cooing! Dear me, as long as one doesn't do anything wrong!"

It annoyed me that we should be subject to a moral indulgence which we did not need, and especially that an ignoble—and undeserved—construction had been put upon this scene. Minna must have shared my feelings, for, while she buttoned the top of her blouse, she shrugged her shoulders and murmured with a comical resentment—

"The old woman always comes creeping in at the wrong moment."

"Do play a little, Minna," I said. "I have not heard you play at all, and I have looked forward so much to it."

Minna implored me not to insist, but I pulled her to the piano. It was still light enough for her to see the music. She opened a Schubert album and played one of the "Moments Musicaux," not without feeling, but nervously, as if she feared to touch the notes.

"It is awful," she exclaimed, just as she played the final chord. "May I not stop? You cannot pretend that it is a pleasure to listen."

"Yes, I can, and also you ought to be ashamed of being nervous before me."

"Nervous? I am trembling all over!"

"You cannot see properly any longer. I will fetch the lamp."

"No, for God's sake, let me, at any rate, have that excuse."

The exceedingly lively, and at the same time fantastic and deeply-moving, impromptu, which she now started, was treated with much more ease and courage, and though she failed once or twice, I had a sincere pleasure in her really musical rendering. After this I expected that she would want to stop, and I was prepared with persuasions to make her continue. But she had scarcely taken her hands off the notes, before she took down the "Sontas" of Beethoven from the top of the piano.

"If it has to be, let it be," she exclaimed gaily. "One might just as well be bold. I should like you to fetch the lamp, Harald, so that I can see all my dropped notes lying upon the floor."

I had expected that she would play "The Marche Funèbre," the first movement of "The Moonlight Sonata," or something equally manageable, one of those pieces about which one can say that they are naturalized in the drawing-room; but to my surprise I heard, while I lit the lamp in the passage, that it was the grand Waldstein Sonata she was attacking, and playing with no lack of passion. She had evidently sent me out for the lamp so that she might begin before I returned, with the idea that when one has taken the first plunge and cannot feel one's feet, one is obliged to swim. And she really swam; even the depth and movement of the waves helped to bear her up.

As I came in just at the moment when from wild runs and violent octave passages she reached the calm of the rich chords that sustain the hymn-like melody, I was struck by a strange expression of energy and enthusiasm on her face. This Beethoven glorification of all her features appealed to me so deeply, that a joking encouragement, which I had on my lips, was suppressed. I quietly placed the lamp on the chest of drawers behind her, and as a big piece of the globe was missing, I turned it so that the light shone through the hole onto the music; a necessary action on my part, for surely this lamp had never given an effective light, and it looked as if it had not been cleaned during the whole of the summer. I seated myself far back in the room, where I

could not disturb her, but could see the soft, shaded bend of her cheek, and her neck where the knot of hair glittered in the lamplight, while I lost myself in an enjoyment, that perhaps is the noblest of all—to have Beethoven played by one's beloved.

In this mood even the unfinished execution was rather advantageous than otherwise; the very modest surroundings were not in accordance with concert demands, and one enjoyed so much more the conquering of difficulties, even if these victories were not won without loss of men in the note-army. In spite of all, her playing was artistic, because she was quite lost in it; she played as a musician who has got a difficult manuscript on the music-stand; now and then she grumbled with disgust at having stumbled, sometimes when she had struck a wrong chord she sent an exclamation after the false note, which was not far from a little oath, and when her hands dragged behind the inspired will, then she loudly sang the melody as if to make the fingers ashamed and force them to follow. In this way she had stormed through the grand Allegro's sunlit mountain-land and descended peacefully to the Adagio's lonely valley, with the deep shadow round the still, shiny water mirror, where the mind searches its inner life, but still with the gaze wistfully uplifted towards a hoped-for glory; then again to soar into the ethereal regions, where the Rondo lives in a heavenly light and undisturbed splendor, joyously warbling and trilling as a blessed spirit of a skylark that dwells not among clouds but between stars.

Minna threw herself back in the chair; I went up to her and pressed a long kiss on her forehead. "Thank you," I whispered.

"What a thing to thank me for!" she said, and looked at me in astonishment, as if she feared I was making fun of her.

"How can you say so! I am absolutely

astonished. I knew well that you were musical, but I had not imagined you could play like that."

A sudden heartfelt joy beamed up to me in her eyes; but she lowered them at once, and her lips curled in a good-natured, ironical smile.

"Yes, is it not true! I am quite a Rubinstein in striking wrong notes."

"Why do you mock? I know quite well that it was not perfect, but all the same you played beautifully."

"Oh! That is what almost makes me desperate each time I play, to hear it so beautifully and not be able to produce it. And especially when, as I sometimes think, I might have been able to play fairly well, if I had ever had the chance to work at it constantly."

"Well, it is not too late yet; it seems to me you have your life before you."

"Perhaps, but there is always the same hindrance in the way. I cannot endure the strain—you have no idea how it affects me; I have now at least played away my night's rest. Why am I so feeble? Ah, if you could imagine the melancholy which in these years I have played myself into, each time I touched the piano! It was just like something closing over me, and the more beautiful the music the darker it was around me. Sometimes I could not leave off, but often it was so dreadful that I dared not go on any longer."

"But all this will disappear, dear one! I shall manage to get you sound and strong, and when your playing makes me happy you will also be pleased. I am a grateful listener, even if you never play any better than you do now, and in the future you will be able to devote yourself to music."

My words did not seem to make much impression on her. She placed the lamp on the table, seated herself in the chair I had left, and leant her head on her hand.

"I can feel it in my head; it strains and thumps in there." She laughed as if by a sudden inspiration. "Do you know, if ever I should wish to get rid of the little sense I have, I think I could play it away."

"What an idea!"

"Indeed, that was also a way to commit suicide. It was the mode of Frants Moor, 'to destroy the body through the mind,' applied to suicide."

"Minna, you must not speak like that —it's a bad joke."

"Anyhow, it is a truly 'practical joke' when it is put into execution. But one doesn't know what tricks one might need in life. 'It is a trick which deserves you as inventor,' " she recited, with a comical imitation of a fashionable actor. "Have you see him here in the Court Theatre? How affected he is! Ugh! . . ." She posed as Frants Moor in the beginning of the second act, and mimicked the face of a scoundrel so funnily that I could not help laughing. Urged on by this applause, she began to imitate the false means of effect which the aforesaid actor had invented for this monologue of meditation: to give questions and answers with two different voices, a high falsetto and a deep ventriloquial voice, while she turned first to the one side then to the other. "What species of sensation should I seek to produce? Anger?—That ravenous wolf is too quickly satiated. Care?—That worm gnaws far too slowly. Grief?—That viper creeps too lazily for me. Fear?—Hope destroys its power. What! and are these the only executioners of man? Is the armory of death so soon exhausted? How? no! Ha! *music!* Of what is not music capable? It can breathe life into stones; would it not be able to kill a Minna?"

She laughed gaily and embraced me.

"I have been very naughty, Harald, and you were so kind and thanked me so prettily for my music, you dear sweet friend! But I did appreciate it, though I do talk such nonsense. I cannot help it, it often pains me so much; it seems to me it must be so beautiful to be an artist, to be able to make others love and admire what touches one so deeply. But I promise to make you a good wife! And do not mind what I said before; as long as you are with me and care for me I shall not destroy myself with the sweet poison. But, Harald, if you should ever care more for another——"

I closed her lips with a kiss—truly not a very logical argument, but in this case, perhaps, more convincing than any other.

Her mother came in with tea and white bread, for which, as a treat, she had bought honey in the comb and fresh butter. When we had finished eating she placed herself in a corner in a queer triangular arm-chair with straight sides. It had originally been the end of a sofa, and the *disjecta membra* of this piece of furniture were scattered about in the flat. In a very few minutes the old lady was fast asleep.

Minna was also tired after the journey, and when the hideous alabaster-columned clock on the chest of drawers, after a long threatening rumble, had made up its mind to strike four strokes, which echoed in the piano with a long note, thereby calling our attention to the fact that the time was really ten o'clock, I insisted that she should go to bed.

Without waking up her mother, Minna lighted me out. To her great terror I went "with my chin on my back"—as she expressed it—down the steep spiral stairs, without being able to take my eyes off her, while she stood bending over the balusters, with a smiling face strongly lit up by the outstretched lamp.

Down below I stood for a long time sending kisses up to her, until she began to scold me, and as that had no effect she suddenly began to make faces and produce such dreadful caricatures à la Wilhelm Busch that at last I broke out into loud laughter and fled.

CHAPTER III

The following day Minna showed me a copy of the letter that she intended to send to Stephensen.

We read it together in the little summer-house, because one of the aunts, who "was not all she ought to be," had turned up, and from her company Minna was anxious to save both herself and me.

The letter calmed my feelings, as it seemed well-fitted to make an end of all this misunderstanding. It was without any bitterness and free from any trace of sentimentality, and was also written with more dignity and calmness than I had expected her to show under circumstances that so deeply moved her feelings and remembrances.

While we were together at Rathen I had sometimes looked forward to walking with Minna in her own beautiful town, and I begged her now not to waste any time.

We went through several rather plain-looking streets and lanes, all alike, which, with their entirely flagged pavement, and without gutters and cellar-stairs, made a neater and cleaner impression than a Dane expects in such quarters. The two-storeyed houses only vary a little in gray or yellowish color; but now and again a low building extends, the big sunken roof of which peeps down on the street through many of those real Saxonian lattice windows, which are shaped like half-closed eyes and, when placed close together, give to the tiled roof the impression of a long wavy movement. The low buildings are old farmhouses, proving that not so very long ago these were the outskirts of the town.

Everywhere a rather comfortable and familiar informality prevailed. At the open window on a ground floor a young woman gave her child the breast; opposite, in a sunlit window above, a man in shirt sleeves smoked his pipe and stared across at his neighbor's roof, on the ridge of which a white cat was walking cautiously. A well-dressed man, who looked like a student, passed us with a glass mug filled with foaming beer, which he had fetched from the beer-house at the corner.

The children playing in front of the houses greeted Minna, and a little urchin of a girl, three to four years of age, with curly hair and a face full of dimples came flying along, with her poor naked legs as bent as swords, and was not content until Minna had chased her into a passage, where she allowed herself to be caught.

Less pleasing was the attention from the bigger children. A tall, bare-headed girl, with dirty stockings and trodden-down slippers, continued to shout after Minna, "Who's 'e?" And a shoemaker's boy walking in the middle of the street, who, to my astonishment, was whistling the Actors' march from the *Midsummer Night's Dream* so that it sounded through the whole neighborhood, must have found something Jewish in my appearance, for he suddenly interrupted his occupation and continued to shout after me "Itzig." Sometimes all voices were drowned in the rumble of an immense wagon, the barrel-shaped canvas roof of which swayed up to the height of the windows on the first floor; a couple of heavy horses, with thick necks and muscular haunches, pulled it with a slow lumbering walk while they shook their shiny brass ornaments of rings and crests; the chains rattled, it creaked in all the fastenings, the wheels grated, and under the enormous moving mass the cobbles groaned so that one was tempted to cover one's ears. Nothing of all this was new to me, but with Minna as my companion it assumed a different and familiar aspect, for I regarded the smallest details with love, because they belonged to the associations which from childhood had both

surrounded her and influenced her imagination.

This cozy bit of the old city was suddenly cut in two by the distinguished Prager Strasse, the modern artery of the residential quarter with its pulsing life of moving carriages, gaily dressed crowds, and handsome shops. We came into new broad streets, which, apart from a few lonely pedestrians and crawling cabs, were quite empty. The rows of flowers on the balconies showed up brightly against the gray mass. There were hardly any shops; on every second door was written "Pension," and over its neighbors "Hôtel garni." This did not suit our taste; in order to reach the villa quarter in our mock "house-hunting," we should have chosen the shortest way, if in this rectangular quarter the distances had not been the same length.

We soon had fine gravel under our feet, and were walking under the shade of a small avenue of maples. Dark acacias, glittering silver poplars, transparent birch tops, massive domes of plane, lime foliage, and copper beech, mixed with numerous varieties of rare bushes and trees, towered on both sides over railings, hedges, and low walls. Here and there the white limbs of a statue shone between flowers and leaves, or the fine spray of a fountain mounted and descended with gentle splashing in the middle of a fertile mass of foliage. Villa followed villa, glorious mixtures of country seats and palaces with fine façades of yellow-gray sandstone which still possessed some of its granulated sparkle. Where the big plate-glass windows stood open the outer pair of cream-colored net curtains waved gently, and in the somberness of the room the prism of a chandelier sparkled or the edge of a golden frame shone with a subdued light.

In a loggia formed of Doric columns with Pompeian painted walls and Caset ceiling some people were drinking coffee.

Down a double zigzag staircase, which was surrounded by flowering plants, a slim lady with the tail of her riding habit over her arm was being escorted by a cavalier in bronze-colored velvet. In a covered drive, which on the side of the villa formed a beautiful portico copied from the Villa d'Este, a landau was waiting, and a pair of chestnut horses were prancing impatiently and pawing the red gravel.

This kind of covered drive especially delighted us, and under no circumstances were we going to content ourselves with one made of iron and glass. It was settled beyond doubt that we were to have a carriage at the time when these luxurious plans were fulfilled. The aforesaid pair of chestnuts pleased us very much; at the same time we also had a strong liking for a black pair. Much consideration was naturally given to the style of the villa, and our tastes coincided, as we both preferred a not too rich Renaissance. An ideal one of this kind we found at a corner near the park. It was a massive building of considerable size, stamped by a real aristocratic simplicity without the slightest sign of parvenu pretentiousness, but with imposing, grand, and noble proportions; it seemed to have been built by Semper himself, or by one of his best pupils.

"That is the one, that is our villa!" Minna exclaimed at once. She laughed hilariously at this castle in the air, but I already took it more seriously. After all, why was it impossible? It was not an unprofitable art in which I indulged; besides, I had good connections and might perhaps inherit something. Eventually, why should not one, after a life of work, be able to retire here as a rich man? My youthful courage seemed to possess unlimited power. And as I knew myself in safe possession of that which is the aim of youth, all my thoughts and dreams began to center themselves towards that

of the man: a glorious fruition of active work. The scepticism of Minna almost hurt me, as if it was a disbelief in my capacity and energy.

"No, to tell you the truth, Harald, I do not believe that it would suit me at all. Just think what such a house involves— all the servants one would have to manage. It also strikes me that with so much money I should be everlastingly wondering whether I was using it wisely, and one would be almost obliged to entertain largely. I am sure that all this would not suit me, and that I should feel much happier in managing a small homely household. For that reason I do not envy the rich at all; on the contrary, it pleases me that others, who are better fitted for them, should have such luxuries. But when I am in a selfish mood I imagine that all this is there for my sake, in order that I should have so many nice things to look at when walking with you, and so that we may have an excuse for such a foolish conversation."

We continued along the Zoological Gardens, entering "Grosser Garten," where we chose the least frequented wood-like road that curved between tall pines and broad oak trees. At last we sat down on a little hillock with a fine view to the north of the Hercules Avenue, the magnificent lime trees of which cast their shadow far away over the stubble fields in front of us. To the left, strongly lit by the sun, lay the heights on the opposite side of the Elbe, with its wood-covered banks and hollows surmounting the villages, which, with the help of the villas, form an almost continuous border of gardens and houses. The steep slopes are intersected by the terraces and walls of the vineyards, and here and there high-roofed country houses, encircled by Italian poplars, are interspersed, while on the heights above are dotted the little cottages of the vineyard workmen, looking like small watch towers. All these details continu-

ally repeated themselves, dwindling and becoming less clear and closer to one another, until they melted into an almost indefinite tone of color at the point where the brow of the hills sloped down towards the plain. This latter stretched far away in a blue mist, and in the dim distance appeared more hazy mountain shapes floating like a sediment of the blue in the atmosphere, rather than a rising of the earth. But as the shadows on the fields grew longer the contours came out more solidly, and among them we recognized distinctly the familiar profile of Lilienstein. While on the right Loschwitzer bank the window-panes flickered like the beginning of an illumination, and we could distinguish the stone-quarries of Lilienstein as a lighter line below. It was queer to think that in this mountain-picture, which was so diminutive that it could be painted on the nail of the little finger, we could with a needle point out the place which had held so much of our happiness. Silently we pressed one another's hands, and our eyes filled with tears as we gazed towards it. It seemed to both of us that the idyll had grown to the place as a delicate flower which will not bear transplanting, and that we had left it there, and only there would be able to find it again; an irresistible home-sickness overpowered and united us.

Though only a few days parted us from that time, and we sat together just as happy as we had been then, and though we looked forward to a happy union,—in spite of all this it seemed to both of us that we saw a lost paradise revealing itself out there in the glow of the setting sun, with tiny rosy clouds like Cupid-feathers floating above in the light colorless sky, little by little to glide away under the shadow of the soft wings of the night, which found us still sitting on the same spot with our arms around each other.

This constant, tender sadness in look-ing back on things, is it but the reaction from an idealizing power which the memory itself possesses, or does it perhaps rather proceed from man's never-ceasing fear—the feeling of everlasting uncertainty with regard to the unknown fate, that by a mere mood is able to rob one of everything, except what one has experienced—an uncertainty that not only threatens from without, but also seems to warn from within, and against which perhaps only our Ego's hidden kernel in rare moments of expansion can place an equal force?

CHAPTER IV

As we came out of the house on the next afternoon, Minna took my arm and turned me round quickly.

"Do you know where we are going to-day? To-day we are going to Zwinger. I want to take advantage of all you have told me about architecture, and especially about the Rococo style. Now we must repeat it in Reality's great picture-book."

And we went to Zwinger both then and on many other lovely afternoons—to Zwinger, this Palace Court of pavilions and galleries, which is an epopee in stone from a time when fondness of life and its pleasures excluded all poems except of the material order, in which one could move and enjoy, drink, dance, fence, love, ride roundabouts, and bathe in the basins of fountains under the open sky. This masterpiece of a luxurious and fantastic style, which an insipid after-taste of the Empire has taught an unproductive generation to look down upon with pseudo-classic contempt, but which now everywhere is again recognized with honor and glory. Zwinger, which seemed to be built by Saxonian gnomes, led by a faun who was in love with a muse. . . .

On other days we visited our godly hostess from Rathen, "the mother Elbe," in her town residence, where she is lodged between both parts of the town in a grand dwelling, which is parted into two banqueting halls by the rows of columns of three bridges. On the famous Brühl-Terrace we intoxicated ourselves at the sunset hour with the glorious metallic colors that shone and glittered between one another in the whirling of the river, until far away it bent into a golden arch in front of the blue vine-hills. Or we walked on the quay, which is ornamented by a long row of small curly poplars that seemed to be taken from a child's box of toys.

I remember a gloomy day when the sun in the last minute broke through the bank of clouds, and the sudden illumination of the windows gleamed down over the stream; it was as if Mother Elbe had unveiled her banqueting hall—a colonnade of twisted columns embossed in the purest gold.

Twice we went on board one of the little steamboats and sailed out to the idyllic vine-trailed Loschwitz, the native town of "Don Carlos," or to the Schiller garden of its neighbor Blasewitz, where Gustel of "the Camp of Wallenstein" lived.

On the way back through the town Minna usually had to make some purchases for our supper. I waited outside the sausage-maker's dainty shop while she did her catering at the marble counter.

One evening, when we returned after a long walk, her mother had gone out, and Minna had no key. We were both very hungry, and, as we had warm sausages with us, we did not hesitate long; Minna went off to the baker at the one corner and I to the beer-house at the other, and bringing respectively a "Zeilen-Semmel" and a tankard of "Kulmbacher" we met in triumph. In the dark summer-house we enjoyed with jokes and laughter the best supper I had ever eaten.

We did not visit the picture-gallery.

Minna never mentioned it, and I dared not propose it for fear of bringing back painful recollections. But we often went to see the excellent collection of plaster casts, in which antique art is so well represented in all its stages.

I was surprised at the instinctive sense of art in Minna and the originality of her criticisms. She was amused over the "Æginets' " set smile, whether they killed or were killed, but at the same time remarked how advanced art already was in the treatment of the body and its movements. It struck her for the first time that an art can be at such a standard that its technique is almost perfect in certain directions, while there is something higher towards which it is moving with the uncertain footsteps of a child. And she questioned whether this was not also the case in a lower degree, with what we recognize as perfect art.

In the Parthenon Hall it was especially the torsos from the gable groups which impressed her. But what struck her most of all were the masterpieces of the post-classic art, "The Gaul," "The Grinder," "Venus of Milo"—most of the other statues of Aphrodites she passed by with indifference. She pointed out to me many details that I had not remarked myself, the life-like touch of reality in a hand or foot, remarking that in statues of modern artists which she had seen these were often made too "beautiful."

Sometimes a personal interest in these plastic studies was awakened: "How nice to have such a beautiful straight Grecian nose," she sighed more than once; "then you would love me still more. Oh yes, you would be bound to do so."

And after having inspected a whole collection of goddesses: "But they have not got such very thin arms!"

"Why should they have?"

"I thought it was ugly to have strong arms," she answered, the blood rushing into her face as she turned away.

But our enjoyments in art, in this town where one *can* enjoy art, culminated ecstatically when we heard Wagner's "Valkyrie." The noble and melancholy love of these two Völsungs etherealized in a beauty of tones, the fervor of which has eternity's clear depth. How profoundly did it not penetrate our souls, uniting them in an endless sympathy! Our love reflected itself in this heavenly flow of melody as a narcissus—and loved itself.

In the beginning we whispered an occasional outburst of admiration to one another; later we were silent.

Minna pressed my hand at the words—

"When in winter's frosty wildness
First my friend I found."

And when Sieglinde distinctly, so that every syllable was heard in the dead silence of the theatre, and with such pathos as only Wagner has ever inspired an opera singer, sang—

"How fair and broad
Thy open brow,
The varying veins
In thy temples I trace!
I tremble with emotion
Resting entranced"—

she gave me a look which I know I shall feel on my death-bed. And at the end, when the curtain did not *fall,* but was drawn together . . . oh! I still see her standing up in the box, clapping with all her might and main, with sparkling eyes and moist traces of tears on her blushing cheek, more beautiful than I had ever seen her, more spiritually beautiful than anything I have seen or shall see!

We went down into the glorious *foyer,* the marble walls and columns of which gleamed in the late daylight. It was overcrowded with well-dressed people. Minna's dress was plain, though not so plain that it was striking, but many eyes were turned upon her. She was too moved to

be worried by the attention paid to her, or even to notice it.

We stepped out upon a balcony where a mild summer air met us refreshingly. The beautiful open square, surrounded by monumental buildings, lay calm and deserted under us, while crowds swarmed over the Elbe bridge; the wood-covered heights were bathed in sunshine and seemed to be quite close. A feeling of endless happiness and richness overcame me.

"You are sighing!" said Minna, who was leaning upon me.

"It is only because I am much too happy, much more so than I deserve," I answered. "Do you know, it was rather presumptuous of me to propose to you."

She looked at me with a questioning smile.

"As I did not know all that was in you, I ought to have waited until I knew you as I do now. I discover new treasures every day. I am getting richer and richer."

Minna said nothing, but pressed my arm firmly to her bosom.

CHAPTER V

Mr. and Mrs. Hertz had now returned from the country. We had each of us visited them in turn; then they wanted to see us both one afternoon to coffee, according to our Rathener custom. The old man was obliged to keep quiet in the evening. Coughing and pains in the chest continued to worry him; he was only able to get up in the middle of the day, and even this was rather the result of an obstinate determination not to give in than because he felt the better for being out of bed, where the doctor wished to keep him.

Mrs. Hertz was rather distressed about him, and thought that it would really be better if we waited for a week or so, but the old man would not hear of it: "But why? Not for my sake, as if I am not able to see anybody! Of course they must come to-morrow, but I will send them away when I get tired. For now I usually get tired a little earlier in the evening," he explained to me.

So, towards four o'clock on the day after we had heard the "Valkyrie," we started into the heart of the Alstadt, where one still sees with pleasure the old Rococo houses, with their irregular roofs and twisted shell ornaments, and the miniature palaces in Baroc style with pilaster-striped façades ornamented with medallions in which were to be seen images of Mars and Athene adorned with helmets and perukes. Between these plainer houses are to be found, in a rather indefinite style but of a thoroughly German character; their cozy bay-windows making a row of cupboards along the street and forming at the corners hexagonal projections tapering down to fine points —inverted cones, scaled like pineapples and ending in a big knob beneath. Several of these houses have stucco ornaments of flower garlands, or draperies made of stone, hanging down from their windows; now and then, too, one comes upon a frieze with enormously stout angels, so thick with paint that at a casual glance one might take the whole thing for a piece of *natura morte* of cabbages, apples, and big branches.

In such a corner house, where four streets met, the old couple lived on the first floor. There was an everlasting rumble of large covered country carts, goods wagons from the railway station, and all sorts of business vehicles, and it was evidently this noise of a busy traffic which pleased the old Königsberg merchant, and made him prefer this situation to a more airy but duller quarter.

The coffee-table was laid in Hertz's study, where he preferred to be. He rarely came into the drawing-room, but liked his wife to take her needlework in to him. It was a middle-sized room with old mahogany furniture, among which no comfortable chairs were to be found, but an arm-chair had now been moved in from the drawing-room.

Against one wall stood an ordinary writing-table with eight fragile legs, a tobacco table, and a bookcase; just opposite was a desk of the same kind as the one beside which Kant was painted (the old color print again presided in its usual place over the writing-table). On each side of the desk hung a couple of valuable oil paintings, life-size portraits of Beethoven and Frederick the Great in their youth. Over it were placed some daguerreotype pictures, on which, however, one could never discover anything but some shining metal spots.

Behind the glass doors of the bookcase there was no show of any special binding, but the outwardly homely-looking company, which displayed sulky, leather-covered backs and torn or dirty bits of cardboard, consisted only of original editions, among which—on the middle shelf —were many of Goethe's and all Schiller's works, from *Zwoote verbesserte Auflage,* of *The Robbers* with the lion rampant as vignette, and the inscription, "In tirannos," to a *William Tell* with a dedication written by Schiller himself. Several of these books we got out, not so much for curiosity's sake, for it was not the first time that the bookcase had been opened for us, but because we knew it always pleased the old man.

Minna was also privileged to unlock a drawer in the writing-table and reveal the most precious of all the treasures; it was a snuff-box which Schiller had sent to Kant, a rather big, circular-shaped box, on the cover of which was painted a beautifully designed miniature copy of the Schiller portrait by Graff. Hertz found in it a resemblance to my most unworthy self—especially in the long neck and nose, a discovery which made Minna so delighted that she kissed him.

It began to rain, and suddenly became as dusk in the room as if it was the hour of twilight. The bluish spirit flame which licked round the copper kettle shone on the old man's white beard and on his moist under-lip while he talked—slowly lisping and interrupted by coughing—about life in Riga, where he had been instructed in mercantile business for two or three years. In the Exchange an old-fashioned custom ordained that the bankrupt had to sit on a sort of stool of repentance, while a doom bell was sounded, a sort of moral execution.

"One laughs at such old symbolic customs and finds them barbaric," he said, "but perhaps they have also had something good in them. How distinctly I remember the day when Moses Meyer had to stop his payments. He was chief in one of the two richest Jewish commercial firms, and had ruined himself by rivalry with Wolff—they had always been enemies. There was a dreadful uproar on the Exchange, some were malicious, but the Jews were all very down-hearted. 'Will Wolff come?' was asked everywhere, but most of the people thought that after all he would not witness the humiliation of his rival. It struck twelve, the hour at which the ceremony was to take place; the chairman was just going to ring the bell, when Wolff's landau drew up at a gallop, and Wolff rushed into the hall and shouted breathlessly: 'The bell is not to ring; Meyer is not to take the bankrupt chair.' He had at the last minute, surely after a hard fight, decided to supply his rival with the necessary amount in order to prevent the Jewish congregation from being humiliated; and the two old men cried in each other's arms."

We stared in astonishment at this old man, who seemed at this moment still more venerable, on account of his remembrances of a time that had such a far-off and patriarchal character.

With what pious meditation did we regard some dust and pebbles in a bottle, earth from the Holy Land, which an old Jew from Riga, who had made the pilgrimage to Jerusalem on foot, had brought home in a pocket-handkerchief.

From such Jewish tales the conversation gradually diverged to the Jews' share in liberal-minded literature and centered principally on Heine,

As soon as the coffee-table was cleared Hertz had his Heine portfolio taken out. It contained many letters both to and from the poet, some proof-sheets, and a few small manuscripts. I took up one of the proofs and, as it was still very dark at the table, I went to the window in order to make out a very much erased portion.

I accidentally looked down on the street corner and started. It seemed to me that the slim, very fashionably dressed man with pointed and well-twisted fair beard, who was passing by, looked like Axel Stephensen. But no, this man was taller and older than the Danish painter, and as he took off his hat to an acquaintance I even saw that he was bald.

My feeling of alarm vanished.

At the same instant Hertz started with his feeble, husky voice to read aloud from a manuscript sheet—

"Once more from that fond heart I'm
    driven
Which I so dearly love, so madly;"

Minna and I exchanged a meaning look; she grew pale, and her pallor showed out still more clearly in the stormy light, which seemed to penetrate through an ashen rain, so dirty and yellow was it.

"It is a beautiful poem," said Hertz; "do you know it?"

"Yes, we know it."

"Oh, they are reading Heine together, the young hearts," Mrs. Hertz exclaimed. "A beautiful time!"

Soon after we took our leave.

We went towards "Grosser Garten."

The rain had stopped. After we had walked a little, Minna exclaimed—

"How strange that he should have the manuscript of just that poem!"

"Yes, a strange coincidence!"

"There is not such a thing as chance." [1]

But as we were half-way up the lovely plane avenue which runs across the fields between the city and "Grosser Garten," it flashed into my mind that the rings which we had ordered were promised us without fail for this afternoon.

We at once agreed to go back, though it took us right into the quarter of the town from which we had come. It was not one of the larger goldsmiths, but a workshop on the second or third floor, of which Minna knew. The rings were ready, and the old woman who gave them to us bestowed them with many congratulations and blessings, to which she also added many regards to Minna's "mamma."

The distress, or rather despondency, which had taken possession of us since that unfortunate poem had been mentioned, gave way to the golden magic of the engagement rings. The weather had changed to the most beautiful sunshine, and we decided to enjoy it on the terrace nearby.

The terrace was swarming with people, as is always the case at this hour in fine summer weather. We heard sounds of the concert in Wienergarten on the other side of the river; it was the finale of the *Valkyrie,* and we stood still and listened. Distance blotted out the defects in the execution. "The renunciation," during which Wotan kisses away the godlike power of Brynhilde, so that the long swooning sleep falls upon her, came clearly over to us in its melancholy rise and fall.

"I heard this very thing on the evening I decided to spend my holiday at Rathen," I said.

"A blessed evening it has been for me," answered Minna, "though I at that time had no notion of it. It is strange to think how quite an unknown human being's decision can so completely alter one's whole life. Therefore I do not believe in chance in such things."

"It has been a blessing for both of us," I exclaimed, "and blessed be the place. I will now show you where I sat, over there, outside the little Café Torniamenti, between the columns. Do you see, just there where the gentleman, no, not the old one, but the one who is now getting up and is paying the waiter——"

I felt myself kept back by a sudden grip on my arm.

Minna had stopped and stared—But, good God, with what an expression upon her face! She was not pale, but her eyes were unnaturally open—Macbeth might have looked on Banquo's ghost in that way when the courtier showed him to his seat.

I followed this look to the spot to which I had myself directed it.

The gentleman, who had paid the waiter, looked towards us and quickly raised his high silk hat.

---

[1] "Es giebt keinen Zufall!"—*Wallenstein,* Schiller.

BOOK IV

CHAPTER I

This smart gentleman was Axel Stephensen.

At once he began to take off his right glove and to walk towards us; Minna also began to unbutton hers, but it fitted tightly, and she was still pulling at it when he stopped in front of us.

"Oh, please, Minna, don't trouble, between old friends——"

But Minna continued determinedly to stare—with a queer smile—at her glove, for the obstinacy of which she was perhaps grateful. At last she got the hand free—the hand that now wore my ring. It appeared to me that she caressed this magic love-token with her eyes, and that Stephensen stared at it morosely. She glanced at him in shaking hands, and with a gesture which made the ring sparkle she introduced us to one another.

"My fiancé, Harald Fenger."

We bowed almost too politely and assured one another that it was a pleasure and an honor, but I noticed that his aplomb in this ordeal was greater than mine, and this added to the irritation that his sudden appearance had already aroused in me.

"You have come here"—Minna was on the point of making the same unnecessary remark which her mother had bestowed upon me, but she had enough presence of mind to insert a "suddenly." "You have come suddenly to Dresden." And in recovering her self-control she looked at him steadily for the first time. "In the letter you sent me a fortnight ago you said nothing about it."

In Germany it is not so unusual as it is in Denmark for young girls and young men—brothers' friends, distant relations, or even acquaintances—to call one another by their Christian names; and therefore Minna could not feel that Stephensen, by still taking advantage of this privilege after she was engaged to a countryman of his, meant to emphasize to me the nature of their intimacy and to equalize our positions.

She turned and began to walk slowly back towards the steps. We accompanied her, one on each side. It was evident that Stephensen was annoyed that this letter was mentioned in my presence, and his annoyance was the greater because I assumed a defiant air, as much as to say, "Indeed, sir, I know quite well your beautiful Heine effusions."

"Quite right," he said. "I got the order after I had written. I have come to copy Correggio's Magdalene. I suppose you remember the copy of it I made a couple of years ago, Minna; you were kind enough to take an interest in it, and to come and watch me at work"—here he smirked under his mustache with a vain and insinuating smile which made my blood boil. "I, at any rate, have not been able to forget the pleasant hours we used to spend together in the gallery." He glanced up in the air with a vague far-away look, and paused so that Minna might have an opportunity to agree with what he had said. But, as she continued to look silently at the ground, he proceeded in a lighter tone—

"As I think I wrote to you, I sold that picture to a merchant. A Mæcenas of ours has now been so uncritical as to fall in love with it."

"You speak a little too modestly about your art for one to be able to believe in your humility . . . especially as I suppose there is no reason for it." This latter I added because Minna looked at me reproachfully, as if she feared that the conversation might take a pointed and personal character.

Stephensen laughed and stroked his beard.

"Well, I have at least reason to wish that this new client will not be too critical, for such a hazardous undertaking does not succeed twice. But, anyhow, it is a good thing to be acquainted with what one is going to represent, and as to the good Correggio I have long ago found him out: the lady is by no means studying the Holy Bible, but reading a pastoral novel, and an improper one, too, I should venture to guess."

Though I, in reality, found this remark quite striking and could not help smiling, there was something so irritating, yes, even insulting, towards Minna in the self-satisfied smirk with which he accompanied it, that an almost irresistible impulse seized me to take him by the collar and push him down the steps at the top of which we were standing. I reflected whether in such case there was any possibility of his breaking his neck, and pictured to myself Minna's terror, the crowd of people round, and how the police would arrest me.

And all the while the unsuspecting man stood expatiating upon the beauty of the town that was stretched out in front of us. He was especially pleased with the Catholic church which, in the foreground, presented its two stories of massive weatherbeaten sandstone, in the elegant forms of a noble Baroc style. Between the clustered columns of the open tower the yellow gleams of evening were shining, and over the copper roof, that just peeped through the balustrade as a green field through a fence, the row of statues were silhouetted sharply in characteristic decorative positions. Stephensen reminded Minna that she had drawn his attention to a group half-way in front of the tower, where a nude arm darkly outstretched on the sky's golden ground made an extraordinary effect.

"Whenever I have thought of Dresden I imagined myself here and at this hour, and it always seemed as if that arm beckoned to me, perhaps also on account of the precious remembrances which were associated with it. But what a lovely place it is! This treasure of a church, and just behind it the palace tower that is so all-powerful, though at the same time so far from being massive. Soon the tower-watchman's light will be lighted above. Do you remember how often we have pondered over that strange life up there above the busy traffic of human beings? . . . And how I love to see the people swarm in and out of the George porch and enter the town through a house. . . . And then on the other side the river quarter, the old bridge under us, and the Maria Bridge which stretches its whole length over the shiny water, and the Lösnitzer Hills, purple-colored and so graceful in shape, they always remind me of the Janiculum by the Tiber. At the same time such comparisons are odious. One calls Dresden the Elbe-Florence, but Florence itself has no square near the Arno which can compete with this, not by a long way."

I, an untravelled man, could never have been able to pay Minna such a compliment, and each word of praise of her beloved town was bound to please her. For the first time she glanced at him with a kindly look, which he caught without turning his eyes towards her, apparently quite lost in contemplation of the town; he even for a minute spread out his arms as if he would embrace it, and this enthusiasm, which was perhaps not wholly feigned, was not unbecoming to him.

"What a pity one does not live here and enjoy this view every day! An artist must live and breathe in artistic surroundings. I feel it every time I get out of Copenhagen: one degenerates there. Don't you agree with me that Copenhagen is a dreadful town?"

"Detestable," I answered, though I had never thought much about it; but I wanted if possible to overtrump him.

"All the same it drew you back when you were there," Minna remarked without lifting her eyes from the broad stone steps down which we slowly walked.

"What can one do? A fellow must live, Minna!"

"But you have just said that an artist must live in a place like this is order to be creative."

"That is right, but one must also sell. And works of art are easier sold where artists mix freely in society; it is not flattering to us, but it is true. It was with a heavy heart I bade good-bye in those days, and I feel it doubly on seeing the town again. No, if I had been happy enough to be born here——"

"Surely then you would have found your way to Berlin," I said sullenly.

The tears came into Minna's eyes at his words, and possibly it was to turn the conversation that she exclaimed—

"Oh yes, it will be hard when some day one has to leave this sweet town."

"Anyhow, you will not have to go away alone, wherever you may go when you leave for your new home," Stephensen answered very emphatically.

"And we shall not stay away for ever," I added quickly, "but even if it is impossible for me to remove my business to Dresden—certainly I shall not have to go out to dinners on account of my wares, to be sure . . . but . . . at any rate, when we are getting old, and I can retire with a good conscience and a little capital, then we will surely live here, I have promised Minna! We have even looked about for a house, and in case I should be a Crœsus we have fixed upon a magnificent villa by the Park. Perhaps Minna might then persuade you, for old friendship's sake, to come and decorate it for us."

Though this was supposed to pass as a joke I was not enough a man of the world to conceal the undertone of satire and insolence, which was much more apparent than it ought to have been. I immediately regretted what I had said, the more so because Minna looked with terrified eyes at me.

"I am not a decorator," Stephensen answered dryly. But directly afterwards he turned towards me with his most suave and courtly smile and continued: "I do not, however, mean to disparage that art, which would give you a false idea of my perception of things. Surely with us there is a certain prejudice against decorative painting with which I do not agree; altogether I do not share many of our Danish prejudices. On the contrary, I highly appreciate decorative art, and when men pretend to be too grand to undertake it, the real fact simply is they haven't got the imagination for it. That is also the case with myself, only that I do not pretend to be too grand. And isn't it the same with all art? We have not sufficient imagination to decorate life, therefore we only copy it and then pretend that we do it out of reverence and love of life. Nonsense! To begin with we are pessimists, so we have neither reverence nor love of life; and besides, even if we still have these—for we are also inconsequent—*la vie c'est une femme*, and they always like to be flattered. By the way, all art is originally decorative, and Apollo is in reality a *maître de plaisir* in Olympus. But to decorate! Great heavens! who can do that? Rubens could. Now we are far too earnest—that is to say, we are morose—and with reason, because we are anæmic and nervous, and get a headache if we have made a night of it. We pretend that we do not want to dance any more and we put on airs, but the truth is that our legs have become stiff and tired. Well, perhaps you do not share these views, Mr. Fenger. I know quite well they are not in vogue."

"I quite agree with you," I assured him, though I did so only in part; but it pleased me to disappoint his hope of a dispute in which he, with reason, expected to get the best of the argument. Nevertheless, I quite understood that he did not mean anything serious by all this palaver, but that from the beginning he merely wanted to make it clear that he was worldly wise enough to understand my sarcasm; and above all things he wanted to show off before Minna. He glanced constantly towards her with his half-closed eyes, and the self-contented smile seemed to say: "Did you notice how quickly I understood that the conversation must be turned away from the shoals on which this fool was just going to strand us? I hope you are thankful. And cannot I discourse about art brilliantly? He ought to try that, but he wisely keeps silent. Well I, too, know when it is time to be silent. *Assez d'esthétique comme ça!*"

When we were outside the theater some ladies and gentlemen came out onto the balconies of the foyer. I thought of yesterday; at this hour I had stood up there with her and had magnified my immense and still growing wealth. "Er stand auf seines Daches zinnen—Polycrates, Polycrates!" [1]

"By the way," Stephensen began after a pause, "I paid your mother a visit and it pleased me to find her so well and active."

"Have you already? And you came yesterday?"

"No, to-day by the morning train."

"And leave again?" I blurted out.

"Not exactly to-morrow," he answered with a mocking smile.

"I almost thought so," I answered, "since you were in such a hurry with your visit."

"And the picture! That will not be finished in one day," Minna remarked.

"No more than Rome! Fortunately the picture is free. I have already arranged everything with the custodian, and I think of starting to-morrow."

I had quite forgotten this picture, and he evidently had also forgotten it.

We had walked slowly through Zwinger, and were now passing through the gardens towards the post-court. Behind a group of acacias, with leaning trunks, a streetlamp, that was struggling with the last ray of daylight, spread a dull yellowish misty glare, out of which the dainty Gothic sandstone portal of the Sophie-Church appeared, while its slim open-work spires stood phantomlike over the dark summits of the trees against a twilight sky, that was almost colorless but for a couple of sloping feathery clouds still beaming in a rosy glow. I had often seen the place in this fascinating light during my evening walks, and now, to my disgust, it was Stephensen who pointed it out and in a way adopted it with his artist's authority.

"Just look how delicately it stands there; it is a pure *Van der Neer.*"

"Oh, one sees beautiful light effects here," I remarked. "The other day we saw 'a real *Poussin*' out in Saxonian Switzerland."

Minna bit her lip. Stephensen, who could not have had any notion of the reference, felt that I mocked at artists' expressions.

"Yes, I quite believe it. One comes upon subjects at every turn. But, *nous voilà!* I live at Hotel Weber, and will take my leave. Perhaps I have already intruded."

We assured him, of course, to the con-

---

[1] Schiller's famous ballad "Polycrates" ("He was standing on his palace roof").

trary, and he disappeared with quick steps which made a crunching sound upon the gravel.

In silence we walked homewards. Near the post office there was a crowd of yellow carriages making their way home like bees to their hives, and every moment a horn-signal resounded.

I silently cursed all letter-writing and the whole postal system.

CHAPTER II

Mrs. Jagemann opened the door to us in rather an alarmed manner. She drew Minna aside in the dark passage and whispered something to her, and as I closed the door of the sitting-room I heard Minna say—

"Yes, yes, we have met him ourselves."

"Oh dear me!" the mother sighed in her stupid way.

This did not improve my temper. I continued to walk up and down, and without knowing it myself I shook my fist at Stephensen's *alter ego* on the sea picture. I caught myself in this act as the door opened, and I quickly dropped the hand and put it in my pocket.

Minna threw herself wearily upon the little sofa.

"What does he want from me?" she exclaimed in a worried tone.

"You? But he has come in order to paint."

She shook her head.

"He wishes to take possession of me again, that's what he wants."

"What a funny fancy! How can you believe that?"

"You have thought the same yourself," she said, and looked at me inquiringly.

"Perhaps for a moment. Queer ideas come to one under such extraordinary circumstances. However, there is no reason to——"

"Did you notice the way he said to me, 'Wherever you go when you leave for your new home'?—those words were quite clear; I know his way only too well."

"But, indeed, it would be too bold. Just as we are engaged! No, had we even been married a couple of years, then I should think it more likely that a fellow with his easy-going ideas might think there was hope."

"For shame, it is nasty to speak like that, you have no right to talk of him in that way."

"You defend him!"

"Is that so strange? You know quite well yourself that it is unjust of you, besides, you ought to remember that it grieves me when you express such a low opinion of him; for, after all, I have cared for him, and, of course, still do. . . . And you have not been at all nice this afternoon; all the time you went on aiming remarks at him, and I was so nervous; you did not make it easier for me, and it was quite difficult enough without that."

"You are right, Minna! Forgive me. I felt it myself; but you must be able to understand—in such a frame of mind and under such conditions."

"It proves that you were afraid of him. You have been as afraid as I have, all the time; not only for a moment, as you said."

"No, I have not. And, after all, it only shows that I feel irritated in the presence of this man, who owns part of your past, and that I must hate him."

"That is just it, he owns my past, all that has any value in it, and he thinks it gives him a hold over me, which perhaps it does."

"Minna, Minna, what is it you are saying?"

"Oh, I am completely confused."

"Do you not know that you are mine, and I yours?"

She nodded slowly, while she gazed in

front of her and pressed her lips together.

"And that you love me; don't you know that?"

Minna got up and embraced me tenderly.

"Yes, my beloved, that I know."

"Then there is nothing to doubt, not even as regards him. He knows you sufficiently to be sure that you would not submit to a marriage of convenience, and of me he knows that I am neither a duke nor a millionaire."

I spoke to her long and soothingly, while we were sitting on the little sofa with our arms round one another; it was so dark I could hardly see her. She seldom answered, and I doubted whether she really listened or whether her thoughts were completely wandering. Suddenly she pressed my hand and said—

"Let us go away from here, Harald! At once, tomorrow."

"Go away, but where to?"

"Out in the mountains, to Erzgebirge, to Blocksberg—anywhere!" And she laughed with the natural gaiety that was always ready to break out.

"Yes, but, Minna, would that be wise?"

"I dare do it. I have thought it all over —I have no relations for whose sake I need bother. I am my own mistress, and I dare."

"That is all very well, and I appreciate that you would in case of necessity ignore —ignore such ideas and formalities, but I think in this instance you ought to understand that your reputation is to me the most precious thing in the world, and I cannot see that it is a necessity."

"Indeed, indeed!" she exclaimed decidedly, almost violently. Whereupon she laid her lips to my ear and whispered in the most insinuating voice: "Let us, Harald; do say 'yes'!"

"Well, yes, dearest——"

"Yes?"

"That is to say, suppose that we really were to leave to-morrow——"

"Yes, yes, what then?"

"I have hardly any money, and I do not know how I, with so short a notice— I only know very few people here, the only one would be Hertz——"

"No, for God's sake! Hertz! What would they say? I haven't given them a thought; how bewildered I must be!"

"Yes, there you are, and it really is an important step, which requires to be most thoroughly considered; one might suffer long for a hasty step."

The turn things had taken was rather welcome to me. I continued to speak soothingly to her, and already thought that I had got her quite away from her idea, when she suddenly said—

"Still, if we had money by us I would do it after all. . . . That money should have such power, it is really dreadful!"

At that moment her mother entered with a lamp, and I was struck by the expression of terror on Minna's face, perhaps exaggerated because of the sudden dazzling light. She seemed compelled to look towards the unavoidable fate, and I myself got a feeling of fear and discomfort as of impending danger, though I could not imagine that such was at hand. For, however painful it might be for poor Minna to receive Stephensen and listen to his undeserved reproaches and fruitless representations, it is the kind of thing one overcomes, and nothing in the whole affair seemed obscure to me.

I did not reveal my own secret forebodings, but so much the more allowed these reasonings to come to the fore. Minna seemed to agree with me.

As we spoke Danish the old woman felt *de trop,* and was just going to creep out in her quiet way when Minna begged her to stay, and began to talk Saxonian dialect and Dresden slang with her; and in this funny language she joked so gaily, and put on such peculiar faces, that I soon quite forgot the feelings which had so recently depressed us, and the mother laughed till the tears ran down her cheeks.

When the old woman fell asleep after tea, Minna sat down at the piano and played a berceuse by Chopin. She also began to play a waltz, but over this she broke down more than once.

"I am not in form," she said and came to me. "I prefer to read to you."

She took *Kätchen von Heilbronn,* which we had begun and hoped to see acted in a few days.

We soon came to the charming episode where Kätchen will not lift her skirt when wading over the brook, and the old man-servant shouts—

"Only to the ankles, child, to the extreme lowest edge of the sole, Kätchen," but she runs away in order to find a plank.

"Yes, Hertz was right when he called you a Kätchen," I interrupted her. "Do you remember at the quarry, when we were going up?"

"Oh, indeed, I can remember it. When you were so obstinate and nasty! And if only you could have imagined how comical you looked, as if you had got on a mask which did not fit at all——"

Then she read the most touching and, in all its naïveté, the most profound love-scene which the whole of dramatic literature possesses: Kätchen reposing in a half-somnambulistic slumber under the elder bush, and answering the questions of the Count. "Verliebt ja, wie ein Käfer bist du mir" ("In love, yes, like a beetle are you").

"That is to you!" Minna exclaimed. "I could also have said that to you in those days."

We laughed and kissed one another.

After having read fluently for about half an hour, she suddenly stopped and blushed crimson; but I had hardly discovered this before I had the book hurled into my face; she had only meant to throw it from her, but, as I was seated

just opposite, it had struck me; perhaps she also had involuntarily been annoyed because I had waited for her to continue.

"What have I done!" she exclaimed, starting up and throwing herself on her knees beside me. "What a wretch I am! Have I hurt you?"

I laughingly assured her that I was more surprised than anything else.

"I could not read it to you—why does he write such things? And I had not sufficient presence of mind to skip it."

I tried to take the book, but she snatched it up, and having smoothed out the crumpled leaves, she put it back in the bookcase.

"Poor man! You had to suffer for it!"

"Yes, just as I look up—Bang!"

And we burst into uncontrollable laughter. The old lady had shown some signs of waking up when the book had come into contact with my head, and our laughter thoroughly aroused her.

"You make such a rumpus, children, that we shall soon have the watchman up," she said. "It is already late. Oh dear me, yes! I wish I was in bed!"

She lit a little bit of a candle, which stood on the chest of drawers, and slouched out.

It was the hour at which I usually left, and I seldom stayed later because I knew that Minna had to get up early.

But she asked me to stay, for she said that she would not be able to sleep for several hours.

"I have read to you, now you might tell me tales," she said, and seated herself beside me on the little sofa. "I have told you so much about my own childhood, and have not heard nearly enough of yours. Do tell me."

I told her of the calm lonely life in a Ranger's home in the south of Zeeland. My mother I could hardly remember, but my recently lost father I described with all the grief which overwhelmed me by the thought that he would have come to love my Minna, and that she in him would have found a second father. He was in some ways rather peculiar, an old disciple of Schopenhauer, and a philosopher of nature; in consequence he was always quarrelling with the parsons of the neighborhood, who had a craze to convert him. I shared his hermit life and, to the disgust of the neighborhood, he brought me up in his free views.

Minna sang the part from the *Valkyrie* where Siegmund relates his youth:

"Friendless fled
My father with me;
Lapsed my youth
While living for years
With Wolfing in woodlands wild."

"By the way, have you wolves in Denmark?"

"Of course we have, and polar bears go about on skates there."

Minna slapped me over my fingers.

"After all, it was not impossible! They have wolves in Poland. I have stayed with a cousin who is married there, and have heard them howl. Yes, just you look at me, such an one am I!—By the way, why did you not take to forestry? I should have liked to be a forester's wife!"

"Well, you ought to have let me know in those days. But you forget, then we should not have met."

"Why not? You might have come to the college in Tharandt. Those who are to meet will meet."

"Fatalist!"

"Oh, you ought to know I am that! But, to be serious, I should think it would have suited you well."

"I also had a taste for it; it was only later I wanted to be an architect, and it had already been decided that I should be one when my mother's brother, who is a director of a large china-factory in London, offered to help me, if I would be a Polytechnic student. Well, it was more advantageous, and my father did not think we ought to lose the chance. Be-

sides, he thought that it would be a good thing for me to take to a practical life, and not become such a lonely misanthrope and dreamer as he accused himself of being."

"I am sure you will be that all the same. You are my sweet enthusiast. And with all this you have not told me a word of those with whom you have been in love. Do you not know that it is the custom for all engaged couples at once to boast to one another of their former sweethearts? To have confessed before the engagement is an exception that confirms the rule, but you seem to imagine that you can break it altogether."

"Not at all. Be it confessed to you under seven-sealed promise of silence, that in my first youth I sighed in secret for the daughter of a forester."

"Well, it is quite an idyll!"

"No, only half a one. For she was so far from being a beauty that it often caused me an effort to keep up the illusion. But it seemed to me I ought to have some one whose initials I could cut on the bark of the trees with a burning heart above."

"Yes, afterwards you men can always speak with irony of your loves, and then it is for poor us to suffer. And who was the next one?"

"There wasn't another."

"What do you say? Look here, Harald, Harald!"

"Indeed, I assure you, none worth mentioning. Perhaps I have fancied some pretty face I have seen in the street. I may have had a dream or two and built castles in the air. . . ."

"Well, for those you are a splendid architect. But I feel certain that you are deceiving me."

"What makes you say so? Remember that I have had so little society, have met so few ladies."

"Yes, that may be the reason. Very likely that is why you care for me. When you discover that I am just like the others——"

"But you are not."

"Well, you don't know!"

"I am sure of it, it's impossible. . . . And, after all, what do I care for the others?"

Minna laughed heartily and pressed me to her.

"That was well said, and it came from the heart, therefore you shall have a kiss . . . if only you would always think so! No, do not promise anything; what is the good of that? Kiss me!"

The tower clock on Kreuz Church struck twelve, it was quite time to part.

The outer door had, of course, been closed long before. Minna had to go down with me and open it. In the cool cellar-like corridor we gave one another a long embrace. I was not to detain her when she opened the door, but quickly slip out so that no passer-by or late neighbor should see her. But the draft blew the folds of her skirt out as she was about to bang the door, and while I helped to free her, I couldn't resist the temptation to steal one more kiss, in spite of the fact that I had seen a man on the opposite pavement.

The light from the little lamp, which she had put down in the corridor, shone round her dark figure with a flickering glare which suddenly went out.

"Good-bye, good-bye!" she whispered quickly, and the door closed.

CHAPTER III

I walked rapidly along: "A dream in the heart, on the lips the last kiss," as one of the German lyric poets sings. With delight I inhaled the fresh evening air; my stick sounded on the pavement, and my firm steps echoed in the empty street. A man whose boots creaked audibly kept pace with me on the opposite pavement. Only a couple of lamps lighted the whole street, and both of them were on my side; I glanced in vain at the stranger, who very likely had witnessed the tender little scene. Suddenly he crossed the road, cleared his throat, and lifted his hat. I was startled to recognize Stephensen.

"Excuse me, Mr. Fenger," he began; "perhaps it surprises you at this hour, it might have the appearance . . . well, why not be straightforward? I *have* been waiting for you."

"Indeed. Then you must have been wearing away the pavement for a considerable time."

"Just as long as you were later than usual in leaving your fiancée. . . . It shows that it was most important for me to meet you."

"You honor me too much. You wish——?"

"I should like to have an interview with you, upon a subject which is of the greatest importance to both of us."

"All right."

"Suppose we drink a glass of beer in a place where I am known and where we can be alone?"

"A glass of beer by all means," I answered, with as cheerful an indifference as was possible, though I felt as if somebody had proposed to drink poison with me.

"I suppose you also appreciate a good glass of Pilsener, or Münchener beer? As far as I am concerned I cannot stand our Danish beer any longer."

"No, it tastes more or less like water with gin in it."

"Quite my opinion! And that we are proud of! Well, *à la bonheur,* as the German says, anyhow it has brought us some statues.[1] Suppose we go to the 'Three

---

[1] A wealthy brewer in Copenhagen made the collecting of modern sculpture his hobby.

Ravens'—very likely you also are known there?"

"No, I have only been there a few times."

"Really! I went there nearly every evening from the very same front door out of which you have just come. Perhaps you know that I lodged there? I had, of course, my own key, and therefore had not the opportunity of being seen out in the pleasant way you were. Speaking of that, do you know the expression, 'A genius, who never has had his own door key'? I find it very applicable to our Danish talents, I came across it the other day in one of our new authors. I suppose you are up to date in our new literature, are you not? Oh, one cannot deny there is a lot of 'go' in it, otherwise I read mostly French novels. Well, here we are at the 'Three Ravens,' they have been illuminated, that's something new. After you."

He stood aside for me to go first into the lighted corridor, and then he took me to the left through a billiard-room, where five or six men were playing in shirt sleeves, to a smaller room which was empty. Before we had taken off our overcoats, a very fat and pale waiter, with leg-of-mutton-shaped whiskers, appeared, and hastened to the assistance of Stephensen.

"Welcome, Professor!" he said, and so that he might leave no doubt as to his personal knowledge of the customers, he hastily added: "Arrived from Denmark in order to paint again, I suppose?"

"That's just it. How are things going on at the 'Three Ravens,' Heinrich?"

"As usual, Professor, as well as usual, I am glad to say; only that last year we stopped drawing Bohemian beer, which the Professor sometimes drank. Well, there was also a waiter on the staff —but perhaps the Professor remembers Frants, the tall fellow with the red beard?"

"Perfectly well; is he not here?"

"Last Easter he opened a bar in Friedrichstadt. He is supposed to be doing well, but I say, 'a bird in the hand——' ' "

"You are right. It would never do for you to leave the 'Three Ravens,' we couldn't do without you. Look here, could we be by ourselves, Heinrich?"

"Oh, dear me, yes, Professor. Shall it be Pilsener?"

"Yes, two—and——"

"With a lid, of course, Professor," the waiter said, anticipating him, and bowing and flicking the napkin under his arm, after which he quickly disappeared.

I sat down on a little velvet sofa with the depressing feeling of inferiority that one gets in a public place in the society of a regular customer, who is treated half as a prince and half as a comrade by the waiter, while whatever attention is shown to outsiders is given as a favor. And what a customer! Arriving here after a couple of years' absence, and being received as if he had left last night. Stephensen, "the Professor," evidently enjoyed his triumph, while he stretched out his legs, glanced in the mirror over the sofa, and fidgeted with his fingers between his neck and stiff little collar.

"What astonishing memories these waiters have," he exclaimed. "Upon my word, he remembers that I always ordered Pilsener beer drawn in a glass with a lid—it is almost absurd! By the way, I also had a curious experience with a porter in Berlin. . . ."

He started to tell some anecdotes in order to pass the time until the waiter returned. I felt as if he was playing with me, like a cat with a mouse, and was almost inclined to get up and go away. From the adjoining room one heard the monotonous counting. A hoarse voice shouted—

"I am naughty,
You are naughty,
We are both naughty."

The waiter entered with the beer and disappeared immediately.

Stephensen lifted his tankard towards me, and took a long drink.

"Well," he started, "it was——— By the way, do you smoke?"

"Not so late in the evening," I answered, though I had a great desire to calm my nerves with tobacco; but my pouch was empty, and the thought of receiving anything from him filled me with disgust.

"Ah, you have principles," he observed, while he lighted his pipe. "Really, with principles, as with trunks when travelling, one ought not to drag about too many of them. . . . There are, for instance, art principles. . . . However, it was our concerns we were to talk about."

"Just so, I think it is time we began," I remarked irritably. . . . "Is there any way I can be of service to you?"

Stephensen smiled in a peculiar way.

"I dare say you can, but it is not about that I want to speak. . . . H'm! I said on the terrace that I had come in order to paint."

"That could not surprise me, as you are a painter."

"Quite right. . . . I am also going to paint, but it was not for this I came. . . . Two letters which I received from Minna, and in which she informed me of her engagement to you, brought me here."

"I don't understand why they should bring you to Dresden."

"Perhaps you will when you come to know what sort of association there has been between Minna and me."

"I know everything concerning this intimacy, but it only makes your presence still more mysterious."

"Indeed! It seems to me you ought to understand that the information that she was suddenly engaged to another man was bound to be a great surprise to me, and that I——"

"Pardon me. A surprise? And why? I think on the contrary you should have been prepared for it, and that it ought to have been welcome news to you. You have in days gone by flirted with her, unfortunately not without success; you have assured yourself of her love in return, though you did not succeed in making her your mistress——"

"Mr. Fenger, what an accusation! I must distinctly refute this insinuation——"

"I am sorry, but you can hardly wonder that I believe more in Minna's assurances than in yours. As you, on the other hand, failed to have sufficient moral courage to take the responsibility which an engagement involved——"

"An engagement? That would be the last straw. My good Mr. Fenger, you are young enough and very likely still sufficiently Danish to be pleased with our four, five, or six years' engagements. For my part I am not. I would do much for Minna's sake, but to bring such an absurdity on myself, to go about as a proper patent Danish fiancé—No!"

"Very well, so after all you also have your principles. Only it is a pity that as engagements are on the same lines in Germany, her German heart and understanding have perhaps not been able fully to value these motives. What, however, is still more to be regretted, is that you did not manage to impart to her your own view of the situation, but that she, on the contrary, believed that there were to be no ties between you and herself."

"In that she was quite right. . . . Of course I wished her to have her full liberty——"

"And you yours, especially the latter."

"What do you mean by that?"

"No doubt you have taken advantage of your liberty; indeed I can mention a certain lady who was sufficiently 'well-to-do' to inspire in you a desire for marriage."

Stephensen laughed mockingly.

"I must say that Copenhagen's old reputation for being a gossip-hole does not belie itself, since the gossip has its echo right down in Saxonia. I can imagine that you have not deprived Minna of this 'tit-bit.'"

"Think what you like, it's no business of mine! But permit me to call your attention to the fact that you are not very consistent, when it surprises and annoys you that she, on her part, has at last made use of her liberty."

Stephensen was evidently very irritated at the turn the conversation had taken; but he checked the sharp outburst that was on his lips. For several minutes he remained staring silently at the ceiling with furrowed brow, breathing deeply and sighing. "What does this mean?" I thought. The voices in the billiard-room had grown more noisy; the musical member sang with sentimental tremor on the long notes: *"Gute Nacht, du mein 'he-rz-iges Kind,"* and several voices joined in, howling the syllable "herz" in a prolonged discord. Stephensen smiled, passed his hand over his eyes, and then looked at me vacantly.

"You do not understand me," he began, and his lisping voice had again attained its gentle, rather sugary tone. "What was it you remarked? I see, that she had only used her liberty, and that it ought not to annoy me. But this is not the point! I do not feel at all wronged. And it is not the fact that she has used her liberty, as you so strikingly observed,—not at all. If I had heard that she had become engaged to a young man whom she had known for a long time, with whose family she had associated, and who was in such a position that he could soon marry her, for instance the son of this Jew where she visits so often, I don't remember——"

"Hertz, I suppose you mean?"

As a mocking chorus they howled in the billiard-room—*"he-rz-iges Kind."*

"That is it, Hertz; of course she could

have married him, and why not? Not a brilliant match, but a solid one. Well, I should have been resigned, and should have silently acquiesced. Indeed, it would have been a case in which my consent would neither have been asked nor required," he added, with a rather self-sufficient irony.

"Your last remark appears to me very sound; would it not also be applicable in the present instance?"

"Not quite. Just place yourself in my position. Minna and I parted as friends, who knew that they were more than friends, not really bound in any way, but with a mutual consent not to lose sight of one another. In consequence of this we have corresponded for a year and a half continually and rather regularly, a fact of which you are probably aware. Well, I am not exactly 'given to sentiment,' and even if our friend perhaps has got a vein of it, it followed naturally that neither of us overwhelmed the other with emotional outpourings or fond assurances. Fortunately, however, the art exists which is called, 'reading between the lines,' and by means of this art I can, without boasting, assure you that the letters, which I received two or three months ago, were written by a lady who was in love with me."

The little Danish Dictionary, which had been Minna's favorite book, came into my mind, and I did not dare to contradict him.

"Then suddenly I receive her confidential announcement that she is engaged to a young man, whom she had only known for about three weeks, and who—forgive my saying so—is not in a position to marry soon and offer her the comforts and security of a home. Excuse me, I must repeat it—it is very painful for me to touch upon your financial position—I know that the thought of not being able to support a family in the near future, or anyhow not to maintain it with ample means, is humiliating in itself, and doubly so when it is alluded to by another; but I place the greatest importance on this point, because it shows that she was not thinking of a marriage of convenience.

"Just the very remark I made to Minna, namely, that you would see this point, and consequently understand that it was serious . . ." I said, and began to stutter, for I was annoyed by my admission that Minna and I had been talking about the possibility of his interference; and he, after a long drink, glanced lurkingly at me over the lid of his tankard, and then sucked the beer from his moustache in a very contented way, as if he was saying to himself: "Oho, my friend, you put your foot into it that time! So you have already been talking about the possibilities!"

"Serious! Oh, no doubt of that."

"It is as much as to say that—that we both—in short, that there was nothing for you to do," I brutally broke through the difficulty, and looked at him fiercely.

"It quite depends, it quite depends, sir! Your reasoning does not hold good. . . . At all events, I quite see what leads you astray. Of course you look upon the expression 'marriage of convenience' as something depreciatory, and forget that I do not share this particular Danish prejudice, nor even all cosmopolitan ones. On the contrary I consider, taken as a whole, that the so-called 'marriages of convenience' are those matches which have most chance of happiness, not forgetting that matrimony altogether is—I won't say a curse—but an anomaly. . . . In this case, however, a matrimony of interest is, as we have already agreed, out of the question; here is supposed to be, forgive me, passion, enthusiasm, love—whatever you like to call it. Please do not misunderstand me! I do not doubt that, as far as you are concerned, it exists, and I will go further: I will grant you that

Minna also feels real affection for you, even—I don't mind saying—is in love with you; only, the question is, of what description is this love?"

"Is it not the most natural thing to leave it to her to decide this question?"

"What are you dreaming of! She is quite incapable of doing that. I am convinced that a certain impatience to break an intercourse, which to her was doubtful and unsatisfactory, has contributed more than a little to this new and sudden love. Besides, I have also a suspicion that the quite accidental circumstance of your being a countryman of my unworthy self has made the transference of certain feelings and impressions easier——"

An intimation in her first letter to Stephensen came into my mind, and certainly confirmed this supposition. I lowered my eyes, bewildered by his inquisitive glance.

"The favorable conditions, the loneliness have done something, and then, what I do not at all doubt, many excellent and lovable qualities in yourself——"

"Shall we not now leave off this rubbish!" I burst out, and got up suddenly. "I understand quite well your ideas, but what the dickens do I care about them? I do not recognize that you have any right to act as Minna's guardian."

"And what the dickens have I to do with your recognition? That is beside the question. I simply *have* the right to do the best I can to prevent Minna from committing one of those follies, which are not easily put right again, and as it is my own behavior towards her which to some extent is the reason for this rash haste, it is even my duty—I don't know what you mean by your scornful laughter."

"I thought the feeling of duty belonged to those cosmopolitan prejudices which you did not share."

"On the contrary, it belongs to those which I *do* share. But there is one motive that very likely influences me still more strongly. It is the circumstance that I love her—love her!"

He also had risen. We stood facing one another with the little table between us, staring firmly into one another's eyes. It struck me that the most natural and, after all, the most proper thing to do, would be to jump at each other and fight like a couple of tigers, instead of which we should no doubt continue to argue and perhaps even drink our beer together and politely say good-night when we parted. This consideration made me so irritated with the situation that I recovered my control. "Since we have begun, let us play the comedy to the end," I thought. Pushing the table away I freed myself from my closed-in position, in which I felt as if I was besieged, and began to walk up and down the room. Our neighbors sang with Teutonic enthusiasm "Die Wacht am Rhein."

"What the deuce, then, do you want?" I exclaimed at last. "Perhaps you think you can make me give her up?"

"Oh no, I don't ask impossibilities."

"Really not! So, after all, you grasp that it is impossible?"

"Of course, for the same reason that the Nürnberger could not hang somebody —they had first to get him."

"I know I have got Minna, just as I know she has got me."

"Those are mere sayings and even antiquated sayings. No human being can get and own another. Do you really think your engagement is going to frighten me? As if I could not long ago have been engaged to her."

"More fool you not to have been so!"

"Perhaps you are right. But I still have a chance, and she will have to choose between us."

"She has chosen."

"No, that's just what she has not done. Under the supposition that I would not marry her, she has given you a promise. Dare you say that you would have been accepted if she, the day before you proposed to her, had known for certain that I loved her and was longing to marry her? . . . Very well, the supposition was false, and if you are a man of honor, you will not bind her to a promise that was given under such circumstances."

"I would never, under any circumstances, look upon her promise as binding if she herself did not feel that she was bound by it."

"Oh, but that is exactly where the shoe pinches, sir. I do not doubt that Minna has most of these esteemed prejudices, which are the chief ornaments of the weaker sex. Indeed, I mean it seriously: I, for my part, would not be without these prejudices in women, though no doubt it would make life easier and more agreeable. It is an extravagant luxury, but what are we to do? Modern nature contains such contradictions. . . . Therefore, it is very likely that Minna is inclined to consider this engagement as a bond for time and eternity. She is not exactly what one would call a character, but she certainly is a nature—and a faithful nature; and it would consequently be easy for you, without precisely forcing your claim or appealing to her constancy, still to keep her amiable, though somewhat narrow-minded, feeling of duty alive in your favor, not stretching the tie, but still holding it firmly, so long as she herself does not untie it. What I demand of you is, that you yourself shall let it go; understand me rightly, 'not give her up,' as you say, but only not make use of the advantage which this half-legitimate position gives you. I demand it of you as a gentleman, and, understand, not for my own sake—you would, of course, willingly see me hanged! But for Minna's sake you cannot wish—I will not believe that of a man to whom Minna has given such a promise—that she should be yours by compulsion, were it even *inward* compulsion, while she secretly grieved over not being able to be mine. If you notice, or even suspect, that she is on the point of committing such a folly, you will know that it is your duty not to accept such a sacrifice, but, if necessary, to open her eyes and give her back her liberty which she herself has not the courage to take. It is possible that you have driven me out of her heart, in that case the matter is already settled. But it is also possible that she loves us both, each in his own way. In that case she will surely have a great struggle to go through in order to come to a conclusion; but she must fight it out alone, and we most certainly ought not to make the battle harder by forcing ourselves upon her and by dragging her in opposite directions. . . . Minna must choose between us; for she *has* not chosen, and no power on earth can relieve her from making a choice. But she must be free to choose—that is all that I demand."

"I shall not put any hindrance in the way of her liberty, either direct or indirect, and I will submit to her decision without trying to shake it. I rely upon you to do the same. . . . And as I suppose your object in this meeting was to obtain such a declaration from me, I presume that we can now part—as enemies."

"But, at any rate, as honest enemies, who are fighting in the open and with equal weapons."

I took my hat down from the peg, gave a stiff bow, and left the room. In the billiard-room the game had ceased; a couple of the shirt-sleeved men, who were standing with their hands on one another's shoulders, were assuring each other of their "absolute affection and unbounded esteem." The musical member, who sat on the corner of the billiard-table, sang: "Ein' feste Burg ist unser Gott." I guessed, with reason, from these manifestations, that the sublimest height of drunkenness had been reached, and that it was very late.

By a stroke of good fortune I succeeded in finding the fat waiter, and in paying for my own beer.

CHAPTER IV

No sleep came to my eyes during that night.

I heard the clock on the Kreuz church strike one quarter after the other while I tossed to and fro on my bed. Sometimes my thoughts began to ramble in the uncertain way that is so often the harbinger of slumber, but then a wave of fever-heat rolled over me, and I was wide awake again. Dull despair took possession of me, and made everything seem lost, and by-and-bye my tears began to flow.

The more impossible a misfortune seems, the nearer is its realization as soon as it comes within the range of possibility, for because it has already taken the leap over the widest precipice, one cannot doubt that it will also have the strength to overcome the smaller chasm. Having developed to something from nothing, why should it not be able to become everything? Certainties exist, which to us seem so incontestable that they are almost argued away, when we are brought to dispute about them at all; for together with their indisputability their inmost being seems to disappear.

What can be a more certain possession, more remote from any danger, than a faithful woman's love? I felt that Minna loved me, I knew that hers was, as Stephensen also had said, a faithful nature.

But the dreadful, Nemesis-like thing was, that this fidelity recoiled upon itself: it was her faithfulness towards older feelings that had been aroused to battle against later ones, by which she was tied to me.

How safely I had rested in my happiness! And now a stranger had told me, in so many words, that he hoped to tear it from me. And as far as I was concerned? Had I laughed in his face or turned my back on him as if he were a poor fool? No, I had entered into a quarrel with him, as if my happiness needed defending; still worse, I had absolutely arranged with him how best to act in the future, and in this way I had agreed to the possibility of his gaining the victory, and admitted that I did not already possess this happiness, but had first to win it.

The danger was not only possible but actual; it was upon me, and I groaned under its weight as if possessed by a nightmare.

How safely I had rested in my happiness! And yet it occurred to me now that I had in reality always suspected danger, and that there had always been a shadow hovering over the clear sunshine of this time. I remember how this suspicious letter had awakened me from the intoxicating bliss of the first kiss. I suddenly felt again the unaccountable terror which came upon me in Schandau when I heard her letter fall into the box. On my first lonely visit to the home of her childhood, a feeling of jealousy had overcome me in a manner that now appeared quite ghostlike. Then again, hardly had I enjoyed the bliss of reunion, before it was embittered by Minna's sadness, and by his reproachful letter which had created a foolish jealousy in me, and a less foolish fear; how persistently I had begged her to leave it unanswered, and she had replied, *"I must,"* with her peculiar fatalism that now also seemed to have infected me. And the following day, when she had written and shown me this letter, and we had sat together in the evening on the small hill in "Grosser Garten," and viewed the distant Lilienstein, did not a melancholy shadow creep upon our hearts, as if we looked back towards a lost Paradise?

In this way the hostile fate seemed to be born at the same time as our compact, and threateningly to have approached, till it now—as Beethoven says—"knocked at the door of our existence." And it was sure to get admittance; the strong one does not threaten in vain.

I forgot that the moment when fate knocks at our door, is the time to show that one is capable of receiving it and, if necessary, of throwing it downstairs; otherwise circumstances, confident of our weakness, might easily take to masking under the cloak of fate.

A prey to such miscellaneous reflections, I was gripped at the same time and with equal force by a state of lethargy, and by a purely physical horror which caused me to rise in agony. I had a vision, I should rather say a feeling, of something enormous and unshapely, of grayish hue, that came out of the darkness and slowly and continuously approached. But even these vague expressions give perhaps a wrong idea of my condition, for this nervous impression was really indescribable, yes, even unfathomable; it seemed to emerge from some part of my own nature which lay under the consciousness, and was as incapable of being bounded by our narrowed conceptions and imaginations, as are the enormous creations of prehistoric times to find a place amongst the now living species.

After awhile I shook off this uncomfortable feeling, dressed, and went out.

It was a cold dawn with mist and fine rain. All the cafés were still closed. Giddy and heavy in my head, and with the sinking feeling that follows a too early rising, I had to go without food for over an hour.

At last I found a café that was being aired and cleaned. I sat down in a corner, and the waiter, who had formed his own opinion of my requirements, proposed "a soda water."

"Coffee," I ordered peremptorily.

But the fire was not yet lighted, so I had to wait. I had a real, though not pleasant, sensation of travelling, with remembrances of hotels and the rush to catch early trains. To travel, away from here! . . . It was just what Minna had wanted yesterday evening. Then I had persuaded her against it,—but now what would not I have given for us to have already started, for her to be sitting with me, and for the cab to be ordered for the early train? Where should we go? Anywhere, only away!

But it was impossible now, even if I had money. Stephensen had, with his frankness, really succeeded in paralyzing me; and very likely that had been his intention, though he had not suspected that we had been thinking of going away secretly. It was not so much that my pride prevented me from flying, though the idea that Stephensen, with some reason, might complain of my action, was revolting to me; worse than this was the fear that I should for ever have the feeling of having gained my best treasure in a deceitful manner; and still worse, the possibility that I might even be guilty of injustice towards her. For my part this flight could only have meaning under the supposition that Minna, after grave consideration, would have preferred Stephensen. But what right had I to prevent such a decision, even if I did so with her consent?

And suppose it proved to be a hasty step; suppose that later on she discovered that she had mistaken her feelings, how bitter would not that repentance be which came too late! No, we ought to remain, happen what would. And still there was an inner voice, which continually whispered: "Go away! Surely she will still go."

Then came the program for the day. The great question was, should I go to her at the first possible moment?

My longing and fear urged me on, but my better judgment said: "Why disturb her at such an early hour? I shall alarm and trouble her, and she requires all her calmness and clearness. Besides, it shows that I myself am out of gear; it makes me appear nervous, perhaps even distrustful! Very likely if I stay away there is a probability of his speaking with her alone; that I cannot, anyhow, prevent, so just as well now as later. . . . Yes, they must speak together, curse it, I cannot possibly propose for him. Well, either I have to run away with her, or leave off playing Argus."

I decided to go as usual to the Polytechnic, and to put off seeing Minna until after dinner.

CHAPTER V

When I entered the little room, Minna was sitting by the open window. I could at once see by the look she gave me, that she had shed many tears.

"Has he been to see you?" I asked at once, while I held her trembling hands in mine.

"Yes."

She allowed me to hold her right hand, while the other, with which she was crushing a small handkerchief, was firmly pressed under her breast, as if she was suffering acute pain.

"What he has said to you, dear Minna, I know beforehand after the interview I had with him last night. . . . He— after all—you were right yesterday, at all events with regard to the motive of his coming . . . unfortunately . . . though perhaps it is selfish of me to say so. . . ."

I hardly knew what I said, and even commonplace words were not any longer at my command, but stuck in my stifled throat. I watched the expression of her averted face, and waited for a word. But she, after one firm grip, suddenly snatched her hand from mine, sank down on the chair, and burst into a dreadfully violent fit of sobbing, with her face hidden in her hands. This heart-rending sound, and the touching sight of this delicate girlish form shaken by the elementary force of weeping, affected me to such a degree that I forgot everything else. I threw myself on my knees beside her, embraced and pressed her firmly to me, called her again and again by name, and implored her with foolish entreaties to stop, not to cry in that way, to take heart and spare herself. Soon my tears fell as freely as hers. Little by little the crisis passed over, she smiled languidly, dried my eyes with the little handkerchief, which was wet with her own tears; and while she tenderly pressed my hand, she whispered several times—

"My dearest friend."

"That I am, Minna, that I am whatever happens. . . . But you must not take it in this way, do you hear? You must not feel unhappy, for you are not going to be unhappy. . . . I would rather suffer anything than that, rather lose you, and so would he, I am quite sure of that. . . . We must be wise and you must make yourself strong . . . you must not consider *me* at all . . . only think of yourself, what is best for you, that must also be best for us. Only do what is right and follow what your own nature dictates, that is the main thing. . . . We shall both be satisfied, if only you will be happy."

"I—no, really I am the last one who ought to be considered. . . . Oh, if I could make both of you happy by giving both of you up, I really think—yes, I am sure—I could make that sacrifice, rather than disappoint one of you. . . . And now I cannot give my hand to the one without taking it away from the other; how then is it possible for me to be happy? That is out of the question."

"Indeed, my dearest, that alone must be the question. I know that at the beginning you will feel very unhappy because you will be bound to hurt one of us so much, but there is time enough for happiness, as it concerns your whole life. . . . When you choose what is best, you will gradually feel content; and the one who does not get the right to call you his—he will also in time resign himself to what is inevitable. Only if you choose wrongly, if you mistake your feelings, well, then you will make all three of us unhappy."

"It is dreadful! To be obliged to make such a choice! If only some one could choose for me, if only a duty existed in this case, which said: 'You must do this, otherwise you will be doing wrong!' . . . But I do wrong whichever way I decide, for I have already done wrong, and it will continue."

"No, no! You must not yield to such thoughts! Do not add scruples of this kind to all the rest——"

"Harald!" she exclaimed, getting up and looking steadily into my eyes, "dare you make the choice for me? Have you the courage? Understand me rightly, I mean is your conviction so strong, that you with a clear conscience can say: 'Your duty is to come with me. You have given me your word, and I cannot give it you back because I am convinced that if you act otherwise it will be your ruin'? . . ."

A shiver of joy passed through me, as I suddenly saw our fate placed in my own hands, and the comforting knowledge that I only had to grasp it made me momentarily forget the seriousness of the responsibility. But before I could answer, Minna stretched out her hand, as if she would place it on my lips, and with an anxious pleading look continued—

"But do remember, Harald, that although you get a wife who loves you, and whom you love much more than she deserves,—indeed I know that—she may not ever be able to make you happy, for she has an inner wound which will never quite heal, and which might kill her. I should never be able to forgive myself for being unfaithful to my first love. . . . No domestic happiness would quite be able to drive away the image of him, to whom I owed my first consciousness, my first thoughts, my independence, the awakening of my best and purest feelings —a life and feelings which rightly belonged to him. Oh, how fondly precious has not his image been to me—and now it must come as a ghost accusing me of giving all this to another, while he confidently waited for me, worked for us both, for our future! No, no, never can I be really happy or give you such happiness as you deserve!"

I stood terrified and almost stunned by the despair of this outburst; my eyes turned away from hers while I tried to collect my thoughts, and to unravel the tangle into which my mind had been thrown. It was quite plain to me, that a girl with her pure and faithful nature could not help putting the most flattering interpretation possible upon Stephensen's conduct. Already in consequence of his letter with the Elegy by Heine she had held forth his faithfulness as a supposition, and after my interview with him yesterday I had not doubted that he, making use of his knowledge of her heart, would let this very flattering, almost melodramatic, light fall upon the obscure interval of time which separated them. For my part I looked upon this through such very critical glasses that every bit of romantic glamor was taken away; and it seemed to me that in time its true character was sure to become clear to her also, for which reason the danger of the ghost did not seem to me quite so great as she had imagined. But, unfortunately, even *I* was not quite sure of my case, and I was obliged to admit to myself, that as I was

possessed with a very natural antipathy towards Stephensen, it was not impossible that this led me to judge him unfairly. And in that case . . .

I still faltered, and already the favorable minute had slipped by.

"See, you hesitate, you dare not!" she exclaimed. "And still you have only us two to consider. The third, to whom you would do the greatest harm, is to you only a stranger, yes, even a man you hate. . . . Then consider how dreadful this choice must be for me, as I know that to whichever side I turn, I must cause unhappiness to one I love."

"It is just that which makes it so difficult for me to put myself in your place. I do not understand this. . . . You say you love me, I feel it, I will not doubt it, but at the same time you mean that you love Stephensen. It is a problem to me. I do not think that what you feel now for Stephensen is love at all, but only remembrance of past love, and that certainly is too frail ground on which to build a matrimonial life, and especially so, when a new passion has sprung up in opposition to the old one."

Minna shook her head.

"You love, really love, two men? Impossible."

"I do not know what is called possible and impossible, my friend! But consider all that you know yourself and then acknowledge, even if you cannot believe it, that I *must* love him. I have shown you, as well as I could, what he has been to me, you know that my love was constant during the long separation, yes, in spite of my belief that his feelings had changed, you saw—it was indeed the first you saw of me—how even a poor dictionary could give nourishment to my enthusiastic remembrances by teaching me words of his language, and by creating the illusion that I was learning it in order to speak with him. . . . And how could I, only some weeks after this, have grown indifferent to him! If I had heard something disparaging about him, or even, that he loved another—but what have I heard! That he, in the midst of an active and social life, which offered him so many different and stronger inducements, has retained his affection more faithfully than I, who had nothing to distract me. Oh, how meanly and miserably have I behaved! If he had held me in contempt! Oh, I have not the heart to wish it, and still perhaps it would have been better for all of us! But instead he comes here, as if his life and happiness depended on my decision—*mine!* Poor me! That so much love should be able to be a curse for one —love which, otherwise, is the greatest blessing."

She turned away, struggling to repress her tears.

"Dearest Minna," I began, laying my hand on her trembling shoulder, "you are right, I could have foreseen all this, and I ought to have. I now think that your feeling towards me is rather an enthusiastic friendship than a real love."

"Why?" she exclaimed, and turned toward me with swimming eyes—"why cannot I love you both? Perhaps I do in a different way, you are not alike and the conditions are also now quite different. Perhaps in reality I love you best——"

"Oh, Minna!"

"And am most in love with him," she added faintly, lowering her eyes.

My outstretched arms fell, and I started as if I had received a blow. Now I felt how that elementary power, which my jealousy had ever secretly feared, was rising against me, scattering my hopes, overthrowing all my nearly victorious efforts, carrying the day with the irresistible birthright of love. But in a moment Minna was embracing me with genuine tenderness.

"No, do not take it in that way, Harald. My God, I have hurt you! I did not mean it like that. It just came to me, but all words express so badly what we mean. . . . Perhaps it is not at all like that, I do not know, I understand nothing any longer. I only feel that both of you belong to my life. I am torn in two directions. Oh, my God, what will become of me!"

"You will become a sound and true woman, my own dear girl, by your own strength, when you have overcome these fights and struggles. . . . God knows how willingly I would assist you, but you see I cannot. Nobody can do it, not even Mrs. Hertz, with all her love for you. It is a temptation to me to advise you to confide in her—there is at least a great probability that her counsel would be in my favor, but that does not matter. I do not think that you ought to ask anybody but yourself. Your own nature will perhaps suddenly, instinctively, choose what is best for it. . . . More important than all, neither Stephensen nor I must from now add to your agitation, and especially not, as to-day, by our alternate presence make the task of deciding more difficult for you. You cannot stand that, and very likely it would end by your taking a rash decision, as was the case just a moment ago. Both of us have now seen you alone and have pleaded our cause. From this time . . ."

"Pleaded your cause!" Minna exclaimed, and looked at me with a candid smile; "but, dearest Harald, you have not done that at all."

"Have I not?" I asked timidly. "Do you think I have taken it too calmly?"

"No, no, my dearest, I understand you so well, you are so tender and loving, so careful for me, you want to save me from the reproaches that you might charge me with; oh, but be sure, so much the more bitterly do I reproach myself!"

"Not for my sake, Minna! You have no right to do that. . . . What should I have to reproach you with? As if I could wish this time had never been, even if it is to bring no future with it! I am so grateful to you for the love I have felt——"

"No, Harald! Oh, don't say that——"

"Does it pain you? Then I will not speak about it any more. Still less ought I to frighten you by picturing the tragic consequences of such a loss to me. . . . What has to be borne must be, and, on the contrary, I promise you that I shall do all in my power to get over it sensibly —and—though I cannot attempt to forget you—nor will——" My lips quivered and my eyes filled with tears. "No, no," I continued, "it was not this I wanted to speak of. Besides, your heart will tell it all to you. . . . I made the suggestion that from now Stephensen and I must agree not to see you again until you have made up your mind. It would be better, if you could leave the town for the present, if you had relations in the country whom you could visit——"

"I have a cousin in the neighborhood of Meissen, her husband has a farm there. I could easily visit them, they asked me only this summer, and I need not even write beforehand."

"So much the better. Can you leave to-morrow?"

"To-morrow? Oh well, I suppose I could."

"Then do it, Minna. It is better not to put it off. And when you have made up your mind, I suppose you will write your decision."

Minna nodded. She had again seated herself on the chair by the window, and was staring at the gardens.

I took my hat, which was lying on the table, and turned it over and over in my hands, waiting for her to look round. At last I approached her and touched her shoulder. She turned her head, and her tearful eyes gazed in astonishment at my outstretched hand, and at the other that nervously fidgeted with my hat.

"What is this? You are not going?"

"Yes, Minna, I must—it is already—I mean, as you leave to-morrow, I suppose you have a good deal to arrange and pack up."

"Well, it is not to Siberia I am going."

"No more it is, but I must go—in order to——"

"It is not true, Harald! But perhaps you are right in going and leaving me to myself, though that is just what I fear, but I must grow accustomed to it. . . . When are you coming again?"

"I am not coming again."

She jumped up.

"Not coming again? What do you mean by that? . . . Will you not spend this evening with me?"

"I do not think it would be right, as we are no longer engaged."

"Not engaged? It seems to me we must be still, as long . . . at any rate nothing has happened so far."

" 'Still,' until you perhaps 'break it off with me.' But you must not be obliged to do that, you must never have the feeling that *you* have severed a pledge. Whatever decision you come to, you tie a new bond. It is *I* who have broken our engagement, you must feel yourself free."

"Oh, Harald, how sad and bitter it is! Who would have thought of this yesterday, when we exchanged rings?"

She looked down upon her ring, which glittered while she clenched her hands.

"By the way, the ring," I exclaimed, and with the feeling of an heroic effort I began to wriggle the ring over my knuckle.

"No, not that," she cried, and laid her hand preventingly on mine, "oh do not give me back the ring, do not demand yours!—Why should we be so cruel to one another?"

I sighed, smiling, pressed her hand tenderly and kissed it, grateful that her unerring instinct spared us an unnecessary pain, perhaps the bitterest of all; because by touching the magic symbol the full meaning of the pledge is realized. How many a knight has felt the announcement of the dishonoring doom less terrible than the breaking of his shield by the hands of the executioner.

"Are you not coming, Harald? Engaged or not, we are after all the same."

"Dearest Minna, imagine for yourself how much determination it will take to remain away. I really hardly know how to bear it myself, when I realize that this is perhaps the last evening I can spend with you."

My emotion overwhelmed me; I pressed my lips together, and while I looked away in order to avoid her glance, my eyes fastened on a boot-shaped spot on the homely gray wall-paper. It would be untrue to say that there was anything pretty in it, but all the same there was real dread in the thought: "Perhaps you will never see it again." Minna looked helpless at my grief, and I was conscious of her expression, though I still kept on staring at that spot. A minute or two passed before I could continue.

"But it is after all the best like this. . . . Quite true that we are the same, but we shall be different to each other, and that will be painful for us. Besides, it is also more correct now that we have taken such a decision,—I mean it looks more fair towards Stephensen."

"But suppose he came this evening!"

"Has he spoken about it?"

"No, I only thought that he possibly might do so, perhaps only to prevent your being alone with me. He very likely thinks you will come as usual."

"You are right, anyhow I will not leave the field open for him. If he comes, then send for me; there is, I suppose, some one you could send such a short distance. . . . Look, here is my pocket-book, I will leave it with you. If I have that sent to me, then I shall know that I am to come. Just let him know that you are sending it to me, it is better for him to

understand that I am not coming uninvited. . . . Farewell, my beloved, no one can forbid me calling you that."

I gave her my hand, which she pressed impetuously, while she looked penetratingly into my eyes with a frightened and questioning smile, and her face approached a very little nearer, perhaps unconsciously to herself. I then drew her to my breast, and our lips met in a long kiss, as if each of us would forcibly imbibe the other's life in order to have it safe and impregnable. At last I felt that she relaxed from my embrace, and in stepping back, still with my arm round her waist, I noticed that she could hardly stand, her head fell onto her shoulder, she gasped for breath and trembled. I led her carefully across to the little sofa, on which I allowed her to slip down, and then I pushed the cushion under her head.

Thereupon I opened the door and called her mother, who at once appeared out of the obscurity of the kitchen, and, when I had told her that Minna was unwell, she again disappeared to fetch some water. Nimble and confused, always bent like some gnome on the stage, she quickly rushed into the sitting-room; the alarmed expression simultaneously made her coarse features still more grotesque and gave them a rather spiritual beauty, inasmuch as it made visible her great tenderness for Minna. When I saw her tending the half-conscious girl I hastened away, for I felt certain that Minna would have no peace of mind while I was present.

CHAPTER VI

On the table in my little room were two letters, the one with an English the other with a German stamp. I knew both hand-writings, and quickly opened the letter from my uncle.

He wrote, in his usual short and business-like manner, that on account of a change in the staff at the factory it would be better if I came to London within four weeks. I should thus be obliged to give up my studies at the Polytechnic, and forego the chance of passing my examination, but it would not harm my career, and it was very necessary not to lose this favorable opportunity of beginning practical work. In a few days he would send me sufficient money for my outfit and travelling expenses. He asked for an answer by return of post in order that he might know that his letter had been promptly delivered. This communication, or rather order, put me into a state of great excitement.

It was evident that if the worst happened, if the bond between Minna and me should be broken, then nothing could be more desirable—if wishes and hopes could then any longer be spoken of— than this arrangement. I should at once be removed from these surroundings that would be so full of heart-rending associations, and where, perhaps, for some time I should be likely to meet her, in order to be thrown into work under new conditions which would require me to strain my energies to the utmost. But naturally my thoughts did not willingly linger over a desire, that was founded upon so painful a supposition. On the other hand if I was chosen, it would be as inconvenient as possible to leave her while she was still shaken by the emotional crisis through which she had passed, and would, more than ever, be needing a faithful support— to leave her just at the instant when a constantly renewed and strengthened feeling that the love, to which she had given herself up, neither could nor would forsake her was of the greatest consequence to her welfare. To leave her alone, perhaps for years, with nothing left to her but correspondence and—the Danish Dictionary! The possibility that quicker

than I expected I might gain a position to justify my marriage seemed not to make up for the misery of a separation at this moment.

But the terms I was on with my uncle, whom I only knew, or did not know, through letters, were not of such a nature that I dared to think of trying to alter his decision; and besides, just at this moment when I was to give an answer, I was prevented from confiding in him.

A bit of English sticking-plaster, in case I got a deadly wound, and if I conquered, a peremptory command, which would draw me away from the happiness I had won, this was the not exactly brilliant promise that the letter held out. I felt even more miserable than when I had entered the room.

Outside it rained heavily, and the narrow street darkened the room so much that I was obliged to go to the window so that I might read the other letter. It was from my friend Immanuel Hertz (he was named after Kant) in Leipzig.

After having congratulated me on my engagement (he begged to be excused for his congratulations being a little late— "much business"), he added that he had been very upset to hear through his mother that his dear old father had not yet got rid of the cold which he had caught in Prague; he feared that his mother might be keeping something back in order not to alarm him, and asked me to say openly what I thought of his father's illness.

I was, of course, too selfishly absorbed in my own grief to let old Hertz's cough appear fatal to me. Therefore this inquiry did not give me much thought, whereas I pondered, with an interpreter's profundity, over his congratulatory remarks, and tried to imagine that they were rather forced. The honest Immanuel Hertz began to have an especial interest for me. I remembered how Minna had always avoided speaking of him; and Stephensen's remark of last evening regarding Minna and him, seemed, though quoted as an example, to have something behind it. All this pointed in the same direction; and, besides, to know Minna and to love her were in my eyes two things so indissolubly united, that my supposition very soon grew into a certainty.

So he had burnt also himself!—How had he got over it? He was surely no easy-going character, but perhaps he had a more self-controlled than passionate disposition, and therefore the wound would hardly have been incurable. New surroundings and hard work had, anyhow, surely been the remedy for him also.

However detestable the thought was that for me also this panacea might be necessary, I, nevertheless, gradually lost myself in fantastic English dreams of the future, which, by the way, left out the most important item—the work—as something taken for granted; but as a reward I imagined my own dear self, two or three years older, galloping in a grand cavalcade through Hyde Park (which I supposed to be like "Grosser Garten"), dancing at balls, which were sparkling with all the diamonds and stars of "high life," or moving as a guest in an old country-seat hidden in tremendous woods and deer parks; an honored guest, the champion at tennis, riding to hounds, and presenting myself in evening dress on the signal of the dinner bell, "the tocsin of the soul," as Byron has it. Of course, in Hyde Park, in the ball-room, and at the country-seat I was surrounded by those young ladies, who have the name of being the most beautiful women of the world, all of whom were heiresses to millions of pounds, though not by any means scornful of the homage that a broken heart still owes to beauty and attractiveness. . . . But then, as the image of Minna appeared very vividly before my mind's eye

on this background, which brought out its unpretentious and simple grace, as a dimly seen tapestry of fantastic, luxurious Gobelin that the effect-seeking hand of an artist has painted behind the portrait study of a dark and calm woman's form —these dreams at once dissolved into nothingness. Not because I looked upon them as impossibilities; but because even the realization was bound to be empty and without value in comparison with the pure and gentle ideal before which all that was noble in me seemed to rise to the surface, and all the baser and lower elements of my nature to sink into the soul's unconscious depths.

Ashamed at having at this moment unfaithfully allowed myself to be led astray by such digressing fancies, I offered them as a sacrifice on her altar, and I hastened to resign all these glories (which naturally would come to a youngster in a subordinate position at a china factory), and to give myself up to the bliss of possessing her or to the grief of losing her.

I was overwhelmed by a feverish longing to see her, and could not imagine how I should bear to remain the whole evening in solitude, knowing that she was also alone and within a few minutes' walk. Dusk had already fallen, and it did not seem as if I was going to be sent for. Now I realized quite clearly that I had all the time supported myself by the hope that *his* presence at the Jagemanns' would also make mine necessary.

At last I began to light the lamp, in order to write to my uncle. At the same moment the bell rang.

I placed the globe of the lamp on the table—or rather on the edge of the table— and heard it crash on the floor before I reached the door, which I only just opened. As far as I could make out, I had been interrupted by a coal-heaver. Furious and desperate, I was going to bang my door, when I heard a weak childish voice exchanging some words with the servant, of which one word had a faint resemblance to my name.

I listened breathlessly. Tiny pattering steps approached, and I heard a gentle tap at the door.

Again I opened it; in front of me stood a tiny girl about seven years of age, with a tear-stained face, which I recognized; the child lived in the same house as the Jagemanns, and old Mrs. Jagemann was very interested in her and her little sisters.

"Do you want me, my little friend?"

The child looked down and snuffled.

"Have you any message, or have you brought me something?"

She now howled and rubbed her eyes with the one hand; the other she kept wrapped up in a handkerchief. I dragged her inside.

"But what is it, then? Perhaps you were to bring me a little book?"

But now she absolutely yelled.

"Good gracious, what does it all mean?" I thought, and fidgeted about in impatient despair.

"It's not my fault," she started at last. "I had—I was to—it was the little Jagemann—she gave me the little book, and the big Jagemann gave me a cake—to eat on my way, and then it happened——"

I rushed forward and seized my hat. The child took her left hand out of the handkerchief, and stretched out the soiled pocket-book to me.

"Couldn't help it, it was a nasty boy—he pushed me, and then the little book fell—into a pool—ugh! in Dibbelswalder Square—ugh!"

I hastened to find a silver coin, which I pushed into her small wet hand, and flew out at the door past the servant and the coal-heaver, whose laughter followed me down the stairs.

In a few minutes—how precious they all were now!—I reached Seilergasse.

CHAPTER VII

Minna opened the door for me. She gave me a firm shake of the hand and whispered, "Thank you for coming."

I stepped at once into the sitting-room, hat in hand. The lamp was lit. Stephensen sat talking to Mrs. Jagemann, who was wearing her linsey dress and best cap. It was evident that the piratical suitor sailed under the neutral flag of a visit to the family. She entertained him about the lodgers: "Bad people, Mr. Stephensen! Indeed, we have often wished you back. But, oh my, there is nothing to say against the present one; he is also a painter, that is to say in another way, . . . he is in the decorative line, you know."

Stephensen had risen. We greeted one another very politely, and I even compelled myself to give him my hand; for, after all, Minna was fond of him, and her feelings should protect him against my dislike. His thin and delicate hand was very cold—the heart perhaps, according to the old saying, was in consequence so much the warmer.

I pressed Mrs. Jagemann's soft and flabby hand, and after a wandering glance round the room I spoke to Minna—

"I thought I had forgotten my pocket-book; it was for that reason——"

"But we have just sent it," the mother shouted. "We thought you were sure to miss it."

"Indeed! Then my landlady will keep it for me."

Stephensen smiled a little ironically, as much as to say: "Is it for my sake you take all this trouble?"

"But you will now remain here for the evening?" Minna said, and bent her head over some music through which she was looking.

"Yes, of course Mr. Fenger will stay.

We shall have a jolly time," the mother said.

I expressed my thanks, and sat down near the window.

The long box with the ferns had been put out on the window-sill. In the midst of all her troubles Minna had still been tenderly careful that they should have the benefit of the rain. The single-leaved ferns, which we had found together, stood in the middle and noddingly moved their slim stalks. Some acacia leaves and a bit of bent cherry branch glittered in the light from within. The thick, fine rain sounded like a low whispering, and with it a water-pipe mingled its babble. From the somber background irregular dotted panes stood out, between which a few staircases mounted up like interrupted columns of light. I stared out, and was suddenly overcome by the strange depressing feeling of the sadness and monotony of human life. It was to me a very extraordinary idea that all these lights were signs of just as many existences, in which possibly there was not to be found any similarity except modest conditions, disappointments, and emptiness, a miserable and joyless fate, like the monotonous darkness, which at the same time isolated and collected the lights. "But," thought I, "could there in any of those rooms be so queer a party as was collected in this?"

"Jolly" was not exactly the correct expression for our mood. Minna, absentmindedly, struck some chords, as if she had not much wish to play, but still would do her best to break the silence. The mother, who had nothing more to say, gave a deep sigh—that was *her* contribution. I felt the pressing necessity of making some remark, but Stephensen anticipated me.

"Is it pretty in the neighborhood of Meissen?" he asked, evidently to let me know that he was aware of the plan.

"Oh no, I cannot say that it is. It is the contrary to that of the south, where Saxonia increases in beauty the farther one descends. Don't you know our beautiful rhyme—

" 'Denn gleich hinter Meissen—
Pfui Spinne!—kommt Breissen.' " [1]

She said this, in spite of a certain nervousness, so funnily, that we all burst out laughing, her mother as heartily as any of us.

"Oh yes," she whimpered, while she dried the tears from her large cheeks, "Why should you now get this sudden idea to visit Wilhelmina . . . when you have been away all the summer? Surely you must have had enough country air! Honestly I believe there is too much fuss made about this fresh air."

The naïve explanation of Minna's trip came as a relief, though I had an idea that it was not quite genuine. If all of us had understood the situation, it would have been too trying, and we should have felt that we might as well speak openly of what we all knew. The good woman's presence placed us on those more conventional terms which are so well fitted to hide the real emotions.

"And such cozy evenings we might have had," Mrs. Jagemann continued. . . . "We might, for instance, have arranged for whist. Can you remember, Mr. Stephensen, how often we amused ourselves in that way when you lodged here, and my good husband still lived? . . . Oh dear me, yes, those were happy times, such a family party, h'm, so to speak, . . . true, I was always being sat upon by my partner."

"Not by me, I hope," Stephensen said with his most amiable smile.

"Oh dear no, Mr. Stephensen! You, who always are so considerate and tactful! But my good husband was often

---

[1] "Then just after Meissen—
Damn it—lies Breissen" (Saxonian for Prussia).

nasty; he also got angry when he had no luck. Indeed, upon my word, he did . . . oh dear! Poor Jagemann could not endure misfortune."

"He was a good player, I remember."

"Good indeed, I should think so; he really was good at everything he undertook, was poor Jagemann. . . . But it's just the same in cards as in other things, what can one do with bad cards?"

Or with a bad partner, I thought.

"Oh dear me, yes, my good husband surely might have been something more than a poor teacher in a public school, but what are we to do? Bad people, Mr. Stephensen! Oh yes, and then fate, as you know—misfortune."

Stephensen tried to look sympathetic. I had not taken my eyes away from Minna. She still sat at the piano, but was half-turned towards us. It was evident that this talk irritated her; the smile round her lips grew more and more mocking, and every now and then she shrugged her shoulders.

"I think it is a good likeness you have caught in your picture there of Jagemann," I remarked to Stephensen.

"Oh yes, something of the old 'Tartar' has got into it, though he could look more amiable."

"It reminds me very speakingly of father," Minna said.

"Oh dear me, yes, indeed!"

"At times I have good luck with such light pencil drawings, but the pastel of Minna, which cost me so much trouble, is really a smudge. I ought not to allow it to hang on the wall."

"Please don't, Mr. Stephensen. How can you say so? That beautiful painting! At that time we had not one other one in colors; at least there was another one with children in a boat, and I honestly thought it was very pretty, but Minna wouldn't allow it to be here, so I had to put it into the bedroom. . . . Well, later on you were so kind as to send that lovely picture over the sofa. . . . But Minna's

picture, no, you mustn't say that, one can clearly see who it is meant for——"

"But only very dimly who it is," Minna said.

"Oh, you really are a naughty child!" Stephensen laughed.

"There you are, Madam! It's no use for you to be so kind, the picture can't be saved. But one might make a new one, and, for instance, just such a pencil sketch."

"Have you painted at all to-day, Mr. Stephensen?" I asked.

"No, the light was too bad. . . . I could only soil the canvas over, so that to-morrow, anyhow, I may not look at the white stuff."

"Do all painters use such disparaging expressions about their art?" Minna asked. "It seems that one never hears anything from you all but 'soiling,' 'daubing,' or, at most, 'smearing.'"

"Quite right," Stephensen answered, smiling; "it is a rather ordinary artistic *façon de parler;* there is a bit of self-criticism in it, and still more affectation and perhaps perverted vanity. I will try to get rid of that habit. By the way, you ladies have a similar habit when speaking of your 'strumming,' what you were doing a minute ago."

"Oh, really you can't compare that!" Minna exclaimed, insulted on behalf of his art. "You are trying to make me appear foolish."

We now both asked her to play seriously. She at once turned towards the piano, opened some music, and started a Prelude by Chopin. Stephensen went into the hall and came back with a sketch-book in his hand. I thought he was going to draw Minna at the piano, though in reality his position was not suitable, but I soon felt that his attention was fixed upon me. I was annoyed that he should sketch me without my permission, but he smiled —one could not deny there was something attractive in his smile—and pointed with the pencil to Minna. "Is it really for her he is going to draw me?" I thought. "It is a queer idea, but in a way rather a nice one." And I sat as still as a mouse, listening to the music.

One Prelude followed the other. She played absent-mindedly and with not nearly her usual amount of expression. One could hardly expect anything else, but I regretted it; I was very proud on her behalf, and should have liked to see her showing off—even to Stephensen. He, for his part, was hardly a very attentive listener, as he was busy drawing, sometimes bending forward in order to see better, or measuring with the pencil in the air.

When Minna had played about half an hour, she turned towards us: "Have you had enough now?" Without waiting for an answer she jumped up and exclaimed, "What is it you are doing there?"

"Oh, it's not bad at all," she said, looking over Stephensen's shoulder. "It's a good likeness."

"Well, it might be worse."

"Oh, I say! Sweetly pretty!" the mother exclaimed.

"If only, I think——"

"What?" Stephensen asked and looked up.

"No, perhaps I'm wrong, and it is impertinent of me to make suggestions."

"Not at all! A fresh eye easily discovers something, and you know the face better than I do."

"I think the chin ought to be larger."

"Really?" Stephensen measured, rubbed out and corrected, bent forward in order to see, and altered again. "Yes, indeed, it improves it; I even think it might stand a little more. You have a good eye, Minna!"

"Perhaps you ought also to let the Adam's apple be a little more prominent, it is so characteristic in him. Just see how it has helped!"

I got up, curious to see my own likeness. The drawing was only lightly sketched, but firm and true in the lines. As one does not know oneself in profile, I could not have much opinion as to the likeness. But Minna was satisfied, and it secretly pleased me that she had taken a small part in the finishing touches. Stephensen's smile betrayed the childish pleasure that an artist always feels when he has succeeded in something. He signed and dated it, loosened the leaf with his penknife and gave it to Minna.

"Thanks!" she said heartily, but without showing any surprise. "It pleases me immensely! There is something much more satisfactory in such a drawing than in a photograph—more charm. I don't know quite how it is, but I believe it makes me think of olden days, when everybody did not have dozens of photographs of themselves to distribute among their friends and acquaintances, and when people must have been so happy to get such a portrait of a person dear to them."

"That hasn't occurred to me before," Stephensen said. "It's more natural to me to think of the art value, but there is much in what you have just said."

"Quite true," I remarked. "It is the way of getting a likeness which always has existed, and it has not only the aristocracy of many ancestors, but is also free from the tiresome democratic point, that Jack and Tom have the same picture which is precious to us."

"Oh dear me, yes!" Mrs. Jagemann exclaimed. "The world has been progressing since I was young! Photography is indeed a wonderful invention, and it produces better likenesses than anything else."

Minna smiled at her mother, who had no notion that her remark was so little in harmony with the reflection to which it was supposed to give support.

"Yes, you are quite right in that," Stephensen admitted with his flexible readiness to smooth over a difficulty, "only there is something in the art of photography which is called re-touching and which indeed can produce strange results."

"Have you never tried to draw yourself?" Minna asked him.

"Not yet. Strangely enough I have not so far received any summons from the Uffizi Gallery in Florence to contribute to its unique collection of self-portraits."

"Suppose I ask you to do so now?"

"Then I will try during these lonely evenings, if the hotel mirror does not make me too crooked. . . . But I must now make use of the time and draw you."

"Am I really to pose? I don't know anything worse."

"At all events it's a long time since I troubled you," Stephensen answered gently, and with a strange sorrowful tone in his voice that was quite new to me, and that clearly enough said: "And who knows whether I shall ever do it again!"

Minna sat down without any further objection, and altered her position once or twice according to his directions. He began eagerly to sketch. But soon he stopped, discontented with the light; I placed the lamp in a better position for him. In so doing I noticed that the old globe with the break had been changed for a new one, in honor of Stephensen, as it seemed; but whether Minna or her mother had been so tender over his artistic susceptibilities I did not know. Most probably Minna would have had more important things to think of than the broken globe, and Mrs. Jagemann had evidently not only a deep reverence for "Mr. Stephensen, artist," but also a certain motherly feeling from the time he had been there as a lodger. She gave him now and then an affectionate side-glance, while she rocked her big head over her knitting, as if she said to herself: "Oh dear me, yes, there he sits again! Yes, my word! Why didn't you come before?"

I did not doubt that, if the choice had been left to her, I might as well have retired at once. And though I was quite sure that Minna was far from wanting to take her advice, and that on the morrow she would be quite free from her influence, I had all the time a painful sensation that I was out of favor.

Minna, on the contrary, shared her kindness equally between us both in a natural and unhesitating manner, which astonished me, as if it did not give her the least difficulty to steer between her two suitors, each of whom seemed to have the same claim to her future. As she had hardly expressed her pleasure over possessing the drawing of me, before she asked Stephensen to draw one of himself for her, so she did not once allow either one of us to get anything at the cost of the other; even if she employed a little art and calculation in this impartiality, she used still more natural feeling and instinctive tact. She talked to both of us— the subject of conversation was the German Theater and Dramatic Art—but as she was being drawn half-profile, she could seldom look towards Stephensen, and even when she answered him her eyes and attention seemed to be fixed upon me. He was very much occupied by his work, but liked her to talk so that her face might retain its liveliness.

Only when he drew the important part round the mouth she was to sit silent, and she then made her mother praise the old days at the theater. Truly enough it did not appear that Mrs. Jagemann had often visited the theater, but she had been captivated by Devrient, whom she had, however, seen more in her father's restaurant than on the stage; and what she had heard from others, who had more idea of art, was so mingled in her rather muddled brain with the little she remembered herself that she grew just as sentimental as if she had lived and breathed in the temple of Thalia and Melpomene.

"Oh dear me, yes, in those days we had

artists! You ought to have seen our thea-
ters then, Mr. Stephensen! Davison!
surely you have heard of him? You know
the beautiful villa which he built, just opposite the Bohemian railway station; in
those days it was something new, we have
so many others now. Yes, he made a lot
out of it, but it was also worth the money
to see him. As Mephistopheles, terrifying!
Now I would not dare to see it for anything. But at last he also went off his
head, you know. And Emil Devrient,
that was in quite a different way, elevated, ideal, Max in Wallenstein, one was
transported; the present generation cannot realize this at all. Poor Jagemann said
the same—he would not go to the theater
any more. Surely you remember, when
you praised anything which you had seen
here, he always said: 'No, you ought to
have seen so-and-so.' *His* favorite, however, was Madame Schröder-Devrient;
indeed, I myself remember her too,
grandly tragic, plastic, 'classic plastic,'
poor Jagemann said; he never missed an
evening when she played. It was before
we were married, she left the theater before she was fifty. Oh dear me, yes, . . .
such artists . . . indeed it was a glorious period."

"But it is everywhere the same, Mrs.
Jagemann; also in Denmark the old generation say they can't stand the theater
any longer, and that we poor things never
have seen proper comedy."

"Well, there you are, bad times, Mr.
Stephensen! . . . No, it was different in
those days, it was nice to be in Dresden
then. One did not see all that stiff Prussian Military, and we were not burdened
with all these taxes. Oh, what couldn't
one get for one's money! Meat has now
gone up one-third in price . . . oh dear,
oh dear!"

And, shaking her head, she got up and
went towards the door.

Minna laughed and recited—

"How love and truth and religion
    From out of the world had fled,
How very dear was the coffee,
    How scarce was the gold, we said."

"Well, you have not forgotten your
Heine," Stephensen remarked.

"Oh no," she exclaimed eagerly.

I thought of the way in which Stephensen had shown his knowledge of Heine,
and I suppose that I did not look very
cheerful. Minna, who seemed to read my
thoughts, sighed deeply. Stephensen placed
the sketch-book on the table, and leaned
back with his hands behind his back.

I think we were all surprised by being
so suddenly brought back to ourselves
and our conditions, and that we felt how
impossible it was to get away from them.

Mrs. Jagemann came in with the table-
cloth, and Minna got up and offered to
help her to lay the table. But at supper
our silence was much greater than our
appetites.

Still the picture was unfinished, and
Stephensen started again directly after we
had risen from the table.

"Well, now it will have to be finished,
it is also getting late, and I suppose
Minna will have to rise early on account
of the journey," he said, after having
worked for about a quarter of an hour.

I went up to him and could not restrain
an outburst of admiration. The drawing
was not so firm and boldly worked as the
one of me, but even this apparent anxiety
gave it a certain pleasing grace, and the
expression was none the less successful
from being given very sketchily; one anticipated something more than was seen.

"It might be better, but even if I had
the time I should be afraid to try and improve it."

He also loosened this leaf with his penknife.

"And who is to have that one?" Minna
asked.

Stephensen handed it to her: "You,

Minna, in order to give it to the one of us whom you think will need it most."

There was a deep and sad earnestness in his voice, which trembled just a little with an exceedingly sympathetic sound. It was the only hint that had been given in the course of the evening of the decision on hand, and nobody had so far been more considerate in keeping the conversation in safe channels than Stephensen. The unexpected plainness almost frightened us—perhaps not the least himself, but I, for one, was pleased that we had not during the whole evening deceived ourselves as to the solemnity of the situation, but for a single moment had looked it straight in the face. It was like a solace for the conscience. I even felt a certain gratitude to Stephensen for the moral courage that he had shown. But, to tell the truth, a bitter feeling soon mingled with it: the recognition of his superiority. I was certain, that had I tried to say something like this I should have failed—it would have come out in a clumsy, upsetting manner, and would only have left a painful discord, instead of being followed by a sigh of relief. Just in the same way as on the previous day upon the terrace, and also during this evening, he had succeeded in keeping everything on neutral ground, so was he followed by the same success, when now, stepping outside this ground, with bold hand he touched what we had considered "tabooed." This success only depends upon assertiveness, and it was this very assertiveness that extorted the silent confession from me, the most painful of all towards a rival suitor —that he was more of a man than I. I tried, to be sure, to console myself with the reflection that this "manliness" was but the outward appearance of manliness, which, after all, only proves greater experience in social life; but all the same it was both mortifying and alarming.

Minna accepted the leaf without a word and with downcast eyes. She placed it in her blotter next to my portrait, and this proximity I considered to be of good omen.

I also remember looking for that boot-shaped spot on the wall-paper, which was not so easily found in the lamplight, so that I might prevent the bad omen which might have been in that fancy, when I took leave of Minna: "Perhaps you never will see this spot again." If I had neglected to look at it, that omen might still be in power! I was in these days as superstitious as an old witch, because only my sphere existed, and everything was bound to have a meaning for it.

Mrs. Jagemann sat in her chair, dozing with open eyes; she understood nothing of the feelings which stirred us, but murmured mechanically—

"Sweetly pretty—oh dear me, yes, that's talent and no mistake."

We still kept on talking for a quarter of an hour about indifferent things—in order to postpone the moment of parting. At last we tore ourselves away.

Minna lighted us out to the stairs. The front door was still open.

I let him step out first. He turned, and lifting his hat, held his right hand towards me.

"You said yesterday evening, Mr. Fenger, that we parted as enemies. Just look, now we have spent quite a friendly evening together. In reality, we cannot hate one another; for whichever of us is going to be the favored one the other is bound to wish him happiness—for her sake."

"You are right, Mr. Stephensen. But our paths lie in different directions. Farewell!"

We parted.

It had stopped raining. Between the ragged clouds a star sparkled here and there over the shiny roofs. The wet stones and the pavements shone for a long distance with a deserted and sad light.

CHAPTER VIII

The following day I went, as usual, to the Polytechnic. But before going I wrote to my uncle.

I visited the Hertzes after dinner, in order to be able to give my friend some information about his father's condition. The old man was in bed; he coughed and had a little fever.

Hertz inquired at once for Minna, and asked why she had not come.

"We thought you were inseparable," Mrs. Hertz added.

It was a good thing that the yellow venetian blinds were down; otherwise the distress caused by her words would have been evident. I felt that I changed color, and that a sudden spasm of pain had taken away my breath. In as indifferent a manner as I could assume I said where she had gone, and gave them her love.

The old people seemed very astonished that she had gone away so suddenly without saying good-bye. "And the day before yesterday she had known nothing about it!"

"She only had the letter yesterday," I said. "Her cousin wished so much that she should come at once, she was not well—depression, I think."

"Yes, then I can imagine she had to go," Mrs. Hertz said; "Minna is always so kind when any one is ill."

"What a pity it should be just now," Hertz complained. "I had looked forward to her coming in these days, she might have played to me. The drawing-room door could have been left ajar, she plays so beautifully."

I hurried to get away from this dangerous subject, and told them about my uncle's letter, which called me to England much earlier than I had expected.

"Already, in the course of the month!" Hertz exclaimed. "Yes, Dresden is just like an hotel, where one comes in and the other goes out. Only such old folks as we are stick, till one fine day we are buried here. Last year the painter Hoym moved to Berlin, and Professor Grimm, who was a very learned Kantian, went to Hamburg a couple of years ago. . . . Well, you are young and had to start work one time or another."

"But there is one for whom that time in Dresden means a lot," Mrs. Hertz remarked.

"Yes, poor Minna——" Hertz was seized by a fit of that dry cough which every now and then interrupted the conversation.

"I have not yet said anything to her, the thought of having to leave her has already made me quite desperate. I have been very doubtful whether I ought not to try to make my uncle give up this plan."

"No, no, dear Fenger," the old man said eagerly, stretching out his hand—"don't do that. Work cannot be controlled, controlled by our inclinations. . . . First duty, work the sooner the better. Man's love works—woman's abides."

"You must not talk so much, it strains you," Mrs. Hertz told her husband. "But it is like that, we two old ones have known it too, once upon a time. . . . Don't worry too much over it. Minna is a sensible girl and a faithful soul, she will also have confidence in you. . . . Be sure she will get through the waiting time more easily than you now imagine."

"I hope so, dear Mrs. Hertz. At the same time I believe that you always had a calmer mind and more balanced temperament than Minna, and therefore in your youth suffered less from such a separation."

"Yes, that's true," said Hertz,—"for Minna, it will be more difficult. . . . But we must all struggle, each one with his burden, and it is well for everybody that it should be so."

"Anyhow it is not in those kind of

struggles that one succumbs," said Mrs. Hertz cheerfully. "I do not think one need even fear a wound, and the hardships one is sure to get over. And of one thing you may be certain, we shall be all we can to the dear girl, and as far as an old couple like ourselves can help her she won't be in need of friends."

"I could never wish better friends for her, and it is the greatest consolation to me that she has here a second home, where she will always be understood, and where the dear remembrances we have together will be treasured."

I got up and gave Hertz my hand.

"Now you must rest and not be tempted to speak. I wish I could play to you. When I get home I shall write to your son, and then I can give him fresh news."

"Yes, give him my love, and tell him not to worry. I mean that he is such a loving son, but you see for yourself it is nothing serious."

Mrs. Hertz nodded, with her calm, habitual smile.

"It is good of you to think at once of writing to Immanuel. Now, you will not see each other for a long time, and he is so fond of you. You must look him up on your way."

"I had already decided to do so. . . . Good-bye!"

During this conversation, I had momentarily forgotten the dreadful uncertainty in which my love was involved. But though this consciousness now returned with full force, the danger seemed less, and I was more inclined to take a brighter view of the future than I had been since my interview with Minna. This kind Philemon and Baucis couple were so intimately interwoven in the peaceful idyll of our love, that it needed only this meeting to refresh its colors and infuse them with a life-like light that drove away all fear of an impending tragic shadow. I had found them true friends, still pos-sessed with the same confidence in our mutual happiness as before, and at a moment when this happiness was, I knew, in peril; and I considered this confidence to be still more valuable, because it rested upon ignorance, a circumstance that would, surely enough, have diminished its value in other people's eyes. But I just needed a support that had not even felt the shock. "Their confidence is not destined to meet with disappointment," I said to myself; "all will turn out for the best,—old Hertz shall not die, and I shall not lose Minna."

This conclusion was not exactly logical. But even had it been so, at this visit to the sick-bed I might, had I been less occupied by my own fate, have remarked many signs to fill me with fear that a stronger Disputant—the strongest of all —would say, *"Nego majorem."*

CHAPTER IX

When I had finished the letter to Immanuel Hertz, I went out for a walk. With yesterday's rain a change in the weather had set in. Clouds drifted over the sky and a piercingly cold wind blew, as if it were November. I strolled about in the Villa-quarter, sauntering through the park—where the ridiculously dressed-up gigantic nurses promenaded with the perambulators—and roamed over the Grosser Garten, constantly looking up the roads and paths where we had walked together. At last I sat for a long time on the little hill at the Hercules Avenue. It was the hour of sunset, just like that evening a fortnight before; but all the fascination of the light was missing, and one saw nothing of the distant mountains of Saxon Switzerland. My head was heavy and incapable of thought; the sanguine feelings that had cheered me after the visit to the Hertzes had disappeared, without, however, allowing the previous melancholy tendencies, which considered everything as lost, to take their place. I was filled with a strange and dull restlessness.

When I went home I lay down on the uncomfortable sofa; so short was it that I had to place my legs over the one arm onto a dirty antimacassar. I did not light the lamp; a street-lamp threw enough light into the room to enable me to distinguish the objects, and to prevent me from being troubled by the darkness; I was neither tempted to sleep, nor in fact to do anything. As I lay in this condition for hours, I mentally reviewed all that I had experienced in these last days, beginning with the previous evening at the Jagemanns', and proceeding backwards from my discussion with Minna, to the one with Stephensen; farther back I did not get. There was sufficient material; I recalled every word that had been exchanged, the tone of voice, the expression of face, gestures and movements, as precisely and carefully as if I had a special purpose in doing so, or as if, somewhere behind me, a secretary had been sitting to whom I was dictating. When, at last, I went to bed, this train of thought, having once been put in motion, could not be checked. But instead of appearing in order, as before, in its proper place and turn for a perspicuous inspection, the whole mass now thrust its way rebelliously forward, while each separate item wanted to assert itself, and the last would be the first. Had all the soldiers in King Mithridates' army appealed at the same time to his famous memory, and rushed forward pell-mell in order to catch hold of him and shout, "Do you remember *me* also? What's my name? What countryman am I? Where have I distinguished myself? Where did I get this scar?"—then that royal master of mnemonics would have found himself in an overwhelmed condition, similar to the one which kept me awake until daylight began to steal into the room.

Late in the forenoon I woke up with a painful heaviness in the back of my head. I did not want to go to the Polytechnic; these last weeks' study would not be of much importance, and, besides, I could hardly remember a single word of the previous day's lecture. I went out in the hope of curing my headache, and strolled about near the Zwinger and in the Theater Square. But I was not accustomed to see the town by midday light with Minna, and it therefore appeared to me without charm and painfully strange; all that I saw displeased me, just in the same way as it would have done to walk about in Berlin or Copenhagen in this state of mind.

On a theater placard stood "Kätchen von Heilbronn." We were to have seen it together this evening!

I soon went back to my house, the lodging-like discomfort of which abolished the idea of "surroundings," and isolated me, as it were, in an empty room. There I lay on my bed—the sofa was too much of a wreck—and kept reviewing the numerous, closely united remembrances, like a dying Alexander who is bidding good-bye to his soldiers; they haunted me on my afternoon walk like a hearse, new crowds joining on at each new street, road, and pathway, and when I at last went to sleep, it was in the shadow of the banners borne by the death-watch.

While I was dressing on the following morning, I felt slack and disheartened at the prospect of the amount of worries that I had conjured up and could not drive away.

I now only wished to get free of the spell.

"Could one but kill time during these dreadful days of waiting," I thought, "or escape from oneself and all one's thoughts."

I recalled the one day of waiting in

Rathen, and how then a fat novel had kept me company. At once I hurried to a library and asked for *The Three Muske-teers,* which I thought would be suitable. While the librarian was looking for it, I opened a thick book lying on the desk. I got a sort of stab when my eye fell on the name "Minna." "Minna's matchless beauty and elevated mind conquered all his hesitations"—I still remember every word of the sentence. I turned the pages over, opening here and there—almost everywhere, "Minna"! She was sailing on the mountain lake in moonlight—was dressing for the ball—was casting herself crying, and sweetly blushing, into her mother's arms.

"Is this book disengaged?" I asked the librarian, who had brought *The Three Musketeers.* He said that it was, and I took both books home with me. I had not even looked for the author's name—both this and the title I have now forgotten. With regard to its contents and style, the Rathen novel was in comparison a true masterpiece, and 1 should surely have thrown it aside after reading the first twenty pages, if the heroine had been named Adelheid or Mathilde; but I now read it faithfully through line by line, and the constantly recurring name put me into a rather excited, but still benevolent mood, while the sometimes trivial, some-times fabulous, incidents that befell only most uninteresting people, just suffi-ciently occupied my mind to keep me from thinking.

During the afternoon I interrupted the influence of this narcotic in order to call on the Hertzes.

"Is Mr. Hertz still in bed?" I asked the old servant who opened the door.

"Indeed the master is in bed, indeed he is," the old woman answered, and shook her head. "Please step into the drawing-room, Mr. Fenger. I will tell the missis; she will be pleased to hear you are here, sir."

The drawing-room gave the double im-pression of too great order, and yet a cer-tain disorder, which a room gets when it has not been used for some days. The chairs stood exactly in their places, but on one of them a forgotten duster was ly-ing. On the corner of the table nearest the hall door several newspapers were heaped up, one on the top of the other, as smooth as when they had been delivered. The draft of air from the unclosed win-dow had blown an open letter to the floor. However natural all of this was, it added to the uncomfortable feeling that had been aroused by the old servant's troubled manner; and a deafening noise from the street corner, where all the different kinds of vehicles passed, quite confused me.

I was still standing with my hat in my hand when, after a few minutes, Mrs. Hertz entered. She had weary, perhaps tear-stained, eyes, and the smile on her lips only seemed to linger there from habit.

"My husband is sleeping, dear friend," she said, giving me her hand. "He is not getting on at all well."

"Is he worse?"

"Yes, the fever has increased; he also has pain in his side when coughing; the one lung is attacked."

"My God! You don't anticipate dan-ger?"

I turned quite cold with fear, not so much because of the dear old man's life being in peril, but because of the fixed idea which had constructed a connection between his health and my love.

"Good gracious," I thought, "suppos-ing he dies after all, and I lose Minna!"

Mrs. Hertz, who could not, of course, have any idea of such a thought, regarded my evident emotion as a pure sign of sympathy and friendship for her hus-band; she thanked me with a grateful look, as she answered—

"Danger there might well be in such an

illness for an old and feeble man. I must be prepared for the worst."

She sat down on the sofa, and asked me to sit beside her.

"I can see you wonder that I speak so calmly and openly about it. . . . Perhaps my nature has something to do with it, but I also think that the parting by death looks much more terrifying to a young person than to one who anyhow can only have a short time to survive and to miss. You are now thinking to yourself, 'If I had the danger of losing Minna, how different and heartbroken should I be—after all she must have a cold heart.' "

I looked down, and the whole room seemed to swim. How did she get this idea? Why did just these words come to her lips, that in quite a different way than she could suspect were exactly upon the track of my most secret thoughts? Wasn't it an inspiration, a voice of warning? Perhaps it meant that I ought to give her my confidence. I could not make up my mind, and all the while I mumbled thoughtlessly—

"Surely not. How can you believe it? I could never entertain such a thought!"

"See, now you already have tears in your eyes!" she exclaimed, and patted me in a motherly way. "You are very sensitive—unusually so, but don't be ashamed of that, at least not towards a woman; you will be a good husband. How can I believe it? Because it is natural for you to think that. But if you had lived a married life with Minna, and you both had grown old in love—for one can do that without love degenerating, believe me—then you would look on death quite differently. You would only see in it a short separation, yes, hardly even that . . . for I don't suppose you are a materialist, Fenger?"

"Materialist? No, I don't think I can be called that, but——"

"But perhaps you have your doubts as

to the life to come. Or perhaps you have not thought much about death, and in that you have done right. Life still for a long time offers you more than enough to think of. . . . With regard to myself, I have always wished that I should be the one to close my husband's eyes. Should I die before him, the thought would trouble me dreadfully that he would be left alone for his last years. It is so much worse for an old man who all his days has been accustomed to be cared for and looked after—we women know better how to take care of ourselves. Then I also have Immanuel, thank goodness!"

"It is a loving and beautiful thought of yours, Mrs. Hertz, but surely you will both still live many years, and your wish may all the same be fulfilled."

"Perhaps. Will Minna soon return?"

"I don't know."

"Have you not had a letter yet?"

I became very confused, and thought that my embarrassment must reveal to her that there was something amiss. But she laughed.

"It's true she has only been away two days, so I suppose it was too much to expect. Perhaps she knows from you how Hertz was when you were here last?"

"No . . . I . . . really have not yet written."

"How is that? It is not like you, Fenger."

The old lady looked at me as if she suddenly suspected that there was something odd about this journey; and, had not her own grief so completely occupied her mind, my agitation must have betrayed me, and she would have compelled me to tell her everything. But now the womanly instinct was unfortunately blunted; she at once forgot her former thoughts, looked past me, and sighed.

"I am going to write to-night; I postponed it until I had been here. And of course I will tell her what you have said. But won't you write yourself? It would be better if she heard directly from you how things are; surely she would come at once, immediately."

"I should like it very much if she came; but it is too painful for me to summon her here, as if to say good-bye—I *dare not*. Perhaps it is *superstitious,* but one ought not to anticipate misfortune."

"But I? May I not ask her to come?"

All my hope came to life. I saw an infallible way to salvation, if she was safe inside this house before she made her choice. Everything here would plead my cause, dumb but insisting, if she was silent; eloquent and persuasive if she gave her confidence. What was Stephensen here? A sick, perhaps dying, old man's blessing would seal her pact with me. My conscience had forbidden me to make her seek advice from the old folk in her trouble, but it surely permitted me to take advantage of a coincidence, which seemed to me a finger of fate.

"Yes, write, dear friend! But you must try not to exaggerate the danger, for her sake also, the dear child! She will take it to heart! She will judge best herself what to do, therefore do not urge her too much to come—perhaps her cousin needs her still more."

"Oh, I do not think there is anything much the matter with her."

"Then I do not understand how you can let her waste several days of the few weeks you still have left here in Dresden. So you have not yet told her that you have to leave so soon for England?"

"I have . . . just to-night I was going to write it—after all I could not call her back the next day, but the combined news will make her come at once, very likely the day after to-morrow. . . . Now tell me, can I help you in any possible way? To fetch medicine? No! But perhaps if I came round to-night to help you with the sitting up?"

"I sit up myself most of the time, and a night nurse is coming, a Sister. Besides

you look yourself as if you needed rest; you must be overworked, my dear! I suppose it is to drive away the monotony while Minna is away that you overwork yourself, but that you musn't do, do you hear? Farewell!"

I went straight home in order to write the letter.

How happy did I feel at again being able to write to her!

Willingly would I have filled one sheet after another, but I only permitted my pen, as shortly as possible, to inform her of Hertz's critical condition and of the curtailment of my stay in Dresden owing to my uncle's altered plans. Certainly I should have liked to have kept back this last information until she had made her decision, and then, if she had decided in my favor, to have told her myself. But it would not do for her to come to Hertz without knowing it.

Though I had considered it my duty not to give way to my feelings, a strange tone had involuntarily stolen into the letter, which disclosed all my despair and anxious longing for her. It struck me on reading it through, and I was pleased by it.

I at once took the letter to the post-office, though it was too late for the night mail, and I might as well have dropped it into a letter-box. It calmed me immensely to communicate with Minna, and in such a way that nobody could blame me for it.

The next day I went at once to Hertz.

The fever had been rather high in the night, but had now subsided, as is often the case in the morning. I only saw the servant; Mrs. Hertz was resting. I promised to call again in the evening.

I spent the day alternately reading and giving myself up to the dreams of memory. I also rang the changes on the following thoughts: "Now she has at least received my letter. . . . Surely there is still a train from Meissen (I got the newspaper from my landlady in order to make sure)—and she has only half a mile's drive to the station. Perhaps—yes, very likely—she will come to-night—and it's possible—yes, it is almost certain that I shall meet her at the Hertzes', she will at once hurry to them. . . . She will be much upset, the motherly Mrs. Hertz will treat her as being engaged, perhaps the old man is conscious, and will enjoy seeing us together. When the evening or night has advanced a little she will have to go home. I will of course accompany her,—that will be almost necessary,—and the whole thing will come right by itself, as if there had never been any Stephensen in existence."

Twice, at the hours when the post arrived, I became excited; never can a lover have been farther from wishing a letter from his sweetheart than I was on that day. But the critical times passed by without result, and after the last delivery I breathed freely.

It was quite dark in the room when I prepared to go to Hertz.

Suddenly the door opened a little: "Here's a letter for you," the girl said, and handed something white to me.

I became completely rigid with terror. At this hour? I told myself that it was impossible!

The letter was large and stiff, and this soothed my feelings. Something from the stationer, I thought.

I quickly lighted a match, and at the same moment gave an involuntary scream. The handwriting was Minna's.

BOOK V

CHAPTER I

My hand shook so violently while I lighted the lamp that I very nearly broke the chimney.

There was no mistake. On the table-cloth was lying the big strange letter, containing life or death, or what seemed to me much more glorious, and much more terrible, than life or death. For a moment I had the greatest inclination to run away. Then I nervously tore open the envelope.

The first thing that met my eye was the pencil drawing of Minna.

Just as suddenly as the image of Portia in the lead casket revealed to Bassanio his happy choice, so in the same manner did these lovely features announce my unfortunate lot.

The room swam round before me. I sat down on the sofa and took up the letter. The words danced and spread out before my eyes; two or three minutes passed before I could read—

"MY DEAR TENDERLY LOVED FRIEND,— It is all over! I must be his. I have lingered and would still like to linger, but I feel that it will not be otherwise. I feel powerless to break with my first youth, to take your dear hand and start anew, and I should have to write a whole book if I would tell you all that moves me. But at the same time it appears to me that after this everything I can write to you is of no account, and besides you know it all. There is only one thing which I must tell you in order that you shall not misunderstand me.

"I have not taken this decision because I expect to be more happy with Stephensen than with you; on the contrary—no, it really is impossible to explain myself properly; still, after all, perhaps you have understood me. I mean to say that it is not regard for myself which has decided me, and—yes, I mean especially—(it was therefore I wrote 'on the contrary!') that if there were no past, no reproaches to be felt, or, in short, had it been something quite fresh that began, then I should have been much more certain of being happy with you than with him. But, do you see, *now,* as it is, I should not be able to make you happy, as you deserve. I should feel a traitor towards my first love. It is true that this feeling perhaps might cease; but circumstances might also arise that made it unnaturally intense, and with your tender loving nature you would in that case suffer terribly under it.

"Perhaps you think I start with over-strained ideas of Stephensen, when I fear to have too much to reproach myself with, if I leave him. Not at all! I know quite well that he will not do himself any harm, and that one would hardly be able to say that I even made him unhappy, though he really loves me passionately; but perhaps I should still do him irrepara-ble harm. A nature like his is exposed to many dangers. It is difficult to make clear to you what I mean; I might easily seem vain, conceited, or overrate my influence —though no, you think much better of me than I deserve, perhaps you, in return, think too little of him. I can only say that he himself fully and firmly believes that a union with me, and *only* with me, will act ennoblingly (I really am ashamed to write it, but it is his own expression) on his character and art. In the past I myself sometimes thought the same, at least not exactly like that, only that marriage and family life may do an artist good, bind him more closely to humanity and infuse warmth into his art. I express myself badly, but hope you will understand,— but in those days (as we have openly dis-cussed, when he lived here and I hoped that he would marry me)—in those days he always stuck to his idea that an artist must be free, without such ties; he had so much to struggle with in relation to his ideal of art. Now he has come to my view, he has learnt, he says, that he cannot be without me; he hardens, gets narrow, has nothing to live for, he stretches out his hand for me, the very hand which has pulled me up out of a moral dullness and the swamp of nothingness. And now is it possible for me to refuse him?—No, no! —You see, it is my duty and my destiny —yes, my destiny!

"May God make it so that we may meet and be together, many years hence, when time has taken away the passion. The friendship it cannot touch; I know that neither of us can forget the other. But I suppose you will have to live abroad; it would be too much happiness to have you near by as friend.

"Farewell, my beloved friend, farewell!
"MINNA."

I read the letter through several times. Its loving tone calmed my pain—yes, there was even a moment when it called forth in me a certain renunciation. But the reaction soon followed.

"No, I will not, I do not recognize this settlement. What is it? It is *I* whom she loves—*I!* With him it is nothing but a reminiscence and duty—yes, and 'a des-tiny'! A nice destiny! To lay her fresh warm life as a plaster on his blasé exist-ence. . . . But it is, of course, my own fault! Why did I not take the settlement into my own hands? What a fool I have been! All this scrupulousness and generos-ity and care, that wind and sun were equally shifted; it was nothing but pre-tense for want of will; and so I allowed myself to be overawed by him. He has indeed 'pleaded his cause,' as she said that day. 'He could not be without her'— no, I should think not, when he has had enough of the flighty girls and been thrown over by rich coquettes, then he has come to think whether 'the best one' might not still be got—for old acquaintance sake. Or perhaps does it only come to this: he could not bear that another one got her, that is the real truth, I suppose."

Yes, I have been a weakling, a young fool! Would a *man* have given up such a woman?

In this way I scourged myself—yes, I even reproached myself for not having that night in Schandau gone to her room, then she would have been mine and no choice left her; I forgot that in order to let this happen, we should both have required different natures. For the nearer an action lies to its opposite, the deeper is often the natural barrier that parts them.

But now, what was to be done? Go to her, take back my words, bind her by her promise and be myself responsible for all, past and future? Yes, but where was I to find her? It was likely that she was no longer in Meissen, or in any case that I should not find her there to-morrow.

My head was aching, my confused thoughts jumped nervously here and there. It was not possible for me to keep my mind fixed to anything. How I needed to seek counsel with somebody, some person with more mature experience! My motherly friend, Mrs. Hertz, seemed my only refuge.

Yes, I would confide everything to her at once.

CHAPTER II

At this moment the door opened, and Immanuel Hertz came in.

His good-natured but plain face had a very alarmed expression.

"Hertz, you here! I hope your father is not——"

"My father is very ill. . . . I got a wire from mother, just in time to catch the train. . . . Father did not recognize me, he was in a high fever. I am afraid . . . that he . . . will pass away."

At any other time these words would have caused me the most acute grief, but now my first thought was: How shall I be able to worry Mrs. Hertz with my own sorrow, when her husband is lying on his deathbed? That Hertz was going to die seemed to me quite natural and necessary, and at the same time I felt my own hope vanish. . . . However, I tried the usual cheering phrases.

"Father is dozing now. I therefore ran over to you. . . . Come home with me, Fenger! And remain with us for the night; I know it will please father to see your face——"

His eyes were filled with tears. I quickly picked up my hat and put out the lamp—at the same instant he caught sight of Minna's picture.

"Oh, how lovely! And I have quite forgotten to congratulate you, but you will understand at such a time. But now I do it with all my heart, for I *can* do so, it is not among the instances where one says it as an empty form. . . . Minna! One can indeed call that good fortune!"

He pressed my hand as in a vise.

"Thank you, dear friend!" I murmured and turned away my face from the faint light, which the street lamp threw into the room,—"it is so kind of you, in the midst of your grief. I know how much I sympathize with you . . ."

We went down the stairs and he kept on talking about Minna. "Well," I thought, "indeed you do wear your heart on your sleeve." And in reality my surmise was right; open-hearted and indiscreet, he expected the same qualities in others.

"Indeed you have reason to consider yourself lucky. Minna, such a girl! How I envy you,—at least, not exactly envy you, though really . . . I suppose Minna has told you that I was very fond of her, more than a mere friend?"

"No, she has never even hinted at anything of the kind; altogether she has spoken very little about you, though I know she likes you. But I must admit, now you touch upon it yourself, that I have had a suspicion . . ."

"You see, I never told her, I mean proposed to her, but she felt it; women always do. No, I kept my feelings to myself; I think her heart in those days did not respond to such a feeling. Her father had just died, and also there was something else, but perhaps you know more about it than I. . . . My mother, in whom I confided,—it's no good hiding anything from her, she looks straight through one, indeed, one can with truth call her a judge of human nature; mother was of the same opinion, however much she would have liked her as a daughter-in-law. Then also I had to go to Leipzig. But I shall never forget her! Well, now you can understand how pleased I am that it should be just you whom she gets."

I felt as if I should begin to yell if this continued, and thought myself lucky when, reaching the corner where the Hertzes lived, he began to express his anxiety about his father: "So changed he looked, quite hollow-cheeked!"

The doctor had just called. I gleaned from Mrs. Hertz, or rather felt, that she had not much hope. He was lying unconscious; the temperature was alarmingly high.

Immanuel Hertz and I soon went into the drawing-room. I recalled the case of a delicate old lady, who for a couple of days had been almost given up with inflammation of the lungs, and who, after all, pulled through; it also occurred to me that I had heard from a doctor that Jews have strong vitality, even in an advanced age, and get through such illnesses. It evidently cheered up my sanguine friend.

He often went into the sick-room, and stayed either for a few minutes or longer; Mrs. Hertz remained there all the time. Occasionally I went with him, but generally I remained sitting in the drawing-room curled up on a chair, a prey to dullness and irritation. I was in the house of sorrow without being able to take my share of the grief and trouble; I was unhappy myself, but could not weep. It was so late that Minna could not any longer be expected. Everything was indifferent and tedious to me. Yes, I really was wearied and had a feeling that this state of tediousness would last forever, and grow more and more unbearable until death at last took me. I would willingly have exchanged places with Hertz—if one could say that there was anything I would willingly do.

In the middle of the night I had at last succumbed to a dull drowsiness, when young Hertz came in and said:

"He has recognized me. Father is conscious; do come in."

The patient faintly smiled when he saw me and said: "Dear Fenger!" "Minna!" he murmured a little while after.

"Surely she will come to-morrow," Mrs. Hertz said.

"Then she will play to you," I added, though I felt tongue-tied and could scarcely speak.

"Beethoven," the old man whispered, and closed his eyes.

Mrs. Hertz arranged the pillows more comfortably; she then took the temperature; the thermometer had gone down to a little under 106°. Shortly after he began to say that time and space were forms of perception, but the soul was a "Ding an sich" (a thing of itself), a substance, a "Noumenon," "Intelligible,"—these words he continually repeated.

The son, who was grieved and alarmed by these thoughts that seemed to indicate death, took his hand and said—

"Now you must not think, father, you must rest."

"Perhaps Kühne will come to-morrow, then you can philosophize together," Mrs. Hertz said.

"To-morrow!" he sighed, with quite a strange accent.

Mrs. Hertz turned away.

"Yes, indeed, wait till he comes; he understands it better than we do."

"Progressus," the old man said.

"Amen!" the Sister murmured, and crossed herself. She thought that he had called upon a saint, or perhaps a prophet.

Immanuel and I, who had heard it, could not help smiling a little. I wondered that I could still find anything to smile at. No one would have been more pleased with the humor that lay in this mistake than Hertz himself; but he was already dead to his surroundings.

For a long while Hertz remained passive, then he began to wander. The fragments which we caught seemed to indicate that he was back in the days of Königsberg and Riga. I several times heard him say: "The bell is not to be sounded,"—and I thought this was a reminiscence of that occurrence on the Exchange of which he had told us so recently. I saw again the whole of that cozy coffee-scene in the dull rainy light, with the glare of the spirit-flame flickering over Minna's dear face; it was so close to me and smiled so confidingly. Mrs. Hertz noticed a tear on my cheek and pressed my hand, touched at my sympathy.

Towards daybreak, when Immanuel and I had fallen asleep in the drawing-room, old Hertz died, without his wife, who had not moved away from his bed or taken her eyes off him, being able to say when death had come.

The nurse had been sleeping soundly for some hours.

CHAPTER III

Hertz was buried three days later in *"Der weite Kirchhof."*

I do not know whether the Jews in Dresden do not keep strictly to the Mosaic churchyard, or whether this unorthodox family had long before left the synagogue. At the time I did not think about it; I thought of nothing,—indeed I hardly realized anything. Therefore I have no idea whether an address was given, or whether it was a Jewish rabbi or Christian priest who performed the ceremony; if an eye-witness insisted that it was a Dervish or a Druid, it would be all the same to me. The whole thing stands to me as a bewildered dream. I remember that the giant Italian poplars rustled heavily and soothingly, and that some little birds twittered in the sharp cool sunlight. And then I see, a little in front of me to the right, Minna's black-draped form. It was for me, for her also I should think, not so much the dear old friend we buried, as our own short and happy life together,—our love. At the gate of the churchyard we pressed each other's hands firmly and long, the last time for many years.

Minna had told Mrs. Hertz everything.

"You have acted rightly," said the old lady to me the following day. "And poor Minna! She anyhow thinks she has acted for the best. But it pains me dreadfully, and not least for her sake."

I heard from her that Stephensen was going to Denmark in a few days in order to prepare everything, and that Minna was soon to follow. With regard to myself —I only thought of getting away. My uncle had no objection to my immediate arrival, and a week after old Hertz's death I was ready to start.

Mrs. Hertz presented me at parting with the little original manuscript of Heine's poems. How truly and bitterly it now suited my case! And still it was so precious to me. I have kept it as a treasure, the unattainableness of which had brought English collectors to despair.

* * *

Year after year passed in almost constant, strenuous work. It followed naturally that at first I hardly saw anybody except the workmen at the factory and the employees, and later on it became a custom that pleased me. I got on well enough with my uncle, though I never became very intimate with him. He was pleased with my capacity for work. After two or three years he feared that I should exaggerate it, be "a business bachelor," as he called it. He tried to persuade me to take some part in social life: a man in such a position ought to form ties.

Little by little I gave in, and gradually changed my habits.

There was neither talk of cavalcades in Hyde Park nor holidays spent in country-seats, but I made the acquaintance of some nice, middle-class families, almost all well-to-do factory owners. The young ladies were not heiresses of millions, but no less beautiful for that (those who *were* beautiful), and none of them would go into matrimony empty-handed. I had, however, another ideal in my heart, and my coolness often irritated my comrades, who considered it humbug.

At last I became acquainted with a young girl, who made a certain impression on me, and who, so my uncle assured me, was not indifferent to me, an assertion that certainly greatly flattered me. She was the only child of the owner of a cloth-factory, who was more than well-to-do, at least after Danish ideas. She showed me much kindness, though only in a social sort of way. I was not quite sure that my uncle was right in supposing that I should be able to win her heart and hand, but I thought that there was a possibility of it. At any rate I partly wished to do so, and began to pass on to less "social" terms.

It was just after Christmas, the fourth since I had left Dresden.

One evening it happened that, at a concert, I was introduced by a friend to a German musician who might have been a year or so older than I, perhaps even more.

He had played a violin Cavatina, it was a small, half-private concert; his appearances at grand concerts were very rare, though I think he was talented enough to do so. He made an ample income by giving lessons in both the violin and the piano. In his appearance there was something distinguished and something rather indolent.

It happened that we walked home together. The German was very talkative, making great game of the good English people's musical ability, and told several anecdotes with a good deal of humor, amongst others one about a rich young lady who had come to him in order to learn to play "The Moonlight Sonata" (of course the first movement) in the course of eight days, although she had never touched the piano before!

We went into a restaurant to have supper, and asked for some ale.

"Your good health," I said, and drank to him. "What an excellent drink it is!"

"Well enough in its way," the German murmured, and brushed a few drops off his moustache. "But still, I say, I wish I was sitting in 'Drei Raben' with a good glass of Spaten-Bräu in front of me, as I have done so many excellent times at this hour of the day."

"So you know Dresden?" It flew out of me. Drei Raben! The whole scene with Stephensen stood quite vividly before me.

The German laughed a little.

"I should think so, but I didn't know that you had been there. For long?"

"For two years. I went to the Polytechnic. It's now four years since I left."

"H'm. I was there two years before. Played with Lauterbach. . . . That was something different to London. What an opera! Oh yes, yes!"

He strummed with his fingers on the table, and glanced dreamily in front of him.

"Waiter, Johannisberger Schloss! With the German remembrance, German wine!"

"The golden days of youth, artist life," I thought. "He also clings to his Dresden memories; but oh, what could they be compared with mine!"

The wine came; he poured it out. "A glass for our Elbe Florentine days!" We clinked glasses, emptied them, and stared long and silently in front of us.

"I suppose you also came often to Renner, in 'Drei Raben,' I mean?" he asked in a distrait tone.

"No, I have only been there once. Perhaps you lived in the neighborhood?"

"Yes, quite close by."

"Where?" I asked at once, for my heart was beating furiously.

"Perhaps you remember a little street —Seilergasse."

"Seilergasse!" I repeated, and stared at him.

He smiled.

"Perhaps you also lived there? What a funny coincidence!"

"No, I did not exactly live there, but I went there very often. I knew a family there."

"I see! Well, well. . . . In these little streets everybody knows one another. Perhaps you have by chance heard about the people with whom I lodged; the landlord was a teacher at a public school."

"Jagemann?" I exclaimed.

The musician just raised a full glass to his lips, and spilt it so that the golden drops ran down the lapel of his coat.

"Yes, it was with them I lived," he said, and wiped himself carefully.

I now knew who my companion was. It was her first, half-childish love, the musician to whom Stephensen had seen her give the farewell kiss.

"And it was those people I used to

visit," I said; "at least—Jagemann was dead—it was madam and the daughter I went to see."

"Minna—she was a lovely girl!"

We both stared down our glasses, as if we, with Heine, saw everything there—

"But most of all the face of my loved one,
That angel-head on the Rhenish wine's gold ground."

"Do you know if she—Minna Jagemann—whether she since—has got married?" he asked at last.

I told him that she had married a Danish painter, made some remarks about his position and circumstances, and related the little I had heard of them from acquaintances; that she had had a daughter, who had died about a year ago.

The musician sat silently opposite to me, often emptying his glass and not always remembering to fill mine—he had ordered another bottle, and dedicated it with a glass to "Die schöne Jagemann." I also was silent. *"Wir schwiegen uns aus"* (We exhausted our silence), as Schumann once is supposed to have said.

When I was in bed on that night I realized that, in a moral lethargy, I had been on the brink of committing a dishonorable and foolish act, though no one would have called it the first, and all would have called it wise. From that day I ceased to visit the house of the owner of the cloth-factory.

My uncle reproached me for my fickleness. I complained of home-sickness, and told him that I wanted to visit my old friends. A week after I was in Copenhagen.

My acquaintances in Denmark were not many, and none of them associated directly with the Stephensens. But, thanks to the gossips of our capital, I heard a good deal about them at second or third hand. There could hardly be anything remarkable in my asking about the fate of a

Dresden acquaintance in Denmark; and if some people suspected a deeper interest, I did not care much what they thought. I wanted to know the real truth.

The usual opinion was that they lived happily together—it was a love-marriage, affection from youth, perhaps first love. Others said that his flirtations—a sharp tongue called them liaisons—could hardly escape her knowledge, and that she seemed to be rather passionate and impetuous. On the contrary, some insisted, she was gentle but silly. "Silly!" several explained, "she can sparkle with original thoughts, but this habit is not always agreeable to everyone; she has a very critical eye for the faults of others." "Anyhow, she's interesting," said an elderly man. "But she's without interests," remarked a young journalist. A lady, however, who lived in the flat above the Stephensens stated that she was at any rate a passionate lover of music, as she usually played half the day. This astonished everybody, as in society she had never been known to touch the piano, and she was rarely seen at concerts. Her appearance was almost unanimously admired.

I had been nearly a fortnight in Copenhagen, and still had not caught a glimpse of her. Should I simply go and call on her? I considered the question for the hundredth-and-which time God only knows, when rather late one evening I entered Café à Porta. In the outer room there were only a few visitors. Looking round in order to choose a place, I heard from a side-room a voice that could not be mistaken: it was Stephensen's, only a degree more lispingly sweet than formerly. I placed myself as quietly as possible where I could best overlook the adjoining room.

The only one I knew of the lively party within was Minna, whom I saw almost in *profile perdu*, hardly half a dozen paces from me. Stephensen apparently was sitting on a corner sofa, of which I could only see a little of the farthest end. A smiling blonde leaned her arm upon it, and evidently conversed with him; her face had a certain vulgar beauty; every minute she laid her head on one side, so that the reddish hair touched her half-bare shoulder, which peeped through a broad insertion of black lace. The laughing glances that she constantly flashed towards the hidden corner, whence Stephensen's voice sounded, proved that she was—I will not say exactly jubilant—but rather in a condition of electric illumination. One of the gentlemen addressed her by a name which I had already heard in gossip connected with Stephensen's. Minna sat leaning back and seemed to be looking down in front of her, but it was evident that she was constantly watching them.

The waiter came up to me to take my order. I was in a dilemma, as I feared that my voice would at once be recognized by Minna. But just then the whole party, with the exception of Minna, began to laugh in the boisterous manner that usually follows a story more vulgar than witty, and under cover of this noise I gave my order without disclosing myself. One of the gentlemen—very likely I should have known the famous name, which I do not doubt was in his possession, had I not been such a newcomer—expressed indignation on behalf of the party at Minna's reserve. "Why do you sit like a stick amongst us, Mrs. Stephensen? Take things more lightly, and don't be a German Philistine. . . . Remember you are amongst artists. . . . Empty your glass."—"I am only tired," Minna said.—"Then you must just drink."—"But I don't care for champagne."—"Ah, ha! Too French, too light and spirituous, it is not for you. But Rhenish wine, that you surely like? . . . Ah, I thought so! Very well! Waiter!" The waiter flew in.—"No more of this foolery, please!" she said, half angry and half amused.—"Really not? I mustn't?"—"No, but I thank you for your kindness. . . . Only let me sit and look after myself; I am so tired, and have a headache."—"You do not want to go home already, I suppose?" Stephensen's voice sounded, this time very morose. Minna did not answer, but yawned in her handkerchief; she leaned back and looked down sideways. She really appeared as if she was tired, not with an acute but with a chronic fatigue. Her face, of which I had by this time obtained a better view, was almost unchanged, only the cheeks were a little less full. I had remarked that she spoke surprisingly pure Danish, the foreign accent was very slight.

The conversation round her now grew very lively. It centered on aestheticism, if one could call it so. Names such as Ibsen, Zola, Dostoevsky, Wagner, Berlioz, Millais, Bastien-Lepage, even such scientific ones as Darwin and Mill, almost buzzed round one's head. In spite of this medley I was not so very much surprised, as during my short stay I had become acquainted with the general tone. At first it had certainly made a great impression upon me. Good gracious! what must not those people have read and heard, such an education and insight, and so many interests! But soon I grew more critical; I perceived that those who talked most were least interested, and that many who "aestheticized" most loudly did not go even so deeply as I myself, who in these years had been too occupied with business to be "up-to-date," and who, through residence in England, had been reading the works of very different authors from those who were fashionable in Denmark. I even had a suspicion that the good Stephensen himself was no adept in literature, though he grew more and more talkative; very likely he wished to sparkle before the blonde, who really seemed to be on the point of fainting with admiration. The gentleman who had wanted to order the Rhenish wine for Minna, a big man with a glorious fair beard, excited him to a constantly growing exaggerated radicalism, and altogether seemed to fool the whole company.

Stephensen's eloquent sentences at last degenerated to an absolute harangue about the art of the future. He flung about apothegms like "the democratic formulae in art," "a scientific illustration of life, in contradiction to the decorative luxury," and finished up with something to the effect that the brush in the true artist's hand ought to be a probe in the wound of society.

"Then my advice is that they should first be thoroughly washed," the fair-bearded man suggested.

The wave of laughter for some time overpowered the discussion, but Stephensen's hollow talk kept afloat like a cork. Minna lifted her eyes and looked at him. Was it possible that she was imposed upon by this bosh? I thought. The expression in her averted eyes I could not see. But then, with eyes half-lowered, she turned her head in more than profile, and I grew almost terrified by the smile of cold disgust that played round her lips, and the annoyance that darkened the brows and shone from her eyes. Thus she had looked at him, and had turned away because she felt that the expression of her feelings was too evident. Little she realized that she turned her face to one who could read its language line by line like his mother tongue, while the others, at most, could only make out a few words of those which are the same in all languages. "Weakling," whispered these firm lips; "Liar, fraud!" this open forehead cried out; "Faithless!" exclaimed those clear eyes, which could look so tenderly and now stared so hard; but the whole hard-set face sighed: "And *he* was the love of my youth!"

"But Raphael!" a youthful individual

of the party objected, "one cannot quite in that way——"

"Bah, Raphael!—'distance lends enchantment,' " the big good-natured man with the fair beard said loudly. "The distance of hundreds of years, that's what makes it. Just let Stephensen be stored for two hundred years, then you will see what kind of fellow he will turn out."

"Yes, but," the blonde exclaimed, "then all this that we now . . . our art . . . would also be antiquated, just like the old one is in our days?"

"Oh, logic!" the fair beard shouted, "your name is *simplicitas profana!* Indeed, madam! everything is relative! Even our great Stephensen is not quite absolute; therefore beware, don't take him too much *au serieux!*"

"You with your irony," Stephensen said. "Yes, let everything be relative, but we——"

He was then brought to silence, even he, by a laughter that seemed to freeze the whole party, and which I can never forget. It was Minna who laughed. She got up, held her handkerchief to her mouth, and burst out again as she turned from the party.

"What is there to laugh about in such a way?" Stephensen said, and his voice was extremely irritable.

"Nien, es ist zu drollig!" (No, it's too funny), Minna murmured. At the same minute her eyes passed over me, but if they stopped, it was only for such an atom of time that it was not possible for me to decide whether she had seen and recognized me. She slowly went towards the adjoining empty room, where the gas had already been turned off.

"Where are you going to?" Stephensen asked.

"I feel suffocated in here," she answered, and disappeared in the dark space. I heard her open a window.

The indefatigable Stephensen started again. Directly afterwards, the robust bearded man got up and went into the dark room. I put on my fur coat, for I also felt suffocated. While I paid the waiter, a strong manly voice called from the inner room: "Waiter! A glass of water."

Shortly afterwards the bearded man rejoined the party:

"Now, enough of your foolery, Stephensen. Your little wife is unwell, and upon my word she's worth more than the whole of your 'art of the future'!"

The following day I had a letter from my uncle in which he asked me when I could tear myself away from Denmark to go to Stockholm and St. Petersburg, where he had business friends with whom he wanted me to become acquainted.

Yes, I could tear myself away from Denmark, I had seen quite enough; help I could not. Run away from the place I could, but not from the miserable impression that I had received; it haunted me day and night. Only the sea-sickness in the Bay of Bothnia had sufficient elemental power to conquer it for one night. In St. Petersburg I remained for about a month, drove in a troika on the Neva, and was every second night at parties till three in the morning. I regretted that my heart was not free, so that I might have lost it to one of these Russian ladies.

It was quite natural that before I returned to England I should visit some factories in Germany. In the course of these visits I went to Saxony, and Dresden attracted me irresistibly; I made the excuse that I wanted to look over the "Art School of Industry," and form a connection with its manager.

On the way I visited Immanuel Hertz in Leipzig. He was married to a brawny Jewess, who had presented him with several children. Into his nature had come something more restless; otherwise he was the same gentle fellow. Tears came into his eyes when he spoke of his mother, who had lived with him and had died six months before, a fact which he had already written to tell me. She was buried in Dresden by the side of her husband.

"And Minna?" he asked. "We had a letter from her when mother died, but in that she spoke so little of herself. Have you seen her?"

"Only in passing; she did not notice me."

"H'm! Do you think she is happy?"

"I suppose she is, that is to say, she has had sorrows—lost a child."

"Yes, at that time she wrote to mother! Oh yes, it must be dreadful for a mother!" Then he started speaking of a Liberal newspaper of which he was half-owner, and about the opposition to Bismarck.

CHAPTER IV

In Dresden I went at once to "Seilergasse." Mrs. Jagemann had long since moved away, and the people in the house did not know where she lived. I looked sorrowfully at the summer-house in the little garden, where everything was unchanged, and I went to "zur Katze" in order to ask whether the widow Jagemann still came there. Here they knew more; Minna's mother had been dead for two years.

I walked round the town, it was to me an indispensable enjoyment to look up our precious spots; not all were untouched by time. On the terrace they had pulled down the dear little Café Torniamenti with its naïve columns, where I had got the idea to go to Rathen, and where we had met Stephensen; the streets, through which we had wandered the last time we walked together, did not exist any longer, and one could hardly find traces of them in the new quarter of pre-

tentious buildings. In Grosser Garten and the Park the buds of the bushes began distinctly to show green—we were at the end of March—and everything looked different; but on the black stems I still read the same names on the labels, which in those days we had studied together, one having a very exotic name, which most likely was easy enough in the mouth of a Maori or Tahitian, but the pronunciation of which had caused Minna to make the most comical grimaces. I remained standing there for a very long time, staring at these dry branches and twigs, and on this little label as if it was a riddle that had to be solved, but that defied solution. And really I had a feeling of not being able to grasp the whole thing; I did not understand that this plant still stood here and had the same unpronounceable name, understood still less that I myself was here and, least of all, that Minna was not here, or that I couldn't go to "Seilergasse" and embrace her. I realized nothing at all.

When at last I turned round, I saw some children a few yards away putting their heads together, laughing and running away. Evidently they thought that I was mad. And who knows? From children one hears the truth!

On my way back I passed the beautiful Renaissance Villa, which Minna and I jokingly had called ours. A new riddle! In those days it had been a matter of course that we two should build a home together, but it was a wild and ridiculous dream that we should ever be able to do it on such a grand scale. And now there was more possibility of my being able to buy this building than of taking Minna to the most modest home. Incomprehensible! Was this perhaps already a madness, that I had a feeling of not being able to understand anything, where I suppose in reality there was nothing to understand, where everything for a cool brain was clear as daylight, *had* to be so, and for me it *could* not be. Madness! Sonnenstein! And why not? "If I am lodged there," I thought, "it will always be an advantage that no Napoleon will come to drive one out."

At sunset a signal shot sounded, which announces that the Elbe rises unusually. The next morning, when I still lay in a half-slumber, I was alarmed by a second shot, by which the danger of flood is foretold. I got up at once. As I was staying at the Bellevue Hotel, I was quite close to the river. Since last evening, the porter said, people had been on the bridge amusing themselves all the night through by watching the rising of the water, and the parapet was now quite black with the crowd. But this bridge itself, which usually was lifted so proudly on its high pillars over the river, now only showed the arches spanning the muddy mass that dashed along, not like water but like a torrent of lava, whirling and grinding, covered with overturned yawls, beams and timber, barrels and bushes, which tossed, went under and came up again. I made my way to the bridge. The whole quay had disappeared and also the little stretch of meadow in front of Neustadt; over there the gardens were under water, and on this side waves foamed and whirled up against the terrace wall.

"Oh, our poor little Rathen," I thought, "what does it look like there? I wonder if the dear house, where we have experienced so much together, is flooded, perhaps even washed away."

I could not resist my desire to know what had happened, and a few hours later the train brought me to Pirna; in Saxonian Switzerland itself there was not any possibility of crossing the Elbe. When I had passed over the bridge, I turned and glanced at the town: I had not seen it since that day on the outer journey to Rathen, when it had shown itself in the frame of the cabin window, shining and wet from the summer rain, with a promising light over the gables of Sonnenstein. Now the town and the somber fortress inhabited by the feeble-minded, lay in sunlight, but it was a cold, cheerless light that contained no suggestion of Spring.

I walked over Dorf- and Stadt-Wehlen and up through the famous Zscherre-Grund, which is passed by all tourists, but was now deserted. The intimate Saxonian mountain landscapes, with their Baroc and steep shapes, moved me deeply and at the same time—strange to say—vexed me. I wished, or anyhow I thought I did so, that one of these overhanging rocks would fall down and crush me. At about four o'clock I at last reached the Bastei, stepped out on the plateau and saw the awful devastation under my feet.

Of Erbgericht's Terrace there were only the tops of the maples over the water, looking like big shrubs on the edge of the stream, which had almost entirely swallowed up its rival the "Rosengarten." Between them the river had flooded the Rathen valley, which usually discharged its modest brook into it. The three little houses, which behind some twigs of the "Rosengarten" were squeezed in between the immovable rock and the tearing stream, presented a miserable appearance. The first one was half under water; the quarry owner's house, which lay a little higher and besides had a base of about six feet, had still its entrance door free, but only for one who did not mind a bath; the water foamed against the hidden stone steps as against a reef. The little summer-house, where we had sat so often, had been torn away. The third house was even more under water. Thanks to my good travelling-glass I saw all this quite distinctly. On the flat opposite bank, round which the river curved, there was nothing to remark, except that it had receded and that the grass grew out into the water without any decided border line.

A sad sight, so much the more as it

had nothing wild in it. Seen from this dominating point the unnaturally broad river seemed, I won't say not to rush, but not even to hasten; one only perceived the enormous irresistible moving mass. Calm and peaceful it had in those days glided by our idyll, as the moving life, occupied with its own concerns, streams past the happy existences that desire nothing from it; it had broken into this idyll, destroying and washing it away; but passionless it had exercised its work of destruction, and indifferently it rushed by —like life—like fate!

A cold wind blew, it had clouded over, now it even began to snow a little. A miserable, depressing outlook, but I would not have exchanged it for a glance over a smiling landscape, through which streamed the broad thoroughfare of a frequented river. In this way I could bear to see Rathen again. I was also content to have never been on these heights with Minna.

A prosaic circumstance prevented me, however, from giving myself up too much to this elegiac mood; I was almost ill with hunger. When I had satisfied my appetite, I thought it was too late to go down to Rathen, and I postponed it to the next day. I went down towards the Elbe by a forest path, which branches off from the descent to Rathen, but is indicated as a "forbidden path." The rough forester came into my head, and I wished I could meet him. This footpath would take me to the one that Minna and I had trodden on the way home from the stone-quarry. But the penetrating wind, which splashed the ever-increasing fall of thawing snow into my face, the farther I came down, soon made me return. Up on the height it surely was easy enough to find shelter, but it was disagreeable everywhere, and I myself was less melancholy than annoyed: this whole expedition seemed to me to be a folly. As soon as the colorless sun had set I retired to my room, where

there was a horrible draught, and at last went to sleep lulled by the monotonous cradle song of soughing pines.

I woke up to find a real spring morning. The view was not changed, but I was told that the river had begun to fall. When I was on the point of leaving, a lonely visitor got up from the table, and said, "I say, is it you, Mr.—Professor! Didn't I think so!" It was the schoolmaster, Mr. Storch. I do not know whether I felt pleased or annoyed to see him, but surely enough I wished him at the bottom of the Elbe when it was evident that he intended to stick to me like a leech and wanted to come with me. He had given a holiday on account of the flood, and had now gone up to Bastei to "get an overlook." There was nothing else to do but to accept his company. I had not time to postpone the trip, unless I had once more stayed the night at Bastei.

"Look, you will get company for dinner, it might even be a whole *table d'hôte*," he exclaimed, while we were going down towards the bridge, and pointed back to a landau, which a couple of steaming horses drew up in front of the hotel. "They have come from Pirna, I know the conveyance; the proprietor of it is a regular shark, he makes the travellers pay a pretty penny."

A lady's hat appeared out of the window and allowed a long black veil to fly to one side.

"I say, there are also ladies. A young one, I bet; that's something for you."

"Now come along," I said irritably, and hurried out to the rock-bridge.

The first part we descended with rapid steps. When we came to more even ground, he began, as I had expected, at once to speak about Minna, pretending not to know that we had been engaged, as indeed perhaps he did not.

"I suppose you remember Minna Jagemann? I am sure you do; I saw myself how you flirted with her on the forest path. . . . Well, and right you were. . . . Now, just imagine, after all, she got married to that painter of whom I told you, your countryman, but 'give a dog a bad name,' you know. I suppose you haven't forgotten that I told you that she had had a sort of——"

"Yes, yes, I remember it quite well."

"And you have not seen her in Denmark? The country is not so very big."

"I have lived all the time in England."

"Oh, I see! I always thought you had got something English about you."

I made him talk about the flood and the damage it caused the poor people, and he told me that in all probability only the two innkeepers and the owners of the three houses by the river would suffer any loss.

When we came down into Rathen itself, I bade him good-bye, allowing the "English" side of my nature to come to the fore, so that the honest German did not feel inclined to force himself upon me any longer.

The flood of the Elbe had not proceeded so far, but the brook was very swollen. The simple planks that led over it were, however, still undisturbed. I went over to the Zedlitz Villa, which, of course, was closed, came past the little birch avenue, and stood suddenly at my destination, the grotto "Sophien-Ruhe." The benches had been taken in; I sat down on the stone table. The birds twittered gaily round me, the bushes breathed the soft spring air with their little green gills, and the buds of the trees showed white in the sunshine against the blue sky.

Again I had that queer feeling of not being able to understand anything: I neither understood that I was here nor that she was not here. Into my head came the remembrance of the little glow-worm, which evening after evening had sat on the same corner of the stone steps, signaling for a mate; and it seemed to me that

if I could only sit here, concentrating all my will-power on my loss, I should be able through the compulsion of nature to enchant Minna to me.

It is said that a dying person is able to review, in a second, his whole life in all its main lines, as if his consciousness was already elevated above the earthly order of time. At this moment my youth died in me, and I reviewed in parting the whole course of my love, all that I have confided to these pages, and still many more half-forgotten incidents. It appeared to me that I saw it all in a flash and from above, just as I had overlooked the whole of its birthplace from the platform of Bastei. And in taking this review, one thing struck me which I had not remarked before, the fact that we had all allowed ourselves to be led and driven almost mechanically by the stream of circumstances, without striking in energetically with a "So it must be!" Even Stephensen's way of behaving, that had certainly had the appearance of spontaneity, had in its essence the same character; he had evidently given in to his jealous longing to see Minna before she was irrevocably lost, and had thought: "Let us see what I can manage. Who knows! Perhaps, after all, she will come with me."

But now? Could nothing be altered? Was there not yet time to step in with an "I will"? A marriage is not any longer an indissoluble tie, hers was an unhappy one. I knew more certainly than any words of hers could have told me that all she had hoped for was irreparably lost, that he was found out, weighed and found wanting; while he, on his part, had long since tired of her. Besides, he was, as he often enough had boasted, a man who did not share the usual prejudices, and I suppose he, least of all, would insist that an unsuccessful union could not rightly be dissolved, or that it was justifiable to bind a wife who stayed against her will. Surely the theories of liberty are not always welcome, when they go against the men of liberty themselves. But even if his vanity shrank, *could* he in the end oppose, when *she* would and when *I* would?

Would she? She had made the trial, and it had failed. Why not give up the impossible to realize the possible? That she had guarded her love and confidence in me I felt with an unswerving certainty.

Would *I?* Yes, I would! I said it for the first time in our relations with one another, said it with triumphant joy. Tomorrow evening I could be in Copenhagen, and the day after speak with her.

Strange indeed is the dream-nature in human beings! Never, perhaps, in those days, when I had Minna at my side, had I felt so happy as in this moment, when I looked back on our first youthful love and forwards to its consummation in a tested matrimonial love, and these two parts in my will united into a single life.

So true are the myths about "Paradise lost" and "Paradise regained": happiness is a remembrance and a hope.

CHAPTER V

At this moment something happened, that at the time seemed to me supernatural, and does so still when recalling it.

The gravel crunched under light quick steps. I started. The situation reminded me so much of the old days when I had sat there and Minna had come, that I fully and firmly believed it was an hallucination. And really, it sounded exactly as if it was a repetition—a copy I could almost say of those steps. "If this hallucination continues," I thought, "I shall see her, and what will then happen to me? God help me, am I really on the point of going out of my mind, as I said, half jokingly, but yesterday . . . ?"

I jumped down from the table with a cry, and with a cry Minna stopped in front of the grotto—yes, Minna herself, no vision!

We had not yet controlled ourselves, when Stephensen appeared and bowed with an astonished, but at the same time a little ironical smile, that clearly enough said: "This is really a coincidence, which looks like a plan."

The usual exclamations: "You here, Harald? That I call a surprise!" "I thought you were in England, Mr. Fenger." "I imagined you in Copenhagen, Mr. Stephensen," masked for a few moments our painful embarrassment.

After the first nervous rapture, which the sudden sight of one's beloved infallibly produces, had calmed down, I felt a painful disappointment. The lady and her husband on a pleasure-trip together! How little did it harmonize with the relations that I had imagined between them, with the plan that had inspired me!

"I suppose southward bound, to Italy?"

"No, we shall limit ourselves to Saxony."

"I imagine you have business in Dresden, Harald?"

Minna was, strange to say, evidently the first of us to regain her self-control; she only continued to breathe somewhat quickly and irregularly. Her smile and voice—yes, even her movements, expressed the most vivid joy at this meeting.

"Very likely you are going back to Pirna? That's capital, then you can drive with us."

"There is plenty of room," Stephensen said. "It is not a victoria. And besides, I would willingly sit on the box."

He forced his usual polite smile; the lips obeyed, but not the eyes. He was obviously irritated; but Minna either did not notice it, or did not care.

"Very likely our talk will tire you, we have so much to speak of after so many years," she said.

We started at once on the return journey. In a window of the school-building stood the master. He leaned far out and continued to follow us with his eyes. Minna laughed.

"Well, my cousin still exists! Do you remember, when he met us on the forest path? God knows what sort of thoughts he has! I hope he will not stare his eyes out of his head."

She continued laughing and joking, a little hysterically, it seemed to me.

"There we have the dear old saw-mill, where I came with the little girls in the morning to drink new milk. Why were you never there? But at that time of course you slept like a log—like you men."

"But you had never told me that you were there at that hour."

"Are you then to have everything given to you with a spoon?"

"I, for my part, prefer to eat solid food, and with a fork," Stephensen said.

Minna looked astonished, not exactly at him, but in his direction, as if she was surprised that any remarks should come from that quarter. When we began to ascend, the conversation soon ceased. To walk uphill was trying to Minna; palpitation of the heart and shortness of breath compelled her frequently to stop. Stephensen walked a few paces in front; she took my arm and leant on it.

At table the conversation was rather halting and indefinite. But when we were in the carriage, Minna seated herself cozily in the corner and said—

"Well, Harald! Now, you must tell me how life has treated you in these years. Everything, good and bad."

I obeyed her command as well as I could. Minna looked at me constantly, so that at times her eyes stared me out of countenance; she also smiled continuously, but often as if she was thinking of quite different scenes. Sometimes she laughed—yes, she even teased me a little about the English beauties.

"Oh, pooh," I exclaimed, a little an-noyed. "Beauties! I have not seen any who came up to you."

Minna threw herself back, and laughed with her handkerchief to her mouth.

"Well, there is a feather in your cap," Stephensen remarked.

He sat on the front seat, and looked most of the time out of the window and lit one cigarette after another. When he threw in a remark or question about art in London or some such thing, Minna re-garded him with an astonished and hard look, in the way one looks at a child who has been naughty, and who, without hav-ing asked pardon, tries to pretend that nothing has happened and joins in the conversation. It was evident that this treatment annoyed him very much; each time he grew silent as soon as possible. But it also troubled me; however painful it would have been to witness a loving confidence between them, it made my heart ache to see their unhappy condition so openly laid bare, and I did not under-stand how she could behave in such a way, even before me.

True, I would have concealed my meeting with the German musician, but when it came to the point I told it all the same. Minna said nothing, but gazed out of the window.

"Funny how small the world is!" Ste-phensen remarked. "One always runs against one another either directly or in-directly."

"And it was then you left?" Minna suddenly asked, turning her head quickly as a bird, and giving me a penetrating look.

This diversion completely threw me off my guard.

"Yes, then—then I left," I stuttered, and turned crimson.

Stephensen looked at us with an in-tensely ironical expression, as if he said: "Now I suppose it will soon come to a declaration *in optima forma*. Well, I shan't stand in the way, don't mind me."

Minna gave him a short glance, and his smile at once disappeared.

"Do tell me, Harald," she asked, leaning forward on her arm, "why didn't you join us, that evening, in the café?"

"What café?"

"Oh, you know very well—à Porta. . . . You thought I had not seen you? Yes, indeed I did, but only at the end; you remember—when I laughed at Stephensen, and at all the others too."

Stephensen put on a very dignified face and stroked himself between the collar and the neck, a pet gesture of his. Minna turned still more away from him, and looked at me with a rather teasing smile.

"I did not know any others of the party,—and—besides——"

"—besides you didn't wish to meet me in that company, and you were right."

But now Stephensen felt that it was high time to assert himself.

"I must say it is a very queer way in which you speak of the company we have associated with."

"*You*—not I. I have been obliged to put up with it."

"It is very regrettable that I could not do better for you! However, they were almost all people of the most intellectual set——"

"Anyhow, I did not feel at home in that society, nor, as a matter of fact, would Harald have done so."

Stephensen compressed his lips and glanced maliciously at her.

"You yourself know best where you are at home."

Minna shuddered and pressed her hand on her breast, as if she was suffering acute pain. I suspected that in these words lay a hidden poison. The idea struck me that I sat here like a priest who accompanies a condemned victim to the scaffold, and that it was a police official who sat opposite to me.

I suffered indescribably, but I felt that the conversation must be turned into a peaceful channel at any price. Pirna had just come into view, and I asked whether they would stay the night there, or go on to Dresden.

"No, we shall stay the night; perhaps we shall go for a while to Bohemia," Stephensen answered. Minna, who had been leaning almost bodily out of the window, turned directly afterwards towards me; her face was colorless and drawn.

"Do you remain for some days in Dresden?" But this question was accompanied by a look which altered it to a petition.

My answer did not come immediately. Should I not take the opportunity of showing my hand—just a little? If I meant to do it at all, no more time was to be lost.

"As a matter of fact," I began deliberately, "when I was discovered sitting on the stone table in the 'Sophien-Ruhe grotto,' I had just come to the conclusion that I would leave to-night for Copenhagen."

At the last words Stephensen involuntarily made an uneasy movement, then straightened himself up and set his features in a highly disapproving manner. So the shot had gone home. I saw this perfectly though my eyes were riveted upon hers, which had not for a moment left my face; and in their wonderful greenish brown depths, I beheld a brighter and brighter golden light.

"I s—see," she said or rather breathed, scarcely moving her lips.

"But now I certainly shall alter my plans. I have work enough to detain me in Dresden for a week or two; for many weeks, if it comes to that."

"I am glad," said Minna.

Stephensen took refuge in his pet gesture—his finger between neck and collar —and seemed disposed to say something bitter, perhaps to the effect that I ought not to upset my arrangements for *their* sakes; but he thought better of it.

None of us spoke after that.

I had previously mentioned that I was staying at the Bellevue Hotel. So I knew that Minna could communicate with me, whenever she wanted to. That she would, I had now no doubt whatever. I was at rest on this point, but I was very uneasy about this strange journey of theirs. "What have they come here for?" I thought. "It is evident that they are not going to Bohemia." Why I found it "evident," I do not know. . . .

"The chariot rolls, the bridge is quaking,
The stream beneath it flows so sadly,
Once more the joys am I forsaking
Of that fond heart I love so madly."

As soon as we had passed the bridge, Stephensen stopped the carriage.

Then I pressed Minna's hand, bowed to Stephensen, and hurried to the railway station.

CHAPTER VI

When I arrived at Dresden, I could not make up my mind to leave the Bohemian station. I had a suspicion that both or one of them would return from Pirna.

The evening train rolled in, and I saw Stephensen's face at a carriage window. He stepped out—alone. I rushed towards him.

"Where is Minna?"

Stephensen regarded me coldly, as if he would beg to be excused from intrusive questions. But he changed his mind.

"You are right, Mr. Fenger, you ought to know it. She is at Sonnenstein."

"Sonnenstein!" I murmured, as if I did not understand. Then I was seized with giddiness, and the commotion of passengers and porters on the half-dark platform made me feel ill. "Sonnenstein! What does it mean?" I caught hold of his overcoat, partly to steady myself, partly to prevent him from getting away. "You

don't mean to say that she—that Minna——"

"Well, don't take it so pathetically!" Stephensen said with a semblance of kindness. "She is not exactly weak-minded or really insane, only very melancholy and a little hysterical. You have seen for yourself. In short, it was the best thing to put her under the treatment of a doctor. What is there in that? In our nervous times, it is nothing unusual. . . . She preferred Sonnenstein, because her home-sickness was rather overwhelming, and then, of course, also to avoid talk in Copenhagen. It is now said that she is visiting her people, though, as I have already remarked, it is in our days so usual, all educated people have got over these prejudices——"

My dull incredulity had, during this explanation, given place to an absolutely conscious fury.

"It is you who have done it, *you—you!*"

My voice was stifled. I shook my fist in front of his face; he tore himself loose, a gendarme stepped towards us. Stephensen whispered a few words to him, shrugged his shoulders, and disappeared in the crowd. I leaned against a pillar; late-comers were rushing about, the conductors shouted, there was a sound of whistling and puffing.

As soon as I had recovered control of myself, I asked the porter whether there was a train for Pirna; but I had to wait until the next morning.

By the first train I was in Pirna, reached Sonnenstein breathless, and fortunately at once had an interview with the Professor. I presented myself as a friend of Mrs. Stephensen's and her husband's, the latter of whom I had met last night, and went on to say that I had promised frequently to give information to him about his wife's condition, as I was remaining in Dresden for some time. But as I myself was also very troubled about my friend, and only had been able to speak to Mr. Stephensen for a few minutes, I had at once hurried out, and now wanted earnestly to know the whole truth.

The Professor calmed me for the time being; there was hardly any cause for immediate fear, it was one of the cases for which in former days one would never have thought of applying to a doctor, and where the asylum essentially served to isolate the patient from mental infection. Further information he could only supply after having her under observation for about a week, but he would then be very pleased to give it.

When, therefore, I called upon him eight days later, he stated that Minna assuredly was suffering mentally, but was not liable to go out of her mind, at any rate not if she was rightly treated and lived under the favorable conditions that an asylum would give her until she recovered her mental balance. She was in a very nervous, excited condition. But the real danger was the heart disease, the seed of which must have been sown several years back. She might grow old with the complaint, but also it might suddenly cause her death. Most of all it was necessary to avoid any agitation of mind, which he thought hitherto had constantly given nourishment to the complaint.

"Do tell me," he suddenly said, "you are a friend of hers and her husband's. Did they live happily together?"

I considered a moment whether I had the right to be candid. "No," I answered, "I almost dare say that they did not."

"There we have got it! Or anyhow the principal cause. It will no doubt be best for her not to return to him. That is to say, if it can be done without too much pain on her part, when the time comes. As far as he is concerned, he seemed to me to be reasonable enough. What do you think?"

"I am quite of your opinion."

My emotion was too strong to escape the notice of an experienced man. He smiled, and looked at me firmly with rather contracted eyes:

"But it will be a long business. . . . I have told her that you have been here, and am to give you her regards. You will remain for the time being in Dresden? That's good. Once a week I should like you to call. I think it has a calming effect on her, but a considerable time will have to pass before I shall dare to allow you to speak to her."

I returned with a good heart, and firmly decided to devote my whole life to Minna, married to her or not, in whatever manner it could best serve her welfare and health. I was satisfied to contribute all that I could to make her as little unhappy as possible, if she could not any longer be happy (though, why should she not still be capable of being so?), without consideration of the harm it might do my career. If it would suit her best to live in her native town, I would try to get a situation in Dresden; if she needed a southern climate, then I would find a means to live in the south. The latter, however, was not very likely; yes, it even was most probable that England, being quite new to her, would be the most suitable place. But all this did not trouble me much. What made me shiver was the consciousness of the sword of Damocles that hung over her head. Had it perhaps at this moment already fallen? And it would remain there constantly, even when the doctor had sanctioned her departure. Yes, even if it was taken away, my fear would still imagine it to be present. . . . But I promised myself that this terror should only make my love stronger, my tenderness more constant. How could I ever leave her in anger or even in a fit of sulkiness after a matrimonial dispute, when an inner voice whispered to me that perhaps when I returned to seize her hand and read love in her eyes, the hand would be cold and the eyes glassy?

My uncle would have to agree to my absence, at all events for a year. I hired a modest room as in olden days, and threw myself into a detailed study of pottery, which I hoped would be useful to our factory, and for which, both in a practical and literary respect, Dresden afforded ample opportunities.

CHAPTER VII

The 3rd of May, in the afternoon, when almost everything was green in the gardens and the public park, I took my usual walk out to Grosser Garden.

At the beginning of Bürgerwiese, my eye was attracted by a portrait, which hung in the window of a curio shop. I rushed across: yes, indeed, it was Stephensen's pastel picture of Minna. But how dreadful it looked now! The pastel powder had fallen away in big patches, especially off the hair, but also on a spot of the forehead and on the cheek; where the one eye ought to have been, the canvas showed light through. It had been put into a worm-eaten, shabby frame in bad rococo style, and under it was written on a scrap of paper: "Unknown master, middle of the eighteenth century."

I stepped into a dark booth, where one could hardly move for old rubbish. The curio-dealer, a tall thin old man, who surely from my German detected the foreigner, and perhaps even suspected something English, mentioned an exorbitant price; it was, he explained, one of those genuine pictures, which now grew more and more scarce, very likely a Mengs. I soon disillusioned him, and bought the picture, certainly for a good deal more than it was worth.

In Grosser Garten, I did not care to walk with a big parcel under my arm, but I needed exercise, and strolled about down the Johannes' street. Of course I had not bought the picture in order to possess it, but only because it was to me an intolerable thought that it should hang there "in the stocks," and later on in a stranger's house—as a Mengs!

I thought I would take it home and burn it.

But, as I found myself facing the Albert Bridge, I was struck suddenly by the thought: "Why not throw it into the Elbe?" Then I should avoid opening it, and seeing it again.

There were only a few people on the bridge. I went out to the parapet of the middle pillar, towards the stream; it was still somewhat high water. Quickly I looked round; there was nobody near. Then I let go the picture. It disappeared under the water, and I heard it crush against the ice-break of the pillar.

Depressed in spirit, I went home.

On my table lay a letter from the Professor.

Minna had died that morning, quite unexpectedly, from apoplexy of the heart.

CHAPTER VIII

The next morning I received a little parcel directed in Minna's handwriting, and with the asylum seal.

At the top lay six sheets of note-paper, closely written; but on the last one the writing stopped at the top of the second page.

"SONNENSTEIN, *April 17th, 188–.*

"DEAREST FRIEND,—The doctor has told me that you have been here, and brought me your regards; he also has promised to give you my love, when you come again. It is an intense consolation to me to know that you are so near.

"I will write to you, only a little now and again, for it always moves me deeply, and the doctor has impressed upon me, most of all, to avoid all agitating thoughts, which, with this one exception, I do. But write I must, because only in that way can I avoid a constant restlessness. For I have the feeling that I might die suddenly; the doctor laughs at me when I say so, but it seems to me that I can see that he himself thinks the same. Still perhaps it is only weakness. At the same time it will be a comfort to me to know that you will get a message from me, if it should happen.

"I have so much resting on my heart that I must tell you. I have collected your letters and some little things that I should not like to fall into other hands; and each time I add to this letter, I will enclose it in the parcel that I have already addressed to you.

"Perhaps we shall one day laugh together at this idea. God grant it may be so!

"I cannot very well bear to write any more to-night. Good-night, my Friend."

"*April 18th.*

"Do you know what made me carry through (by the way, with great difficulty) this trip to Rathen, before the asylum closed its doors behind me, and why I came to the Grotto? Not only that, which likewise brought you there, but also the idea, that something would happen to me there, something extraordinary. However, not what happened, which was in reality still more wonderful, no, I thought that the agitation of mind in coming there would be too overpowering for me—that it would either kill me or drive me mad, even this I would prefer to the state of mind in which I was.

"But how blessed it was to meet you there, Harald! I saw that you were the same, and you also felt that I was unaltered—towards you. Towards *him* I surely was changed.

"I know quite well how painful it was to you that my indignation towards him was so apparent, and still I could not help it. So nasty I have already become, so much bitterness—yes, hatred—has risen up in me.

"This you will very likely not understand.

"How is it possible to detest a human being one has loved? Or perhaps better ask (for very likely, to you, that is what seems incomprehensible): 'How can one love a being whom one comes to look down upon to such a degree, when by daily intercourse one gets to know his true character?' And here we are not speaking about a passing falling in love, for I did know something of him.

"This I have thought of more than anything else, and in order that you may understand me thoroughly, I must tell you what I think of it.

"A nature like Stephensen's, in which from the beginning, after all, there were some noble seeds (without them I suppose he would not have been an artist, not even the artist he is); when such a nature, still young and not quite debased, feels love for a young girl, then he grows higher and nobler, and she comes to know—and to love—a different being from what he was before. Still, this is not a deceit; on the contrary, she knows and loves just what he will be through their relations to one another, and in her something corresponding takes place, she develops, her character gets stronger and her views broader.

"All this is beautiful and true.

"But then the difference between the different natures appears in the course of time: such men in whom the nobler seeds are strong enough, really develop towards this ideal and gradually strengthen in it, but the others cannot keep themselves on the height to which they have been raised, they even sink below it."

"*April 20th.*

"What I wrote last strained and affected me very much. It was so sad to think of and so difficult to make plain. Yesterday I could not write anything. I will not try to develop this idea any further, though it is of great importance to me that you quite understand, for it is in this point alone that my excuse lies. But surely you have understood. I dare not insist that it answers generally, but in this case it must be so.

"It was about my life in Denmark I wanted to tell you something.

"I wonder if you remember what Sieglinde says about her life with Hunding—

" 'Foreign seemed all until now,
　　Friendless I was and forsaken;
　　I counted strange and unknown,
　　Each and all that came near.'

"Still it was not because of my being 'a foreigner' in a national sense, though I suppose that has also done something. Besides, you know well that there is a good deal in the German nature and also in our art—apart from the great classics —with which I have never sympathized.

"In the beginning I really found everything lovely: liberty, broadness of mind, education, and all that sort of thing.

"But soon I felt how hollow the kernel was. I had indeed had a quintessence of the whole in Stephensen to observe too closely. After all it was no wonder that I did not blend with this circle, as it consisted of my husband's friends, anyhow by name. Some few, of course, appealed more to me. But none of them resembled you. When I now and again met a person sympathetic to me, it was as a rule one who belonged to another set, and by some chance came in touch with ours, but soon retired. That our circle, however, was the most spiritual in Denmark and represented the highest intellect of

the country, I heard almost every time we met. Indeed, it was also the most honorable; for the others were not only more or less idiots, but also sworn enemies of truth and righteousness. Ah, I could write much about these things, for I have a good memory, and I have heard many brilliant speeches!

"There was a time when I tried to settle down and give in to it; it was my duty, Stephensen said. I thought that perhaps they were right and I was wrong, possibly I was queer and absurd. I shrugged my shoulders with the others at things that at the bottom of my heart I found noble and elevating, I tried to admire what was repulsive to my inmost self, I pretended to believe that the quality of virtue was hypocrisy and the word itself an absurdity, no, an 'indecency,' as one of Stephensen's intellectual friends said. In short, I tried to howl with the wolves I was among (after all you have wolves in Denmark, haven't you?—do you remember when you made fun of me?—but no lions). I did not succeed in getting my stiff neck bent, perhaps the fault is mostly yours, and this is not the least I have to thank you for."

"*April 26th.*

"We lived very sociably, as Stephensen had a real mania for diversion, and this sociability often lasted far into the night. As I had to get up early in the morning— after the German custom I was a rather industrious housewife, and had to be so to make two ends meet—this added considerably to the breaking down of my health.

"Sometimes I tried to excuse myself, which always made Stephensen most irritable. Very likely I should in the end have got my way, had it not been for one thing: my jealousy.

"How I have suffered from jealousy, I can hardly make you understand. I do not believe any man can understand it, though your sex is supposed to have produced Othellos.

"One would think that when a wife has lost so much respect and love for her husband, and when hardly any relationship exists, she would be able almost with indifference to see him run after others. With me it was almost the reverse. The cooler I felt towards him, the more burning was my jealousy. As a painter's wife I had besides a special enemy—the model. I have lowered myself to listening at the door when he had models. No wonder I could fight against sleep at insufferable parties in order to keep an eye on him.

"These efforts, unfortunately, were crowned with a terrible success. I had for a long time suspected the blonde lady you saw at Café à Porta. One day, shortly after that evening, I discovered that he had locked himself up with her in the studio, under pretense of having a model. I was so insistent that he confessed. Once having got into a sort of talkative repentance, he poured forth much more than I had suspected. I heard that his unfaithfulness went as far back as the first years, nay, even to the period when he most of all——

"No, I cannot write about it.

"How I hate him!"

"April 30th.

"When my child died I grieved dreadfully, but a year had not passed before I looked upon it as a blessing. I have told you so much about my father; you see I feared that I might have been a mother of the same kind. For I felt the same process of petrifying beginning in me, like the one the effect of which I had felt as a child, and which later I have understood.

"There was now no duty to prevent me from retiring into myself. My one and only life was to read our great poets and cultivate music—especially Beethoven and Wagner, whose piano scores I possessed. It was a world after my own heart, and so different from all that I was doomed to come in contact with.

"You know how passionately fond of music I am, but also how strongly it affects my nervous system to play much. I once said to you jokingly that if I wanted to kill my reason, it would be through piano-playing. Perhaps I really have tried mentally to take my life through this heavenly poison.

"Had I seen any light, had I known what I am now aware of, surely I should have spared myself more."

"2nd May.

"I wish I knew really what you think of death. Do you believe in a reunion? It is difficult to realize, still, I cannot understand that my own self should quite vanish. I often think of old Hertz, whom I have heard talking about the soul and immortality on many different occasions. As it was, in the main, the doctrine of his beloved Kant (or so I understood), it is no great wonder if I, poor unlearned creature as I was and am, should not have mastered it at all. Nevertheless, it struck me deeply at that time, and in later days the mystic lore he was so fond of has recurred to me in many a lonely and desolate hour. One sentence, and I trust, the very one fitted to be the key to this whole train of thought, has stamped itself upon my memory almost word for word, because Hertz used to recapitulate it on every possible occasion, with many variations, to be sure, but it always came to this: 'What we call Self is not Self as it is in reality (only for this he had a queer phrase, 'in itself,' I think), but only as it appears in our sense-consciousness.' Now, over this sentence I have pondered many and many a time in my own stupid way, because I wanted very badly to know what my self in reality was, hoping that it might turn out to be something better than what I did know of myself. And often I have fancied that *that* which I do not know of myself, because it does not appear in the little dim mirror of consciousness, and that which *you*—for the same reason—do not know of yourself, are in reality, if not exactly the same thing, at last two things that are very closely allied to one another, so much so, indeed, that it shall one day seem to us only a bad and mad dream that we could ever have been separated.

"These are odd thoughts, one may say. But they have their comforting side for all that.

"And perhaps you will not find them so very odd, after all, nor of a wholly unfamiliar stamp. For you have told me that your father was an old disciple of Schopenhauer's, and that he used to speak to you of his beliefs and his views. Now, I certainly have read nothing of Schopenhauer myself, but I remember that Hertz often mentioned him as a great thinker of the school of Kant, though rather too mystical for his taste. So, perhaps, what I have said may even have a familiar ring about it.

"But I really am glad that I have a good safe lock to my writing-case, and can shut up these sheets. For I have a shrewd suspicion that if the Professor read these 'odd thoughts' he would have me removed at once to the other part of this great castle, where the incurables are lodged."

For a long time I sat musing with the sheet in my hand. Alas, but one remained, and only the first page was covered with writing. I had no need to hurry! It seemed to me that all that was worth reading was there, on the last sheet of note-paper.

So I mused over these "odd thoughts," which touched me deeply. Minna was quite right: they reminded me of my dear father, recalled to my mind many a

ramble by his side through our great woods, rambles on which he liked to indulge in metaphysical speculations about the "will in nature," as manifesting itself in the lives of the trees and animals of the forest. How much had I lamented, in the days of my engagement to Minna, that I could not take her to him, who would have been as sure to be a father to her as she to be a daughter to him. Both were deep and original natures and had so much in common. How fond they both were of plants and animals, how responsive to every beauty of nature! Both, too, had a strain of melancholy and a golden touch of humor. And now they had, as it were, already met; they belonged to another world, and I was left alone—oh, so utterly alone!

But in the last lines Minna was so vividly present that I could hardly realize she was no more where I could reach her. That little humorous touch of hers that gushed forth fountain-like amid thoughts of deepest earnestness and sadness, that note of subtle irony at the expense of the worthy professor, whom she had long found out as the up-to-date man of science, with no mystical nonsense whatever about him, was so thoroughly in her own dear manner, that I almost fancied I could see the arch smile on those sweet lips which now . . . alas . . . alas! . . .

And now there remained but the last page of the tiny manuscript!

At last I took heart of grace to read it.

"But why am I speaking of death and of the beyond the grave today? It is strange, for I have not for a very long time been in so hopeful spirits as to-day.

"The weather is so lovely. All the forenoon I have been sitting with my sewing in the Professor's garden. He is an excellent man.

"To-morrow I shall tell you more about

how time goes here. But to-night I am not writing any more. I will read Schiller. The other day, when I was turning over the last volume, I got such a desire to try if I could grasp *Ueber das Erhabene.* The Professor is afraid that this kind of reading may prove trying to me, and recommends historical works. I also began to read Schiller's *Thirty Years' War,* but it wearied me dreadfully. I cannot help it; it was already like that in my schooldays, everything historical bored me.

"Good-night, Harald!"

The reading of this journal had created so deep and solemn an impression upon me that I had been unable to find relief in tears; I had not yet wept since her death.

But as I finally clutched for the remaining contents of the parcel, and got a strangely crumpled and curled letter in my hand, that letter from me which she had carried on her breast, then I pressed it to my lips and sobbed like a child.

I have read again the first of these leaves. How could I write those foolish words—

"And have I ever regretted it? Even to this very day, it is now five years ago, I am unable to answer this question."

As if I, for any prize in the world, would give up our love, give up the remembrance of Minna! As if any happiness could be to me so precious as my grief!

I arbitrarily undertook to look after the funeral. To my joy—yes, it really was a joy to me!—I secured a grave on "Der weite Kirchhof," quite close to the resting-place of Hertz and his wife, under one of the giant poplars.

On the tomb I ordered a broken column of the most beautiful Saxonian Serpentine to be placed, without any other inscription than the name:

MINNA

THE LIFE AND WORKS OF
KARL ADOLPH GJELLERUP

By F. J. BILLESKOR JANSEN

KARL GJELLERUP was born in a country parsonage on June 2, 1857. He came from a family of Danish Lutheran clergy; his father, Carl Adolph Gjellerup, who died only three years after his birth, was a practicing minister. The young Karl was brought up in Copenhagen by one of his mother's cousins, another Protestant clergyman, Johannes Fibiger, who had a decisive influence on the intellectual development of his adopted son. Fibiger was both poet and scholar, a man of great philological learning who, like all Protestant theologians, knew Greek and Hebrew, as well as Old Norse and Egyptian, and also read the holy books of Persia and India in the original. He was particularly interested in the origins of the Danish spiritual heritage.

Young Gjellerup finished his schooling in 1874, and took up the study of theology. However, contemporary Positivist theories soon began to influence him. The historical and critical elucidation of the Bible had greatly advanced, and such questions as the authenticity of the fourth Gospel were being widely discussed. With the enthusiasm of youth, Gjellerup associated himself with the more radical scholars. By the time he had passed his final exam, he had lost his faith, and had embraced the literary theories of Georg Brandes, of whom he remained a fervent disciple for several years. Brandes, born in 1842, was a literary critic of genius, a tempestuous orator, and a ruthless, polemical writer. In the poem *Ave*, Gjellerup even calls him "Our knight of the Holy Ghost, our Saint George."

Gjellerup had always written poetry. His favorite poet was Schiller (whose looks he was pleased to note resembled his own); and it would be impossible to appreciate Gjellerup's poetical work without some knowledge of these Germans: Goethe, Kant, and Schiller. Gjellerup's work came at the culmination of a philosophical and literary movement which had begun about 1790, when Germany could justly claim the title of "the land of poets and thinkers"; thereafter, all Germany's great minds felt and thought in the same way. "Teeming millions, I embrace you!" cried Schiller. Kant discovered deep in the human soul a "moral imperative"; and Goethe said that "Every human fault is redeemed by humanity's essential nobility." According to this Teutonic conception, the life of a man who sacrifices his idiosyncrasies and desires to become part of the human generality acquires a new harmony. Purified in this way, the individual becomes a personality, and his being attains its highest level.

Danish literature was inspired by both

German classicism and German romanticism. In his play *Aladdin* (1805), Oehlenschläger, the head of the Danish romantic school, revived *The Arabian Nights*. In much of his poetry he did the same for the myths and legends of Scandinavian antiquity. In 1835, Hans Christian Andersen used the popular fairy tale as the basis for those exquisite inventions which tell us so much about mankind. Toward the middle of the century, however, these romantic notions came under severe attack. The philosophy of Hegel regarded the life of the cosmos as the achievement of an eternal idea, compared with which the life of the individual is nothing. It was not until 1870 that Darwinism, Positivism, and naturalism came into conflict with idealism in its essential form. The protagonist of this dynamic movement was Gjellerup's mentor, Georg Brandes. Gjellerup's work may have its origins in the great idealist traditions of Germany and Denmark, but he reached manhood at the moment when Brandesism was in full flood.

It was with a prose work that Gjellerup began his official literary career. Having aligned himself with the Brandésian school, he began by writing about contemporary Danish problems. In his first book, *En idealist* (An Idealist, 1878), the hero, an erudite youth, rails against theology and organized religion. In concert with the ideas of the German thinkers, he believes that our spirits belong to the cosmos, and our souls to eternal ideas, of which our thoughts are the manifestation.

Gjellerup published his great problem novel, *Germanernes Laerling* (The Apprentice of the Teutons) in 1882.

Niels Hjorth, its hero, is born into a peasant family in Schleswig, the province that Bismarck seized from Denmark in 1864. He is consumed with hatred for Germany, but by the irony of fate his spiritual life is nourished by the German classics, in particular by Schiller. With great difficulty he becomes a schoolmaster and then, having passed his exams, begins theological studies at the University of Copenhagen.

German idealism sows the seeds of doubt in the young theologian; his faith gradually declines, and Lessing's book, *Nathan the Wise,* opens the way to free thought. Having expressed doubts about the authenticity of the fourth Gospel in his examination, he is refused entry to the oral exam by the faculty and the Ministry of Ecclesiastical Affairs. Victor and vanquished at once, he returns to his native village across the border, where he meets the charming young niece of a German pastor, who provides him with the companionship he needs. Rid thus of his religious and nationalist prejudices, he prepares to teach his Danish countrymen the lesson of modern renunciation, which holds that we endure the evils of this earth without demanding the rewards of heaven in return.

After this book, so filled with aggressive naturalism, Gjellerup came under the influence of the psychology of Slavic realism. The novels of Turgenev, in particular, left their mark in two of his short stories, *G-Dur* (G Major) and *Romulus,* both written in 1883. *Romulus* was completed in Italy, where Gjellerup traveled during 1882 and 1883. Also during this period he wrote *En klassisk maaned* (A Classical Month, 1884) and *Vandreaart* (Wander Year, 1885), his two books of travel impressions in which he contrasts the beauty of the Greek temples with the ugliness of modern literature. In *Vandreaart* he broke off from his alliance with the Brandésians. Naturalism, he said, could depict not only the baseness of life, as in the contemporary French novel, but also the highest aspirations of humanity.

After his travels, Gjellerup began to exhibit two main tendencies. In keeping with German classicism, he praised free will and the moral responsibility of man; and under the influence of Schopenhauer, he emphasized the intrinsic suffering of the human condition.

Gjellerup became a Wagnerian fairly early, while in Germany, where he first heard the *Meistersinger*. Then in Rome, during his travels, he heard a complete performance of the *Ring of the Nibelungen* tetralogy. It was to him a revelation of both the grandiose and the modern in art. Following Wagner's example, he selected the same subject and wrote a play. In the Nordic tradition, he called his hero Siegfried and the Walkyrie Brynhild. In his verse drama *Brynhild* (1884), the first of his works to be received with excitement, he depicts the fidelity of those great souls who can love only one. The heroine, when the man she loves is assassinated, places herself beside him on the pyre and dies. Here we see the heroic and tragic character as a law unto itself. In this work, the austerity of the characterization and the somberness of the action are mitigated by the magic of the verse. With astonishing flexibility, Gjellerup alternates the trimeters of Greek tragedy with verses suitable to the song of the Nibelungen, adding the alliterative versification of the Scandinavian Edda and the blank verse of Shakespeare. With its analysis of heroic feelings and with its variety of the poetic language, this tragedy, at once ancient and modern, achieves universality. The inspiration as well as the poetic quality place this work beside that of Hebbel or Swinburne.

From the summer of 1885 to the fall of 1887, Gjellerup lived in Dresden. Here he worked on his plays and completed the dramatic-lyric poem "Thamyris" (1887). This poem, along with *Brynhild,* earned him a state pension for life and enabled him to continue writing. In October of 1887, Gjellerup married for a second time: this time to a cousin of Georg Brandés, Eugenia Bendiz. He had first met her in 1880, but it was seven years before they were able to marry. The couple settled in Hellerup in Denmark after their marriage and Gjellerup continued to write.

His next work to appear was *Hagbard og Sign* (Hagbard and Signe, 1888), a lyrical tragedy in which Gjellerup alternates verse with prose, and which follows the original ancient Danish tale faithfully. The events of antiquity are transported into the Middle Ages, introducing the lovers to a feeling of guilt unknown in the ancient version. Because they succumb to the temptations of love, they are doomed to death.

Among his important works completed at Hellerup are the novel *Minna* (1889), and the collection of poetry *Min kaerligheds bog* (The Book of My Love, 1889). *Minna* is more or less an autobiographical account of Gjellerup's own childhood and the events which led to his first broken marriage. In March of 1892, Gjellerup moved with his family back to Dresden. He brought with him several completed plays which he hoped to have produced in Dresden.

Whereas the tragic blemish that brings about the downfall of a superior personality is the essence of Gjellerup's early plays, he now began to transform heroic plays into contemporary drama. He often dealt with problem plays in the manner of Ibsen and his imitators, and the two modern dramas he brought to Dresden treated contemporary problems; the relationship of a heroic figure to love, marriage, and career. The hero of *Herman Vandel* (1891) is a young schoolteacher who, consumed by guilt at contracting a loveless marriage, commits suicide. Gjellerup took this play to the Theater Royal but it was turned down. It was finally performed only once at the free theater of the *Studentersamfundet,* the association of radical Socialist students.

The other play, *Wuthhorn,* met with more success. It was produced in 1893. The action takes place near the mountain which gives the play its name, and it is the story of two people in love who are prepared to die together if they cannot live life together. *Wuthhorn* met with some popular success and was performed at the Dagmar Theater over one hundred times.

Two other plays, *Kong Hjarne* (King Hjarne, 1893), a tragedy, and *Gift og modgift* (Toxin and Antitoxin, 1898), a verse comedy, were also performed at the Dagmar Theater. During this time Gjellerup wrote the play *Hans Excellence* (His Excellence, 1895). Its story of the corruption of a high government official was perhaps too controversial and was also refused by the Theater Royal, but, like *Herman Vandel,* it too found a home at the *Studentersamfundet.*

Several other minor works followed and then, as Gjellerup himself put it, he "bade farewell to Danish poetry." In 1894, he wrote his first work in German. *Pastor Mors* is a curious novel. In it Gjellerup ridicules a professor of Protestant theology who believes he will survive in eternity as he is on earth.

Next came one of Gjellerup's more important works, *Møllen* (The Mill, 1896), also written in German. Here the most methodical realism is combined with pronounced idealism; no other naturalist could have better adapted the setting to the action. Set in the Danish countryside, it is the story of passion, jealousy, and murder, in which the author skillfully makes use of the popular faith in Providence to express his own doctrine of universal justice. This concept was further developed in the novel *Stens Landpraxis* or *Reif für das Leben* (Ripe for Life, 1913). It is the story of a young doctor's conversion to belief in the mysterious ways of Providence.

In his later drama and novels the influence of Oriental religion and tradition is strong. In the legendary drama *Die Opferfeur* (The Sacrificial Fires, 1903) he moves to a religion of pure spirit. *Das Weib des Vellendeten* (The Wife of the Perfect One, 1907) tells the story of the conversion of a woman to Buddhism through her own understanding of the way in which life continues even after death. In the novel *Der Pilger Kamanita* (The Pilgrim Kamanita, 1906), this theme is further developed when two lovers, forced in life to live apart, are united after death. *Die Weltwanderer* (The World Travelers, 1910) is set in India, telling the story of two lovers who recognize themselves in a previous existence.

When Gjellerup was awarded the Nobel Prize in 1917, Germany might reasonably have claimed a part of the glory for he was always a pupil of the Germans. Schiller, Wagner, and Schopenhauer had successively helped to form his mind, even leading him to the sources of Buddhism. He died in 1919 in Klotzsche, near Dresden, Germany, in his adopted country.

F. J. Billeskor Jansen is a professor at the University of Copenhagen.
Translated by Anthony Rhodes.

THE 1917 PRIZE

By A. JOLIVET

It was 1917. The World War was in its third year and still raging. After the terrible slaughter at Verdun, when the antagonists had sunk into apathy, a renewed frenzy of fighting had broken out, covering a much wider area than the land round the forts of Vaux and Douaumont. In February, Germany had launched total submarine warfare in the oceans, which was to bring the United States into the war. In Russia, the imperial colossus tottered on its feet of clay. The February Revolution in Petrograd was pursuing its fateful course, beginning with the Czar's abdication and culminating in the Communist seizure of power in October. Clouds of catastrophe were gathering on every horizon.

At the time, awarding a Nobel Prize for Literature hardly seemed appropriate. The hitherto honorable task of choosing the laureates had become a wearisome burden without glory, one which was no longer able to arouse interest. The small scene which was being played out at the same time as the immense drama of the century was bathed in an atmosphere of dull indifference. There were no Prize celebrations on December 10, therefore.

In addition, there were political worries. Sweden felt it was important to remain strictly neutral. But this posture was not without risk. Sweden's neutrality was, to say the least, delicate: the nearness of the German seaboard on the Baltic and her diplomatic relations with Germany produced serious tension between Sweden and the Allies in 1917. The Allies' suspicion of Swedish policy contributed toward provoking a governmental crisis in March. In Sweden it became urgently necessary to prove a neutral stand did not necessarily mean going along with Germany's warlike designs.

Sweden stiffened her attitude toward Germany in 1917, and, as it happened, neither France nor England proposed any Nobel candidates. The Germans proposed only one of their writers, Paul Ernst, a star of lesser brilliance. The Swedish Academy looked for a graceful means of getting out of the difficulty unscathed.

In December of 1914, the Kings of Denmark, Norway, and Sweden had met at Malmö. The presence side-by-side of the three neutral monarchs revealed the existence of a new cohesion in this corner of the planet. It also marked the end of the dissension that had formerly troubled the Nordic atmosphere, and it quieted the repercussions that had occurred after the separation of Sweden and Norway in 1905. The famous meeting of the three kings, repeated again in Christiania in 1917, showed a happy willingness for cooperation and the wish to support each other in this time of strain. People began to think of themselves more emphatically as Scandinavians. And so the Nobel Prize for Literature was awarded in 1917 to two Danish writers, Karl Gjellerup and Henrik Pontoppidan. Gjellerup, who had had a German philosophical education and had strong Germanic spiritual affinities, had lived in Dresden since 1892. His books had a wide circulation in Germany. Like Gjellerup, Pontoppidan had also been one of the group of young men enlightened by Georg Brandes.

Now the question arose as to whether the prize should be divided or not. In the eyes of certain Academicians this was an abomination, an intolerable half-measure. Albert Nobel had expressed the wish in his will that his money should be a substantial means of support, not merely a source of tips. A certain number of Academicians wanted to give the whole

Prize to Gjellerup, and were deeply disappointed when the idea was abandoned. Others pointed out that a division was justified and that this praiseworthy concession to literary fairness would be appreciated by future generations. Neither Gjellerup nor Pontoppidan were after all of such far-reaching importance. The division was necessary as a sort of happy medium that allowed the problems of a delicate situation to be resolved.

Thus it was that the Swedish Academy, when it met in plenary session on November 8, 1917, decided to award the Nobel Prize for Literature to Karl Gjellerup "for his varied and rich poetry, which is inspired by lofty ideals" and, more laconically, to Henrik Pontoppidan "for his authentic descriptions of present-day life in Denmark."

Translated by Dale McAdoo.

Paul Heyse

1910

"As a tribute to the consummate artistry,

permeated with idealism, which he has

demonstrated during his long productive

career as a lyric poet, dramatist, novelist,

and writer of world-renowned short stories"

Illustrated by AIMÉ D. STEINLEN

PRESENTATION ADDRESS

By C. D. AF WIRSÉN

PERMANENT SECRETARY OF THE SWEDISH ACADEMY

MANY FAMOUS WRITERS from several countries have been proposed for this year's Nobel Prize for Literature. The Swedish Academy has awarded it to a writer whose nomination has been supported by more than sixty German experts on art, literature, and philosophy. His name is Paul Heyse. The name revives the memory of our youth and manhood; we still remember the literary pleasure that his novellas, in particular, gave to us. Now an old but still active man, he is a figure that the jury could not pass over if it was to express its admiration by awarding the high distinction to the most significant literary work. Nor was the jury to be swayed by considerations of age or, indeed, anything other than true merit.

Paul Heyse was born in Berlin in 1830. His father was the philologist Karl Wilhelm Heyse, a gentle but determined scholar. From his Jewish mother, Julie Saaling, Heyse perhaps inherited his warm and lively temperament. Heyse, who was nature's favorite in so many ways, had the good fortune of growing up in a carefree home. His school years passed quickly. He was an easy learner. For a while he was a student in Berlin and later he studied Romance philology under Friedrich Diez at Bonn University. In 1852 he received his doctorate in Berlin *multa cum laude*. Subsequently Heyse was awarded a scholarship that enabled him to travel in Italy, with whose art and literature he was to become so familiar. He soon became engaged to Margarete Kugler, the daughter of the art historian to whose house he had been introduced by his patron, the poet Emanuel Geibel. Not sure where to look for a position, he was freed from all material worries by Geibel, who once more helped him. At Geibel's recommendation Maximilian II offered him a titular professorship at Munich. His only duty consisted in taking part in the literary soirées of the King. On May 15, 1854, he was married to Margarete and the happy young couple settled in Munich, where Heyse has lived ever since, with the exception of occasional sojourns in his beloved Italy. Soon he became the central figure of a thriving cultural life. Since this is not the place for a detailed biography of Heyse, suffice it to say that several years after the death of Margarete he married again, this time the charming Anna Schubart.

Between 1855 and 1862 Heyse wrote the first four volumes of his prose novellas, a genre in which he became a master. Among Heyse's many novellas we may mention here *L'Arrabbiata* (1853); *Andrea Delfin* (1859), rich in Venetian colors; the deeply felt *Nerina* (1875), an episode from Leopardi's life; the profoundly moral *Bild der Mutter* (Portrait of a Mother, 1859); and the marvelous troubadour novella *Marion* (1855). In his novellas Heyse observes strict rules of composition without doing violence to the charm and freedom of the story. He developed his own theory of the novella. "A novella of literary value," he wrote, "should represent an important human destiny. It must not be an everyday occurrence but should reveal to us a new side of human nature. The narrow scope of the tale calls for strict concentration."

It has rightly been said that Heyse is the creator of the modern psychological novella. He is rarely tendentious in his novellas, and that is probably the reason we prefer their Goethean objectivity to his longer narratives *Kinder der Welt* (*The Children of the World*, 1872) and *Im Paradiese* (*In Paradise*, 1875), which deal with moral problems, the former with the independence of morality from narrow dogmas, the latter with a defense of art against an austere puritanism. Both works unmistakably show the humanism of their creator. In *Im Paradiese* there is in addition a vivid description of the artists' world in Munich. In *Gegen den Strom* (Against the Stream, 1904) Heyse courageously challenged engrained prejudices by turning against the practice of duelling. A curiously youthful power is evident in the book *Geburt der Venus* (Birth of Venus, 1909), which appeared last year and in which he consistently and emphatically develops his lifelong esthetic convictions both by defending the freedom of art from a one-sided asceticism and by polemizing against the naturalistic technique of copying the low, the common, and the simple-minded.

Heyse, however, is not only a writer of novels and novellas; he is the most important lyrical poet of contemporary Germany. He has written delightful novellas in verse, of which the admirable *Salamander* (1879) in terza rima is especially memorable. Although drama was not his natural medium, he has nonetheless written excellent plays, among them —to select two from a total of over fifty—the patriotic play *Kolberg* (1865) and the interesting drama *Hadrian* (1865), in which the wisdom and sadness of Hadrian are combined and represented in a most moving manner.

Heyse's taste is very independent. While he had great admiration for *The Pretenders* and *Vikings at Helgeland* by his friend Ibsen, he liked neither *Ghosts* nor the following symbolic plays. He is deeply musical, but not so much moved by Wagner as by Beethoven, Mozart, Schubert, Chopin, and Brahms.

In all critical situations of life Heyse has maintained the same independence. When his friend Geibel lost his salary as a poet at the Bavarian court because of a poem to King William in which he expressed his hope for a united Germany under Prussia, Heyse, too, in a respectful letter offered to resign his position, since he agreed with Geibel on every point and therefore wished to share his fate as well.

Heyse is almost as popular in Italy as in Germany. His numerous brilliant translations have made Italian literature known in Germany. It is due to him that Leopardi, Manzoni, Foseolo, Monti, Parini, and Giusti are now widely read and admired there.

But it would be wrong to assume that the brilliant Heyse, so often called the laurel-crowned favorite of fortune, was always free from cares or was always acknowledged in the leading circles of his country. As a father he was deeply afflicted by the loss of several of his beloved children. He expressed his grief in deeply poetic songs which despite their gloom radiate an unending beauty.

As for literary opinion, it is true that the Apollonian and charming poet enjoyed early popularity, but it is equally true that there was a time when the situation changed. Naturalism, which burst forth in the eighties and dominated the scene for the next decade, directed its iconoclastic attack especially against Heyse, its most powerful opponent. He was too harmonious, too fond of beauty, too Hellenic and lofty for those who, slandering him at any price, demanded sensation, effect, bizarre licentiousness, and crass reproductions of ugly realities. Heyse did not yield. His sense of form was offended by their uncouth behavior; he demanded that literature should see life in an ideal light that would transfigure reality. In his detailed and sensitive story *Merlin* (1892) he expressed his sense of injury in a manly way. Now the tide has turned again, and Heyse would probably have been proposed earlier by his country for the world Prize had it not been for the partisan dislike of the naturalists. Now a miracle seems to have changed everything. The honorable veteran has been the object of admiration everywhere; he is an honorary citizen of Munich, where a street has been named after him; he has been flooded with honors. To the manifold distinctions, the Swedish Academy, acting at the recommendation of many critics, has now added its token of admiration by presenting to the old poet the rare homage of the Nobel Prize.

Heyse has gone his own ways. Esthetically he has been faithful to truth, but in such a manner that he mirrored inner in external reality. Schiller's well-known words, "Life is serious, art serene," properly understood, express a profound truth which can be found in the life and work of Heyse. Beauty should liberate and re-create: it should neither imitate reality slavishly nor drag it into the dust. It should have a noble simplicity. Heyse reveals beauty in this aspect. He does not teach morals, which would deprive beauty of its immediacy, but there is much wisdom and nobility in his works. He does not teach religion, but one would look in vain for anything that would seriously hurt religious feelings. Although he puts greater emphasis on the ethical than on the dogmatic side of religion, he has expressed his deep respect for every serious opinion. He is tolerant but not indifferent. He has praised love, but it was its heavenly and not its earthly aspect that he glorified. He likes men who are faithful to their nature, but the individuals to whom Heyse is most sympathetic adhere to their higher rather than their lower nature.

On this festive occasion, which Heyse has not been able to attend because of illness, we thank him for the joy that his works have given to thousands, and we send our regards to the house in the Louisenstrasse in Munich, which has been for so many years the home of the Muses.

L'ARRABBIATA

By PAUL HEYSE

Translated by Harry Steinhauer

The sun had not risen yet. Over Mount Vesuvius hung a broad, gray layer of fog, which stretched towards Naples and darkened the small towns situated along that stretch of coastline. The sea was still. But on the marina, located in a narrow bay beneath the high, rocky shore of Sorrento, some fishermen and their wives were already bustling about, hauling in their boats with heavy ropes and their nets which had been lying out at sea overnight for a catch. Others were preparing their barks, readying the sails, dragging out oars and masts from the big shuttered caverns built deep into the rock and in which the fishing equipment was stored overnight. Not an idle person was to be seen, for even the old men who could no longer undertake a sea voyage joined the long chain of those pulling the nets, and here and there an old woman stood on one of the flat roofs with her spindle or looked after her grandchildren while her daughter was helping her husband.

"Do you see, Rachela? There's our Father, the priest," said an old woman to a little girl of ten, who was swinging her little spindle beside her. "He's just getting into the boat. Antonino is to ferry him over to Capri. Holy Mother Mary, how sleepy the reverend gentleman still looks!" And she waved her hand to a slight, pleasant-faced priest who had just settled down in the boat after carefully lifting the tails of his black soutane, which he spread over the wooden seat.

The other folk on the shore interrupted their labors to watch their priest start out as he sent friendly nods and greetings to right and left.

"But why does he have to go to Capri, Grandma?" the child asked. "Don't the people there have a priest, do they have to borrow ours?"

"Don't be so silly," the old woman said. "They've priests enough there and the most beautiful churches, and even a hermit, which we don't. But there's a great *signora* there, who lived here in Sorrento for a long time and was very ill, so that the *padre* had to go to her often with the Blessed Host when they thought she wouldn't live through the night. Well, the Holy Virgin helped her back into health and vigor, and she's been able to bathe in the sea everyday. When she left here for Capri she donated a pretty pile of ducats to the Church and the poor folk, and she refused to leave, so they say, until the *padre* promised to visit her over there, so that she could confess to him. For it's remarkable how much she thinks of him, and we can bless ourselves for having him as our priest, for he's as gifted as an archbishop and the high folk ask for him. The Madonna be with him!" And with that she waved down to the little boat which was just on the point of pushing off from shore.

"Are we going to have clear weather, my son?" asked the little priest, looking doubtfully toward Naples.

"The sun isn't out yet," replied the boy. "It can overcome this bit of fog."

"Then let's start, so that we may arrive before the heat does."

Antonino had just grasped the long rudder to steer the boat into the open water, when suddenly he stopped and looked up at the head of the steep road that leads from the town of Sorrento to the marina. A slender, girlish figure became visible above, hastily striding over the stones, waving a cloth. She carried a small bundle under her arm and her attire was rather poor. But she had an almost noble, though somewhat wild manner of throwing her head back, and the black braid that she wore in a coil about her forehead looked like a diadem.

"What are we waiting for?" the priest asked.

"There's someone else coming to the boat, probably going to Capri too. If you'll permit, *Padre*—it won't take us any longer, for it's only a young thing of scarcely eighteen years."

At this moment the girl appeared from behind the wall that surrounds the winding road. "Laurella!" the priest exclaimed. "What business does she have in Capri?"

Antonino shrugged his shoulders. The girl approached with swift steps looking straight ahead of her.

"Hello, *l'arrabbiata!*" some of the young boatmen shouted. They would probably have said more if the presence of the *curato* had not imposed respect on them; for the defiant, silent way in which the girl received their greeting seemed to stir the mischievous among them.

"Good day, Laurella," the priest now said. "How are things going? Do you wish to come to Capri?"

"If I may, *Padre*."

"Ask Antonino, he's the owner of the boat. Everyone is lord over his property and God is lord over us all."

"Here's half a *carlin*," said Laurella without looking at the young boatman, "if I can come along for it."

"You can make better use of it than I can," the boy mumbled, and he pushed several baskets of oranges together to make room for her. He was to sell them in Capri, for that rocky island did not produce enough to fill the needs of the many visitors.

"I won't go for nothing," the girl replied and her black eyebrows quivered.

"Come child, come," said the priest. "He's a good lad and doesn't want to get rich on your bit of poverty. Here, step in"—and he stretched out his hand to her—"and sit down here beside me. Look, he's put out his coat for you so that you'll have it softer. He didn't make it so comfortable for me. But that's the way young people are. They take better care of one young girl than of ten clergymen. Now, now, you needn't apologize, Tino. It's the way our Lord has arranged things, that like and like should hold together."

Laurella had meanwhile stepped into the boat and, after pushing the jacket aside, sat down without saying a word. The young boatman let it lie there and mumbled something between his teeth. Then he gave a vigorous shove against the pier and the little boat shot out into the bay.

"What do you have there in your bundle?" the priest asked, as they glided over the sea, which was just brightening with the first rays of sunshine.

"Silk, yarn and a loaf of bread, *Padre*. I'm to sell the silk to a woman in Capri who makes ribbons, and the yarn to another woman."

"Did you spin it yourself?"

"Yes, sir."

"If I remember rightly, you learned to make ribbons too."

"Yes, sir. But things are worse with Mother again, so I can't leave the house and we can't afford our own loom."

"Things are worse? Oh! Oh! When I

was at your place at Easter, she was sitting up."

"Spring is always the worse time for her. Since we've had the big storms and the earthquakes she's been on her back with the pains."

"Don't abate your prayers and requests to the Virgin Mary, my child, to intercede for you. And be good and industrious, so that your prayer may be heard."

After a pause: "As you were coming down to the beach, they shouted at you: 'Hello, l'arrabbiata!' Why do they call you that? It isn't a nice name for a Christian who should be gentle and humble."

The girl's brown face glowed and her eyes flashed.

"They make fun of me because I don't dance or sing or talk a lot, like other girls. They should leave me alone; I don't do them any harm."

"But you could be friendly toward everyone. Let others dance and sing, if they have an easy life. But to exchange a gentle word is proper even for a soul in distress."

She looked down before her and contracted her brows even more, as if she wished to hide her black eyes beneath them. For a while they sailed on in silence. The sun now stood in splendor over the mountain range, the peak of Mount Vesuvius jutted out over the bank of clouds which still encircled the foot of the mountain, and the houses on the plain of Sorrento gleamed white between the orange groves.

"Has that painter, that Neapolitan, who wanted to marry you, Laurella, never communicated with you again?" asked the priest.

She shook her head.

"He came to make a picture of you that time. Why didn't you let him?"

"What was the point of it? There are other girls more attractive than I am.

And besides, who knows what he would have done with it? He might have used it to bewitch me and hurt my soul, or even kill me, Mother said."

"Don't believe such sinful things," the priest said earnestly. "Are you not always in the hands of God, without whose will not a hair on your head can be touched? Do you think that a human being with such a picture in his hand can be stronger than the Lord?—Besides, you can see that his intentions toward you were good. Would he have wanted to marry you otherwise?"

She was silent.

"And why did you refuse him? He's supposed to be a good man and quite handsome, and he could have supported you and your mother better than you can do now with your bit of spinning and silk winding."

"We are poor folk," she said vehemently, "and my mother has been sick for such a long time. We would only have been a burden on him. And I'm no good for a gentleman. He would have felt ashamed when his friends came to visit him."

"What nonsense you talk! I'm telling you he was a good man. And besides he wanted to move to Sorrento. You won't soon find another man like him who seemed directed by Heaven to rescue both of you from your distress."

"I don't want any husband, ever!" she said, full of defiance and as if to herself.

"Did you take a vow, or do you want to enter a convent?"

She shook her head.

"People are right to accuse you of stubbornness, though the name they call you is not pretty. You should consider that you are not in this world alone and that your stubbornness is only making your mother's life and her illness the more bitter to endure. What solid grounds can you have for rejecting every honest hand that is offered in support of you and your mother? Answer me, Laurella!"

"I do have a ground," she said softly and with hesitation. "But I can't say it."

"Not say it? Not even to me? Not to your father confessor, whom you normally trust as having your interest at heart? Or don't you?"

She nodded.

"Then unburden your heart, child. If you are right, I'll be the first to admit it. But you are young and have little knowledge of the world, and at some later time you might regret it if you should throw away your happiness for some childish whim."

She cast a fleeting shy look at the boy, who sat at the back of the boat rowing industriously, his woolen cap pulled far down over his forehead. He was staring down the side of the boat into the water and seemed to be wrapped in his own thoughts. The priest followed her eyes and bent his ear closer to her.

"You didn't know my father," she whispered, and her eyes took on a dark look.

"Your father? Why, I believe he died when you were scarcely ten years old. What has your father, may his soul be in paradise, to do with your stubbornness?"

"You didn't know him, *Padre*. You don't know that he alone is responsible for my mother's illness."

"How so?"

"Because he mistreated her and beat her and kicked her. I still remember the nights when he came home in a rage. She never said a word but did everything he wanted. But he would beat her so that my heart felt like breaking. I would pull the bedcovers over my head and would pretend to sleep, but I cried all night. And when he saw her lying on the floor, he would suddenly be transformed and pick her up and kiss her till she cried out he was choking her. Mother has forbidden

me to mention a word of it; but it affected her so much that in all these many years he's been dead, she has not yet recovered from her illness. And if she should die an early death, which Heaven forbid, I know who has killed her."

The little priest kept shaking his head and seemed undecided to what point he should agree with the communicant. Finally he said, "Forgive him, as your mother has forgiven him. Don't let your thoughts dwell on those sad scenes, Laurella. Better times will come for you and let you forget everything."

"I'll never forget that," she said, and shuddered. "And you must know, *Padre*, that is why I don't want to marry, so that I needn't depend on anyone who would first mistreat me and then caress me. If any man wants to beat or kiss me now, I know how to defend myself. But my mother couldn't take care of herself, she couldn't resist his blows or his kisses because she loved him. And I don't want to love any man so much that I'll become sick and wretched because of him."

"My, but you're a child, and you talk like a person who knows nothing about what goes on in the world. Do you think that all men are like your poor father, that they yield to every whim and passion and treat their wives badly? Haven't you seen enough decent men in the whole region—and women, who live in peace and harmony with their husbands?"

"No one knew how my father behaved toward my mother either, for she would rather have died a thousand times than tell anyone or complain. And all because she loved him. If love is the kind of thing that seals your lips when you should be crying out for help and makes you defenseless against worse things than your worst enemy can do to you, then I never want to make my heart depend on a man."

"I tell you, you are a child and don't know what you're saying. When the time comes, your heart will ask you precious little, whether you want to love or not; then all these ideas that fill your head will count for nothing."—And after a pause: "And that painter, did you think he would treat you harshly too?"

"He had a look in his eyes like my father's when he begged mother's pardon and wanted to take her in his arms and speak sweet words to her. I know those eyes. They can also belong to a man who can bring himself to beat his wife who has never harmed him. I felt horrified when I saw those eyes again."

After that she was stubbornly silent. The priest was silent too. He was probably going over in his mind the many pretty speeches he could make to the girl. But the presence of the young boatman, who had become more restless toward the end of the confession, closed his lips.

When they arrived at the little harbor of Capri after a two-hour trip, Antonino carried the clergyman from the boat over the last shallow waves and set him down reverently. But Laurella had been unwilling to wait till he waded back and did the same for her. She gathered her skirts, took her wooden boots in her right hand and her bundle in her left and briskly splashed to shore.

"I'll probably be in Capri a long time today," said the *padre,* "so you needn't wait for me. Perhaps I won't return before tomorrow. And you, Laurella, when you get home, give your mother my regards. I'll pay you a visit before the week is out. You're going back before night, aren't you?"

"If I have the opportunity," the girl said, and adjusted her skirt.

"You know that I have to go back too," said Antonino, in what he thought was a very indifferent tone of voice. "I'll wait for you till the Ave Maria. If you don't come by then, it's all one to me."

"You must come, Laurella," the little man interrupted. "You mustn't leave your mother by herself all night. Is it far you have to go to?"

"To Anacapri, in one of the vineyards."

"And I have to go toward Capri. May the Lord keep you, child, and you, my son."

Laurella kissed his hand and uttered a good-bye that was meant to be shared by the *padre* and Antonino. But Antonino did not accept it as intended for him. He took off his cap to the *padre* but did not look at Laurella.

But when they had both turned their backs to him, his eyes followed the clergyman only briefly as he trudged laboriously in the deep gravel, then he fixed them on the girl who had turned right toward the mountain slope, shading her eyes with her hand against the strong sun. Before the road withdrew between walls above, she stopped for a moment, as though to catch her breath, and turned around. The marina lay at her feet, round about her the jagged rocks towered up, the sea shone blue in rare splendor—it was indeed a sight worth stopping for. Chance would have it that her eyes, sweeping past Antonino's boat, met that look which Antonino had sent in her direction. They both made a gesture of people who apologize for something that happened in error; whereupon the girl continued her way with a set expression about her mouth.

It was one o'clock in the afternoon, but Antonino had already been sitting for two hours on a bench before the fishermen's tavern. Some thoughts must have been troubling him, for he jumped up every five minutes, went out into the sun and carefully surveyed the roads that lead to the two island towns from right and left. The weather seemed to him doubtful, he told the woman who ran the inn.

Sure, it was clear, but he knew this color of sky and sea. It had looked just like that before the last great storm when he had barely managed to bring the English family to shore. She must remember it.

"No," said the woman.

Well, if there was a change before nightfall, she could think of what he had said.

"Do you have many visitors over there?" the hostess said, after a while.

"It's just beginning. We've had a bad season so far. The ones who come to take the baths are taking their time."

"Spring came late. Have you been making more money than we here on Capri?"

"If I were wholly dependent on my boat I couldn't eat macaroni twice a week. Delivering a letter to Naples now and then, rowing some *signore* out to sea who wants to fish—that was all. But you know that my uncle owns those large orange groves and is a rich man. 'Tonino,' he says, 'as long as I live you shall not suffer want, and after I'm gone you'll be looked after too.' In this way I have survived the winter with God's help."

"Has he any children, your uncle?"

"No. He never married and was abroad for a long time, collecting many a *piaster*. Now he plans to start a large fishery and wants to put me in charge of the whole works, to keep an eye on it."

"Then you're a made man, Antonino."

The young boatman shrugged his shoulders. "Every man has his burden to bear," he said. Then he jumped up and once more looked to left and right to check the weather, although he must have known that there was only one weather side.

"I'll bring you another bottle. Your uncle can afford it," said the hostess.

"Just one more glass, for you have a fiery brand here. My head already feels quite warm."

"It doesn't get into your blood, you can drink as much of it as you want to. And here's my husband coming; you'll have to sit with him a while and talk."

True enough, the stately *padrone* came down toward the tavern from the mountain heights, his net slung over his shoulder, his red cap over his curly hair. He had delivered fish to town to that aristocratic lady who had ordered them to serve to the little priest from Sorrento. When he caught sight of the young boatman, he waved a warm welcome to him, then sat down beside him on the bench and began to ask questions and tell stories. His wife was just bringing a second bottle of genuine, unadulterated Capri, when a crunching noise was heard on the beach road at the left, and Laurella came from the direction of Anacapri. She gave a curt nod with her head and then stood silent, undecided as what to do.

Antonino jumped from his seat. "I must go," he said. "That's a girl from Sorrento who came this morning with the *Signor Curato* and wants to get back tonight to her sick mother."

"Well, well, it's a long while still till nighttime," said the fisherman. "She'll certainly have time to drink a glass of wine. Hello there, Wife, bring another glass."

"Thanks, I'm not drinking," said Laurella and remained standing at some distance from them.

"Pour out a glass, Wife, pour it out. She's being coy."

"Leave her alone," said the boy. "She has a hard head; when she's made up her mind that she doesn't want a thing, not even a saint can talk her into it." And with that he took a hasty leave, ran down to his boat, loosened the rope and stood there waiting for the girl. She waved her hand again to the landlord and his wife and then walked toward the boat with hesitating steps. First she looked all about her, as if she expected other passengers to join her. But the marina was deserted; the fishermen were asleep or sailing about with rod and net, a few women and children sat in front of the doors, sleeping or spinning, and the tourists who had come over in the morning were waiting for the cooler hours to return. She was not able to look about too long, for before she could prevent it, Antonino had taken her in his arms and was carrying her, like a child, into the boat. Then he jumped in after her and with a few strokes of the oars they were on the open sea.

She had sat down in the bow of the boat with her back half-turned toward him, so that he could only see her in profile. Her features were now even more solemn than usual. Her hair drooped low over her forehead, her delicate nostrils quivered with a stubborn air, her full lips were pressed tightly together. —When they had been sailing through the water in silence for a while, she felt the hot sun burning her, took the loaf of bread out of the cloth and spread the kerchief over her head. Then she began to eat the bread for dinner, for she had eaten nothing in Capri.

Antonino did not watch this scene very long. From one of the baskets that had been filled with oranges in the morning, he took out two and said: "Here's something for your bread, Laurella. Don't think I kept them especially for you. They rolled out of the basket into the boat, and I found them when I put the empty baskets back into the boat."

"You eat them. I'm quite satisfied with the bread."

"They will refresh you in this heat; you've walked a long distance."

"They gave me a glass of water up there, that was enough to refresh me."

"As you wish," he said, and let them drop back into the basket.

A new silence. The sea was as smooth as a mirror and could hardly be heard around the keel. Even the white gulls which make their nests in the caves on the shore were flying silently in search of prey.

"You could give those two oranges to your mother," Antonino began once more.

"We still have some at home and when they're gone, I'll go out and buy some."

"Why don't you give them to her with my compliments."

"But she doesn't know you."

"Well, you could tell her who I am."

"I don't know you either."

This wasn't the first time she denied knowing him. A year ago, shortly after the painter had come to Sorrento, it happened on a Sunday that Antonino and some other youths from the town were playing *boccia* on an open square near the main street. It was there that the painter had first met Laurella, who walked past him, carrying a jug of water on her head, without noticing him. The Neapolitan, struck by the vision, stopped and looked after her although he was standing right in the path of the game and could have left it by taking two steps. He had to be reminded by a bowling ball, which hit him roughly in the ankle, that this was not the spot for being lost in thought. He looked around, as if expecting an apology. The young boatman, who had thrown the ball, stood among his friends, stubborn and silent, so that the tourist found it advisable to avoid an exchange of words and to go away. But the incident was talked about and there was more talk when the painter openly courted Laurella. When he asked her if she was rejecting him for that rude boy, she replied irritably, "I don't know him." And yet she too had heard about that talk. Since then, when she met Antonino, she had certainly recognized him again.

And now they were sitting in the boat like the most bitter enemies and the hearts of both were beating like fury. Antonino's normally good-natured face was a deep red color; he struck the waves so that he was sprayed with foam, and his lips trembled at times as if he were uttering angry words. She pretended that she noticed nothing and made her most innocent face, bent over the edge of the boat and let the water glide between her fingers. Then she took her kerchief off and arranged her hair as if she were all alone in the boat. Only her eyebrows were still trembling and she made a vain attempt to cool her burning cheeks with her wet hands.

Now they were in midsea, and not a sail was to be seen, near or far. The island had been left behind; the coast lay a long distance away in the haze of the sun; not even a seagull flew through the profound solitude. Antonino looked about him. A thought seemed to enter his mind. The color suddenly left his cheeks and he dropped the oars. Involuntarily Laurella turned around to look at him, tense but unafraid.

"I must put an end to it," the boy exploded. "It's lasted too long and I almost wonder it hasn't destroyed me. You say you don't know me? Didn't you watch me long enough as I walked past you like a crazy man with my heart full of things I wanted to tell you? Then you made an angry face and turned your back to me."

"What was there to talk about?" she replied curtly. "I saw, of course, that you wanted to strike up a friendship with me. But I didn't want people to gossip about me for no reason at all. For I don't want you for a husband, neither you nor any other man."

"No other man? You won't talk like that always. Because you rejected the painter? Bah! You were still a child then. Some day you'll feel lonely and then you'll take the first man that comes along, you mad thing."

"No one knows his future. Maybe I'll change my mind. What business is it of yours?"

"What business?" he burst out, and jumped up from his bench so that the boat rocked. "What business is it of mine? You can ask that when you know how I feel? May the man who gets better treatment from you than I have die a miserable death!"

"Have I ever given you a promise? Can I help it if you're crazy in the head? What right do you have over me?"

"Oh," he exclaimed, "it isn't there in writing, of course, no lawyer has written it in Latin or put his seal on it; but this I know: that I have as much right to you as I have to get into Heaven if I've been a decent fellow. Do you think I want to stand by when you go into Church with another man and the girls walk past me and shrug their shoulders? Am I going to stand for that insult?"

"Do as you wish. You won't scare me with all your threats. I'll do as I wish too."

"You won't talk like this very long," he said, his whole body shaking. "I'm man enough not to let my life be ruined any longer by a stubborn creature like you. Do you know that you're in my power here and have to do what *I* want?"

She gave a slight start and turned her flashing eyes on him.

"Kill me if you dare," she said slowly.

"Nothing should be done by halves," he said, in a softer voice. "There's room enough for both of us in the sea. I can't help you, child"—and he spoke almost sympathetically, as though in a dream—"but we must go down, both of us, at once, and right now!" he shouted and suddenly seized both her arms. But the next instant he withdrew his right hand. The blood was flowing; she had bitten it fiercely.

"Must I do what you wish?" she cried, pushing him away with a sudden turn. "Let's see if I am in your power." —With that she leaped from the boat and for a moment vanished in the depths of the sea.

She appeared again at once. Her skirt clung to her tightly. Her hair had been loosened by the waves and hung down heavy over her neck. She was pulling vigorously with her arms, swimming silently in powerful strokes away from the boat towards the coast. His sudden fright seemed to have paralyzed his senses. He stood in the boat, bending forward, his eyes fixed on her as though a miracle were taking place before him. Then he shook himself, seized his oars and pursued her with all the strength that was in him, while the bottom of his boat turned red from the blood that kept flowing.

He was beside her in a moment, in spite of her swift strokes. "By the Holy Mary!" he cried, "come into the boat. I was crazy; God knows what clouded my brain. It rushed into my head like a flash of lightning from Heaven, so that I burned with a fire and didn't know what I was doing or saying. I don't ask you to forgive me, Laurella, only to save your life and come into the boat."

She kept on swimming as if she had heard nothing.

"You can't get to shore, you have two more miles to go. Think of your mother. If you had an accident, she would die of horror."

She measured the distance to the shore with a look. Then, without replying, she swam to the boat and grasped the edge with her hands. He stood up to help her. His jacket which had been lying on the bench glided into the sea when the boat tipped to one side from the girl's weight. Nimbly she pulled herself up and climbed into her former seat. When he saw that she was safe, he took the oars again. But she wrung out her dripping skirt and squeezed the water out of her braids. As she looked down on the floor of the boat, she noticed the blood. She cast a swift glance at the hand, which was handling the oar as if it were unhurt. "There!" she said, as she handed him her kerchief. He

shook his head and kept on rowing. Finally she stood up, went to him and tied the kerchief about his deep wound. Then, in spite of his resistance, she took the one oar from his hand, sat down opposite him without looking at him, fixing her eyes on the oar which was reddened by the blood, and rowed with vigorous strokes. They were both pale and silent. When they came closer to land, they were met by fishermen who were casting their nets for the night. They hailed Antonino and made taunting remarks to Laurella. Neither of them looked up or said a word in reply.

The sun was still high over Procida when they entered the marina. Laurella shook her skirt, which had almost wholly dried in the crossing, and jumped ashore. The old spinning woman who had seen them set out in the morning was again standing on the roof. "What's that you have on your hand, Tonino?" she called down. "Lord Almighty, the boat is swimming in blood."

"It's nothing, Godmother," the boy replied. "I tore it on a nail that was sticking out too far. It'll be all right by tomorrow. My damn blood is always ready to flow, so that it looks more dangerous than it is."

"I'll come down and put some herbs on it, Godson. Wait, I'm coming."

"Don't bother, Godmother. It's been attended to and tomorrow it'll be all over and forgotten. I have a healthy skin that grows quickly over any wound."

"Addio!" said Laurella, and turned to the path that leads up the slope.

"Good night," the boy called after her, without looking at her. Then he took the equipment and baskets out of his boat and climbed the little stone stairway that led to his hut.

There was no one beside him in the two rooms through which he was pacing up and down. Through the open little windows which are closed by wooden shutters the air streamed in somewhat cooler than over the calm sea, and he felt comfort from the solitude. For a long time he stood before the small icon of the Virgin Mary and stared devoutly at the halo of stars made of silver paper that had been pasted over her head. But he could think of no prayer to say. And what could he have asked from Her, since he had lost all hope?

And the day seemed to be standing still. He yearned for the darkness, for he was tired and the loss of blood had affected him more than he was willing to admit. He felt a throbbing pain in his hand, sat down on a stool and loosened the bandage. The blood which had been held in check streamed out again and his hand was swollen badly around the wound. He washed it carefully and cooled it for a long time in water. When he took it out again he could clearly discern the mark of Laurella's teeth. "She was right," he said. "I was a beast and deserve no better. I'll send back the kerchief to her tomorrow by Giuseppe. For I don't want her to see me again." —And now he washed the kerchief carefully and spread it out in the sun after he had bandaged his hand again as well as he could, using his one hand and his teeth. Then he threw himself on his bed and closed his eyes.

He was awakened from a half-slumber by the bright moon and by the pain in his hand. He was just getting up again to soothe the pounding of his blood by immersing it in the water, when he heard a noise at his door. "Who's there?" he exclaimed, and opened it. Laurella stood before him.

She came in without saying much. She took off the kerchief that she had thrown over her head and put down a little basket on the table. Then she drew a deep breath.

"You've come to fetch your kerchief," he said. "You could have saved yourself the trouble, for tomorrow morning I would have asked Giuseppe to take it to you."

"It isn't about the kerchief," she replied quickly. "I've been on the mountain looking for herbs that help against bleeding. There!" And she lifted the lid from the basket.

"Too much trouble," he said, without any trace of harshness, "too much trouble. I feel much better already, much better. And even if it were worse, it would be what I deserve. What are you doing here at this time of night? If someone met you here! You know how they gossip, though they don't know what they are talking about."

"I don't care about any of them," she said vehemently. "But I want to see your hand and put the herbs on it because you'll never be able to do it with your left hand."

"I tell you it's not necessary."

"Then let me see it so that I can believe you."

She took hold of his hand without any further words; he put up no resistance and she took the bandage off. When she saw the big swelling she shuddered and shrieked: "Jesus and Mary!"

"It's swollen a little," he said. "It'll pass in a day and a night."

She shook her head: "You won't be able to go to sea for a week."

"I think I can the day after tomorrow. Besides, what does it matter?"

Meanwhile she had fetched a basin and washed the wound again, which he allowed her to do like a child. Then she placed the healing leaves on it, and they relieved the burning at once. She bandaged his hands with strips of linen that she had brought with her.

When it was done he said: "Thank you. And listen, if you will do me a favor, forgive me because I couldn't control my madness today and forget everything I said and did. I don't know myself how it happened. You never gave me a reason for it, truly you didn't. And you won't hear anything that might offend you from me again . . ."

"I who owe you the apology," she interrupted him. "I should have explained everything to you differently and better and not irritated you by my silence. And now this wound—"

"It was self-defense and it was high time that I should regain control of myself. And, as I say, it doesn't mean anything. Don't talk about forgiving. You did me a favor and I thank you for that. And now go to sleep and there—there's your kerchief that you can take along now."

He handed it to her, but she kept standing there, apparently going through an inner conflict. Finally she said: "You have lost your coat too because of me, and I know that the money for the oranges was in it. I didn't think of this until I was on my way home. I can't give it back to you at the moment because we don't have it, and if we did, it would belong to my mother. But here is the silver crucifix that the painter left on our table the last time he came to our house. I haven't looked at it since then and don't want it lying about in the box. If you sell it—it's worth a few *piasters,* my mother said at the time—it would make up your loss, and if you fall short, I will make it up with my spinning at night when mother is asleep."

"I'll take nothing," he said shortly, and thrust the shining crucifix, which she had taken out of her pocket, back at her.

"You must take it," she said. "Who knows how long you won't be able to earn anything with this hand? There it is, and I never want to see it again."

"Then throw it into the sea."

"But it isn't a present I give you; it's no more than your just right and what is owing to you."

"Right? I have no right to anything

from you. If we should ever meet in the future, do me a favor and don't look at me, so that I may not think you remember my guilt toward you. And now good night and let this be the end."

He put the kerchief into her basket and the crucifix beside it and closed the lid. When he then looked up into her face he got a shock. Big heavy drops were rolling down her cheeks. She did nothing to stop them.

"Maria Santissima!" he cried, "are you sick? You're trembling from head to foot."

"It's nothing," she said. "I want to go home!" and she staggered to the door. She was overcome by a fit of weeping, so that she pressed her forehead against the doorjamb and now sobbed loud and convulsively. But before he could go to her to hold her back, she suddenly turned around and threw her arms about his neck.

"I can't bear it," she cried, and pressed him to her like a dying person clinging to life. "I can't listen to you giving me all those good words and sending me away with all that guilt on my conscience. Strike me, trample me under foot, curse me!—or, if it is true that you love me, even after all the evil I have done to you, then take me and keep me and do with me as you will. But don't send me from you like this!" —Renewed vehement sobbing interrupted her.

For a while he held her in his arms speechless. "Do I love you?" he finally exclaimed. "Holy Mother of God! Do you think this little wound has drained all my heart's blood away? Don't you feel it pounding there in my chest as if it wanted to get out and go to you? If you're only saying this to test me or because you feel pity for me, then go and I will forget even that. You mustn't think you owe it to me because you know how much I suffer."

"No," she said firmly, and looked up

from his shoulder into his face with her tear-filled eyes, "I love you, and let me confess, I have feared it for a long time and fought it stubbornly. And now I want to change, for I can't bear it any longer not to look at you when you pass me on the street. Now I want to kiss you too," she said, "so that you can say to yourself when you're in doubt: 'She kissed me and Laurella kisses no man unless she wants him for her husband.' "

She kissed him three times; then she freed herself and said: "Good night, my dearest. Now go to bed and heal your hand and don't come with me, for I'm not afraid of anyone except you."

With that she slipped through the door and vanished into the shadow of the wall. But he stood at the window for a long time, looking out to the sea, above which all the stars seemed to be dancing.

When the little *padre* left the confessional in which Laurella had been kneeling a long time, he smiled. "Who would have thought," he said to himself, "that God would take mercy on this strange heart so quickly? And here I was reproaching myself for not having uttered harsher threats against the daemon Stubbornness. But our eyes are too shortsighted for the ways of Heaven. Well, may the Lord bless them and may I live to see the day when Laurella's oldest boy ferries me across the sea instead of his father. My, oh my, *l'arrabbiata!*"

THE WINE GUARD

By PAUL HEYSE

Translated by Harry Steinhauer

In September of a year which has vanished from human memory as far as its rural history is concerned, a young lad was sitting, during the sultry noon hour, in the luxuriant vineyard that covers the southern slopes of Mount Küchel near the city of Meran. The arbor walks of more than human height, in which the wine is grown here, were so heavily laden with the blessing of that year that a dark green twilight hung over the long, noiseless streets, as well as a heavy, stagnant heat, in which not a breath of air stirred any waves. Only where the narrow gray stairways of rock run steeply up the mountain between the individual vineyards could one barely feel that one was emerging into the open air. For the sea of boiling heat that surged in the spacious valley-kettle here attacked the unprotected head with double force. Rarely could a human being be seen walking along the road. Only numerous lizards, proof against fire, ran up and down the steps and rustled through the tough ivy thickets which opulently entwine the foundation walls of the vineyards. The dark blue grapes with their large thick-skinned berries hung densely from the latticework on the vaulted arches and a strangely bubbling note could be heard now and then in the profound midday silence, as though the juice were circulating audibly and were seething in the noble growth under the fire of the sun.

But the lad, who was sitting alone under the vines halfway up the mountain, seemed deaf to these mysterious voices of nature and wholly absorbed in his own gloomy thoughts. He wore the ancient, bizarre dress of the wine guards or "saltners": the sleeveless leather jacket, with wide shoulder straps that held the leather cuffs firm above the shirt sleeves through small straps or little silver chains, breeches and braces likewise made of leather and encircled by a wide belt as thick as a thumb, with the owner's name embroidered on it in white; short white hose with an openwork pattern; about his neck all sorts of ornamentation made of small chains, boar and marmot teeth. But the principal items of his official garb lay beside him in the grass: the tall three-cornered hat, whose rim was covered by cock and peacock feathers, fox and squirrel tails, no small burden at the time of the grape harvest, and the long, weighty halberd which the wine guards are able to use, to give emphasis to their threatening appearance when an unauthorized intruder into their territory is not willing to lay down the security money.

Day and night, without relief, without Sunday rest or time for Church, in return for a moderate wage, each of these "living scarecrows" roams through the territory assigned to him, from the middle of July, when the first berries turn sweet, until the last grape has reached the wine press. Their hard service in heat and wet weather, without shelter except for the wretched protection of their shed made of corn husks, is nevertheless a service of honor for which only the most dependable lads are chosen. Besides, the mild, star-clear nights in the free heights have their attraction, while in the houses below, the sultry heat hardly ever evaporates and the owners of the vineyards make a special point of supplying the guards with plentiful wine and food so that they may remain strong and in good spirits.

This recipe, however, did not seem to work on the morose lad whom we have approached. The jug of red wine, the bread and the large slices of smoked meat which a little boy had just dragged up the mountain for his midday meal lay beside him, untouched, on the flat stone that served him for a table. His very small carved pipe with a silver chain had long gone out, and gloomily he sank his teeth into the soft wooden stem. He was about twenty-three years old, his beard curled lightly about his chin and cheeks; the sharp features of his face indicated early passions; in the fashion of the region, his forehead was hidden by his hair which, from an early day trimmed close to his eyebrows, had been trained into individual locks and hung down in curls about his temples and neck. This restored to the head all the freshness of youth which the shadows under his dark eyes threatened to take from him.

A slow step approaching by the footpath below caused him to look up suddenly, put on his hat and seize his halberd. It could now be seen that his height was somewhat below what was customary in the country but still stately enough and, at first sight, striking the eye with the beautiful harmony of the curved chest and the firm thighs. Only his head seemed to be almost too small and his hands and feet actually those of a woman. The supple figure glided noiselessly along under the vaulted latticework, without as much as touching a grape, and peered down the road from the nearest rocky promontory.

A slender figure in a black coat with a high, very shabby felt hat was strolling down the broad lane between the vineyard and the meadow, in the shadow of the willow trees, holding an open book in his folded hands and peering contentedly and without desire at the beautiful grapes. Even without the long coat, which reached down almost to the ankles of the black stockings, anyone would soon have recognized the ecclesiastic in the contemplative stroller, specifically from some of the most amiable traits which, under certain skies, are characteristic of this large and variegated species. At that time the violent party strife in favor of a unified creed in the promised land of Tyrol, where the milk of faith and the honey of superstition flow so pure, was still an unheard-of thing, and even the capital of the old county, Meran, in which formerly many stirrings of a new spirit had rudely disturbed the peace, had sunk back into a deep contentment. And so the servants of the Church had no cause for brandishing their croziers like weapons; they were able to practice the idyllic virtues of their condition with perfect equanimity. At that time it was not uncommon to meet those modest ecclesiastical faces on which one could clearly read a certain embarrassment caused by their own dignity, a constant concern to yield nothing to the majesty of the dear Lord, whose cloak they wore, and yet to face their unhallowed fellow creatures solemnly but not too unapproachably.

To be sure the friendly little gentleman in the shabby hat was none of your lofty Church luminaries, but a mere assistant pastor in the parish Church of Meran, whose duty it was to say Mass daily at ten o'clock, for which he received a daily income of a guilder, a little room in the Laubengasse, as well as few other emoluments. The people, who held him in honor because of his mild manner and, next to the Capuchins, placed the greatest confidence in him, insisted on referring to him as the "ten o'clock Mass-er" and bestowed many sorts of favors on him. There was not a house, far and wide, which did not, when he appeared, place a wine jug and a bite of something on the table, so that in the course of time the good man succeeded, if not in ameliorating the natural slenderness of his form, at least in enhancing the dignity of his appearance by a modest little paunch. This paunch went so badly with the cut of his figure that to the profane eye it looked comical, sitting there buttoned up tightly, askew and anxious under the thin coat. But the embarrassing burden went very well with the modest expression on his face, and it occurred to none of his communicants to ridicule this late arrival of nature. Nor was anyone able to accuse the ten o'clock Mass-er of any immoderate act, unless it was in giving alms. For the fact that everyone hastened to treat him to the best of their vineyards was due in part to the reputation he enjoyed: that for many miles around there was neither ecclesiastical nor worldly tongue better able to judge the quality of the wine and to determine how long it would keep and, when it was possible to improve it by some formula, who could produce that formula as well as he. After a while the greatest compliment one could pay a connoisseur was to say that he "had a wine tongue like the ten o'clock Mass-er's."

But among the many gifts and virtues of our good man, courage was simply not the strongest. Although he came from a peasant family in Passeier, which had given many a brave sharpshooter to Andreas Hofer's wars, his nerves left his eas-

ily shaken soul in the lurch at every unexpected test, except when the saving of a strange soul or some other lofty duty dictated by his conscience was at stake. Even then he preferred to help out his moral strength by physical fortification and saw to it that a moderately sized keg filled with white Terlaner wine, to which he ascribed the most inspiriting effects, should never dry up in the cellar of his house. But today, as he was returning from a sick visit in the village of Algund without refreshment, he was no match for any strong test and was most violently frightened when a dark figure suddenly jumped down beside him from the high wall of the vineyard and grasped his hand.

"Praise be to Jesus Christ!" he exclaimed, trembling in his whole body.

"For ever and ever!" the boy replied.

"It's you, Andree, my son? I really thought the Evil One was descending on me with force, for he slinks about in the vineyard of the Lord to see whom he may swallow up. Well, well, when you are lost in thoughts and meditations it can happen to you that a hat looks like the horned head of Old Nick himself. So you're here, Andree? This is your own soil that you're guarding, I mean your mother's?"

The boy's eyes darkened and the blood suffused his cheeks. "Heaven forbid," he said, "that I should set foot in my mother's estate. Since she slapped my face at Candlemas, because she thought I had set a fire in the barn, I am no longer her son and will not cross her threshold by day or night."

Only now did the clergyman remember that he had touched a sore spot. He shook his head earnestly and sympathetically and said: "Ah, Andree, you talk as no good Christian should talk. Did not Our Lord on the Cross forgive His bloody enemies, and shall a son bear a grudge against his mother even if she punished him unjustly? I know it may be a hard thing for you and that it was not the first time your mother forgot herself. But we are asked to forgive seven times seventy, Andree. Have you already forgotten this since Sunday school?"

"No, Your Reverence," the boy replied firmly. "I took a vow never to think of that day and I can keep that vow as long as I keep away from the house. But if I came back, my mother herself would remind me of it, because she hates me and does nothing but scheme how she can torment and needle me. She'll deprive me of my inheritance in her will, I know this for certain and don't care much about it. I won't perish even without it and don't begrudge it my sister. But we are separated and no one can do anything about that. I've hired myself out to Steirer, over in Gratsch, as head hand, and this year I'm doing guard duty and making a living without getting a penny from home. But mother could send seven messengers to me and try to get me back with four horses, I wouldn't go. Everything must have an end sometime."

The little priest looked pensively in front of him and seemed to be of the opinion that it was more advisable to let matters take their course than to offer still more ecclesiastical admonition. He looked with expert eyes at the vines on the wall above and said:

"Steirer did well to plant Hertlinger grapes here instead of the Bratvines that used to grow here. They are still young but next year they will bear double."

"They are only planted at the edge here," the boy replied. "Up there it's mostly red Farnatsch and some Goateyes in between. What he has up there, below Tyrol village, are red Ferseilen, but he's going to remove them this year and plant slips, for they've borne almost to the point of exhaustion."

"How many hogshead do you expect, approximately?"

"A hundred and forty to a hundred and seventy, at least."

"And how does guarding appeal to you, Andree? It can be hard work in the long run."

"Oh, it's passable, Reverence. I don't feel it in my limbs yet."

"Do you keep your eyes open at night too?"

"Mine, yes. But they're only two and I'd have to have a dozen to keep watch everywhere at once. The white coats are beginning to poach again at night; the grapes are just juicy enough for them to moisten their army bread in. And they always come in large numbers at the same time, but singly, and when we catch one, the others have a free terrain meanwhile; so it's no use, we can't get any justice from the captain."

"The city ought to lodge a complaint."

"Yes, the city! Then we'd have to have witnesses and proof. But who is willing to swear, when, in the morning, we find long stretches in which the best grapes have been stolen and to left and right the vines have been cut down like weeds with the sword, either from vandalism or malice, that it could only have been done by the soldiers? When we nab one by the collar he knows as little about grapes as a child in its mother's womb. So there's nothing left for us but to make him walk the plank ourselves, so that he'll think twice before coming back. But the next one, on my oath, we'll hang from his legs, he can do his drill in the air till day comes."

"They're poor devils, Andree, and the temptation is great. You should treat them humanely."

"Don't they act like beasts? Look there, Reverence"—and he pointed to a vine that was cut clean through the middle so that the leaves were already hanging limp and yellow from the tendrils—"it makes your heart bleed to see such a healthy, peaceful plant which is in this world only to fill its master's keg, ravaged by these scoundrels out of pure meanness, just to get our goat. If I catch one of them at work, may the Lord have mercy on him!"

He shook his halberd menacingly in the direction of the city and then stuck it vehemently into the sand.

The ecclesiastic gave a slight shudder but did not forget his dignity and said: "I'll talk to the captain, this very day, to keep a sterner check that the men don't leave the barracks after taps. But you, my son, control your passion and remember that you are in the service of the authorities here and must leave judgment to them. May God protect you, Andree. I'll probably go up to Goyen today, to see Hirzer. Have you any message for Franz or Rosina? Greetings, for instance?"

"No, Your Reverence. My relations with the farmer are still the same. He refuses to recognize our existence, so I don't ask about his. The others are very decent, so I wouldn't want to spoil it for them with their father by sending my greetings. But if you should possibly meet my sister—no don't say anything to her either, it was just an idea."

Quickly, as if to hide his confusion, he bent down and kissed the priest's hand reverently and swung himself back on the wall with the help of his halberd, disappearing behind the thick foliage.

Shaking his head, the ten o'clock Mass-er continued his way, and the conversation with the youth occupied his benevolent mind for some time. But the sharpest sting of sympathy had already been blunted by the long daily exercise of an extensive ministerial office and the ecclesiastical duty of pouring the oil of patience on his own and others' troubled waters. He had not the faintest inkling of how things now looked in the mind of the boy who lay up there beside his straw hut, his face pressed against the stone floor, as though he wanted to bury himself alive in the womb of Mother Earth in order to find sanctuary from an all too great grief.

He lay there for a full hour, finally finding release from his desperate thoughts in a compassionate half-sleep, when bright laughter on the road below finally awakened him. For a moment he lay still, wondering whether it had been a dream. But a bright voice penetrated to him and the same innocent trilling and cooing girlish laughter, which from a distance almost sounded like the song of a bird. In a flash the youth was on his feet and rushed to a peephole which afforded his eye a clear vision below. On the same road under the willows which the cleric had taken before, but from the direction of the town, a girl was approaching, who could not be more than seventeen years old, blond, short rather than tall, wearing the dark, sloppy local dress. But the movements of the attractive figure, though she strode along slowly and comfortably, were so light and graceful that every eye had to follow. She was clasping her hands loosely, in the manner practiced by girls here when they have nothing to carry. But her round head did not remain quiet for a moment on the slender neck, but turned restlessly, like that of a bird, in every direction, but most frequently toward her companion, whose joking remarks caused her to break constantly into new laughter. He was a lively, smart fellow, whose linen soldier's jacket, tight-fitting blue trousers and rimless blue cap sitting askew on his head made him look not unhandsome. His dark face and black eyes betrayed his southern blood. He had great difficulty in making himself intelligible to the girl in his broken German. But the mere sound of his mutilated, foreign-sounding words seemed to amuse her immensely. Several times he cast a searching look about him. Lingering deliberately, he allowed a peasant, who was driving a calf to the next village with the aid of his dog, to get ahead of them, and now that the peasant had disappeared around a turn in the road, he was obviously preparing to make closer physical contact with the girl, when his roving eye suddenly discovered the threatening figure of the wine guard, who had stepped out from an opening in the path between the vines and was motioning to him silently with his raised weapon.

The foreign soldier stopped in an uncertain silence. The girl too checked her measured step and looked up. "Good afternoon, Andree," she called out without the least embarassment. "It's my brother," she added to the soldier. "You'd better get going; he's not to be trifled with."

The soldier seemed to appreciate fully the well-meant counsel but to feel secure as yet by the departure of the enemy. "No 'fraid, Miss," he said; "I give him dime *a comprar tobacco;* then be still, good friend."

He put his hand into his pocket and was just taking out his small supply of cash when he heard the lad's thundering voice above: "Back, soldier, or this spear will fly at your head so that you'll forget to come back here by day or night."

The Italian stood as though rooted to the ground, measuring the wine guard with a furious eye.

"German bear!" he muttered between his teeth. *"Maledetto!"* —Still he could not decide to turn around and reveal himself in so disadvantageous a light before his beautiful friend. She stood beside him calmly, obviously delighted by his vehement and impotent gestures, laughing without constraint. But to the boy above the scene seemed to be anything but a merry one. With swift leaps he raced down the slope, twisting through narrow openings in the arbors, and before the Italian could collect his wits, two flashing eyes beneath the waving hat looked into his pallid face.

"Have you ears, buddy?" he shouted,

his face red with anger. "Don't you know that this road is out of bounds for the likes of you? Shall I tear your jacket from your back as evidence, you Italian fox? I suppose you forgot to get grapes last night, so you come to get some now for your supper? Get out of here this moment or—"

"Take your hands off me!" the Italian snarled, feeling himself being seized violently and shaken. "If I had my *sdegena*—"

"Louse!" the youth shouted. "Bring your sword along next time and your rifle too; it would be a worthwhile pledge. But now, by the Cross, off with you or I'll spear you like a frog and hurl you back into your barracks so that you'll never live to complete your last prayer."

With that he hurled the tall fellow a few paces so that, stumbling over a stone, he fell to his knees. The next moment he was on his feet again and, shaking his two fists threateningly against the enemy like a woman and spewing out a flood of Italian curses, he yielded before superior force and, limping and looking back frequently from the protection of the willow trees, he trotted off toward the nearby city gate.

"You made things bad for him, Andree," said the blond girl as she looked coldbloodedly after her defeated gallant. "He talked such funny stuff that I had to laugh all the time. Why did you get so wild?"

Her brother did not reply, his thoughts were still on his anger. "It isn't over between us yet!" he muttered to himself. "He'll come my way again; for all I care, I'll keep it on ice for him. —Lassie," he continued, suddenly turning to the girl, "and you—you're still singing the old tune, 'I'll dance to any fiddler'? Aren't you ashamed to listen to such a malicious devil and to walk along at his side? If any man who can make you laugh is good enough for you, then you can keep away from me. For you know very well that laughter is as rare with me as snow at Pentecost."

The girl had become silent and looked ahead of her with an absent look. With the palms of her two hands she stroked her hair, which was combed back smoothly over her head and was held together at the nape of her neck with a large round comb, and her very very delicately colored face turned red with embarrassment. "Andree," she finally said without looking at him, "shall I go now?"

"No, stay!" he replied. "Did you come on my account?"

"Of course," she said eagerly and dared to look straight at him for the first time. "It's been a week since I was able to get away. You never show your face, you know. Mother fell asleep, it was so hot in the kitchen, so I thought I'd skip out and see how you are. And here, I've brought you half a bun; Franz Hirz bought it for me yesterday after Church. I don't care for it, it's far too sweet."

"Franz Hirz? What business has he giving you presents? If his father knew about it, there'd be the devil of a row. Did he make you laugh too?"

"That fellow? All his laughter is in his pockets, when the florins rattle in them. Besides, Mother was there, you know that; when she looks at anyone, he doesn't feel like joking, like the mice when they scent the presence of a cat. I'm surprised myself that I can still be merry. But without my laughter I'd have been dead long ago, I feel so horrible sometimes, alone with her up there in the cottage."

They were silent for a while. —"Don't you want the bun?" the girl said. "Then put it there on the bench, it won't run away. And here are a few figs too, from our tree up above, the ripest ones. I picked them for you. There! They'll taste good in this heat!"

"I thank you, Lassie," he replied. "Come, we'll eat them together, up there in the shade."

He led the way up the steps to the vineyard, and she followed him, chatting about all sorts of things to which he owed her answers. On his old spot near the vine arbor he threw himself down and she sat down beside him on the broad stone and coaxed him to eat the figs. In time, as there was no new disturbance, he seemed to relax. A light wind arose, wafting toward them the sound of a distant mill on the Adige River and the roar of the Passeier, from time to time also the bang of a rifle fired by the marksmen who were performing target practice over in the shooting range. The time passed quickly for them. He coaxed her to drink from his wine, which soon brought her back to her old merry mood. The seclusion of the shady retreat further increased her high spirits and he could not take his eyes from her, letting her go on, responding monosyllabically but no longer with irritation. Finally she put on his heavy guard's hat, took his spear in her hand and walked up and down the arbor lane with giant steps, holding the two foxtails under her chin with her left hand, so that they completely framed her face. "Andree," she said, "I think they'd really be afraid of me, and if it weren't for Mother, I'd come to you every night and do guard duty while you took a few hours off for sleep. I'd make those rogues, the soldiers, respect me, wouldn't I?"

The youth laughed for the first time. When she saw that she had broken the ice of his gloom she came to him quickly, put away the hat and halberd and, crouching close to him in the grass, she said: "See, Andree, you look a thousand times better when you laugh occasionally like other boys, instead of having creases on your forehead all the time and wearing a look on your face like the Lord Jesus on the Cross. Aren't you a young lad full of fresh life who doesn't have to play second fiddle to anybody? That thing with Mother—yes, that's a sad story, but it's no fault of yours, people know that, and you needn't grieve about me either, I'll come to you as often as I can, and Mother must not say one bad word about you to my face if she doesn't want to drive me out the door, she knows that quite well. So what's wrong with you, that you always hang your head, look at me with such angry eyes, as if I weren't your loving sister but an enemy? And when another boy says an innocent word to me, the roof is on fire in an instant. Say, do you want to make a nun of me or do you expect me to be Mother's poultry maid for the rest of my life and turn into an ancient spinster?"

While she was speaking she had moved toward him in close intimacy and put her arm lightly about his neck. But he leaped up as if a ghost had seized him and shook off her caress. His chest heaved. "Leave me alone," he panted, "don't touch me, don't ask me anything, go away from me as far as you can and never come back!"

He had jumped up as if he wanted to flee, but he was unable to move from the spot. He had to look at her kneeling in the grass, petrified, her hands folded in her lap, with a look on her face that cut him to the heart. Her eyes seemed to have grown larger, her half-open mouth was fixed in a cry of anguish, her delicate nostrils quivered. It was not the first time that this expression on the girl's face caused him fright. Sometimes in the midst of her laughter, which often sounded childish anyway, she was overcome by a sudden terror and lost consciousness for a while, as if she were the victim of a destructive convulsion, which would then dissolve more or less violently. Until now he could not reproach himself with having caused such a scene. Rather he used to be called to exorcise the evil spirit, which he was able to do

without difficulty. But when he saw her kneeling in this breathless fainting fit brought about by his guilt, his own mind was paralyzed for a moment.

He struck his forehead with the palm of his hand and gave a deep groan. Then he bent down to her, seized her hands, which had grown ice-cold, and gazed intently into her eyes. "It's me, Maria," he kept repeating, "it's Andree; look at me, listen to me, pardon me, I'm crazy, but it's over now; let this be enough and forgive me, you don't know how I feel, or you would have sympathy for me."

With his hot hands he pressed hers and, kneeling before her, waited with passionate anxiety for life to flicker again in her features. But rigidity still remained in control of her, her eyelashes did not stir, he could scarcely feel any breath coming from her lips, and her wide-open eyes seemed to stare right through him, like empty air. Then the bells of the parish church began to peal for vespers with their deep tones and they broke the spell, slowly but with beneficent effect. A deep sigh came from her breast, first her eyelids closed, then when they opened again and her awakening soul became aware of the world and herself, big tears gushed forth and, leaning on his shoulder, she came out of her shock in silent tears.

He held her in his arms silently, pressed her to his beating heart, listening to the vibrant tone of the bells, muttering confused prayers to himself. When the bells stopped tolling, he took the jug and handed it to her. She brought her lips toward it, like a sick person who is afraid to hold the vessel, and took a long draught from it. Then she closed her eyes without drying them and fell asleep beside him, still on her knees and her hands folded motionless.

When he heard her breathing calmly after a while, he lifted her up and laid her down comfortably on the sloping floor; he placed his jacket under her head without waking her. After making a swift turn of his territory, he lay down beside her, resting his head on his hand; he gazed fixedly at her sleeping face, on which there was now a peaceful smile as if she were having a pleasant dream. When a leaf stirred and the light played fleetingly on her forehead, she would give a gentle sigh. But she felt serene, while he was seething with dark pain and difficult decisions, and every glance at these peaceful features gave him new nourishment for his torment.

What mysterious fate surrounded this brother and sister? —To explain it, we must go back many years, to a time when the mother who stood between them with such strange hostility was not much older than the blond child who is sleeping up there under the vines, though in every other respect they are completely antithetical. The grandparents of the blond lassie owned a simple farmhouse up on Mount Küchel; it had a pretty view into the valleys from every direction, from the left to the Passeier, from the right into the Vintschgau, straight ahead over the city of Meran into the broad plain of the Adige to the Bozen Mountains. Old Ingram had inherited the property from his ancestors; he appreciated the lovely situation as something extra, but primarily he valued the extensive vineyards that adjoined it from every direction and were a substantial help in feeding his many children. Of these the youngest, Maria, called Lassie in the local vernacular, was a source of genuine worry to him, while there was nothing special to report, either good or bad, about the others. This youngest, however, was not only the ugliest and looked more like a mandrake than a Meran child, most of whom grew up clean-limbed and comely, but behaved so badly that she earned many beatings and few good words from her mother; the father, too, who was a moderate man and clung to tradition, began more and more

to feel ashamed of this youngest child. With time the beatings ceased, since it was evident that they merely increased the evil they were supposed to cure and since, moreover, it became evident, even to a peasant's eye, that not everything was right in this sad head. True, the priest had given her an extensive examination and been inclined to trace her perversities to the wild instincts of a vain and weak heart; and truly, if you didn't look too closely, you could find no crack or spar in her intellect; for whenever she was catechized, she was able to collect herself smartly and to make even her obvious follies appear in a half-favorable light. The worst of these was a wholly useless and pathetic mania for preening herself, with which, wherever she was or went, she deliberately drew the attention of everyone to her ugliness, which was remarkable enough even without this. She thus earned a score of the most malicious nicknames; those who liked her best named her "the black peacock," or the "ugly lass," while her own brothers just called her "Black Lassie"; for not only did her face have a very dark color, with thick, bushy eyebrows, but her hair was, through a strange fluke of nature, curly like that of a Negro woman and resisted stubbornly the ministrations of comb and ribbons. We will leave open the question whether it was the Moorish King among the Three Magi on a painting her mother had once seen in a Bozen church who was responsible for this embarrassing biological sport. But it was a fact that the "ugly lass," instead of bearing her fate with a smiling face, had recourse to the most ridiculous means for remedying it and making her person more attractive and presentable through the application of all sorts of finery and frippery which she put on in the face of local custom. All the money she could scrape together, not always in the most honest way, she hastily converted into gay ribbons or artificial flowers which she stuck into her wooly hair. Decked out in this outfit she would appear in church on a Sunday, to the great annoyance of the old and the jeering of the young. The fact that her mother, whenever she met her in this garb, angrily tore the decorations off and punished her with hunger and blows made no impression on her.

This sorry impulse in her improved somewhat when she reached a more mature age and developed a greater sensitivity for the mockery of the young lads. Unfortunately that first childish folly was succeeded by an even more harmful one, which caused her to act with still less self-control, though with greater excuse. She cast her eye on the handsomest of the many boys who associated with her brothers, the one who had from the beginning treated her with the most pronounced aversion. He was a lad of the good old Meran stamp, both physically and mentally, a somewhat sluggish temperament in a strong, marvelously built body, an avid churchgoer, an expert wine grower, a boy of few words and thoughts only for his domestic needs. He wasted neither time nor money on useless amorous affairs, since in these romantic valleys love and marriage are approached in a far more businesslike way than casual tourists dream of. At that time, when the black lass became stuck on him, his father was still alive, old Aloys Hirzer, who had purchased, from a debt-ridden heir, an old castle situated below the Ifinger River, on a height far above the city, and here he had established his wine business in the grand style amid the feudal ruins. Besides his son Joseph, he had a daughter who was getting a superior education in Innsbruck from her godfather and hoped to train as a schoolteacher. When the father suddenly died, her brother asked her to come home and help him run the estate. She was a gentle, pale girl with beautiful eyes, older than her brother Joseph. His friends, some of whom no doubt cherished a desire to marry into a piece of the castle, did not dare approach Anna, who was too refined and gentle for them and was soon virtually surrounded by an odor of sanctity, for she could be found in every church and in every cottage where there was a sick or needy person; she never passed a child that she did not take into her arms and present it with a holy picture or have it recite a prayer. Her brother was well contented with her, since she quietly kept house for him, that is, that part of the house that was still habitable. He had always got along excellently with her. Since he was a calculating man, not to be swayed by emotional storms, it seemed to him practical that his sister should remain unmarried. When he stood on the balcony, which clung to the gray castle wall like a swallow's nest and looked out on the spacious land, in his peasant dress, a loden jacket trimmed with red facings, a broad black hat with a red cord on his head, his tanned hands grasping the slitted suspenders, his eyes rested with satisfaction on the small cloister towers that raised their crosses here and there out of the mist, and he liked to think that in former times the noble lords of the manor had settled their unmarried sons and daughters in them. It would not have inconvenienced him if his sister, too, had sought a contemplative refuge from the dangers and temptations of the world. But as she showed no desire to do so, he was satisfied for the present with the reflection of her halo, which cast some radiance on him as well, and he showed no little pride when ecclesiastical dignitaries came to Goyen because of his sister and delivered edifying speeches about the affairs of the Church over a glass of red wine.

Only occasionally did he think of his own matrimonial future, as when there was once some talk of a rich heiress, but even then without heated or ugly greed, but with a quiet sense of duty, that it was fitting for him to increase the paternal estate by a handsome round addition. Since, as we said, he was one of the trimmest and most elegant youths in the region, he carried about with him the calm assurance that he could lack nothing for which he felt a serious want. At first he merely accepted with a dignified superciliousness the undisguised demonstrations of favor shown him by the black lass. But in the long run, when the gossip became louder and more pointed, when he could not appear at a market place or church fair or any other public occasion without being baited about his conquest, anger mounted within him and he considered it appropriate to get rid of the importunate courtship through the most contemptuous jesting.

To some this courtship would perhaps have appeared to be pitiable, for it expressed itself only through the touching stubbornness with which the girl's eyes, as soon as the boy met her, clung compulsively to his regular features and his red and white complexion, and followed him everywhere, heedless of the anger that darkened his face, which showed no sign of returning her love. Even in church, when he stood behind her, she was able to arrange it so that she at least turned half her face toward him, and at such times she seemed to be so wholly absorbed in her admiring devotion that she was oblivious of everything else. Anyone who reflects on the simple and cool customs of the people and the commendable indifference with which the families meet there, will understand the deep irritation which such behavior occasioned. Moreover, most people were wholly convinced that the lass was only half-sane and she had to be left alone since it was, after all, not possible to keep her from going to church without granting the evil spirits even greater power

over her. But the young boys had less Christian thoughts about the matter and simply called her man-crazy and since the girls, too, kept their distance from her, even more attention was drawn to the girl, who was already marked by nature, as she went down Küchel Mountain to Mass alone, her penetrating eyes fixed straight ahead of her, seeking her chosen one among the men gathered on the church square. It could then happen, especially after vespers, when the wine dictated the tone, that one of the most hard-hearted began to sing the lament of the fair spinster of Passeier:

> What can a poor lass like me do
> To catch a man before I die?
> I've lost the esteem of all the men
> Who run from me and hide.
> Fate is most unkind to me
> No man will ever lie with me.

And when the chorus of laughter had subsided, the second stanza:

> I've tried every ploy in the business,
> Novenas more than I have years,
> Praying the Lord might send me
> A man whom I could wed.
> With Shrovetide past, my hopes are gone
> For a joyful marriage bed.

Though he considered it beneath his dignity to join in the singing, Joseph listened to the song with visible satisfaction, hoping that this musical running of the gauntlet would drive the amorous whims out of the poor crazed girl's head. But as soon as she caught sight of him she seemed to become completely deaf, so that she neither heard nor was affected by the abusive ditty. She was equally insensitive to the embittered scoldings of her brothers, said not a word in reply, but did not alter her behavior a jot; and even the sharp admonition of the priest, who had heard something about the situation, had as little effect on her as a warning to the iron when it comes too close to the magnet.

Finally one of the girls took pity on

her and decided to put her straight. She reported to her—whether truthfully or as a deliberate invention, we do not know—that Joe Hirzer had said: if he were interested in getting black poodles in his cradle, he would marry Lassie. The sermon on this short and concise text seems to have been effective enough. For from that day on Black Lassie was as though transformed, appeared nowhere, stole away to early Mass before dawn, knelt in the remotest corner of the church. When a boy met her up on the mountain, she averted her face and countered any words with silence. Her need for primping was completely gone. She favored the meanest and coarsest clothes and her curly hair waved wildly about her temples, untouched by a comb for weeks on end, so that she looked almost weird and no one would have anything to do with her.

For the rest she performed her hard labor without grumbling, so that her parents were wholly satisfied with her and left her entirely alone. And so the winter passed. When the meadows began to turn green in the spring, she came to her father one day and begged his permission to move to one of the Alps, the highest and most lonely in the Passeier. Her father, who had more understanding of her unhappy state of mind than anyone else, agreed without hesitation, and so, for the length of a summer, the black lass disappeared altogether.

All the greater was the general astonishment when the herds came home from the mountains in the fall and brought the rumor with them that told Ingram's daughter had brought a boy with her, a child as clean, blossom-white and rose-colored as had ever had to make do without a father, with black but by no means Moorish hair, a regular prince of a baby. In spite of the shame of it, the reports continued, Lassie was well satisfied, had received her mother's blows without complaint but, when her father subjected

her to the most rigorous examination, she had refused to confess who the guilty man was. The mother had driven her out to the shed so that she would not have to endure the disgrace before her eyes; here the daughter had fixed up a warm nook for her child as best she could and refused to be separated from it by day or night.

Anyone who found all this incredible, especially the boy's famed beauty, had an opportunity the following Sunday to convince himself that the report was true. For in the full light of day the much-abused girl came down from Küchel Mountain, carrying the child in her arms as though in triumph, wrapped in the best linens and cloths; with defiant maternal pride she was bringing the infant to be baptized. When anyone approached her and peered with curiosity at the little world wonder, she stopped at once, threw back the old veil that covered the sleeping little face and said almost mockingly: "You'd like to look at the black poodle, wouldn't you? There, it's nothing special. Why should it be?" And then she laughed to herself with great self-satisfaction when the viewer, surprised by the child's beauty, could say nothing; then she added: "He's only a black poodle; he should be thrown into the Passeier, that would be best." And she laughed again as strangely as if the blessings of motherhood had not improved her poor wits.

Rarely has a baptism in Meran taken place amidst such an onrush of spectators. But when the priest called for the godparents, it turned out that Lassie had completely forgotten this point. No one responded to the question as to who in the assembled congregation would show the child this service of love; for no one felt the urge to establish a closer relationship with the mother, and the grandparents had gone to the church at Lana a few hours distant, to escape the disgrace. Finally old Hirzer's daughter, who was ready to make every sacrifice demanded by the love of one's neighbor, and who was kneeling in the front pew, rose, went up to the baptismal font and took the child out of Lassie's arms. This loosening of the dubious bond appeared to everyone to be the simplest, since Hirzer's Anna, with the overflowing treasure of grace represented by her pious life, could be of greatest help to the poor sinner. So the boy was baptized Andree after the sexton, who was willing to help out too by offering his name; he was carried back through the city by his radiant mother, followed by a large throng, into the wretched shed where he was to take his first looks into the world in the company of the domestic beasts.

Before long no one spoke about these remarkable events anymore, especially as Lassie never showed herself anywhere, lived only for her child and seemed to have concentrated all her former follies into the one passion of the most tender, doting love. For she now adorned and bedecked little Andree with everything that seemed to her appropriate, as she had formerly done to her own person. One could see her sitting for hours up above on a shaded rock, winding wreaths for the child and stitching strange clothes for him out of old pieces of colored silk, with which she tricked him out as one does a doll and showed him off to every passerby. Since this activity, though it was surprising, was perfectly innocent, no one interfered. Only Joseph Hirzer reacted with the utmost horror toward her and forbade his Anna most sternly to have any relations with her godchild.

Lassie seemed to ask for no such relationship. When, a year later, her once so painfully beloved married a very rich peasant's daughter from Algund, she remained quite cold and did not show the slightest sign of a broken heart. The whole past, up to the hour when the boy came into the world, was as though wiped from her memory, nor did she ever speak of the mysterious nameless father and she seemed to make no attempt to inform him about herself and her child.

Then it happened that, first her parents, then her brothers were cut down, one after the other, in the course of a single year by a disease that claimed many victims in these valleys. Now the fate of Black Lassie was transformed with a single stroke. For if, during the lifetime of her brothers, she had merely had no cause to fear poverty, she had now become a wealthy match, as the sole possessor of the house and the substantial vineyards; more the pity that the dowry of her dark skin and the even darker first amour was bound to frighten off many a choosy suitor.

But the practical instinct that is powerful among the people here came to her aid; in fact she did not have to be indulgent in any way toward the suitor who came to court her. He was a very dapper farmer's son from the village of Tirol, which is situated not far from the famous fortress with the same name at the end of Mount Küchel, where the wall of the Muttspitze rises steeply aloft. His father had persuaded him to move in and although the son was not one of the most resolute of men, the whole important enterprise was nevertheless carried out with few words.

The same was true for Lassie. She seemed to find it perfectly natural that, in spite of all that had happened, it should now be her turn. During the courtship she made jests with little Andree, who was already in his fourth year and regarded the strange young man with shy and defiant eyes. But when, following his mother's advice, he drew a large bag of candy out of his pocket and handed it to the child, Lassie's last doubt was conquered. True, in a comparison with Joseph Hirzer, Franz Wolfhart came off with second prize. His flat, round, comfortable face, framed in pale blond hair, reminded one strongly of the Madonna pictures we meet in large numbers on houses, gateways and especially in churches, as if they were reproduced from a stencil. But Lassie had enough black in her to cast a shadow into his excessive white, and she did not seem to feel the least bit honored by the courtship of the fair young man. After the swift, absolutely businesslike course which such matters take hereabouts, Franz moved into the house of his newly wedded spouse on Küchel Mountain four weeks later, and with that the reawakened gossip concerning the destiny of Black Lassie was silenced and died for the second time.

But not for too long. A little more than a year later a girl was born from this marriage, who gave the interested neighbors as much cause for gossip as little Andree had done before. She was the spitting image of her father, beautifully white and red, with smooth blond hair, resembling her mother in no feature except that, from an early age, she began to show tendencies of a fantastic disposition, an easily swayed imagination and feminine vanity, but less extreme than in the mother and softened into pleasantness through the charm of her little person, but still dangerous, since the child lacked a firm hand that might hold her wantonness in check and tear out the beautiful wild flowers from the young soul with care.

For little Maria was hardly able to let her first childlike ingratiating tricks have free play when she stole her mother's heart so completely that she robbed her brother of even the compassion that his mother owed him as an act of duty. He, who had formerly been his mother's idol, now suddenly became the defenseless prey not only of her indifference but of a positive dislike, which with the years grew into open hatred. It did not help

much that the good-natured stepfather took the boy's part. In fact, when the little sister grew up and joined her brother in passionate tenderness, she, who was able to get her will in everything, failed to tame her mother's antagonistic spirit. On the contrary, her intercession seemed to fan the flame of the unnatural hatred, which was now joined by a kind of jealousy, a hard and evil resentment at the pleasant intimacy with which the little girl approached the sudden outcast.

The intercession of little Maria on behalf of the poor boy won this much for him that he was protected against physical maltreatment. For the first time that the degenerate mother laid a hand on her one-time darling was also the last. That was the first instance of that nervous convulsion to befall the little girl, an example of which we described in the beginning of our narrative. Fortunately the father was at home to check the senseless remedies that the terrified mother sought to apply as she swooped down on the child. By gentle stroking with his trembling hands, the brother succeeded in controlling the rigidity, until the girl threw her arms around his neck and was finally carried by him to her bedroom soundly asleep.

Since this incident, which was followed by similar ones resulting from other sudden causes, the old Lassie never again lifted her hand to her son. But her dislike of him only became more sinister and furious, because it no longer dared to vent itself in scenes of violence. She seemed to want to wholly deny the boy's existence in order to dedicate herself solely to the girl. For her sake she was tireless in seeking counsel from doctors and herb women, making pilgrimages, having Masses said and, wherever possible, in removing every obstacle from her path through the most complete indulgence. The weak and softhearted father let her have her way. He did not feel happy in his home. But the city lay so close by at his feet that he saw the green shrubs in front of the tavern doors beckon right up to him. And so he conscientiously celebrated the numerous peasant holidays which color almost the whole Tyrolean calendar red and told everyone who was willing to listen that in the last fifty years three members of his family had died from delirium tremens, which is not the worst form of death.

To his wife he had long become a thing of indifference. She loved no one in the world except her blond child. More and more she gave up associating with her neighbors and relatives, since her unnatural whims inspired horror in people. The house was situated on a solitary spot on the naked rock, far removed from the road which winds its way up Küchel Mountain toward Tyrol village. No one called in as he passed by; she went to no one; in church, which she attended before dawn, the pew beside her remained empty.

Under these circumstances it is small wonder that Joseph Hirzer avoided any contact with Lassie and her house more resolutely from year to year, and that he inexorably prevented his sister from doing so when her conscience impelled her to concern herself about her godchild. He forbade his own children, who met Andree and the blond Lassie in school, most strictly from speaking about them at home. He himself had prospered mightily on every count, was regarded as one of the most capable administrators, most ambitious winemakers and most respectable citizen, while his sister increased in like measure in the grace of God and men, especially since in her will she had bequeathed her whole estate to churches and cloisters, in return for which the priests promised her that she would infallibly get to heaven the moment she passed away. Her brother had not been able to interfere. His son and his splendid three daughters were adequately cared for, even without their aunt's inheritance, through the prosperous extensive estates of both parents. And when their mother, the heiress of Algund, died in the prime of life, Aunt Anna took her place and, by her loving care for them, saw to it that even without any palpable inheritance her brother's children would preserve a favorable memory of her.

But the children, although they feared their father, could not obey him so blindly that they avoided Andree and his sister even in the school at Meran. Lassie, with her bright disposition, so given to laughter, associated with them without constraint as she did with everyone who was friendly toward her. Andree at least tolerated them since he knew that his Aunt Anna, his godmother, was so holy and that she was only not permitted to concern herself about him because of his mother. For the rest he was a pensive, taciturn boy, easy to boil up with anger, who preferred to be by himself and from a very early date showed a strange jealousy of his sister. He felt happiest on holidays, when they remained alone, without other children, up there in this merry solitude all day and the little girl dressed up for no one but him. They had set up a hermitage under a projecting rock on which wild berries grew in abundance and whose rough wall was covered with thick ivy, containing many carefully guarded hiding places known only to the lizards, where they could play their childish games. In high summer, when the vine leaves fell luxuriantly down to the foot of their refuge, they would sit there for half-days while the little girl tirelessly strung the shiny yellow kernels of sweet corn on long threads with a sharp needle until a gay necklace took shape. When these chains were finished, her brother would kneel down before Lassie and twine the finery about her brow, neck and arms in artistic rings. This was accompanied by all sorts of confused, religious ideas and the wearer of the ornaments felt an obscure joy from the knowledge that she was the object of inspection and admiration, and indeed that she was wearing something like a halo about her foolish little child's head. The boy was even more solemn, and woe to him who would have dared to appear at such a moment to disturb his act of homage. He was even annoyed with his sister when she suddenly began to laugh and to tear up the yellow chains out of wild spirits and boredom, scattering the kernels down the mountainside and suggesting some new game for them to play.

During the first few years the mother left them alone to pursue their secret games and haunts. But as Andree grew bigger and met her hatred with increasing astonishment and reproach in his sharp eyes and skeptical expression, she tried to turn the little girl against him by all sorts of nasty words and base suspicions and seized every opportunity to separate the children with spiteful malice. She even urged her husband to send the useless boy, who showed no inclination to work, to the ten o'clock Mass-er for schooling, to be made into a clergyman. As the boy had revealed a quick intelligence and much zeal for learning in school, the plan appealed to both men and so Andree moved down into the city and took up residence with the priest. He parted from the little girl in silence and deep sorrow, but she laughed and understood nothing of what the separation meant.

The assistant pastor lived in Meran's long Arbor Lane, which derives its name from the two rows of stone arcades to which the sun has no access. The narrow houses with their tight, rectangular courtyards and gloomy hallways, mostly very ancient and mostly unkempt, have a considerable depth; behind them extensive vineyards stretch northward to the foot of Küchel Mountain, while to the south they open out to the city wall. There is more light here, and from the windows one has a view of the quays and, beyond the river, of the broad valley of the Adige. The pastor's modest quarters enjoyed this prospect too; but the boy, who was accustomed to the free air on the heights, felt himself to be a prisoner. In fact he would gladly have exchanged his sunny attic bedroom for a dark window facing north, which would have enabled him to see the mountain and the little rocky promontory beyond the last vines, the place where he had played his childhood games. He became even more taciturn than before, in spite of the encouragement given him by the friendly teacher. He suddenly lost all pleasure in learning; he ate little and slept badly, so that in four weeks he became pale and hollow-eyed. And one day he came to his teacher and told him he was going to die if he were kept in the city any longer. He had never once mentioned the name of his sister; but it was clear to the sympathetic pastor that he was being consumed by a burning homesickness for her; in dismay he undertook to persuade the mother of the need to take him back. She raged and scolded and would not hear of it. But in the evening of that same day the boy knocked on the door of the hut and, after a violent scene which once more ended with a convulsive attack suffered by little Marie, the mother yielded to the inevitable on condition that the former student would work for his father as a hired hand and sleep in a corner of the shed behind the house.

The little girl was very happy to have him back and he seemed to find no hardship and setback too high a price to pay for this reunion. He was willing to do any job his stepfather assigned to him, worked in the vineyards, went willingly with cross-country messages and saw his mother only at meals, where there was never a word exchanged between them. Since he received no money and only the minimum in clothing, he remained a stranger to the other boys of his age, as well as to taverns and bowling alleys, and he did not seem to miss them. For he used to spend the holidays with his sister, as he had done before, for hours on end. Although they were both growing up, he into a vigorous youth and she to become the target of both timid and more aggressive courtships, their association was still that of two children and their conversation silly chatter. She did all she could to ease his hard life, shared with him all the good morsels she got from her mother or, since she had a sweet tooth, that she bought in town. Though he scorned the former, he accepted her own gifts with visible joy. Often after a hard day of labor, especially at harvest time, when the Sunday sun could not awaken him in his windowless shed, she stole to him and sat in the dark beside his bed of straw, which was a bed only by virtue of his cheap sheet and horse blanket. It amused her when he could not see in the dark that she was there beside him and sleepily sought to remove her hand which was rumpling his hair as if he were warding off a field mouse. When he did wake up he would hear her bright laughter near him and lie there a while longer, pretending to be asleep in order to endure her teasing a little longer. She insisted that he accompany her to church, where his heart received many a stab of jealousy from the boys who approached her and whose advances she showed no inclination to reject. Here he also met his godmother, Aunt Anna, whom he would gladly have cultivated since she always greeted him with a quiet and friendly eye. But Joseph Hirzer, who on these occasions kept a strict watch, let it be clearly known through his fixed stare that he would not tolerate any familiarity from the fatherless boy. And so the children too did not go beyond exchanging an occasional greeting, although Lassie often

told her brother laughingly that Rosina, Hirzer's youngest daughter, who was now alone in the house since the marriage of her two sisters, had again given him that long stare and was certainly in love with him.

Every time they talked about this matter or when they discussed a wedding, the youth would become pensive and break off the conversation abruptly. All girls seemed to be a source of embarrassment and all jokes about love an abomination to him. No one could guess whether he ever thought of setting up a home of his own. But whenever his sister let her frivolous thoughts dwell on her future and expressed the possibility of a separation from him as something that could be endured, he would look at her with a strange expression of profound anxiety. "You're a child," he would then say. "Who could marry you? The men are all bad and domestic life but leads to strife. You'll stay with me, I'll work for you and make a good life for you. Why do you chatter about other men? The Passeier will sooner flow into the Ifinger before I find anyone who is good enough for you."

She would laugh at such talk and enjoy it because it flattered her. Nor did any serious love seem able to take root in her frivolous mind. Her mother did her share to scare off any suitors who came from outside. And so for many years the strange little society lived up there on Küchel Mountain with no change in prospect.

Then one day the husband succumbed to that star that had lighted the way of his worthy ancestors to their grave. He died in an alcoholic stupor. From that day on the widow made the most zealous efforts to get her son out of the house. We will spare ourselves a detailed description of the wild and angry scene that helped her attain her goal. The brother and sister became separated; the blond Lassie lacked the spirit to encourage her brother to expose himself to a repetition of his maltreatment. "Go," she said. "It's better that way. I won't abandon you. You know I can have my way with her; if she closes the door to me, I'll jump out the window and come to you."

And she kept her word. But what good was it that not a week passed but she sought him out, in addition to their meetings on Sundays? He had been accustomed to have her near him every day, every hour. That childish homesickness that had driven him away from the ten o'clock Masser often enough came over him with such power when he sat under the branches of a chestnut tree after a hot day's work that he would storm down the steep mountain close to the village of Gratsch just to see the roof of the little house before he went to bed or, better still, something that looked like the girl herself. It also happened more than once, especially on holidays, when she failed to appear at their prearranged trysting place that he would keep watch at the road leading to her house to see if some visitor was with her. At such times he lay in virtual ambush. If a visitor came walking down the mountain, he would pretend to be asleep in order to study his features. He did not feel comfortable in doing this. A faint suspicion began to dawn on him that this behavior was not right or admirable. Why would he not allow his sister what all girls enjoyed: freedom in their wishes and inclinations? With passionate anxiety he drove these thoughts away, but they only returned with greater urgency. True, her father was not his; but were they any the less brother and sister because of that?

Often enough the thought crossed his mind that he must go away, that the constriction about his heart would vanish out there. What stood in his path? What held him back? He had to fight for his existence just as much here as in the great world beyond. And who could tell: he might meet his father out there; a change of air was in every way advisable. If only he could muster enough strength to take the first step!

He turned these thoughts over in his mind again as he sat beside the sleeping girl under the vines today and watched the rays of the sun play on her brow. The shock from which she was now recovering, refreshingly and without memory, still made him tremble throughout his system, and the sight of her innocent calm merely increased his confusion. He searched within himself for the courage to take a solemn vow now that would drive him from this place, where the most natural bonds had become so ruinously intertwined. At her side he understood only too well how necessary it was to flee. But when he was alone he felt that it was impossible.

He did not touch the sleeping girl; since his childhood years he had not dared to kiss her red, laughter-loving mouth. But the shyness with which he studied her was mingled with a dull, passionate torment, and her light breath which grazed his face drove the blood pulsating to his heart.

Evening was already beginning to descend, for Mount Marling in the west hides the sun early. The sleeper now came to life, sat upright in the grass and looked about her with wide-open eyes. When she caught sight of her brother beside her, she gave him a friendly laugh. "How long did I sleep?" she asked in wonder. "How does it happen that I lay down here?"

"It was hot," he replied. "But now go home, Lassie. I must have a look over there to see that all is well."

She stood up and gave him her hand. "Good night, Andree," she said hastily, for she began to have a dim memory of what had taken place. "The day after tomorrow is Sunday. You're coming to church, aren't you?"

"No, Lassie. You know that I have to stand guard as long as I'm a *saltner*."

"It's true," she replied thoughtfully. "But I'll come to see you again. Good night."

He went through an inner struggle whether he should ask her not to come again. But before he could arrive at a decision she was gone. He stood at the exit of the arbor and looked after her as she nimbly climbed the steep stairway. Her long skirts with their hundred pleats danced gracefully about her ankles, opening and closing the pleats like a fan at every step she took. From the top she waved her hand to him. He did not return the greeting; the railing against which he was leaning trembled, and a sigh that he had suppressed a long time did not free his oppressed heart.

At this moment he heard a swift male step coming up from below and recognized one of his comrades, a strong lad with a long beard, who also wore a military hat, but with a big pine club in his rough fist instead of a halberd. He swung the heavy end of the club in a merry greeting. "Andree," he said when he was close enough, "how do things look for tonight? Shall I watch with you? I noticed that you had trouble with the Italian. And you may be sure he won't forget it but will probably return with reinforcements. Look, here's something I've got that'll spoil the fun for those dogs!" And he drew a pistol from the breast pocket of his leather jacket and cocked it.

"No thanks, Köbele," Andree replied. "The Italian is as cowardly as sin itself. He certainly will not come alone, and if there's a whole gang of them, the two of us will be too weak against them. I will then give the sign for you to tell the others. That thing there," he pointed to the pistol, "leave it alone. It has little use in the dark, you'll only fire away at the plants. But if we catch one of them, the jacket full of blows we give him will be worth more than a hole in his skin, which he can trot out as evidence against us."

"As you wish," the lad answered. "I meant just in case. But I wish they'd come. They've run up a nice bill with me and Hans is quite eager to get at the rogues too. We'll have to give it to them proper once."

Andree was silent, and the bearded one went down again with a brief greeting. People were used to leaving the taciturn fellow alone and not forcing themselves on him.

Now the sun had set behind the mountain, but several hours more passed before the night took control. For to the right, streaming high out of the Vintschgau and down to the girdle of the Ifinger, the light of day still prevailed, and a bluish haze formed a cloud over the river, shot through by a streak of sunshine here and there, which stole into the valleys behind the wall of mountain. The shepherds drove their herds together down in the meadows below and all the roads to the villages above came alive with beautiful fallow cows which had spent the day grazing at the brooks below. But in the south the Trientine Mountains and the beautiful Mendel Peak, looking boldly in, were veiled under the damp vapors which the sirocco blew into the valley.

Only late did a narrow sliver of a moon emerge, casting an uncertain look into the silent depth and soon disappearing behind the heavy mist that sluggishly drifted to the mountains. The last noise in the city, where work stops early, the last sound from the towers near and far died away. Only the swift mountain waters roared on, and from a distance the south wind hummed away, driving the dust on the roads up in light swirls and rustling through the leaves of the past autumn. That too died away at about eleven o'clock and now the motionless black night hung moist and warm over the earth, without stars, without breath pouring its dew of sleep over a thousand eyes.

The wine guards were not asleep and they knew why. It was not the first moonless night in which the insolent thieves had tried to break into the vineyards and done heavy damage. Above, beside his little hut of maize straw, Andree sat smoking his pipe, drinking from time to time from the jug that his master had sent him. He scarcely felt the heavy drops of rain that penetrated the roof of leaves and fell onto his thick hair. But he listened intently in the direction of the city, and when eleven o'clock had struck he stood up gently and crossed the street stealthily at a certain spot in the arbor where there had been built a lookout made of large pumpkin leaves with a protruding little wall. Here he ducked behind the stones, his halberd conveniently beside him, and lit a new pipe. His blood was much calmer than it had been in the daytime. It was good for him that he had something to do, that he could vent his hot unrest through some danger. For he felt certain that the Italian would not let the night pass without attempting an act of revenge.

But the enemy was taking his time; he seemed to wish to lull the watchers into a false sense of security. One could hear midnight strike from the tower and still there was no stirring. One of the *saltners,* who was guarding the neighboring vineyard, went by Andree on his round. "They're not coming tonight," he said. "I'm going up to the huts. If anything should happen, you need only whistle." "Good night," murmured Andree. It pleased him that his comrade chose to sleep. He preferred to handle the Italian all by himself, man to man.

Another half-hour passed, when the lonely watchman suddenly pricked up his ears. Not far from him, where a farmhouse leaned against the mountain between the vineyards, there arose a tremendous roar and immediately after that a dark mass, unlike anything human, came storming out amid the violent crash of splitting railings. The listener jumped to his feet, his heart beating wildly, and involuntarily crossed himself. He was separated from the arbor beyond by a staircase and a wall; in a moment he was standing at the edge of the parapet, leaning on his halberd, peering breathlessly into the neighboring territory out of which the noise was coming. It came closer and closer, a howling like an animal that had been shot in the desert, furiously stalking its hunter. And now there was a dull rustling in the wall beyond, the stones collapsed and rolled down the steps with a clatter; through the breach the mysterious monster came tumbling down the steps into the arch over the staircase with such force that the wall on which Andree was standing shook as if struck by an earthquake.

At once there was total silence, only a weak groan penetrated to the ears of the listening wine guard from the depths below where the heavy mass had collapsed. The boy had no further doubt that it was one of the cows belonging to the neighbor whose stable was located near the vineyard. A furious suspicion flamed up within him. He gave two shrill whistles on his fingers, then leaped down and swung himself over the wall into the roadway.

The felled animal lay at the edge of the road, half-wedged in among the stones, kicking wildly with its legs, boring its horns into the ground. However, it seemed to be free from the pain that had driven it through the arbors before; only from time to time it emitted a dull roar as though calling for help; when Andree came up to it, the animal lay there tame and patient.

Three or four of the other lads now appeared from various directions, exchanging vehement words in undertones before they prepared to help the animal to its feet. Andree was examining the ground around him in silence. Suddenly he lifted something gleaming from the ground with the iron of his weapon. "Right!" he said. "I thought so and I smelt it as I came down. It's one of their knavish tricks. Look here!"

He held out a piece of tinder that was still burning in spite of the dampness. "Shameful brutes!" he flared up. "They put it into the ear of this innocent creature to madden her. If she hadn't fallen down it would have burned its way through her brain and she would now be ready for the knacker. But she shook the tinder out and the farmer can consider himself lucky. If I had the fellow here, Holy Cross—!"

Köbele cocked his pistol. "Will you come with me, Andree?"

"No. Leave that thing alone," the boy replied grimly. "Get the cow back on her feet again and take her home. I'll go alone."

With great leaps he raced noiselessly through the willows on the other side and over the meadow and swamplands; a savage lust for battle glowed within him, sharpening all his senses. The rain was now falling steadily and noisily, and the wind roared more loudly than before. In spite of this Andree heard distant steps under the willows as he approached the city gate and now discerned two fleeing figures far ahead of him. With a joy he was scarcely able to conceal, he recognized the white jackets of the hated enemy. Scarcely a hundred feet more and they would reach the gate. But they were moving slowly. One of them—he was close enough now to be seen distinctly— was limping laboriously along, supporting himself on his comrade's arm. The animal had probably defended itself with its sharp horns. They were talking about their mischievous deed as they walked, the fellow who limped was laughing in a tone that the avenger remembered all too well from that morning. But the laughter suddenly turned into a cry of horror. For, struck by a furious blow of the halberd, the wretch fell to his knees whimpering for pardon. A second blow felled him mutely. His companion, who was about to rush to his aid, was gripped by two steel fists, a savage struggle began in the darkness, no one uttered a word. The embittered opponents only gnashed their teeth and gazed into the whites of each others' eyes. Then the soldier saw his advantage and pushed his foe close to the edge of the ditch, so that his foot slipped on the wet ground and he fell backwards. Before he could get to his feet again the white coat had sped away and Andree stood alone beside the Italian, who was lying there motionless, showing no sign of life in response to the cries and shaking he received.

"He's dead!" the boy said aloud to himself, as the lifeless mass slipped out of his hands again. At the sound of his own words he shuddered involuntarily. Suddenly his whole wretched life stood before his mind's eye.

It was not the act of homicide that weighed so grievously on his conscience. They had broken in like ruthless robbers in the dead of night, and what had befallen them was just vengeance for their malicious deed. If it had been the other white coat, the one who had fled and who was a total stranger to him, that lay there before him with a cracked skull, his face bathed in the pool of his own blood, it would scarcely have moved the defiant boy very deeply. But that it had to be *this one,* whom he had hated, hated because Lassie had been friendly with him—his sister! His blood seemed to congeal into clumps of ice as he now, for the first time, saw his cursed fate before him with merciless clarity. All day and through half the night he had lurked at the roadside with thoughts of vengeance and blood. What did the crime against the vines and the innocent beast concern him? He had a crime of a very different sort to avenge: that this insolent fellow had flirted with the girl, that the girl had laughed at his jokes, that she had defended him against her brother's anger. This was what he had to atone for; that was why he now lay there silent in his blood, and he who stood before him was not a guardian of the law but a murderer, outlawed by his own conscience.

Köbele now came up and his steps startled the boy out of his hopeless brooding. He said nothing in reply to all that the other whispered and said. He motioned to him with silent gestures that they should lift the dead man and carry him to the Capuchin Monastery which one can see from the gate of Meran over the city wall. At the gateway to the monastery, as they unloaded their burden on the threshold, Andree said dully: "Ring the bell, Köbele, and wait till they open. You can tell them that I did it. And may God preserve you; you'll never see me again."—With that he turned away abruptly and vanished in the dark street.

He was in no hurry to carry out his plan, yet he could drag his feet forward only slowly, so powerfully did his thoughts paralyze him. When he reached the dark archways of the Long Arbor, where he was protected from the rain, he sat down on one of the stone benches and leaned his heavy head against the pillar. In the daytime the old woman sat here, roasting chestnuts on her coal stove. The ground was still strewn with shells, which crackled under Andree's heavy hobnailed boots. How often had he appeased his hunger here when he had been too proud to ask his own mother for food. And there, a few houses further up, was the confectioner's store to which Lassie used to take the pennies she had saved up. He could still remember clearly the large heart-shaped biscuit, the first sweet she had bought for herself. She had wanted to share it with him; when he refused his share, she had thrown it into the Passeier, although she very much wanted to eat it, for she cried as she threw it in. Even now, as he thought back to those childish tears, he felt a triumphant joy at having possessed so much power over her flippant, stubborn little heart, and at the same time he was frightened by his joy. He leaped up again in agitation and groped his way forward in the desolate arched walk until he came to the house in which the ten o'clock Masser lived. The front door was unlocked, the hallway with its decrepit angular stairway was so dark that any unfamiliar intruder ran the risk of breaking his neck. Andree went up on his tiptoes, he knew every step. When he got to the top under the roof, where the priest had his quarters, the bats flew out. He stood there for a while before the door, listening if he could hear the breathing inside. Then he decided to enter.

But the room was empty; nor did he find the priest in the adjacent bedroom in which he himself had lived as a boy. As if he now felt himself more than ever forsaken by God and man, he sat down on the undisturbed bed and thought once more of all those years and brooded about the grim decisions that faced him.

The big cat, the ten o'clock Masser's housekeeper, crept softly up to him, for she had recognized him and purred ingratiatingly around him. Then she leaped into his lap, rubbing her soft back against his chest. Involuntarily tears came into his eyes and he buried his face in the silken hide of his old darling. After finding relief in this way, he gently lifted the cat from his knees, stood up and groped his way down the rickety stairs again. For outside the clock struck one and he dared not delay if he was to set his plan into motion successfully.

He took the road which his ecclesiastical friend had wanted to walk that morning, up to the castle where Hirzer lived. The ten o'clock Masser was especially welcome there; he could have become entangled in an ecclesiastical discourse with Aunt Anna up there or been detained at a winetasting and was spending the night there. At least they would know where he had gone. So the fugitive strode through the Arbor Lane and the Passeier Gate with a freer step and walked over the stone path across the raging Passeier. The rain was now coming down more gently, the clouds became airier, and the wind blew vigorously from the northeast, clearing a section of the sky, so that weak moonbeams fell into the foaming waves of the rocky canyon. Up the mountain to the left, after a walk of about fifteen minutes, he could have looked into the window behind which his sister was sleeping. And here, over the stone breastwork—a final prayer and a swift leap—and he would be relieved of all earthly torment. But, as if he felt an equal horror in the face of both temptations, he now strode more hurriedly over the reverberating stone slabs of the bridge, wiping the sweat from his brow as he reached the slopes of Obermais on the other side.

The guards challenged him as he climbed up through the streets and footpaths. He exchanged the sign with them but gave no reply to their further questions. With increasing impatience he kept looking up to the height from which the old castle beckoned down to him, a black, shapeless pile of stones, with the tops of the chestnut trees whistling about it and around which the brooks flowed through the vineyards down into the valley. Andree had not walked this road since his seventh year, when he had once called on Hirzer's children up above, secretly hoping to see his gentle, pale godmother with the beautiful eyes, his Aunt Anna. At that time the farmer had driven him away from the farm with harsh words and forbidden him to show his

face there ever again. He had gone grinding his teeth, and nothing could have persuaded him to cross that threshold again. But the distress he found himself in now made him forget that old feud.

Only when he had reached the top, after laboriously wandering and losing his way over the rocks, it flashed through his mind that he did not know his way through the old labyrinthine structure, and for a moment he stood helplessly under the vaulted entrance that leads into the lower courtyard. He saw the narrow wooden stairway that clung to the decrepit wall under the open sky and which you had to climb in order to reach the rooms that were still habitable. If he should awaken the hostile men and fail to find the clergyman, in what sort of light would he stand there and what could he tell them to excuse his nocturnal visit? His head felt so empty and desolate that he had difficulty in straightening the muddle out. And he almost turned around, when the howling of the watchdog, who slept at the head of the stairs in a hole of the wall, freed him from his embarrassment.

After the old watchdog, who in the course of the years had become too lazy to move from the spot but who heard every strange step in the courtyard in his light sleep, had barked away to himself peevishly for several minutes, the little door near his sleeping place opened and a feminine figure appeared on the staircase above. Andree heard her talking to the dog; she scolded him for his restless dreams and for making this noise which would disturb Aunt Anna in her sleep. "Rosine!" he called to her. The girl started and stepped back into the doorway. For a moment she listened and the dog was silent too. When she heard her name called a second time, she came forward and peered over the railing. "Who's down there?" she said in a trembling voice. "Is it you, Andree?"

"It's me," the youth answered. "Is the ten o'clock Mass-er up there?"

She did not seem to hear the question. In a flash she had vanished in the house and left him waiting below in angry impatience. "Rosine!" he cried too loudly, so that the ruined arches echoed his voice. Then she came out again, a shawl flung over her shoulders, and whisked past the dog down the steep stairs. "Andree! Is it possible?" she whispered rapidly, hastening up to him. "What are you doing here at this hour? Has anything happened to Lassie or—"

"I'm looking for the ten o'clock Mass-er," he interrupted her. "Tell me if he's upstairs or where I can find him."

"He is upstairs," she replied swiftly. "Come up. I'll bring you to him; father is sound asleep, nobody will know about it except Aunt Anna."

"Not even she," the boy said in a commanding tone of voice. "I've no time left. Good thing you were at hand. I was just ready to turn back."

They went up the stairs; the dog whimpered in displeasure but let them enter unchallenged.

"I dreamed about you just before you came," the girl said as she lit a small lamp in the kitchen near the entrance hall. "It was dreadful. You were lying dead on the breakwater; they had pulled you out of the Passeier and tried to bring you back to life, and I stood beside you and kept saying: 'Leave him be, it's no use!' and at that my whole body turned ice cold and I was frightened at my own voice but I had to keep on saying: 'It's all no use, he's dead'—and then the dog barked and now you're standing before me alive, Andree, thank God!"

"A dream can become true," he murmured between his teeth, but he did not want to worry her still more, so he added aloud: "I'm still alive, Rosine, but I must get away from here, you'll know soon enough why. And I must go this very

night, as soon as I've spoken to His Reverence."

The girl let the lamp slip from her hand so that the oil flowed on the hearth. Her delicate pale face turned a deep red and her beautiful brown eyes looked up at him in distress as if they had seen a ghost. "You want to go away?" she said. "Is it possible, Andree? You want to leave Lassie and all of us, and when will you come back again? But what has happened? Has your mother again—"

"Don't talk about mother," he interrupted her. "Don't ask any more questions, it will all come out. And now tell me where His Reverence is sleeping. I haven't a minute to spare."

She took the lamp in humble silence from the hearth and led the way through the tidy hall, from whose whitewashed walls a few ancient, brown saints' figures, which had been spared by the painter, looked down at them out of sad, almond-shaped eyes. A narrow stone staircase led to the upstairs rooms; there was a pervasive smell of beautiful ripe apples, which lay piled up in a corner. An old wall clock ticked away with a hard sound, and the mice, frightened by the approaching steps, scurried helter skelter back into their holes.

"Here!" The girl said, pointing to a large, old-fashioned door. She put the lamp into the boy's hand and remained out in the hall until he had entered the room. For a moment she felt a temptation to put her ear to the keyhole. Then she shook her head sadly and crept down the stairs back into the desolate kitchen, to wait until he returned.

But he stood for a long while upstairs in the huge drawing room, with its walls paneled in dark wood, where a bed had been prepared for the clergyman in a niche. He could not bring himself to wake the man from his peaceful sleep. For the first time he had an obscure feeling that his beloved teacher and spiritual mentor lacked the power to calm the storms that were raging in his bosom. He had been driven here by a vague anxiety, to seek refuge with his heavy conscience in a secure place. But the peace that lay on this face, slightly flushed and breathing calmly, was not for him. To what end should he put his distress into words, since no one could help him?

He drew back his foot, resolved to leave the hall as softly as he had come, when the sleeping man, disturbed by the light of the little lamp, made a movement and, with his eyes still shut, spoke to himself: "This year's vintage will be good, but last year's was better. Take a good look, Andree, the red Farnatsch—"

"Your Reverence," said the boy, raising his voice, "I'm here and beg your pardon for disturbing your night's rest. But I wouldn't like to go away without saying good-bye to you."

Startled, the dreamer sat up and stared at his nightly visitor with wide-open eyes. "Heavenly mercy!" he exclaimed, "what has happened? Andree, is it really you, up here in Goyen Castle, in the middle of the night, and with a face that looks more dead than alive?"

"I feel like that too, Reverence," the youth replied. "I must go away, like Cain I've killed a man and will find no rest on earth any more."

"Andree!" the horrified priest cried. "You have—" The word died on his tongue; he sat there on the bed with a lifeless face and mechanically clasped his hands on the red checkered comforter. In a few clear-cut words the boy told him everything that had occurred. He mentioned nothing about his sister.

He ended with the decision to seek refuge in a monastery for the time being and asked his Reverence to give him a letter of recommendation, so that they would not turn him away when he knocked without any identification papers. Then he was silent, waiting patiently to hear what his spiritual mentor would say.

But the priest gazed fixedly into space, absorbed in his thoughts. "That won't do, my son," he said at length with a worried look on his face. "The courts will demand your extradition, and since you haven't taken orders yet, you will be brought back. But what real harm can they do you? You were not the aggressor and you struck him in the dark; the wretched soul of the shameful robber cannot accuse you before the throne of God. So I believe you'd best go quietly to the police and make a deposition and wait for the verdict of the court. Just think, if you became a fugitive, what would your sister do, who has no one to protect her except you, once your mother has closed her eyes."

The boy's face turned a deep red and he looked away. "There's simply no other way," he said dully. "To stay here, answer the charge, be punished and pitied? I'd rather go down to Hell at once—may God forgive me my sin! If you won't help me, Reverence, I'll say 'God be with you' and go my way. It's something," he continued more hesitatingly, "I can't tell you, that's driving me from here, so that I feel I'll stifle if I try to breathe any longer between these mountains. And even if everything were to go smoothly in the courts, I still couldn't stay. I'd go to the monastery anyway, since Our Lord has forbidden us to take ourselves out of this world, which is what I'd most like to do. But I must go to some place where I'll be dead and buried in the eyes of everyone and where I can forget that there are still people in the world. Then I can perhaps endure life, but in no other way, as truly as I stand here before you."

The priest raised his thin eyebrows with an alert expression of significance, and rocked his head back and forth. "What sort of *secreta mysteria* are these?" he said in a tone of disapproval. "You won't tell them even to your confessor?"

"I will tell him," the youth replied evasively and turning a deeper red in the face. "But only when I'm in the monastery. And that's why I beseech Your Reverence to help me regain my peace of mind and not let me go without a letter of recommendation."

"So be it, my poor son," the little priest said compassionately. "You once made a good beginning toward your ecclesiastical studies and I believe you've retained a good bit of your Latin. I will recommend you to Pater Benedictus—" and he gave him the name of a Capuchin Monastery situated high up on the Vintschgau, that was rarely frequented because of its harsh climate—"give him my regards, and tell him I'll send him a letter tomorrow describing your situation. And so I commend you for the time being to the protection of Our Lord Jesus and His merciful Mother, and when you feel it in your heart, Andree, that you want to pour out your secret grief, you know that you can write to me and that you will always find willing concern and sympathy in my heart. God be with you, my son."

Visibly moved, he gave the boy his hand, which Andree silently pressed to his lips. Then he went away with a lightened heart, softly closing the heavy door behind him.

But however softly he descended the vaulted hallway—for he was afraid to meet the old farmer, although he was otherwise without fear of any human being—downstairs two beating hearts were listening for his steps; a slender, pale hand opened a bedroom door near the kitchen and a tender, prematurely aged face peered into the shaft of light that fell down the narrow stone stairway. Aunt Anna had awakened when she heard the girl stirring about the hearth and had summoned her into her bedroom. "He refuses to see anyone except His Reverence," Rosine had told her. "He'll just have to see me," came the soft but deter-

mined reply. And then the aunt had dressed hastily with her niece's help and, without saying another word, had waited in her armchair beside the bed until the late guest would come downstairs. They had no light in the little bedroom except the faint glow of the narrow moon that penetrated through the small window panes. The crucifix above the bed, the hassock in the corner, the neat furniture that stood against the walls, all had that melancholy mystery which an old spinster usually generates through her essence and activity when she has renounced all earthly hopes. This room had seen many a tear shed and had heard many a passionate prayer whispered. And now Rosine saw that her aunt's lips were moving silently, and did not dare to disturb her pious thoughts.

When she heard steps upstairs, the woman stood up from her prayers and went to the door. "Andree," she called softly into the hall.

The youth stopped on the stairs, undecided. He felt an impulse to begin his nocturnal journey without delay, and yet he could not hurry past with a hasty greeting, especially since he did not expect to see these calm, loving eyes ever again in his life.

"You're awake, Godmother?" he finally said. "I asked Rosine—"

"I woke up myself," she replied. "But come in, Andree," and she drew him into the bedroom, "and now tell me what you're about and what has occurred to bring you here at this hour. Aren't you a guard down below on Küchel Mountain, and how does it happen that you've left your post?"

She had taken his hand and spoken these words rapidly, as if she wanted to put an inner anxiety to rest. He looked down at the floor gloomily, turning over in his mind to what extent he should confide in her. For years he had not exchanged a word with her, though he had thought much about her and yearned passionately to meet her alone sometime and tell her with deep emotion how close he felt to her and how bitter it was for him to have to avoid her. And now he felt that, if he could confess his secret sorrow to any human being, it would be no one else but she. But Rosine was standing by the window, and time was pressing, and besides—what good would it be? Even this saint had no power to give him back his peace of mind.

"Godmother," he said, "His Reverence will tell you everything tomorrow, why I must leave the region. I was a wretched person from my very birth, without father or mother, without fortune or a lucky star. It's for the best that I should die to the world, before I become a bad man. And that's why I want to enter the monastery, and I'm glad that I saw you before I do so; for I have always felt a great love and veneration for you, and Heaven knows, things would be better for me if I had been permitted to see you and talk to you more often. For you alone in the whole world have given me quiet and peace of mind by your presence, and I thank you, Godmother, for having raised me out of holy baptism that time when I was a helpless infant and I beg that you will pray for me in future that God may have mercy on me. For truly, I have need of it."

With that he pressed her hands and wanted to leave the room with a "God preserve you!" But the old woman held him back and said: "To the monastery? And I shall never see you again? I must know everything, Andree. Leave us, Rosine, and bring him a glass of wine, he's quite pale and cold as death. Holy Mother of God, what has happened?"

"Don't send Rosine away, Godmother," he replied anxiously, for he felt that if he were left alone with the old woman, she would lure the innermost secrets of his heart to his tongue, so much

power did her gentle voice and her large, pain-filled eyes have over him. "Don't be angry with me," he continued, "but you can alter nothing, and if I had to think that I had saddened your heart, too, with my sorrow, I would be even more wretched. But if you want to show me your love, place your hand on my head and give me your blessing to take along with me, because it is farewell for eternity."

He fell to his knees before her and she did what he had asked. Then she raised him up and, as she looked into his pale face with tears in her eyes, she did not restrain herself but drew him firmly into her arms and kissed him passionately on his lips and eyes, so that he too broke into sobs like a child. For quite a while they stood in this passionate melancholy, and in the comfort of their embrace and their mutual possession of each other the old woman forgot everything that was to come and the youth what lay behind him.

"Godmother," he finally said, "I'll never forget how good you have been to me. Don't you forget me either, and so enough. The cocks will soon be crowing. I must not delay."

"Andree, my poor child," the old woman sighed and sank back into her chair when he crossed the threshold. Suddenly she stood up, a thought raced through her head, she called his name as if she had something else to give him on his way; then her eye fell on the crucifix above her head, she stopped as though suddenly starting back before a threatening danger, shook her head sadly and went to the window with tired steps to see whether she could follow his course through the night. "To the monastery!" she said to herself. "Merciful God! Thy will be done."

Outside under the front door in the dark stood Rosine, who had crept out of her room. "Andree," she said when the lad came toward her, "why, you have no hat and you're wearing your guard's jacket. I fetched a garment of my brother's for you and one of his old hats. He's in Innsbruck and won't need it."

The youth hastily took the loden coat and gave her his leather jacket in exchange for it. "I thank you, Rosie," he said. "You too are good, like your aunt. Do think of me when I've gone. I'll send these things back to you one day soon."

The girl was silent until she had controlled the tears that were breaking out of her. "Does Lassie know about it?" she finally said.

"No. You can tell her, Rosie. Say goodbye to her for me for the last time and then—good night forever, Rosie."

And lightly touching her trembling hand, he went down the open staircase by the wall, hurried across the gloomy courtyard and vanished in the noiseless night, which now stood clear and cool above the mountains and gorges and promised a bright morning.

Very early next morning one could see the ten o'clock Mass-er hurrying down from Goyen Castle, with Rosine at his side. She was to bring Aunt Anna further details about the bloody adventure of the night before and the final greetings from the fugitive to Lassie. Down in Meran they found no little excitement; the country folk were standing about on the streets in groups, exchanging hostile words against the soldiery, and Andree's name was on everyone's lips. Whenever a uniform appeared, the talk became lower but the looks more savage and fists clenched threateningly.

The little man of peace continued his way with growing anxiety. But his face brightened once more when he heard at the Capuchin Monastery that the Italian was not dead; after lying unconscious for hours he had once more opened his eyes and lips and the doctor gave every hope of having him on his feet again soon and

able to go home. What he learned at police headquarters was reassuring too. They felt inclined to quash the matter if the fugitive would for the time being stay in the cloister quietly or indeed take the vows. Stricter discipline would prevent a recurrence of such nasty brawls. The buddy of the Italian soldier was in jail; the farmer whose vineyard had been devastated would receive compensation. And so there seemed to be good promise of comfort and reconciliation and the troubled humanitarian could send good tidings back to Aunt Anna and two beautiful, edifying letters to Vintschgau, one to his friend the prior, the other to his communicant, to whose conscience he appealed earnestly not to delay, if he felt burdened by a grave sin, in making a frank confession by return mail to the ecclesiastical friend of his youth.

But such a letter obdurately failed to come, either in the immediate future or in the weeks and months that followed. To be sure, he soon received a friendly answer from the prior, stating that Andree Ingram had duly arrived there and had been put at once into a lay cowl, since he had repeatedly and most urgently stated his firm resolve to live and die in the monastery. A subsequent letter, written at Christmas time, merely mentioned briefly that the novitiate Andreas was behaving to everyone's satisfaction, performing his services silently and modestly and studying the monastery books during his leisure hours, but that he could not be persuaded to write to his family. The ecclesiastical letter said nothing about a confession.

The little assistant pastor shook his head thoughtfully at this news; Aunt Anna locked herself in her bedroom for a whole day to commend the salvation of her godchild to Heaven undisturbed amidst fasting and prayer; Rosine went about the house with reddened eyes and absent-mindedly; even his mother, the

Black Lassie, betrayed a human impulse, accusing herself in private of hardness and malice toward the poor outcast. Only his sister, to whom his departure was the greatest loss, seemed to be least concerned about his fate. She declared it made her laugh herself sick to imagine Andree in a cowl with a tonsured head. And she really couldn't believe that he was living up in the monastery. He didn't have an ecclesiastical disposition at all, and he had merely planned the whole thing to throw sand in the eyes of the military authorities. He was sitting up there in Vintschgau, shooting deer and drinking new wine, and one fine day he would appear again without his long Capuchin beard and as secular as when he had left.

The prior's Christmas letter baffled her at first. For three days she walked about without laughing once; finally she sat down to write her brother a letter that was full of nonsense but which ended with a serious appeal to come back soon, since "she needed him very badly." She showed the letter to Rosine, whom she often saw now; for, once Andree had gone off to the monastery, the farmer of Goyen had no further objection to his children associating with the lonely girl, who was of no more concern to him at all. Rosine read the letter silently and put it down. It was not nearly cordial enough for her taste. "If he doesn't come in answer to that," said Lassie, "he must have a girl up there in the Vintschgau mountains." —"How can you say such things?" the other girl replied. "The messenger from Algund himself saw him in the cowl." —Lassie turned pale. "If it were really so, I would grieve myself half to death," she said. "Then no one would be to blame but—" she wanted to say "Mother," but she was silent. For she heard the old woman coughing and groaning in the next room, where she was lying on her back as the result of a severe fall on the slippery ice. Those were bad

days, and every night the fever came and drew wild, strange words from her, in the midst of which her daughter fortunately used to fall asleep. The ten o'clock Mass-er made frequent calls and when her condition became worse in the spring, Aunt Anna too climbed Küchel Mountain several times. On these occasions her nephew, Franz Hirzer, who had returned from Innsbruck, accompanied her to the door of the house, and while the two old women were talking inside, he carried on a casual conversation in the customary style of the prominent young men with the fair Lassie, who found much to laugh at, although he intended everything he said to be taken seriously. "Lassie," Rosine said to her one day, "is it true that you've straightened things out with Franz? He says so and I'd certainly wish it to be so, but I don't know, I can't believe it." —"Why not?" asked Lassie defiantly as she smoothed her hair behind her ears with an air of indifference. "After all, I've got to marry some man, and Franz is as good as the next. But the last word hasn't been spoken yet and you know, Rosie, I can't leave Mother. And I'm really in no hurry, but it's so boring in the world since Andree left, and when Franz comes and tells me something new or just sits down on the bench and looks at me lovingly, nearly burning the tip of his nose with his hot pipe, I get a few laughs out of it."

The other girl listened silently. She could not understand how anyone could find love such an amusing thing.

Meanwhile spring came, the meadows had long turned green again, the chestnut trees bore new buds and, down below at the dam, the Passeier roared past, swelled by the waters of the melting snows, so that the thundering noise could be heard in the little house up on Küchel Mountain and the last nights had gone by sleeplessly for both Black Lassie and her poor daughter. She had not written her brother that her mother's condition was low. She knew that that would not bring him back and her mother showed no desire to see him again before her end, although she mentioned his name often enough in her feverish dreams. Indeed, it was almost the last word to come from her lips when, on a stormy night in April, she died after a hard struggle.

Her daughter shuddered at the thought of sharing the lonely dwelling with the dead woman. She closed her mother's eyes, said a few Pater Nosters and the Angelic Greeting, and then stole out with a beating heart into the stormy spring night. She stood up there and looked down into the broad valley of the Adige, where the lightening night clouds raced above the swollen rivers and she felt so wretched and alone, that she broke into bitter weeping. A fierce anger against Andree possessed her. He could now sit snugly in his monastery cell and leave his helpless sister, who loved no one in the world better than him, here alone amid all the terrors and stresses of her young life. —The rain came down more heavily and the wind swept chill over the open mountain slopes. Trembling, the orphaned girl groped her way along the walls up to the shed in which Andree had had his bed during his childhood. There in the darkness she lay down on the same spot and when she thought of it she cried more vehemently and finally fell asleep on the bed of corn rushes, sobbing and hungry and in superstitious horror of her dead mother lying nearby.

But with the levity of her eighteen years she slept through everything that troubled her, and when she awoke late next morning, she had to think for a moment before she realized that her mother had really died. Nor was she able, try as she would, to force a feeling of real sadness, only an eerie sensation held her back a long time from opening the door and entering the house again. Inside she found the ten o'clock Mass-er and her friend Rosine and she was glad to be relieved of all further care. The day after the funeral she was once more sunning herself on the bench in front of the house, laughing gaily as she watched her young kittens romping about on the ground, playing with a corn husk. Two weeks later she sat beside Rosie in a light cart; Franz was driving on the coachman's box; they were riding up Vintschgau Street, and whoever passed them stopped to look at the beautiful blond girl who was driving by, dressed in mourning but scanning the spring landscape with the merriest pair of eyes in the world.

Only when she perceived the old monastery perched up on the mountain on a bald, dark granite cone, with a sparse stand of trees around it and the gorge behind it looking black and gruesome even in the early afternoon like a gate of Hell, she grew silent and serious and exchanged no words with Rosine who, equally taciturn, looked up at the belfry surrounded by swallows in flight. A poor village lay down below at the foot of the slope, without the noble chestnut trees, vineyards or fig trees that grew so gaily about the villages near Meran. Lassie too was struck by this difference. She had never been a whole day's journey away from home and had imagined that the world was more splendid the farther away it was. When they stopped before the shabby village tavern, she got out of the cart, feeling quite weak and sad. She did not want to enter but urged Rosine to accompany her at once up the mountain road, so that she could speak to her brother before night fell. Franz stayed behind with the horses; he had always preferred to keep out of Andree's way.

So the girls went alone at an even, comfortable country pace, holding hands, but with drooping heads and not saying a word. Only when they had come so close to the gray old monastery that they could see the grass that grew on the roof, Lassie suddenly stopped in her tracks, looked at the bare walls like a frightened child and said, drawing a deep breath: "Would you like to live there, Rosie?" Her friend only shook her head. "It would crush my heart," Lassie continued; "not a spot of green around the place, not a vine, not a wheat field. You'll see, it isn't true that he spent the winter here. We won't even find him. Who knows where he is in this big world?"

To this too Rosine made no reply. She knew only too well that they would find him and dreaded it without quite knowing why. When they rang the bell up at the cloister gate and asked the gatekeeper for Andreas Ingram, the old man nodded his head and gave the pretty girls a searching look. "Ask him to come out," Lassie said swiftly. "There's a messenger here from Meran. But don't tell him who it is."

They sat down on a stone bench near the gate and waited. "You're right, Rosie, he is here; how could he stand it?" his sister said. She drew her hands across her forehead, which was glowing, and fidgeted with her clothes in order to conceal her uneasiness. Rosine sat still, leaning against the wall, both her hands in her lap, her eyes shut tight, as if she were blinded by the sunset up on the mountain peaks.

Then the gate clanged again and with a cry of "Andree, God be with you, it's me!" Lassie threw her arms about his neck. But in the same instant she drew back in fright. It was he, and yet not the same person any longer; the one winter seemed to have aged him by ten years. He stood before her speechless, gazing at her fixedly with brooding, anxious eyes as if he were waiting for her to sink into the ground like a ghost or for himself to awaken out of a dream. She had pictured herself teasing him if she really saw him

in a cowl. But now she was closer to tears than to laughter.

"Andree," she finally said, "you look at me so wildly. Did I do wrong to come here myself? Rosie is here too; won't you even say 'God be with you' to her? Franz drove us over; we're going home again tomorrow, it's so desolate and sad round about here, how can you stand it? To be sure, it shows in your face, you've become quite skinny and pale as if you had already been underground. But things will improve again, the air here is so harsh, you must now come back to Meran, the ten o'clock Mass-er will write to the prior, the year is still far from being over, and then you'll live in our little house up there, for you don't know yet, Andree, Mother is dead."

As she spoke her tenseness had relaxed and her features had become once more gay, so that, strangely enough, her last words, the report of their mother's death, were spoken almost with a laugh on her lips. He too seemed to have collected himself and now said in his old tone of voice: "I thank you, Lassie, for coming yourself, and you too, Rosine. But the fact that Mother is dead makes no difference whatever in the situation, and there can be no thought of my coming home and living in Meran again; quite the contrary, I might go still farther away, into a monastery in Italy or even France. For you are quite right, the air up here is not good for me."

He looked down at the gray stone floor, gloomy and self-conscious.

"Andree," she began again, "you mustn't talk like that if you don't want to make me quite sad and angry too. I had no fun all winter without you and now, as soon as I could, I left everything and came to you and now you talk of going away to distant lands, as if I didn't concern you at all. When I hear you say such things, I could almost believe Mother was right when she kept saying to herself in her fever that you weren't her child at all, she had only taken you off the hands of another woman to be able to boast a healthy boy of her own, since she was such a miserable creature. Imagine, she could talk for half-hours at a time about this, and when I must see how little I mean to you, I really begin to fear that you're not my brother at all, because you can be so hardhearted to me."

He had retreated a step involuntarily and stared at her with gaping eyes. "Lassie!" he stammered with a thick tongue, "is this true? Can you swear that Mother really said that?"

She tried to grasp his hand and became sad once more when he hastily withdrew it from her. He cast a nervous look at Rosine, who had remained standing by the little bench to let the two have a private conversation. Then he looked at Lassie again with a glance that made her tremble. "Rosie," he now said, "I have something to say to Lassie, we'll be back in a minute." —With that he motioned to his sister to go with him, walked with rapid steps around the corner of the high monastery wall and entered a vegetable garden by another door. A sole brother was digging and planting under the apple trees. Andree's whole being was suddenly transformed, his face was glowing, he seemed younger again by ten years and he walked briskly as in the days when he kept watch in the vineyards.

Now, when they were alone in the little garden, he turned to her. "Lassie," he said in a trembling voice, "repeat all that you told me about Mother, everything, and as you value your salvation, neither add nor subtract anything—life and death depend on it."

He had now taken her hand and was pressing it feverishly. "I don't understand your strange talk," she said calmly. "What if she did say that? And she did say it, to be sure, word for word and more than once. But you know that she

had a hate against you. Perhaps she only said it so that you'd get no share of the inheritance, because she wanted me to have it all. Perhaps it was just idle talk, because she felt remorse for the evil she had done you all her life. She wanted to persuade herself that you had been someone else's child because she hadn't treated you like her own. But what does it matter?"

"Try to recollect," he urged. "Didn't she say who gave her the child? Was there no one else present when she said it? Was it always in a state of fever or did she say it at night too, when she woke up and thought you were asleep and she then talked to herself the way she used to do when Father was still alive?"

"Who brought you to her? No, she never talked of that," the girl replied, as she tried hard to remember everything. "But wait, I just remember that the ten o'clock Mass-er was once sitting beside her bed when she was talking in that crazy way, and then she sat up and asked for her clothes, she wanted to go down to the Dean, to the courts, right up to the Emperor, so that it might be proclaimed everywhere that you were not her son. I came running in from the kitchen and saw how his Reverence stood there beside her, quite frightened, holding her back; when he saw me enter, he bent down to her and whispered something in her ear, quite a long time, something I couldn't make out; after that she became calm again. What difference can it make to you, Andree, whether she said it in a fever or just out of her imagination? And if it really were so, must you love me the less because of it? Haven't we been like brother and sister in spite of it, as long as we can think back, and now it's to be all over between us suddenly? Look here, Andree, I can't change my nature this way. And even if the Emperor himself should proclaim it the way Mother wanted it, you would still be my brother and the little house would be yours and the vineyard and everything. Besides, I'm not going to live on there. For you must know, I gave my word to Franz Hirzer and we'll be married in the fall and then I'll live up at Goyen. I hope you're not mad because I didn't ask your permission."

She did not dare to look at him when she said this, she didn't know why, but at this moment it seemed to her like a grave sin that she had pledged her troth to Franz and she would gladly have taken it back; for of course she knew that he and her brother were not good friends. She stood there trembling and humble as a child, waiting to be scolded. But when he kept silent, she only felt more anxious and sadder at heart. She would have preferred to be scolded, so that she could defend herself and bring him back to an even temper. But this deathly silence between them was eerie to her, and finally big tears came into her eyes and rolled down her young face. Then he broke the silence.

"Lassie," he said, "did you do it willingly, or did they urge you to take him so long until you finally said yes?"

She looked up at him nervously and still weeping. "Oh, Andree," she said, "do forgive me. I don't know myself how it happened. They sent for me up at Goyen when Mother died and I slept with Rosie and was like a child of the house. And Aunt Anna too said that Franz is a nice boy and if I took him it would be best for all of us, especially since he acts as if he were crazy about me, and you weren't there for me to ask you."

"And if I had said no, would you have grieved?" he asked quickly.

She put her arms about his neck and looked at him full of touching, serene love. "Of course, I don't love him as much as I do you," she said, "and would rather do what you say than what he wants me to do. But now it's happened this way and there would be a new hatred to the death if I now came and said: 'I don't want him.' Be a good boy again and come over yourself, Aunt Anna sends you her love many, many times over and she'd so much like you to come, she has so much to tell you, and I believe, saint though she is, she'd be very happy if you would take that horrid cowl off again, you don't look the trim Andree in it that you always were before. Do it for my sake, I don't feel very happy at the thought that you live here so sadly, and if anything should happen to you, an illness or the like, I won't be here to look after you. Promise me, Andree, that you will at least come down for the wedding and talk things over with Aunt Anna."

At these words she stroked his face affectionately and he suffered it with his eyes closed tight, while a gentle trembling of his lips betrayed the inner struggle he was going through. "Not another word now!" he finally exclaimed, breathing heavily. "Tomorrow morning I'll come down to the inn to see you once more. I'll tell you then what is to happen. Take your hands from my face. Be of good spirit, Lassie. Everything will happen according to God's will. Have a good night."

He did not look at her again, but withdrew quickly, walked through the little garden toward the monastery buildings and vanished in the door without turning around to look at her. But she looked after him, lost in deep thought, turning over in her mind the few words he had spoken to her, in the hope of guessing what he meant by them and what he had in store for her. Shaking her head and in deep sorrow, she finally left the garden and sought out Rosine once more, who had been waiting outside in anxiety and concern. It cut her to the heart that Lassie came back alone and Andree did not even think of wishing her a good night.

"I don't know what's wrong with him,"

the blond girl said. "I knew of course that he half-resents the fact that I'm marrying Franz. But what am I to do? He's going to come down tomorrow morning and give me his opinion. He hardly looked at me and will hear nothing of going back home. If I only knew why I have to submit to this. I could pay no attention to him and do as I wish without asking him. But I've been used to act this way as far back as I can remember, and he was always good to me. Oh, why did everything have to turn out like this?"

Amidst such useless talk they went down the mountain, and the rest of the day passed in depression and monosyllabic conversation. Franz had never been a great talker, and he didn't care a damn as to what would happen to Andree. He was still smoking and drinking merrily with the few farmers in the bar when the girls were already long in their beds.

But in fact only one of them was asleep, that was Lassie. Rosine didn't close an eye all night.

When the dawn was still far from appearing, she heard a step approaching outside over the courtyard, coming toward the low windows of their bedroom. The dogs set up a howl but were appeased at once. Her heart beat fast and she hurriedly got out of bed in fretful anxiety. Lassie went on sleeping peacefully.

Sure enough, the steps stopped in front of the window and a hand tapped softly against the window pane. "Lassie!" the familiar voice said.

"I'm awake, Andree," the girl replied in a whisper; "Lassie is still asleep. Shall I wake her?"

"Do so, Rosie. Tell her to get dressed and to do it fast; I still have a lot to say to her before you go home."

Fifteen minutes passed, then the back door of the tavern opened softly and out came Lassie, her face turning to her brother in a mixture of sleepiness, curiosity and fear. "Good morning," she said.

"But you are early. If only you bring good news, Andree, it'll wake me up."

"Wrap your coat around you," he said by way of answer. "It's cool and you're not used to the air here. We'll walk a few paces together."

She obeyed willingly and came out to him wrapped in her winter cloak. The silence around them, the strange place, the nocturnal desolation over the mountains, her brother standing there facing her in his Capuchin cowl—it all seemed so strange to her and awakened her old desire to laugh. She drew one corner of the pleated cloak over her head. "Now I'm your Capuchin sister," she said and nodded to him mischievously. He took her hand and walked with her silently through the courtyard. The horses stirred in the stable, the chickens flapped their wings, a young cock prematurely crowed the advent of the morning. But the people in the lowly huts were still asleep, except for one poor young soul who stared in pain through the dim window into the courtyard and lay down again in bed with profound sighing, glowing and shivering alternately, waiting for the day to come.

But the sun was already high and the brother and sister had still not returned. Franz Hirzer sat in the bar with furrowed brow before a bottle, ran out into the street every minute or so to see whether there was any trace of his betrothed, and finally unhitched the horses, cursing Andree. Rosie did not say a word, she felt mortally sad about the heart; no matter what happened now, as far as she was concerned, all joy and hope were gone.

Finally, at about ten o'clock, one of the monastery brothers brought a letter which Andree had written to Rosine the night before; it said that he had vowed to join a penitential procession to a holy image to pray for the soul of his mother. He supposed that Lassie would accompany him, so they need not wait for her return but could go home. In due time Lassie would get back to Meran.

When Franz had read the letter, he struck the table with his fist so that the glasses rang, and in his first burst of anger he was all for setting out in search of Andree. But since the letter did not mention the church to which the pilgrimage was to be made, and as the Capuchin brother knew nothing about it except that the prior had given Andree permission to make the pilgrimage, the boy's fury and hatred had to be stored up for a future occasion; for the time being he had to think of the return journey.

It was a hard trip for poor Rosine beside her furious brother, who raged on incessantly against the malicious abductor and swore mighty oaths that, once Lassie was his wife, he would lock the door against Andree as his father had done these many years. He had from the first objected to the stupid trip to the good-for-nothing foundling, who wouldn't even be a real brother-in-law to him. But the women had gotten it into their heads, Aunt Anna most of all. He had been a fool to yield. But he'd tell that Lassie a thing or two, and he wouldn't forget Aunt Anna either. But above all it was Rosine's fault; she shouldn't have allowed him to go off with Lassie in the morning—and there followed a flood of brotherly scoldings, which did not penetrate her very deeply. For a much harsher sorrow had fortified her soul.

Summer came, the vines on Küchel Mountain had long since passed their bloom, and the wine berries swelled and turned red; the first fig harvest, too, went by without a trace of the two runaways; there were few who still believed that they would ever turn up again. Since no one had any precise idea as to what might have lured Andree out into the world, and since most people had taken little interest in his doings and goings, the talk of

the fate that might have befallen the brother and sister soon came to an end. At first, of course, there had been much speculation about it. For the strangest thing about it was not the sham pilgrimage, for the Tiroleans are a race that loves to undertake such wanderings on foot, but that one hour's walk beyond the monastery all trace of the two young people had completely vanished. The village goatherd had seen them slowly climbing a bridle path up the mountain slope, absorbed in eager talk. They were a striking couple, the pale young novice with the serious face and the beautiful blond girl in her peasant cloak at his side. And yet, when a few weeks later a search was instituted in the nearby mountain villages at the urging of the ten o'clock Mass-er, there was not a tavern-keeper nor farmer who could remember such a couple knocking at his door. The help of the police was sought, with no more success. The couple remained lost, as if the mountain had split open to remove them forever from the sight of man within its secret chambers.

When this strange report was brought up to Goyen Castle by the little assistant priest, it stirred up a tempest of the most diverse emotions. Only old Hirzer calmly finished his glass of wine and said he was glad that he would never hear another word of the whole Ingram clan for the rest of his life, or so he hoped. If that frivolous creature, Lassie, ever dared appear on his threshold again, she'd really get to know him and harvest a curse into the bargain, of the sort he was not accustomed to utter in front of the ten o'clock Mass-er. He ordered his son to set out the very next day to court a rich young widow in the neighborhood, whose land holdings were very appropriately situated for them. Franz did not take the matter so cold-bloodedly. Lassie had really bewitched him; the thought of her was the only thing that had ever sparked his sluggish nature into flame. So he disregarded his father's orders for the present and vented his rage in every conceivable way, so that his family had a lot of grief from him. Aunt Anna vanished into her bedroom for several days, put on mourning, for she firmly believed that the couple had perished in an accident, if not actually by their own hand, and she wept day and night and would see no one except His Reverence and Rosine. With this silent sufferer she sat at the hearth through the sleepless nights, a rosary between her pale fingers, spending the hours half in prayer, half in conversation. The girl alone was of the firm opinion that the two were still alive and kept trying to persuade the aunt of it. But since the farewell in Vintschgau she did not believe for a moment that they would ever return.

The calmest person of them all was the little ecclesiastic, in spite of his old pastoral friendship. In fact, it almost seemed as if the self-banishment of his pupil had taken a burden from his chest. He still came up to Goyen regularly, listened benevolently to them all according to their different natures, said a good word to everyone and was able to turn the conversation very soon to the new vintage and the hope for an exceptionally noble year, a subject he had fathomed with the deepest science and which he put ahead of even his theological discussions with Aunt Anna.

And so it had become late November, the empty house up on Küchel Mountain stood bleak among the bare vineyards; down below in the city of Meran the busy activity of an annual slaughter and cattle market surged through the narrow streets; the Saturday noise had died down and the ten o'clock Mass-er, who did not intend to go out that evening, had taken his old fiddle from the wall, to improvise a tune or two in the evening dusk before the maid brought up his evening meal and the lamp. The tomcat lay in the easy chair, purring comfortably; a small fire crackled in the stove, since the night promised to be cool; from the window, where a couple of handsome geranium pots stood, came a sweet scent, which the delicate nose of the ecclesiastic inhaled with satisfaction; and while he surpassed all the happiest flageolet tones of the forest birds on his violin and strode up and down in measured steps between the four low walls of his room, he indulged himself in his thoughts of divine contentedness. He really lacked nothing essential to attain perfect bliss, especially since one of his brother priests down in St. Valentine had sent him a sample of the precious red wine which the pious brethren make in their sunny valley at the foot of Mount Ifinger and which was to enhance his modest meal this evening.

There was a knock on the door; thinking it was the maid bringing the guest from St. Valentine, he called out "Come in" without interrupting his playing. But he nearly dropped his bow when the door opened and the figure of the missing Andree stood before him like a shade from another world.

"Don't be frightened, Your Reverence, it's me," said the youth, coming in all the way. "You see, the tomcat recognizes me; he would certainly arch his back if I were a ghost. I would have sent you word of my visit in advance, but the place we come from has no mail service."

He bent down to the purring animal to conceal his emotion. There was a softness and gentleness in his manner that made him seem completely transformed.

The priest had stopped in the center of the room; he felt hot and cold all over. All that he could say in his first wave of astonishment was: "And Lassie?"

"She's here too, you shall know everything, for I have no one but you, and if you can't help me with counsel, I'm a wretched man both in this world and the next."

At that moment they heard the steps of the maid on the stairs, and while the old woman, who recognized Andree with no less fright but with greater joy, set the table for the evening meal, put down the candle and vented her surprise in strange exclamations, the two men had time to collect themselves and to prepare silently for the conversation that was to follow. The maid went out again hesitatingly. She would have liked to get the answers to a hundred questions. But she felt afraid of the unusually solemn expression on the face of her reverend master, who had taken his place behind the table, daubed his forehead several times with his colored handkerchief and silently poured out the first glass of the red Valentine, but without bringing it to his lips with the usual ritual of the connoisseur. For his tongue felt bitter from the foretaste of the many unpleasant words that would have to be said in the next hour.

But Andree broke the silence and said: "Your Reverence will pardon me if I sit down. Today we walked for fourteen hours across the mountains, and in addition there was the anxiety and distress regarding the poor girl and hunger and sorrow—my knees refuse to support me any longer. If Your Reverence knew what we have endured, you would really not avert your face from me so sternly, for you have always been a merciful gentleman and have never sent away a remorseful sinner without comfort and encouragement."

The little pastor seemed touched by these humble words. He raised his glass, let it play against the candle in its red glow, drank a slow draught and then handed it to his pupil, whom he now for the first time dared to look directly in the face. "Have a drink, Andree," he said; "you can use one. It's Valentine, from the best locations, scarcely four weeks from the press. I received it only today."

Andree took the glass, emptied it at one draft with a reverent bow toward the ecclesiastical gentleman and, handing it back to him over the table, said: "I thank Your Reverence. But what I wanted to ask you and what you must tell me before God's countenance: Am I the son of Maria Ingram—may she be with God!—or am I not?"

Then he stood up again; in spite of his exhaustion he could not stay put, he pressed both his clenched fists against a plate that stood before him and fixed his sad eyes tensely on the face of his ecclesiastical friend, who squirmed in his armchair with no less uneasiness.

"My son," he then said, "if you will promise me to ask no further questions, I will answer this one. Your mother brought only one child into the world: Lassie. Now that you know this, leave everything else alone; for my ecclesiastical vow of obedience forbids me to say any more, and it would be of no use to you in any case."

The tension on the young man's face relaxed suddenly and his features merely expressed grief and hopelessness. "I thank you," he said, "but it doesn't help me much, for I knew that already. Even if no one had told me so, I would have known that she could not be my mother. And I would ask no further, for after all, if my parents can get along without me, I must learn to do without them too, and I've done that long enough. But the poor woman, Your Reverence, who has no peace by day or night, because she thinks that all this talk by her mother is just a lie, because she hated me too much, and that I am lying because I loved my sister too much—no, Your Reverence, the only remedy for it is a letter with a seal, otherwise I fear she won't last long, for it's really pitiful the way it has affected her mind, and you know perfectly well that she has a weak spot somewhere in her head that you can do nothing with."

He sat down again with an expression

of profound weariness on his face. The assistant pastor ate and drank mechanically, more to conceal his confusion than because he felt a desire to eat, for he did not taste the food at all. "Tell me first," he said, "how things have got to this stage. Then we'll see what can be done to improve matters. Where have you been all these months during which it was impossible to find any trace of you?"

"Not in the cowl, Reverence," said the boy, and his features brightened a little at the memory of dangerous and cunning exploits. "You see," he continued, "when Lassie first told me that her mother had brought me down from the meadow or God knows where else as a foundling, I felt as if I were suddenly freed from glowing chains and bonds which I had perpetually dragged about with me, and which refused to fall from my limbs even up in the monastery. For not even in holy confession could I bring my tongue to utter what I endured in these last years because of Lassie, and that I could not live on if another man should marry her. And I knew, of course, that it was a mortal sin if I had really been her mother's son; and yet I could not rid myself of it, for it was more powerful than my puny reason and my religion and everything I had learned from you and read in the holy books. But when I was finally able to grasp palpably that I had fretted uselessly all these years and that there was nothing sinful in loving the girl more than my own life, I suddenly became quite merry and I resolved at once that she must be mine, even if the Emperor himself should want to keep us apart. But that same evening I showed no sign of any change, only as I sat in my cell I could have sung and shouted so loud that they would have heard it right down to Meran. But I had all sorts of things to attend to, also the letter to Rosine which had to be written, and so the night ended at last. And then, though the dawn had not quite broken yet, I was already down there and fetched the poor thing, who had no idea of what was to come. At first I acted quite rationally, until we were a few hours' distance away; I kept talking about the pilgrimage, and she was not angry because I was taking her along with me. For she wanted to look a bit further into the world. But when we were high up between the mountains and she kept asking with greater and greater curiosity where we were going, I had her sit down for a bit on the moss, went behind a stone and came out again at once but no longer as a Capuchin monk, but in a jacket and trousers and everything I had worn on the night when I fled from Goyen; for I had still not returned to Franz the clothes that belonged to him. At first she laughed uproariously and said she liked me better this way than in the long monastery cloak, and we ate up what I had secretly brought with me. But then she suddenly became quiet and I must have looked very strange to her, for she subjected me to a sharp interrogation, and when, in my heartfelt joy, I finally burst out with the news that I would never put on the cowl again nor was I going on a pilgrimage but was abducting her to a distant place as my wife, she became terribly frightened and began to sob pitifully. But I talked to her most kindly and remained quite calm, so that she might not get another attack of her old cramps; and so, while her tears flowed less and less, I explained to her that it was not practical to go back to Meran and ask Pontius and Pilate whether they had nothing against the marriage. That would cause an even greater uproar than if we didn't return at all, and if we ever felt homesick for our little house and made our appearance in Meran as husband and wife, they would all have to accept it. I asked her to think of old Hirzer and Franz and how they would flare up if I suddenly went up to them and said: 'Lassie is mine and I'll never give her up.' And Aunt Anna and the Dean and the whole city that had known us for so long as brother and sister, and the outcry and the documentation at City Hall and all the deviltry. And finally I played my trump card and said: Of course, if she preferred Franz to me, she need but say so boldly, it wasn't too late yet to turn back and to part for evermore.

"She could stand it no longer but threw her arms about my neck and, amidst laughter and tears, she cried that she had no will but mine and she helped me roll large stones over the cowl so that no one would find it and ferret out traces of our route. And on that same day we walked for many more hours, happy at heart and always alone, looking back occasionally to the region in which Meran lay, enjoying a malicious pleasure in the fact that Franz would now have to go home without his fiancée and endure the ridicule of all the people. Of course, I thought of you too, Reverence, that you might resent my deed and of my godmother and Rosie, both of whom had always treated me well. But this mood did not last long. For when I looked at Lassie beside me, whom I could now embrace and kiss as much as I wanted to and who patiently let me do it—well, you can't of course know, Reverence, how one feels when he walks along under the open sky so completely alone with his sweetheart; but if you had ever felt a joy like this, especially after such a long period of privation, you would not regard it as such a grave sin for us both, but would gladly grant us the bit of happiness that has not been ours for very long."

He was silent again and looked sadly straight ahead of him. The assistant priest pushed his plate back, gave a sigh from the depths of his heart and filled his glass again and handed it to his communicant. The boy drank, sighed too and continued in his quiet, monotonous manner:

"The first night we slept on a meadow; the dairy farmer gave us food and didn't ask any questions about ourselves; for he no doubt guessed easily enough the relationship between us. He promised us the next morning not to tell a soul that he had given us shelter in his hut, and so we went on in good spirits in the high mountains and were even happier and more deeply in love than the day before. The region was wholly strange to me but I knew that if we kept going towards the west we would finally reach Switzerland, and because they enjoy the freedom to live the way they want to and no police, I thought of staying there for the time being, nor did I fear that they would ask us for a passport at the border; for where we were walking, high under the ridge of the mountains, from one dairy farm to the next, it's too precipitous for the militia, and in fact we weren't stopped a single time. But I must also tell you, that on that second day we came to a place where a steep ridge rises right in the middle of the meadows, far higher than the Mutspitz or the Ifinger. I persuaded Lassie to climb up the ridge and look down at the world from there. But I had a special reason for doing this; for I didn't care about the glaciers and snowfields at all. On the peak stood a crucifix with Our Lord Jesus hanging on it, a crude piece of woodcarving, probably the work of some dairy farmer that he had whittled with his pocket knife. But it was good enough for my purpose. For when we were at the top and Lassie was looking about her, quiet and contented, I took her gently by the hand and knelt down with her before the Cross. At first we prayed together, then she wanted to stand up. But I said: 'Remain on your knees, Lassie; it isn't over yet.' And then I recited in Latin the whole marriage ceremony and then I took her silver ring from her finger and gave her mine in exchange for it and I placed my hand on her head and hers on mine, while I spoke the blessing. I simply thought that a man must know how to help himself in an emergency, and just as there is a private baptism, so there must also be a private marriage, no offense meant, Your Reverence; later on it could be done all right and proper. She must have thought as I did, for she let me do what I wanted and knelt before the crucifix in sincere devotion. When I was through with my Latin, I kissed her warmly and said: 'Now I am your husband and you are my wife, and death alone shall part us.' She nodded and her happiness laughed in her eyes and then we stood up and remained up there a while longer and we had a wonderful feeling in the great silence and mystery as we looked down together on a hundred miles of lands, cities, and rivers, and there was no one with us except the Lord God Himself, before whose countenance we had just vowed our troth until death.

"You know Lassie, Reverence; you know that she would rather laugh than cry, and that for a girl her age she has too many childish pranks in her head. But throughout our whole wedding day we didn't laugh at all nor did we talk much to each other but walked along beneath the beautiful sun, as solemnly as if the whole mountain range had been a great church, except that as she walked, Lassie picked flowers and fastened a bridal bouquet to my jacket and plaited a little wreath for herself and hung it from her arm. We still had some money and at the next dairy farm we were able to order whatever the farmer had to offer us. So it was a very merry wedding and neither of us thought of what lay behind us or of what was still to come.

"We did think of these things when our money began to dwindle; perhaps a week had gone by and we were still far away from Switzerland, since we did not follow any route but walked wherever we pleased. On the first night when we looked for a bed with empty pockets and were just about to crawl into a haystack, my eye was caught by a large solitary farm and I thought: try your luck there. Sure enough, we found a night's lodging there, but the one night turned into half a year. For the farm belonged to a widow who lived there with a few hired men and maids and she had just been on the point of marrying her head man, but he had been killed by a falling tree and the widow mourned him as she did her first husband. When I told her that I had had to flee because I had killed an Italian and my sister there—I passed Lassie off as such because I supposed the woman would not have saddled herself with a married couple—and that Lassie had refused to let me go by myself and we were now penniless, she offered me the opportunity of entering her service and there was work for my sister too. Of course, we were glad of that, but Lassie later reproached me for not recognizing her as my wife and I had some trouble appeasing her. So we stayed, and the summer passed, and we had no grounds for complaining. The fact that the peasant woman had cast an eye on me, as I noticed by and by, and made me her head man, intending to promote me even more later on, I could accept for the present undisturbed and still say 'no' at the right moment. But suddenly Lassie became so sad that I had no more peace by day or night. About a week ago I was mowing on the highest meadow and suddenly saw my wife coming up with a very distraught look on her face. And when she reached the top, she fell down before me and implored me with outstretched arms to put her out of her misery in grace and mercy; she could not live with the sin on her conscience, she was bearing a child, and the night before, her mother had appeared to her in a dream and had whispered to her: 'Andree is really my son, and your child and his will be cursed to all eternity.'

"You can imagine, Reverence, how frightened I was; for since she remained obdurate and firm, I finally felt afraid and anxious because I had no real and clear proofs that everything was what we had believed it to be and the dream was merely a delusion. Lord in Heaven, I thought, suppose it were true after all, and an ice-cold chill ran through me and, as I saw the woman lying before me on the ground wringing her hands, I really thought for a moment: 'The best thing would be if the two of us went off to a spot where there was a sharp and deep precipice and we both closed our eyes and leaped straight to hell. But then I for my part became calmer; I thought it all over and finally remained convinced that it couldn't be so. But the poor woman was not to be comforted by that. She no longer wanted to die, since this would constitute a double sin because of the child, but to go back to Meran, where the truth must be ascertained. For me it was a bitter thought; I knew that here at home the matter would not be settled quietly. But since Lassie developed a more and more confused look in her eyes and the peasant woman suspected that there was something wrong and advised me to send my sister away but to stay on myself, there was nothing else for me to do but to pack our things and set out on the hard road of atonement.

"I will not tire you with an account of our wretched mental states on our journey home, especially when we came to many spots where we had been happy six months ago, but where now the poor woman thought she heard in every wind voices that accused and condemned her. If we committed a sin going out into the world as husband and wife without asking anyone and without the blessing of the Church, we have atoned for it a hundredfold on the return journey, especially I who had to bear the burden for her as well. And just imagine, when we came to the mountain peak where in the spring we had been joined together, the crucifix had vanished. It was probably torn down by the stormy winds. But it cut Lassie to the heart, as if it had merely been a trick of the devil, who had wanted to ensnare us into the sinful marriage, and fell into my arms in a swoon and it took me an hour to bring her back to consciousness."—

He was silent; the memory of all the hardships he had endured visibly went through him like a fever chill. The ecclesiastic had risen long ago and had listened to the confession pacing up and down the room, taking more and more frequent pinches of snuff from his birch-rind box. He held the last pinch between thumb and forefinger a long time and stood still before a large copper engraving representing the Magdalen in the desert, the only decoration on his four bare walls. He did not trust himself to turn his face to the young man who sought his counsel and help, for the case was so difficult that he had little hope of bringing it to a happy conclusion.

"Where is she now?" he finally asked in a low voice.

"Up on Küchel Mountain in our little house," the boy replied. "We arrived a few hours ago by way of Tirol village, and the people recognized us and pointed their fingers at us, and when I came down alone through the arbors, it must have been common knowledge, for they kept out of my way as if I had a disease or the plague. But up there the poor woman sits waiting for me to bring you back with me, and if you have no comfort for her, I vouch for nothing. For there is a spirit of despair in her eyes, and her poor reason hangs by a fine thread. One more tug, and it will fall into the bottomless pit; you may be sure of that, Reverence. Three weeks can bring things far for such a poor woman."

He now stood up too, as if hoping to

force a decision by this act from the silent clergyman. But the pastor still stood for a while before the copper engraving, although he could hardly distinguish a single line of it on the dark wall. Only the clock on the tower striking eight seemed to warn him that there was danger afoot. He turned away from the wall, made a sign to Andree that he would return at once and, taking the only candle from the table with him, went down the stairs until the last glimmer of light vanished.

But before a Pater Noster had passed the light appeared again and the worthy gentleman emerged panting from his effort, carrying on his arm, like an infant, a quart bottle filled with delicate yellow wine, followed by the maid with two clean glasses. "See," he said to Andree, who was staring ahead of him absent-minded and impatient, "this is the true spiritual comfort and fellow soldier, and before we comfort others it behooves us to strengthen our own spirits. Drink, my poor son; you will recognize it, no doubt. It has become sharper in the last ten years but more mature and more sedate; see, it no longer blows any bubbles."

And with a serene look on his face he held the pure gold against the light before drinking and clinked glasses cordially with his worried pupil. "I hope things may yet turn out well," he said, for the presence of the noble liquor was already producing its invigorating effect on him. "It is written: *Gaudete in Domino semper,* and therefore drink, my son, and then we will fill another bottle for the poor penitential girl, for she will need it."

After that they said nothing more, but the ten o'clock Mass-er kept pacing up and down the room, like a general in his tent reflecting on his battle plan, taking large drafts from time to time, replacing the glass on the table each time with a more vigorous thrust. When the large bottle was half-empty, he took the fiddle from the wall with a sweeping gesture and began to play a beautiful old Italian cantata, still striding up and down, a number that was ornamented with many intricate *fioriture* and which he always played on significant occasions. It was also the favorite piece of the tomcat, who leaped to the table purring joyfully, circled about the candle and looked at Andree with his big green eyes, as if urging him to be of good cheer too. But he, in his impatience, felt the ground burning under his feet, and only his respect and his own sense of guilt prevented him from interrupting the ecclesiastic in his concert and reminding him that Lassie was counting the minutes till he brought her comfort.

Finally, however, the clergyman put down the violin, mopped his brow with the sleeve of his dressing gown and then quickly put on his black soutane. The maid came and poured the remainder of the Terlaner into a small bottle which Andree had to put in his pocket, brought her master his hat and lighted their way down the stairs. Meanwhile it had become quieter in Arbor Lane; only from the taverns could one hear the singing and laughter of the Italian masons and day laborers, and here and there quarreling and vehement words exchanged, and the watchmen sat before their open booths and got ready for the night, which promised to be a cold one. When they came to the square on which the church stood, the ten o'clock Mass-er stopped and said: "Now you go ahead, my son; I have some business to attend to with the Dean first; I can't have you there while I transact it. I'll follow you in half an hour; meanwhile tell Lassie that I said everything would turn out well."

He gave Andree his hand, which the boy kissed reverently, and then stood a while longer down at the parsonage before he could persuade himself to go up. But the Terlaner helped him and he reached the parsonage above with only a slight acceleration of his heartbeat, caused by the steep stone stairway.

What he said there that evening and what reply he received he refused to betray to anyone. But when he descended again a quarter of an hour later, his whole being was greatly altered, the spirit of the Terlaner had receded and been replaced by a profound dejection. He sighed frequently as he climbed the rough road to Küchel Mountain and when he finally saw the little house at the top, casting a weak glimmer of light through its little windows, he sighed even more profoundly and would have preferred to go back down. But if he could not help, he at least did not want to leave the poor couple alone in their misfortune, and so he opened the low door without knocking and crossed the familiar threshold.

He found the couple in the kitchen, in which the mother had died; Andree was standing at the hearth, blowing up the fire to cook polenta; Lassie sat silently and apathetically on the bed against the wall, the cloak she had worn on her long pilgrimage still about her shoulders, as if she was not at home yet and would never find a home again anywhere. When the clergyman came up to her and wished her a good evening, she started, made a movement as if to get up but sank back on the bed and sat there huddled up, her hands pressed against her face, without uttering a sound.

"Lassie," the little man said, "don't you recognize me?"

She nodded quickly, without looking at him.

"Won't you even look me in the face, and have you no trust in me?"

She did not reply, but he saw how her whole body was trembling. He shook his head sadly. "Andree," he said, "you go into the bedroom for a while, I'd like some words with Lassie in private."

The boy obeyed at once, but he did not go into the bedroom; instead he went outside, because he felt too constricted and stifled in the house, where he had experienced much suffering.

"Now, my daughter," the ten o'clock Mass-er began again, "take courage and listen to what I'm saying to you. It is true that you have both committed a sin, and if things have gone hard for you, you should accept it as a just punishment and atonement from the Lord. But your sin is not so grave that you cannot make it good again, and what most alarms you and burdens your conscience, I can—thank Heaven for that—take from you, when I tell you and testify that Andree is not your mother's son and that the sacraments of the Church can and will make you a Christian husband and wife. So be comforted and lift up your face and do not sadden me and Andree with your delusions, which merely increase the evil and come from the wicked enemy who wants to destroy souls."

He expected that these words would calm her and that she would finally say something. But she sat there motionless, as if everything he said was not intended for her at all. He came even closer to her and took her hands with gentle force from her face; they were cold and moist. Then he saw that her soft, childlike features had been painfully transformed in the few short months. She kept her eyes tightly closed, her eyebrows were drawn taut as though by a powerful emotional struggle, her lips were half-open, and her pale cheeks, whose outlines appeared to be more delicate and sharper, were suddenly suffused with a deep red when the clergyman removed her hands from them.

He studied her with profound sympathy. "Say something, Lassie," he said emphatically. "I can't help you if I don't know what's wrong. Isn't it enough for you if I assure you that Andree is not your brother?"

She shook her head vehemently and opened her eyes; the rigid, wild look in them terrified him. "I know better," she said to herself dully. "Mother told me not to let myself be led astray, she deceived everyone, the men of the Church and the city officials and everyone. But no one can deceive the Lord. And how could it be otherwise? Where is his mother, and why doesn't she help him now, when he's in misery? I know better, no one will help us, no one will join us together except death, and now go and leave me alone, what do you want here? But first I must —the child—"

She stopped and her whole body began to tremble again and she closed her eyes once more. Suddenly she became calmer again, as though she were reflecting about something. "Is it true," she said with fear in her voice, "that I am to go to Church with him and you will say the blessing over us? Yes, if that could be done, it would be fine. But I know better, you are all deceived; if you were to do it and you came to the place in the service where you say: 'If any of you know just cause or impediment why these two should not be joined together in holy matrimony,' you would see his mother suddenly standing at the high altar, laughing because she had deceived you and you would not be able to give us the blessing. That's what will happen, I know it."

"Lassie," said the priest in a firm voice, "you are an ignorant creature, and what you are babbling there is a delusion inspired by the evil enemy to ensnare you in still greater sin. Is it not enough for you if I tell you that I know who Andree's father and mother are, but I mustn't reveal it because I have been forbidden to do so by those to whom I owe obedience?"

She suddenly looked hard at him without uttering a word. But in her face there was such an anxious, imploring expression that he was deeply shaken by it and had to turn away to regain his composure. Then he heard her laughing cynically to herself. "You see," she said, "you can't look me in the face as you talk, it's all deception, to make me cheerful again; Andree must have asked you to say this, he is so deeply concerned about me, but who can help us? If you knew who his parents are, you would surely go to them and tell them that people are pointing their fingers at Lassie and Andree because they say that they are brother and sister and are nevertheless bringing a child into the world. But you can't summon the parents, for where are they? I know the mother well, she told it to me in a dream, no one can confuse me, I know better!"—

With that he resisted no longer. "Listen to me," he said and came close to the bed. "I can't hear your wretched words any longer and will tell you what I know and what is as true as that there is a merciful God in Heaven. But first you must vow to me on your poor soul that you will never tell anyone, least of all Andree, what I am going to confide to you against my duty and clerical vow of obedience, because your mind is severely disturbed and things would get even worse if I were to remain silent. Will you promise me on the Holy Sacrament to keep it to yourself?"

She nodded three times with an attentive look on her face, on which a faint ray of hope was beginning to dawn. "You see," he said, "Andree doesn't need it, he has no doubts or torments of conscience and will lead you into the Church without fear. And I think that his mother will surely be sitting there among the others and silently join in the blessing, but it will not be the departed spirit of Maria Ingram, your poor mother, but"—and he put his lips close to her ear—"Rosine's aunt, Anna Hirzer, who lifted him out of the baptismal font; she will join in the prayer and raise no objection."

He had uttered the words in a hasty whisper and, as though frightened by his own speech, he jumped up to see if no third person had heard it. The young woman sat still and rigid; it was as though the revelation of this secret had made no impression whatever on her disturbed mind.

"Now that you know this much, my daughter," the little priest began again after a pause, "you shall know too how all this happened; otherwise you would think that this too is but a delusion. But you know very well that your mother brought little Andree down from the meadow that time. On that same meadow Anna Hirzer gave birth to him. A year before that, in fact, a foreign gentleman had come from Germany to Innsbruck, an officer, who had taken part in a campaign against Napoleon, and when his wounds had healed, the doctors sent him to the Tirol because the air where he lived was not good for him. Well, he saw Anna Hirzer on the street and a relationship soon developed between them, for he was a resolute and courtly gentleman, and whatever he took into his head had to happen, just as Andree has been from his childhood. But there was a serious hitch in the situation, for the officer—you're listening to me, aren't you, Lassie?"

She nodded her head quickly and raised both her hands if as to beg him not to be astonished at her stiff behavior but to continue with his story.

"Well, my child, the gentleman was normally a gallant man, an aristocrat and rich, and intended to marry Anna. But he was a Lutheran and refused to have anything to do with our Holy Church, and Anna wept day and night because she knew that he was damned but could not help him. And when she noticed that her prayers and supplications had no effect on him, she went to her confessor, who advised her to sacrifice her heart to God and flee before the tempter. And because

she had a pious and holy heart, she did indeed leave Innsbruck, very secretly, so that her fiancé learned about it only after she had returned to Goyen to her brother's house. He praised her highly for preferring flight to the commission of such a grave offense; for you know that the Hirzers have always shown great zeal for our Catholic faith and Joseph used to say that he would rather lose his right arm than a member of his family to the heretics or to Anti-Christ. But Anna had overestimated her strength, for after only a few days she became a different person, walked about like a shadow, hardly ate a mouthful, so that I thought she would go out like a lamp that is not refilled with oil. Her attachment to the foreigner was already too deep and Heaven knows what I would have given to see the two poor people united in marriage. I carried on elaborate negotiations with the Dean at the time, but in the end all efforts failed because we didn't want the children to be damned too, Anna could not have brought herself to cause that. And so six or seven days passed; then one day Joseph came to me in rage and aggravation and told me that the heretic, the fiancé, had followed her here and was now living at Trautmannsdorf Castle, because he was acquainted with the Count. What was to happen now?—I went to the Dean again and got the same answer; and then I went to see Anna and then the foreigner; I'll remember those days as long as I live, they cost me no little sweat and heartblood. But while we were all still busy with worries and talk and counsel and I almost began to believe that we would bring back a prodigal son to the Church in this foreigner, whose behavior toward me was very respectful, the headstrong and reckless man was able to get to Goyen Castle secretly in the night and to see his love again in spite of Joseph's vigilance. These secret meetings lasted about four weeks. But one morning, long before the first Mass was said, as he was about to leave her in the gray dawn by his usual route, which was the window, where there was a pine tree growing so close to the rough wall that he could use it as a ladder to climb up and down, Joseph Hirzer had awakened earlier than usual and seen the figure climbing down and knew everything. There was a savage fight in the silent gorge above, where it declines sharply toward the Naif, and Anna had to see from her window how her brother finally overcame her fiancé, got him down to the ground and trod him under foot. But the foreigner had fallen against a rock and had injured himself so badly that he was barely able to drag himself with great difficulty before day broke to Trautmannsdorf, where he collapsed miserably. As soon as he regained consciousness he wanted to get away, so the Count had him taken to Venice in his own carriage, and after scarcely three weeks had passed the news came that he had died."

The little priest was silent for a time, thoughtfully took a pinch of snuff from his box, looking straight in front of him and said: "May his soul rest in peace. He was a fine and noble gentleman and stately of face and figure. Andree is his veritable image, except that he is not so tall and has his mother's eyes. Never did I come so close as then to wondering why there must be different religions among men, granting salvation to one and damnation to the other. But God has so ordained it and we shortsighted humans must simply accept it. I was the one who had to bring Anna the news from Venice. That too was a bitter mission, my daughter. But afterwards things were peaceful up there, Joseph and Anna dared not hurl harsh words at each other, they both had reason for seeking forgiveness. And when summer came, Anna ostensibly took a trip to Bozen, but in reality she went up to the meadow to your mother's place,

for apart from the five of us, not a living soul has ever learned what happened that night. They didn't even know at Trautmannsdorf whom the foreign gentleman was visiting at night. And when it was all over and your mother had brought the boy home with her from the meadow, Anna made her will and left half her fortune to the Church at Meran and the other half to the Church at Innsbruck, where she had first spoken to her fiancé and she founded a number of sacred Masses to be said every year for the soul of the dead man, in the hope that the Lord might have mercy on him. That is the way it all happened and it's not to be altered and it's better not to stir up the old griefs which have now been laid to rest. Besides it would ill become Andree to try to upset the will and thus rob his father's soul of the Church's grace. So it is more salutary that he too should learn nothing of his father and mother as long as he lives, especially as he has no desire to do so. But you, my daughter, will bear in mind what you promised me on your oath, then the Holy Mother of God will intercede on your behalf that your sins may be forgiven you and you may lead a peaceful life together and one that is acceptable in the eyes of God after your many trials. Amen."

He had spoken the last words with elevated voice in a solemn, hortatory tone and now he waited to hear if she had any questions to ask or an objection to make. But she sat quite still on her bed with her eyes closed, her head leaning back against the wall, her hands folded in her lap. The anxious wildness had gone out of her face, the forehead under the unruly blond hair was smooth and serene, her breast rose and fell gently. After a short while her head sank down to her shoulder and her clasped hands parted. The little pastor's tale had lulled her to sleep like a lullaby, and she had sunk into a deep, dreamless sleep for the first time since the difficulties and distress of the past months.

The assistant pastor stood up with an uncertain look on his face; he had not expected this effect from his pastoral activity. It now first struck his conscience that he had delivered up the delicate secret into the hands of a poor, distracted creature who was hardly a wholly responsible person. And she hadn't even spoken the vow to keep silent but had merely nodded to everything with an absent look in her eyes and perhaps with deaf ears. But what had been done could not be altered and this much at least was gained, that she was asleep and so could do no mischief this night. Tomorrow would have to take care of itself.

Softly he left the bedside and went out by the door. Andree was still sitting on the bench outside, but he did not stand up when his clerical friend came out to him. He, too, knowing that his poor wife was well cared for, had allowed his overstrained senses, after such a long period of tension, to take their natural course, and so he had succumbed to sleep, the best spiritual mentor of youth.

At that same hour no one was thinking of sleep up at Goyen Castle. Late in the evening a boy from Tirol village, who had been one of Lassie's suitors in the past, had come to Franz and given him the news about the return of the two fugitives and about Lassie's condition. All the people were in great anger, he reported, and there was general talk that such goings on should not be tolerated; the clergy should step in and wipe such gruesome behavior from the face of the earth with excommunication and fire as a fearful example for all time.

This news reached Franz when he was in the vilest mood. He had just returned home from a suitors' quarrel with the young widow, and since the people of the house were careful to keep out of his way when he was in these moods, he eagerly sized upon the new development for venting his spleen. He could not deny himself the pleasure of going down to the room in which his father sat behind a bottle and an old newspaper and his aunt and Rosine at their spinning wheels and to treat them to the pretty story of the two vagrants in his crudest style. No one gave him a word in reply; but it was enough satisfaction for him to see that his aunt turned deathly pale and sank into Rosine's arms. She had always taken Andree's part; now she could see him end his career in the most miserable way. With a sneering "Good night" he left the room and strode down the steep paths with his companions, through the leafless chestnut trees, toward the city, where they spent the night drinking and forging sinister plans.

The three who remained behind at Goyen sat together in silence for about a quarter of an hour; the aunt, who had recovered from her fainting fit quickly, seemed to be praying; Rosine stared at her father, incapable of generating any thoughts of her own; he kept his eyes fixed on the newspaper, smoking furiously. Finally he got up, thoughtfully put his small pipe out and ordered his daughter to go to bed.

When he was alone with Anna, he went up to her and said: "Forget your praying for once. You can't pray away what the devil has put in your path. You've heard that the tramp—I don't want to name him—has turned up again. Maybe he has gotten wind of the way he came into the world and wants to make a row to help himself out of the pinch. But I tell you he shall not cross my threshold, neither he nor his wench. Our family has not existed in honor for close to forty years only to experience overnight the disgrace that a Lutheran foundling should force his way in and bring the name of Joseph Hirzer's own sister in her old days on every tongue. If all your praying and holiness have done you no more good than to make of you, after twenty years, an object of derision to every child, then I wish you—" He swallowed the curse that he had on the tip of his tongue, for her serious, proud eyes had met his head on. —"It's all right," he continued in a somewhat gentler tone, "we don't have to waste words on the subject, you know as well as I do what will happen if you don't act reasonably. I'll have the horses hitched up tomorrow morning and drive with you to Lana, first to Mass, then to our cousin's, where you can stay until the air has cleared here. I don't think it will take long. I'll put my hand in my pocket and offer him a sum of money if he will undertake to leave the district and never return. In any event, one could buy the house and the estate from him and give him the wench into the bargain; in that way we would be rid of him and have no cause for reproaching ourselves. I'll think the matter over, there's time enough on our trip tomorrow, and after lunch I can come home and arrange the deal with the ten o'clock Mass-er, he still has the greatest influence on the madcap and he will realize the need to avoid a sensation. But if you act contrary to my wishes, Sister, let me tell you: I'll do everything I can so that I don't have to pay out a penny, even if the lawsuits should bring me to the grave. Now you know my position, be sensible and don't argue with me and don't look for any tricks and subterfuges. For they would be useless; you can take the sacrament on that."

He left the room without waiting for an answer from her and she heard him going down into the cellar to fetch a nightcap for himself, which he might well need, for all his firm and self-assured talk. Rosine crept in again and looked at her aunt with nervous, tear-stained eyes. "Come," the old woman said, "we'll go up to my room; I have something to tell you."

She stood up calmly from her spinning wheel and her hand, which held the candle that was to light their way across the hall to her bed, did not tremble. While her brother had revealed his harsh terms to her, an unshakeable determination had hardened in her as well. She was a Hirzer too, and her brother well knew it. And that is why he needed the nightcap; for in spite of his blustering confidence he foresaw no good issue to this dispute. His Anna had given him that look only once before in her life: that time after the fight when he first dared to face her alone.

But the nightcap did its duty. When the bells were rung for early Mass down in Meran, the lord of Goyen Castle still lay in a deep sleep and even failed to hear the dog barking joyfully and rattling his chain. Franz could not hear it either, for he had spent the night in Meran. So the two feminine figures, in their Sunday clothes, went down the wooden staircase by the wall unnoticed and began their walk through the misty winter morning silently and swiftly.

They had both spent a sleepless night, yearning for the morning to come. For the old woman had told the young girl the whole story, which the latter had till now only dimly suspected and which she had been able to piece together from chance phrases dropped by her father in his drunken bouts. The aunt had unlocked the most secret drawer of her clothes-press, and old letters, a small portrait of the dead man and the faded presents from him which she had preserved, were for the first time exposed to other eyes than those which did not grow tired of weeping over them. On this night alone they shed no tears; rather they shone with a magnificent, heroic courage, which rejuvenated her whole face miraculously, flushed her cheeks and now, as she strode along through the morning, gave youthful wings to her walk, so that the young girl found it an effort to keep up with her.

A mist lay over the valleys of the Naif and the Passeier, so that they walked as though in a cloud and perceived through the haze only the tops of Küchel Mountain and the topmost pinnacles of old Zeno Castle in ruins. They could still hear the ringing bells and intermittently the roar of the Passeier and on the many footpaths to the left and right they heard churchgoers, who remained invisible to them in the thick fog, eagerly talking to each other and occasionally mentioning the two names which caused their hearts to beat faster. On the stone path below there was already a lively assembly of men and women, who greeted them reverently as Anna Hirzer, the saint, walked through their ranks with unusual haste. They all stopped and put their heads together. For the old woman did not, as usual, join the stream of people going to the left through the city gate toward the church, but they were seen turning into the steep street at the right that leads up to Küchel Mountain. Many people followed them, especially since the street was uncommonly animated, as if there were astounding things to be seen up there. After all, it was Anna Hirzer, the saint, Andree's godmother, who was going up there. What will she have to say to the misguided couple, who have returned home in sin and disgrace? Does she intend to protect the poor sinners with her holiness against ecclesiastical and secular judgment, or will she herself pronounce the word of condemnation over them?

This is what the peasants and their wives whispered among themselves. But Anna looked neither to right nor to left, scarcely returned the greetings with a slight nod of her head, but went up the stony road as though she were already a departed ghost who could neither feel earthly burdens nor heed human speech. Close behind her walked Rosine with the quiet face, which was familiar to them all. But today it was so pale that the sympathetic women called it to each others' attention, while the face of the old woman was suffused by a fresh red color. She did not take the time for resting at half-distance, where a bench stood beside the rock. It was as though she were driven forward by a premonition that she had not a minute to lose.

And indeed the night had brewed misfortune and toward morning a threatening storm had gathered about the little house on Küchel Mountain. Soon after midnight Andree had been awakened by the cold from his sleep in front of the door. He crept into the hall quietly and when he found his wife sleeping gently, he stretched out before the hearth to get a few more hours of rest. When he awoke out of his anxious dreams in the half-light of the white morning mist, he heard voices in front of the window and saw figures peering in through the window panes, only to disappear and make room for others. He listened through the front door, which he had fortunately bolted at night, and heard scraps of phrases that left no doubt as to what was going on out there. But if he had been able to see through the mist and survey the streets and gardens, his heart would have sunk and his hair stood on end.

For outside there had gathered, in dense masses, half the population of the villages of Tirol, Gratsch and Algund, through which the fugitives had wandered on the previous day in their miserable walk home, and no one was concerned about missing the first Mass. Nobody really knew what they wanted here and why they surrounded the house. But an obscure feeling was stirring within them all that something unheard of was bound to happen to two people who had committed such an unheard-of sin; there was curiosity about the position which the authorities would take toward the horrible crime, and in a very few cases sympathy. For whatever affection the fair Lassie enjoyed on the part of the neighbors was fully counterbalanced by the low esteem in which the word-shy Andree stood, indeed by the hostility which his dominating character stirred in the young lads.

And so one could hear among the crowd of curious folk only sinister talk and see only stern faces. They were joined by no few people from Meran and by a liberal troop of white jackets, who had not yet forgotten Andree's adventure with their Italian comrade, and the longer the church bells rang the more numerous became the stream of country folk that moved from the Passeier villages up the steep mountain paths. For as long as vines had been grown and wine pressed on Küchel Mountain many a savage and bloody deed had been done and many a revolting crime had been committed, but no one could remember a mortal sin being perpetrated so openly and freely before the eyes of the multitude.

While the buzzing and grumbling of the mob was still increasing, without anyone knowing just what to do, when the church bells finally ceased tolling, one could hear a rough voice shout with unnecessary loudness: "Kick in the door! I'll drag the rascal out with my own fists, I'll tear the wretch to shreds, I'll finish him off, I've sworn it, as true as my name is Franz Hirzer, he shall be torn to pieces by four horses and thrown into the Passeier limb by limb, that's what the hound of hell deserves and anyone who opposes this will have me to reckon with."

An absolute silence had suddenly descended on the throng that was packed in head beside head. The thousand curious eyes turned to the street on which Franz Hirzer was staggering forward, supported on either side by a drinking comrade, with whom he had spent the night carousing in the tavern below. He was without a hat, his face very red; but his walk and general behavior were not those of a drunkard. His hatred and the consciousness of being the spokesman for the great multitude and of carrying out a meritorious act of vengeance had sobered him completely after a brief sleep.

The prisoner in the house heard the raging words clearly and immediately afterward the hurricane roar of the thousand voices that broke loose from every direction and shouted encouragement to the executor of the punishment. He heard the throng surging in closer and a deathly chill ran down his spine. He would have given up his own life easily enough; the world had been hostile to him from his youth. But the poor young creature, who was resting in there so innocently after the distress of many weeks, how could he save her, how could he tolerate it that she should suffer a fearful martyrdom because of him? Should he step out to sacrifice himself and assume the whole guilt? But who would listen to him, who would believe him, even if he invoked the testimony of his friend the priest? And yet it must be tried, whatever the risk, for the din outside was getting louder every moment. He now heard his old friend Köbele trying to intercede, attempting to push Franz away. Why didn't they wait, he urged, till the officials passed judgment; the Dean ought to be called or the ten o'clock Mass-er, who had been the confessor of Black Lassie; there was something wrong about the whole affair, the courts would prove it. And then once more the cursing and provocations of Franz, mixed with the shouts of the Italian soldiers, a call to order by a few old men, the women screaming woe and lamentation, and even to the most distant groups the muffled echoes of an agitated mob torn hither and thither by blind passions.

The captive gave himself up for lost.

He was already considering whether he should wake Lassie, take his rifle from the wall and shoot her and himself, to save them from a worse fate. But suddenly it became quiet outside and he heard many cries of order and silence, to which Franz alone paid no attention. But suddenly his voice too grew silent, and in its place the listener in the hall heard the gentle but firm voice of Aunt Anna, who could now be only a few steps from the house.

"You should be ashamed of yourself, Franz," he heard her say, "to be raging and cursing here on a holy Sunday, stirring up the other people, who don't know what they are doing here. Go home this moment and put on your Sunday clothes and then come to Church and pray to our Savior on your knees not to call you to account for graver sins than those committed by poor Andree and Lassie in there, whom you, you wretched being, want to bring to justice, as if you were the judge, and yet you are only an ignorant, sinful person, as we all are. Don't stand here in my way any longer," she continued, raising her voice, "and you others go your ways too: I alone have a right to knock on this door, for you must know that in that house lives my son, whom I bore in pain and denied for many years, because I have been a weak woman and feared disgrace in the eyes of the world. But now I state and testify before the countenance of God the Father, the Son and the Holy Spirit and within hearing of all who are assembled here: he is *mine* and whoever would accuse him or scorn him, let him accuse me, for it was by my fault that he fell into guilt and misery, because I withdrew my hand from him as no mother should do to her child, but turned him over to a stranger who could not love him. Now you know it and now go down to Church and pray for a great sinner whom you regarded and honored as a pious and just person

and who must be the last and most despised of women if God in His grace will not have mercy on her remorse and suffering."

When she had finished, there was a complete silence and no one stirred from the spot, except Franz who retreated in confusion and disappeared in the crowd. Anna pounded on the door, which was opened at once. On the threshold stood Andree as if in a dream. He saw his mother's eyes fixed on him and saw them overflowing with tears and saw her knees sag as she took a step forward toward him and she would have fallen at his feet if he had not thrown both his arms around her and brought her to her feet again so that she could rest on his chest and exhaust her tears. Only now did life return to the crowd; the people dispersed noiselessly, whispering to each other, the women dried their eyes with their handkerchiefs, the men went away in silence. Many stayed behind and stared at the open doorway into which mother and son had vanished.

It was not long before they came out again, the mother in the center between Andree on her right and Lassie on her left, all three holding hands. They did not speak to each other, they looked straight ahead, their faces as if transfigured. And when Lassie caught sight of Rosine outside, she let go of the mother's hand and threw her arms about the loyal friend, her eyes full of tears. Then she drew the friend into the group and the four miraculously united people walked through the ranks of the silent multitude along the street that leads down to the city. A noiseless stream of devout people joined them.

Below, where the market square was teeming with people, a broad path was opened for them. The rumor had preceded them, the town and country folk stood at their front doors and windows to see Anna Hirzer, the saint, who was leading her son to show him to the whole city and to testify to the fact that she had committed a great sin and needed the mercy of her God more than many of those who had pronounced her a saint.

An hour later, when the bells tolled for ten o'clock Mass, the mother and her two children knelt well forward in the Church between the pews on the cold stones. The clergyman at the altar saw them clearly. His voice trembled as he spoke the first words. Then it rang out more sonorous and joyful through the lofty space, and when the organ joined in at the end, he raised his eyes aloft, as though he wished to implore all the blessings of Heaven on the bowed gray woman and the two young people who knelt beside her.

THE LIFE AND WORKS
OF PAUL HEYSE

By GENEVIÈVE BIANQUIS

TODAY PAUL HEYSE is a writer who has been forgotten. Literary historians label him an imitator and dismiss him in a line or two. Nevertheless, he had his moment of celebrity and even of glory, climaxed by the Nobel Prize. His prolific work appealed to a large audience with a taste for pretty stories charmingly told. But, perhaps because he was never a groundbreaking writer, he was soon passed by.

Heyse was born in Berlin in 1830 to an intellectual university family. His father, a teacher, was a well-known philologist; his grandfather had made a reputation as a grammarian. It is hardly surprising that their scion should write in so disciplined a fashion. His Jewish mother was related to the Mendelssohns, the influential Berlin family of bankers, musicians, and patrons of the arts.

In 1848, when he was eighteen, Heyse made his first step into literature with a little volume of verse called *Frühling* (Springtime). The following year, obviously proud of his son's precocity, the elder Heyse surprised him by having his story, *Jungbrunnen* (Fountain of Youth), printed anonymously. By this time a student in Bonn, Heyse was working uninterruptedly on a tragedy, *Francesca da Rimini,* which he finished in the same year. After study at the universities of Bonn and Berlin, where he specialized

in philosophy, romance philology, and art history, Heyse earned his doctorate. He did not immediately settle on a career; but for the time being was content to take an active part in the literary life of his native city.

The home of Franz Kugler, Professor Heyse's friend and colleague, was a center for young intellectuals. There they encountered older, more established figures, such as Jacob Burckhardt, with whom young Heyse formed a strong friendship. It was Burckhardt who inspired Heyse's love for Italy and his taste for the Renaissance. For a long time they maintained a cordial correspondence which has since been published. In the same house Heyse met his future wife, Grete Kugler, whom he married in 1854.

The atmosphere in the Kuglers' home was marked by the uneasiness of the years after the political disappointment of 1848. One was a "liberal" but one never talked politics; esthetics was a much more welcome subject.

Young Heyse, who was already stirred by literary ambitions, also moved in the Berlin group known as the "Tunnel Over the Spree," where he came to know the men who were to be his masters in the art of the novella: Gottfried Keller, Theodor Storm, Theodor Fontane, as well as a then famous novelist, Felix Dahn, and

Emmanuel Geibel, who was his mentor in poetry and his fatherlike friend.

By 1852, though still a student, Heyse was already established as a writer. A grant from the university made it possible for him to visit Italy, where he sought out unpublished old Provençal songs for his dissertation. But he had little enthusiasm for scholarship. Besides, through the monsignor in charge, the Pope ordered that he be forbidden to copy a single line from the Provençal manuscripts in the Vatican Library, so Heyse abandoned the dissertation and proceeded to employ his grant toward less ascetic ends. He roamed through Italy from Rome to Naples and finally to Venice. In Italy he had found the land of his heart's desire. The Italian landscape, the sky, the light, the colors were unending magic to him. He loved the Italian people, so impulsive, so gay, so passionate, and so naturally beautiful. He was enchanted by the vivacity of Naples, even though he did not like the carnival vulgarity. It was during the first time in Italy that he met in Sorrento the beautiful dark-haired girl whom he transformed into the heroine of his best novella, *L'Arrabbiata* (The Angry Woman, 1853). Subsequently, he visited and lived in Italy, especially in Rome and Naples. During the last part of his life he spent every autumn in his villa at Gardone on the shore of the Lago di Garda.

On his return to Germany following his discovery of Italy he continued to write, though without quite knowing where it might lead. His teacher and friend, Geibel, had left Berlin for Munich at the summons of Maximilian II, King of Bavaria and a patron of arts and letters. Now Geibel brought Heyse to the attention of the king, who, in spite of the writer's youth, invited him to join the royal retinue. Maximilian enjoyed surrounding himself with writers and artists for whom he provided comfortable livings and whom he liked to receive at his table, demanding only that they devote themselves zealously to their chosen arts and contribute to the intellectual awakening of a kingdom somewhat entrenched in materialism and in the depths of superstitious religiosity. These royal favorites were anything but popular with the people, who called them the "Northern Lights" because in most instances the king had brought them from northern regions, Prussia or Saxony, where minds were more enlightened and the arts and sciences were more advanced. Such a policy of colonization of the south by the north had been inaugurated earlier by Maximilian's predecessor, Ludwig I. He too had imported artists and scholars who were unwelcome because they were Protestants or unbelievers, as well as products of northern Germany.

But in 1854 these prejudices were much relaxed, and on the whole Heyse had no reason to complain of his reception. When Maximilian died in 1863, Heyse's position was secure and he no longer required a patron, but he paid poetic tribute to this "truly human" king who had found his greatest pleasure in his strolls through the "Grove of the Muses." Still unknown and very young, Heyse was grateful that at the Bavarian court he had savored that very rare privilege, "freedom for every man to find his own path according to his tastes."

In his memoirs Heyse has described Munich, then still half rural, where peasants walked the streets cracking their whips, resoundingly, and loggers carried their loads on their shoulders and smoked their pipes furiously. It was a strange little city of merchants, court functionaries and servants with no concerns but the material ones. "At that time," he wrote, "there was never a word about literature even in the most cultivated circles; at best people talked about the theater. On the other hand, I was received coldly, not to say antagonistically, by a crowd of fellow-practitioners, and this attitude toward an outlander such as myself tempered my character and incited me to excel in my efforts."

There was, in a manner of speaking, no social life: "In the evening men went to their favorite taverns, and ladies, in very informal attire, remained at home; at the very most they might occasionally entertain some other lady, or a 'friend' who could not possibly be offended by their informal dress. If a guest from another city called on a friend in Munich, his host invited him to dine in the tavern, or, if he entertained him at home, the serving woman came to ask what the gentleman would like to eat and then went out to the tavern to get it, not forgetting to include a decent bottle for the evening's libations."

Actually, Heyse adjusted very quickly to Munich—amazingly quickly for a north German. He soon had his own circle of friends, most of whom, like himself, came from other parts of Germany but were firmly ensconced in that royal favor that made life so easy.

A number of books of verse, seven novels, some forty plays, more than one hundred and fifty novellas, excellent translations of some Italian poets (Leopardi, Giusti, Monti, Manzoni, Zendrini), anthologies of Italian and Spanish songs, all testify to his remarkable diligence in his work. This sizable and varied inventory of his production must have had a certain influence long afterward on the decision of the Nobel judges.

Though literary work might not have been much esteemed by the public in Munich, it very easily assumed quasi-official aspects. The king gave "evening teas" at which there were readings of the most talked-about theatrical works. At the Crocodile Club, which Heyse founded, writers gathered for solemn "symposia" at which full evening dress was mandatory and guests were welcomed by a royal

aide or a marshal of the court. The members included novelists of the historical school like Felix Dahn or Victor von Scheffel, Orientalists like Bodenstedt, lyric poets of a slightly outmoded breed like Geibel, Strachwitz, Hermann Lingg. Among these there were a few more authentic poets, unclassifiable or individual, like Graf Platen or Heinrich Leuthold, the Swiss. For the most part these were gentlemen of letters, the very opposite of a venturesome or innovative Bohemian group.

From then on, Heyse's life proceeded with the utmost calm, alternating between Munich and Italy. There were no sterile periods in his output, few upheavals in his life. He had good friends, a loyal following, eminent correspondents, but he had no contact with the ebullient life of the new schools. He turned out an unbroken flow of novels, plays, and innumerable novellas that he put together in collections every two or three years. In 1862, when he was the father of three children, his wife died; a year later he married Anna Schubart, who was very young and who gave him three more children. It was like a second springtime for him. But within a very few years all the children of his second marriage died, and this became the great trial of his life. There is little more to be said of his uneventful life until 1910, when he received a title of nobility and the Nobel Prize for Literature. He died in 1914 at the age of eighty-four.

One must seek in Heyse neither bold ideas nor new forms. He lived on the profits of the previous generation, in communion with the great masters of his form—less humorous than Keller, less melancholy than Storm, less aware of the social problems of his time than Fontane. He moved through a very active period of German literature without any contact with it. Wagnerianism, naturalism, symbolism, he denounced all these young men's movements, which he did not understand. To him naturalism seemed to derive from pathology. He criticized impressionism and symbolism for the vagueness and imprecision of images and symbols, and Wagnerian music left him unmoved. On the other hand, he condemned the romantic fashion of medieval subjects and troubadour style, and he had no affinity with Catholicism. His thinking was comfortable in the course set by Goethe and Humboldt, but his style had nothing of classical rigidity: it was precise, plastic, and soberly and expressively realistic.

Paul Heyse suffered throughout his life from an unrequited love for the theater. He never stopped writing plays, both tragedies and comedies, which never reached the stage. The subjects of his dramas were taken from ancient tradition (*Alcibiades, Meleager, The Sabines, Hadrian*) or Biblical themes (*King Saul, The Wisdom of Solomon, Mary Magdalen*), or from the rather anecdotal history of Germany (*Ludwig of Bavaria, Elisabeth-Charlotte, Hans Lang, Colberg*) and Italy (*Francesca da Rimini, Vanina Vanini, La Fornarina, Maria Moroni*), and on one occasion from French history (*The Goddess Reason*). Gifted above all for narrative prose and the analysis of emotion, he lacked the dramatic temperament.

Heyse's lyric poetry is graceful, harmonious, and usually short. His model was Geibel, himself an emulator of the brilliant generation of lyricists that adorned the first half of the eighteenth century. In a series of sonnets dedicated to various German poets, Heyse indicated those whom he considered as his forerunners: Eichendorff, Mörike, Lenau, Rückert, Geibel, Chamisso, Keller, Storm, Annette von Droste-Hülshoff.

His first collections were almost exclu-sively picturesque: Italian landscapes and *genre* pieces, most of them Neapolitan or Sorrentine; children dancing the *tarantella* as their mother watched, a woman spinning and singing her child to sleep; a little thief, a black-eyed hussy, a Neapolitan prostitute, a festive dinner of forty Neapolitan servants, a buxom peasant woman suckling her child in a museum. Laurella, the "Angry Woman," first appeared here, charming and bashful, refusing love, dancing as if she were challenging, biting into an orange. There is a sonnet for each of a dozen Italian cities and for Capri, where all the girls were beautiful and willing. The poet is barely visible in these admirably drawn miniatures, except occasionally in the guise of an amused or fleetingly moved traveler.

Heyse's first two novels have acquired a reputation for naturalistic daring that they hardly deserve. Both deal with a kind of Bohemianism—in Berlin in the first, *Kinder der Welt* (*Children of the World*, 1872); in Munich in the second, *Im Paradiese* (*In Paradise*, 1875). The children of the world are a group of impoverished young artists and virtuous artisans—a painter whose only good pictures are of battles, a sculptor, a young teacher without a job, and his interestingly invalid brother, a poet and wood carver, the family of a struggling shoemaker, an old journeyman painter who supports his daughter and himself by mass production of little landscapes that sell well; and a minor actress. Generally chaste idyls are acted out parallel to one another, occasionally intersecting but always remaining distinct; there are pathetic incidents, but in the end, almost everyone finds happiness and a good marriage. The basic theme is that the children of the world are better people than the children of God. Their natural virtues consist of courage in their work, faith in their art, gaiety, mutual help, and all the proper affectionate bonds. The only unsympathetic character is a Moravian pastor, covetous and lecherous, whose sinister schemes are finally unmasked. The plot seemed daring in its anticlericalism and its advocacy—more theoretical, to be honest, than concrete—of the prerogatives of passion and of equality in love.

Im Paradiese was of the same stripe; it dealt with the same relaxed, impoverished Bohemia facing the same problems of daily bread and career, the same kind of sentimental involvements that quite naturally culminate in marriage. He also wrote four subsequent novels, *Merlin* (in three volumes, 1892), *Gegen den Strom* (Against the Stream, 1904), and *Geburt der Venus* (Birth of Venus, 1909).

But it was in the novella that he found the form and the means of expression that best suited him. He excelled in this form, one easily accessible to a reading public made up of a comfortable middle class tormented neither by needs nor by rebellions, and he made it his business to interest, distract, move, and occasionally instruct such readers by offering them touching or amusing, sometimes dramatic, stories that would reveal to them the recesses of the human heart and the whims of destiny.

In the novella Heyse exercised the full range of his talent. Its short length and its comfortable atmosphere made the novella appropriate to an age that no longer pursued either high purpose or great ambition. The form flowered in Germany during the period of apathy that followed the unsuccessful revolution of 1848 and again in the complacent climate of the years from 1870 to 1900. Heyse was a displaced writer, a Berliner transplanted to Munich. His work could not have that strong tang of the earth to be found in that of the Swiss Keller or the Lower Saxon Storm or the Prussian Fontane. The lowly people that he preferred to depict were Italians at the humblest levels, as he had learned to know them during his travels and sojourns: innkeepers, serving women, ferrymen, coachmen, small artisans. His description of landscape is never intrusive. He had his own explanation for this: "Nature should remain in the background of the picture; the theater of the world does not begin to be worth the price of admission until the human actors come onto the stage."

The essential element of his novella is a tightly woven plot, an enigma resolved. What interested Heyse above all were his characters' psychological problems, especially the women's, for by inclination and taste Heyse was a portraitist of women and particularly of young girls. Occasionally he described the lives of aristocratic families in their great castles in northern Germany, or the middle-class ways of the Rhinelanders; he even set some novellas in the "days of the troubadours"; but as a general rule he preferred to restrict himself to his own time, and to the Italian regions that he knew so well. Essentially he clung to the traditional values: order, regularity, thrift, family, and fatherland. But he knew that often this splendid order could be thrown into confusion by lack of discipline and the dangers of love. Toward genuine love he had complete tolerance—so much that he hesitated to condemn it in the evolution of his plots and strove always to find a pleasant solution. He believed in love as he believed in beauty. All his heroines were beautiful, as almost all his heroes were young and charming. Beauty illuminated life and shone even more brilliantly against the background of the ordinary or even the wretched. Tragedy itself was endowed by beauty with a sorrowing grace or a sublime dignity.

Heyse referred to Boccaccio as his model in the art of the novella. He defined the form as a reasonably short narrative of a surprising event, outside the realm of the ordinary, that determines a whole life. This was the part played by chance intervening in destiny. So the themes of his novellas were difficult or thwarted betrothals, ill-made marriages, sentimental misadventures that came to unexpected solutions by way of a belated meeting, an unforeseen encounter, an unexpected coincidence.

Nerina (1875) is based on an actual incident. The high-born but ailing Leopardi loves the beautiful young peasant, Nerina, who is also ill and who understands his desperate verses so well. This romance is doomed from the start. Leopardi is strong enough to withdraw and to urge the girl to make a more appropriate marriage. He goes away for years, returning only to learn that she died remembering him to the end. In *Donna Lionarda,* a son seeking to redeem his mother's honor kills her lover. She dies of grief and her son goes off to join the Foreign Legion and seek death in Africa. In *Tantalus* a painter who has been scorned by his beloved goes blind and throws himself into the Isar. The title character of *Vroni* yields to her father's ban on marriage to the man she loves. He goes away to forget; when he returns, he finds Vroni married to someone else. She decides to die and throws herself under a train. *Ninon,* an actress in love with her work, has a child by a painter. She decides to abandon the theater in order to bring up her child. But drawn again by her passion for the stage, she neglects the child, who sickens and dies. There is no choice for Ninon but to die of grief.

These few examples show that the tragic is not ignored in Heyse's novellas. But they do not always end so gloomily. The ill-tempered Laurella, *l'Arrabbiata* (1853), first rejected her admirer and bit him savagely, then softened, tended his wounds, and was willing to give him a hearing. The young boatman's sweetness won the beautiful Sorrentine away from an aversion toward marriage that she had conceived from watching the brutal treatment inflicted on her own mother at home. In *Resurrection,* a neurotic young noblewoman who has withdrawn into a gloomy fortified castle on the Tirolean border after a forced marriage, is at last touched by the kindness of her old husband and "comes back to life."

There are many happy stories in these novellas; there are also some that are comic, or, at the very least, humorous. One is the account of the misadventures of two young Germans traveling through Italy. They thought it would be easier and cheaper to pass themselves off as newly married, so that one had to disguise himself as a woman. There was nothing questionable in this: it was a kind of student joke.

In *Marriage on Capri,* an enthusiastic young German takes his mother to the island in order to introduce her to the peasant girl whom he wants to marry. The mother, a fat beer merchant from Munich, is shocked at every turn by the permissiveness, the vulgarity, the poverty, and the dirtiness of the Neapolitans. In the meantime, fortunately, the girl has changed her mind and chosen another husband. Then there is the satirical sketch of the redeemed prostitute turned scheming landowner. She passes herself off as a widow in an effort to marry the model tenant on whom she lavishes little attentions.

It is undeniable that in writing so prodigiously Heyse repeated himself somewhat. His earliest novellas are the best. Yet he has the virtue of a pleasant, careful style and unlimited good will. He himself said he was in love with all his heroines and would have been incapable of creating a character in whom there was absolutely nothing likable. His favorites, and those he portrayed best, were women and particularly girls, so that when he was still being read people spoke of *Heysesche Mädchengestalten* (Heyse's feminine types). They were neither rebellious nor resigned; they adapted themselves quite easily to the laws of the family and society. But let no one wound them in their feelings; they were proud, vigorous girls who knew what they wanted and how to get it. They were not easily won, they were capable of protracted resistance. When love ' caught, they flamed, and then they did battle for their love. They were capable of the most difficult disciplines, of silences that lasted for years, of the greatest renunciations. They were adept at keeping the secrecy of their hearts and guarding the modesty of their emotions. Everything in them was healthy and good, even if at times love led them into a breach of the civil law. There were among them few flirts, few decadents, and few melancholics.

A Berliner transplanted to Munich and in a way naturalized as a Bavarian, Paul Heyse was essentially a chronicler of the Italian countryside, of Italian popular customs, of the Italian character as he understood it through living intimately among the people. This love of Italy is a deeply rooted German tradition that has been handed down from the classicists to the romantics and well beyond, from Goethe to Platen and Hofmannsthal. An excellent humanist, a keen student of the human heart, Heyse applied his analytical talent to the study of a host of delicate problems raised by the dialectics of love. Social and political problems did not attract him; he was the opposite of a committed writer. That is why the pleasant stories he knew how to tell so charmingly soon came to seem somewhat irrelevant. He has been called the German Mérimée —a paler Mérimée, less capable of understanding fundamental passions. *The Angry Woman* is a most decorously behaved little lady, compared to Colomba. Nevertheless the comparison is not inappropriate and it cannot do injustice to either of these writers.

Geneviève Bianquis is a literary critic who has written a history of German literature. Translated by Charles Lam Markmann.

THE 1910 PRIZE

By GUNNAR AHLSTRÖM

The young century was beginning to grow up, and the calendar bore the date 1910. The sensational news value which had at first accompanied the Nobel Prize had been exhausted, and the superlatives it called forth had all been uttered before. The annual event no longer made headlines.

Besides, the most recent awards had filled the press with vehement prose. In 1908 it had protested violently because Selma Lagerlöf had not been given the Prize, and in 1909 the press had celebrated her triumph just as noisily. The author of *The Wonderful Adventures of Nils* had, without a shadow of a doubt, collected more applause than any other laureate. After this peak it was only too natural that the attention of the public should have lapsed.

It was probably because of an article in the Paris newspaper *Le Soleil* that the name of Sâr Péladan was mentioned as one of the writers whose names rumor had placed on the list of candidates. Another Frenchman's name also appeared: this was old Henri Fabre, still living in the same rustic retreat from which he had one day sent his *Souvenirs Entomologiques* to the publisher, but his name was put forward too late.

The actual candidates that year were twenty-five, of whom some were being proposed for the second time, and several had by now become veterans. One candidacy had been preceded by widespread efforts at persuasion. This was to get the Prize awarded to Gustav Warneck of the organization of Protestant Missions and a former history professor at Halle University.

Several members of the Academy were ardent Christians, notably the Permanent Secretary, and it seemed reasonable to suppose that the mission should find a hearing. It also seemed that, in principle, the study of history and ideas was as deserving of the award as descriptions of the doubtful morals of the Roman emperors. But Professor Warneck's work had too little artistic merit.

The name of Anatole France was once again sent in by Paul Hervieu, and the candidacy of Georg Brandes came up again, presented by two erudite Finns. A comeback was also made by Maurice Maeterlinck, John Morley, and Antonio Fogazzaro. A new writer, Pierre Loti, was sent to join the ranks by Gabriel Hanotaux.

Paul Heyse had celebrated his eightieth birthday on March 15 in Munich, and the homage paid to him had assumed enormous proportions, transforming the occasion into a truly national celebration of German literature. It was not the first time that birthdays and jubilees had contributed toward the selection of a Nobel

[355]

Prizewinner: one thought of Björnson, Sienkiewicz, Carducci, and Selma Lagerlöf. It was understandable therefore that scholarly circles in Germany and Austria considered it their duty to gather up an abundant harvest of important names in behalf of Heyse. And Heyse was chosen.

Contrary to the usual custom, the name of the laureate was not kept secret until the solemn day of December 10. The decision was publishd in November, after Paul Heyse had been informed and had accepted. He announced at the same time that his health prevented him from going to Stockholm to receive his Prize. "What shall I say about this gift?" he said to a German journalist who interviewed him in Munich. "The news surprised me as much as it did the rest of the world. I do not know who recommended me, or who the other competitors were. The only thing I got wind of was that the proposals also mentioned a Frenchman, a pronounced mystic who, in my view, could not be called the incarnation of French literature. Naturally, one is pleased to see one's life work crowned, because then one can say, without too much pride: 'What I have done cannot then be entirely bad.' "

The choice raised no enthusiasm. The people who criticized the Academy for only rewarding august old gentlemen were again vindicated. And besides, rumor had it that the beneficiary was rich, indeed a millionaire. The Permanent Secretary took steps to deny this rumor: Heyse was comfortably off, but he was not rich, and it was announced that the laureate had immediately set aside 40,000 marks of his Prize money for the financing of good works.

In Paul Heyse's case, the Nobel laurels came as an addition to the other prizes his talent had already earned for him. The award was made, the Diploma stated, "as a tribute to the consummate artistry, permeated with idealism, which he has demonstrated during his long, productive career as a lyric poet, dramatist, novelist, and writer of world-renowned short stories."

Translated by Camilla Sykes.